COLLECT
AIRCRAFT
ON STAMPS

Stanley Gibbons
Stamp Catalogue

COLLECT
AIRCRAFT
ON STAMPS

2nd edition 2009

Stanley Gibbons Ltd
London and Ringwood

By Appointment to Her Majesty The Queen
Stanley Gibbons Ltd, London
Philatelists

Published by Stanley Gibbons Ltd
Editorial, Publications Sales Offices
and Distribution Centre:
7 Parkside, Christchurch Road, Ringwood,
Hants BH24 3SH

First Edition – December 1994
Second Edition – March 2009

© Stanley Gibbons Ltd 2009

ISBN-13: 978-0-85259-706-4
ISBN-10: 0-85259-706-1

Item No. 2862-09

Printed by
MPGi Limited

About this book

This catalogue is a listing of stamps depicting aircraft issued by countries throughout the world. It is based on *Stanley Gibbons Stamps of the World* simplified catalogue, published annually in five volumes. This edition contains over 24,000 stamps which depict over 1,600 identified aircraft types plus more than 180 identified airships and balloons. It has been updated to include all aircraft stamps that have appeared in *Gibbons Stamp Monthly* catalogue supplements up to and including the October 2008 issue.

What is Included
All issues depicting aircraft (including gliders, airships and balloons). Miniature sheets are included.

What is Excluded
All stamp variations of watermark and perforation outside the scope of *Stamps of the World*.

Designs showing symbolic or stylised aircraft (unless it is clear that a particular aircraft type is intended) or those where only a small part of the aircraft is visible.

Very small representations of aircraft which cannot be identified and which are of insignificant importance to the design. These are frequently included in designs to indicate airmail use.

Children's toys (other than flying models), kites, meteorological balloons, all forms of spacecraft including space shuttles, and hovercraft.

Countries Section
This section lists, in alphabetical order, with prices, the various countries and territories which have issued aircraft stamps. Within each country the stamps are listed in chronological order with the year of issue and catalogue number taken from the *Stamps of the World*.

Each aircraft is identified, where known, by the manufacturer's name, aircraft type name and number. Individual aircraft names are shown in italics and unofficial type names in quotation marks. Specific mark or model numbers are given where it has been possible to establish them, as are the airline or private user's name.

Identities
Identifying the aircraft shown on stamps is a difficult art due to the small size involved and the degree of artistic licence that is sometimes apparent. As much care as possible has been given to identification, but it must often be a matter of opinion. There are bound to have been some errors and possible disagreements about identities. **Similarly there are many aircraft that have yet to be identified. I would be grateful for any corrections or suggestions that may be used for a future edition.**

Chronology Section
The Chronology of Aviation Events is intended to be used in conjunction with the Index to provide the collector with useful information which can be used when planning or writing-up an aircraft collection.

Index Section
This is in two parts, the first being a general Classification Index which is cross-referenced to the more detailed Sectional Index. This is divided into sections which cover the various types of aircraft listed in the catalogue. They list, in alphabetical order of country and by catalogue number, all stamps depicting the type of aircraft covered by that heading. Many aircraft types have experienced changes of manufacturer's name, due to amalgamation, take-over, etc. All such aircraft are listed under the current manufacturer's name, with previous manufacturer's name in brackets.

Acknowledgments
This book would never have happened without the support and computer knowledge of my wife Jeanette, who deserves all my thanks.

I would also like to thank Hugh Jefferies, Clare de la Feuillade and all the staff of Stanley Gibbons at Ringwood for all their assistance and hard work whilst I compiled this new edition.

Ian Hamilton

Bibliography
The Encyclopedia of World Aircraft, Silverdale Books
The Chronicle of Aviation, Chronicle
    Communications Ltd
Jane's Encyclopedia of Aviation and
other Jane's publications
World Encyclopedia of Military Aircraft, Guild
    Publishing
Encyclopedia of the World's Air Forces, Patrick
    Stephens Ltd.
The X-Planes, X-1 to X-45, Midland Publishing
Who's Who in Aviation History, Airlife
Flight, Carlton Books
Aviators – a history in photographs, Times Books
Biplanes, Triplanes and Seaplanes, Amber Books

The Author
Ian Hamilton was born in Glasgow in 1933, he was a National Serviceman with the RAF between 1951 and 1953, which is where his interest in aircraft began. He was based most of the time on a training station in Yorkshire where they flew Gloster Meteors and de Havilland Vampires. He was part of a mobile bomb disposal flight.

In 2006 Ian and his wife, Jeanette decided to return to their native soil and ended up in Portknockie, near Elgin on the Moray Firth. On their return Ian become a member of the Moray Stamp Club. He is still collecting aircraft stamps, but his collecting activities have been put on hold while he plays his part in producing *Aircraft on Stamps*, Second Edition.

List of Airline Abbreviations
B.E.A.	British European Airways
B.O.A.C.	British Overseas Airways Corporation
B.W.I.A.	British West Indian Airways
C.F.R.N.A.	Compagnie Franco-Romaine de Navigation Aerienne
C.S.A.	Ceskoslovenskie Statni Aerolinie
L.A.N.	Linea Aerea Nacional de Chile
L.I.A.T.	Leeward Islands Air Transport
S.A.A.	Saudi Arabian Airlines
S.N.A.M.	Service de la Navigation Aerienne de Madagascar
T.A.P.	Transportes Aereos Portugueses
U.T.A.	Union des Transports Aeriens

Arrangement
The various countries and territories are listed in the same order as in *Stamps of the World*. Those few which are not in alphabetical order are covered by cross-references. Each entry includes the geographical location and details of the currencies used. The dates quoted against these currencies are those on which they were first used for stamps in this catalogue.

Illustrations
These are ¾ of actual size, except for oversize issues which maybe shown smaller. One design from each issue is depicted, but only those overprints and surcharges required for identification are included.

Listings
These are divided into years by dates and into individual issues by the illustrations.

For philatelic details *Stamps of the World*, or the 22-part standard catalogue, should be consulted.

A * against the catalogue number indicates an issue where unlisted stamps in the set depict designs other than aircraft.

Miniature sheets are indicated by a **MS** prefix.

Prices
Those in the left-hand column are for unused stamps and those in the right-hand column for used.

Our prices are for stamps in fine average condition, and in issues where condition varies we may ask more for the superb and less for the sub-standard.

The prices of unused stamps are for lightly hinged examples for those issued before 1946, thereafter for unmounted mint.

Prices for used stamps refer to postally used examples, though for certain issues they may be for cancelled-to-order.

The minimum price quoted is 10p which represents a handling charge rather than a basis for valuing common stamps.

The prices quoted are generally for the cheapest variety of stamps, but it is worth noting that differences of watermark, perforation, or other details, outside the scope of this catalogue, may often increase the value of the stamp.

All prices are subject to change without prior notice and we give no guarantee to supply all stamps priced. Prices quoted for albums, publications, etc. advertised in this catalogue are also subject to change without prior notice.

Guarantee
All stamps supplied by us are guaranteed originals in the following terms:

If not as described, and returned by the purchaser in the original transaction, we undertake to refund the price paid to us. If any stamp is certified as genuine by the Expert Committee of the Royal Philatelic Society, London, or by B.P.A. Expertising Ltd., the purchaser shall not be entitled to make any claim against us for any error, omission or mistake in such certificate.

Consumers' statutory rights are not affected by the above guarantee.

Plane Crazy

Welcome to a new fully updated Second Edition of Stanley Gibbons' *Collect Aircraft on Stamps*. In the years since the First Edition was published, the aviation world has seen the arrival of many new types, while a number of old favourites have departed to that great hangar in the skies.

In the world of postage stamps, a proliferation of new issues has marked many significant aviation events, including the 200th Anniversary of Manned Flight, the 75th, 80th and 90th Anniversaries of the Royal Air Force and, most significant of all, the Centenary, in 2003, of the Wright Brothers pioneering flight. There has even been a stamp issued illustrating an aircraft yet to make its first flight, the Boeing 787.

In the aviation industry, recent history has seen mergers and takeovers resulting in the disappearance of many pioneering names – Bristol, Douglas, Gloster, McDonnell to name but a few. These illustrious names live on, featured on many stamps from around the world, and new names have appeared in countries with no previous aircraft industry. Supersonic flight is once again the preserve of military pilots. Only two civil aircraft with supersonic capability – Concorde and the Tupolev Tu-144 – have taken flight and both have now been retired.

Lindbergh's Ryan NYP Special, *Spirit of St. Louis* retains its title of 'most depicted individual aircraft', despite a challenge from Concorde. However, there were many Concordes, and only one *Spirit of St. Louis*.

I'm sorry to record that the immortal Douglas DC-3 has lost its title of 'most depicted type', having fallen to the might of Boeing's 747. Interestingly, but for the personal whim of one man it could have been the Douglas DC-5 holding the top spot until now. Dramatically superior to the DC-3, Douglas expected the DC-5 to receive massive orders when large numbers of transport aircraft were needed at the outbreak of World War II. However, General 'Hap' Arnold chose the DC-3 instead, and told Douglas to stop DC-5 production and, as the saying goes, the rest is history.

This new edition incorporates many changes, all of which we hope you will see as improvements. The most obvious one is the introduction of full glorious colour and a fresh graphic layout. Less obvious is the introduction of issue titles, but only where the entire issue is devoted to aviation. The inevitable result is the greatly increased number of stamps listed – more than double the 12,000 or so in the First Edition.

Who can tell what the future holds? Airbus and Boeing will continue to compete for industry domination and stamp issuing authorities have thousands of aircraft types yet to appear on stamps to choose from. As a subject for thematic collectors, aviation can only become more popular as thematic collecting itself appeals to more and more collectors, encouraged we hope by this exciting new catalogue.

Ian Hamilton

ABU DHABI

Arabian Peninsula

1000 fils = 1 dinar

1968.
| 50* | 10f. Vickers VC-10 and other airliners at Abu Dhabi Airport | 4·00 | 80 |

1969.
| 53* | 60f. Westland Whirlwind helicopter | 2·75 | 95 |

1970.
| 71* | 25f. Douglas DC-8 airliners at Abu Dhabi Airport | 1·80 | 65 |

1971.
| 79* | 150f. Hawker Hunter FGA.76 jet fighters | 16·00 | 5·00 |

ADEN

Arabian Peninsula

16 annas = 1 rupee

1949. As Nos. 114/15 of Antigua, but surcharged.
| 32* | 2½a. on 20c. Airplane | 50 | 1·50 |
| 33* | 3a. on 30c. Jet-powered Vickers Viking | 2·00 | 1·50 |

ADEN PROTECTORATE STATES

Arabian Peninsula

1949 16 annas = 1 rupee

1955 100 cents = 1 shilling

1966 100 fils = 1 dinar

Kathiri State of Seiyun

1949. As Nos. 114/15 of Antigua, but surcharged.
| 16* | 2½a. on 20c. Airplane | 15 | 70 |
| 17* | 3a. on 30c. Jet-powered Vickers Viking | 1·25 | 1·50 |

Qu'aiti State in Hadhramaut

1949. As Nos. 114/15 of Antigua, but surcharged.
| 16* | 2½a. on 20c. Airplane | 15 | 20 |
| 17* | 3a. on 30c. Jet-powered Vickers Viking | 1·40 | 85 |

APPENDIX

The following stamps have either been issued in excess of postal needs or have not been made available to the public in reasonable quantities at face value. Miniature sheets, imperforate stamps, etc are excluded from this section.

1967.

Amphilex International Stamp Exhibition, Amsterdam. 75f. (Curtiss JN-4 "Jenny", on United States of America stamp No. A548 with centre inverted).
Space Research. 250f. (Wright Flyer I).

AEGEAN ISLANDS

Mediterranean

100 centesimi = 1 lira

1932. Nos. 326 and 330 of Italy overprinted **ISOLE ITALIANE DELL'EGEO.**
| 82* | 50c. Leonardo da Vinci's drawing of a "Flying man" | 60 | 1·25 |
| 86* | 7l.70 +2l. Leonardo da Vinci's drawing of a "Flying man" | 85 | 2·25 |

1933.
116	3l. Airship LZ-127 *Graf Zeppelin*	32·00	90·00
117	5l. Airship LZ-127 *Graf Zeppelin*	32·00	£110
118	10l. Airship LZ-127 *Graf Zeppelin*	32·00	£180
119	12l. Airship LZ-127 *Graf Zeppelin*	32·00	£225
120	15l. Airship LZ-127 *Graf Zeppelin*	32·00	£225
121	20l. Airship LZ-127 *Graf Zeppelin*	32·00	£225
116/121 *Set of 6*		£180	£950

1933. No. 379 of Italy overprinted **ISOLE ITALIANE DELL'EGEO.**
| 123* | 5l.25 +44l.75 Savoia Marchetti S-55X flying boat | 27·00 | 75·00 |

1934. Nos. 418/21 of Italy overprinted **ISOLE ITALIANE DELL'EGEO.**
133*	50c. Marina Fiat MF.S flying boat	4·25	25·00
134*	75c. Savoia Marchetti S-55X flying boat	4·25	25·00
135*	5l. +2l.50 Marina Fiat MF.5 flying boat	12·50	50·00
136*	10l. +5l. Marina Fiat MF.S flying boat	12·50	70·00

1934. Nos. 435/41 of Italy overprinted **ISOLE ITALIANE DELL'EGEO.**
168*	25c. Italian "P" Type airship	38·00	50·00
169*	50c. Marina Fiat MF.5 flying boat	38·00	50·00
170*	75c. Marina Fiat MF.5 flying boat	38·00	50·00
171*	80c. Italian "P" Type airship	38·00	50·00
172*	1l. +50c. Caproni Ca 101	29·00	50·00
173*	2l. +1l. Pomilio PC type biplane	29·00	50·00
174*	3l. +2l. Marina Fiat MF.5 flying boat	29·00	50·00

1940.
210*	50c. Savoia Marchetti S.M.75	85	1·90
211*	1l. Savoia Marchetti S.M.75	85	1·90
212*	2l. +75c. Savoia Marchetti S.M.75	85	3·75
213*	5l. +2l.50 Savoia Marchetti S.M.75	85	6·00

EXPRESS STAMPS

1932. As Nos. E348/9 of Italy, but in different colours, overprinted **ISOLE ITALIANE DELL'EGEO.**
| E104 | 2l.25 +1l. Savoia Marchetti S-55A flying boat | 38·00 | 70·00 |
| E105 | 4l.50 +1l.50 Savoia Marchetti S-55A flying boat | 38·00 | 70·00 |

1934. As Nos. E442/3 of Italy, but in different colours, overprinted **ISOLE ITALIANE DELL'EGEO.**
| E175 | 2l. +1l.25 Caproni Ca 101 | 30·00 | 48·00 |
| E176 | 4l.50 +2l. Caproni Ca 101 | 30·00 | 48·00 |

AFGHANISTAN

Central Asia

100 poul (pul) = 1 afghani (rupee)

1939.
280a	5a. Potez 25A2 (?) (orange)	5·75	4·50
280b	10a. Potez 25A2 (?) (blue)	5·75	4·50
280c	20a. Potez 25A2 (?) (green)	11·50	7·75
280a/280c *Set of 3*		22·00	16·00

1948. As Nos. 280a/c, but colours changed.
300	5a. Potez 25A2 (?) (green)	23·00	23·00
301	10a. Potez 25A2 (?) (orange)	23·00	23·00
302	20a. Potez 25A2 (?) (blue)	23·00	23·00
300/301 *Set of 3*		70·00	70·00

1951.
| 339 | 5a. Douglas DC-3 of Ariana (red) | 3·25 | 65 |
| 339a | 5a. Douglas DC-3 of Ariana (green) | 1·80 | 40 |

340	10a. Douglas DC-3 of Ariana (grey)	7·50	1·80
341	20a. Douglas DC-3 of Ariana	10·50	3·00
339/341 *Set of 4*		22·00	6·00

1957. As Nos. 339/40, but colours changed.
| 415a | 5a. Douglas DC-3 of Ariana (blue) | 2·10 | 60 |
| 415b | 10a. Douglas DC-3 of Ariana (violet) | 3·00 | 1·10 |

1960.
467	75p. Douglas DC-6 of Ariana	65	25
468	125p. Douglas DC-6 of Ariana	80	40
469	5a. Douglas DC-6 of Ariana	1·50	90
467/469 *Set of 3*		2·75	1·40

1964. Inauguration of Kabul International Airport.
511	10a. Kabul International Airport	80	25
512	20a. Kabul International Airport	1·00	40
513	50a. Kabul International Airport	2·75	1·20
511/513 *Set of 3*		4·00	1·70

1964. Inauguration of Kandahar International Airport.
514	7a.75 Kandahar International Airport	65	40
515	9a.25 Kandahar International Airport	90	80
516	10a.50 Kandahar International Airport	1·20	1·00
517	13a.75 Kandahar International Airport	1·40	1·10
514/517 *Set of 4*		3·75	3·00

1965. 10th Anniv of ARIANA (Afghan Airlines).
551	1a.25 Douglas DC-3 of Ariana	35	10
552	5a. Convair CV 240 of Ariana	90	15
553	10a. Douglas DC-6A of Ariana	1·60	60
551/553 *Set of 3*		2·40	70

1971.
| 714 | 50a. Boeing 727–200 of Ariana at Kabul Airport | 4·50 | 4·50 |
| 715 | 100a. Boeing 727–200 of Ariana | 5·75 | 3·50 |

1972.
| 729 | 25a. Mil Mi-4 helicopters | 4·50 | 1·20 |

1984. 40th Anniv of ARIANA (Afghan Airlines).
970	1a. Antonov An-2 biplane	10	10
971	4a. Ilyushin Il-12	15	10
972	9a. Tupolev Tu-104A	60	15
973	10a. Ilyushin Il-18	80	15
974	13a. Yakovlev Yak-42	1·10	15
975	17a. Tupolev Tu-154	1·40	15
976	21a. Ilyushin Il-86	1·60	15
970/976 *Set of 7*		5·25	85

1987.
1170	42a. Douglas DC-10	4·50	1·00

1988.
1196	20a. Airplane	80	50

1989.
1286*	4a. Boeing 727	6·00	1·00

1996. As No. 1286 but surcharged.
1290*	1200a. on 4a. Boeing 727	6·00	1·00

AITUTAKI

South Pacific
100 cents = 1 dollar

1983. Bicentenary of Manned Flight.
442	18c. Sports balloon	55	30
443	36c. Sports balloon	75	50
444	48c. Sports balloon	90	60
445	60c. Sports balloon	1·00	80
442/445 Set of 4		3·00	2·00
MS446 $2.50 Sports balloon		1·50	2·00

1995.
686	$4 Supermarine Spitfire/Junkers Ju87 Stuka	9·00	8·50
687	$4 Grumman TBM Avengers	9·00	8·50

AJMAN

Arabian Peninsula
100 dirhams = 1 riyal

1967.
138*	4d. Boeing 707	10	10
143*	70d. Sikorsky S-58 helicopter	40	10
147*	5r. Boeing 707 (air)	2·30	95

APPENDIX

The following stamps have either been issued in excess of postal needs or have not been made available to the public in reasonable quantities at face value. Miniature sheets, imperforate stamps, etc are excluded from this section.

1971.

Space Flight of "Apollo 15". 1r. (Helicopter).

ALAND ISLANDS

Northern Europe
1992. 100 pennia = 1 markka
2002. 100 cents = 1 euro

1999.
157	2m.90 Avions de Transport Regional ATR72	1·20	1·30

2007.
292	2 klass Junkers F. 13 flying boat	1·60	1·50
293	2 klass SAAB 340	2·00	1·80

ALAOUITES

Middle East
100 centimes = 1 piastre

1926. Nos. 192/5 of Syria further overprinted ALAOUITES in English and Arabic.
44	2p. Bleriot XI overprint	1·80	8·25
45	3p. Bleriot XI overprint	1·60	8·25
46	5p. Bleriot XI overprint	1·60	8·25
47	10p. Bleriot XI overprint	1·50	8·75
44/47 Set of 4		5·75	30·00

1929. Nos. 225/9 of Syria further overprinted ALAOUITES in English and Arabic.
59	0p.50 Bleriot XI overprint	2·00	7·00
60	1p. Bleriot XI overprint	3·25	15·00
61	2p. on 1p.25 Bleriot XI overprint	20·00	48·00
62	15p. on 25p. Bleriot XI =overprint	2·50	8·25
63	25p. Bleriot XI overprint	17·00	32·00
59/63 Set of 5		40·00	£100

ALBANIA

South-east Europe
1925. 100 qint = 1 franc
1947. 100 qint = 1 lek

1925.
186	5q. Airplane	3·25	3·25
187	10q. Airplane	3·50	3·50
188	25q. Airplane	3·50	3·50
189	50q. Airplane	5·00	5·00
190	1f. Airplane	8·25	8·25
191	2f. Airplane	11·00	11·00
192	3f. Airplane	19·00	19·00
186/192 Set of 7		48·00	48·00

1927. Nos. 186/92 overprinted Rep. Shqiptare.
204	5q. Airplane	10·00	10·00
205	10q. Airplane	10·00	10·00
206	25q. Airplane	8·50	8·50
207	50q. Airplane	8·00	8·00
208	1f. Airplane	8·00	8·00
209	2f. Airplane	9·75	9·75
210	3f. Airplane	17·00	17·00
204/210 Set of 7		65·00	65·00

1928. Nos. 186/92 overprinted REP. SHQYPTARE Fluturim' i l-ar Vlone- Brindisi 21.IV.1928.
222	5q. Airplane	9·25	11·50
223	10q. Airplane	9·25	11·50
224	25q. Airplane	9·25	9·50
225	50q. Airplane	10·50	14·50
226	1f. Airplane	95·00	£110
227	2f. Airplane	£100	£110
228	3f. Airplane	£100	£120
222/228 Set of 7		£300	£350

1929. Nos. 186/92 overprinted Mbr. Shqiptare.
270	5q. Airplane	8·00	12·00
271	10q. Airplane	8·00	12·00
272	25q. Airplane	15·00	12·50
273	50q. Airplane	45·00	60·00
274	1f. Airplane	£250	£250
275	2f. Airplane	£275	£350
276	3f. Airplane	£500	£550
270/276 Set of 7		£1000	£1200

1930.
288	5q. Junkers F-13	2·10	2·10
289	15q. Junkers F-13	2·10	2·10
290	20q. Junkers F-13	2·10	2·10
291	50q. Junkers F-13	3·75	3·75
292	1f. Junkers F-13	6·25	6·25
293	2f. Junkers F-13	21·00	21·00
294	3f. Junkers F-13	24·00	24·00
288/294 Set of 7		55·00	55·00

1931. Nos. 288/94 overprinted TIRANE-ROME 6 KORRIK 1931.
295	5q. Junkers F-13		
296	15q. Junkers F-13	9·00	9·00
297	20q. Junkers F-13	9·00	9·00
298	50q. Junkers F-13	9·00	9·00
299	1f. Junkers F-13	50·00	50·00
300	2f. Junkers F-13	50·00	50·00
301	3f. Junkers F-13	50·00	50·00
295/301 Set of 7		£170	£170

1939. Nos. 288/9 and 291 overprinted Mbledhja Kushtetuese 12-IV-1939 XVII or surcharged also.
348*	5q. Junkers F-13	4·25	3·75
349*	15q. Junkers F-13	3·00	3·75
350*	20q. on 50q. Junkers F-13	7·25	7·25

1939.
365*	20q. Fiat G18V of Avio Linee Italiane on Tirana-Rome service	45·00	10·50

1940.
366	5q. Savoia Marchetti S.M.75	1·25	1·25
367	15q. Savoia Marchetti S.M.75	1·75	1·60
368	20q. Savoia Marchetti S.M.75	4·00	2·40
369	50q. Savoia Marchetti S.M.75	4·50	4·75
370	1f. Savoia Marchetti S.M.75	6·00	6·00
371	2f. Savoia Marchetti S.M.75	13·50	14·00
372	3f. Savoia Marchetti S.M.75	55·00	24·00
366/372 Set of 7		75·00	49·00

1950.
539	0l.50 Douglas DC-3	90	90
540	1l. Douglas DC-3	90	90
541	2l. Douglas DC-3	1·60	1·60
542	5l. Douglas DC-3	5·50	5·50
543	10l. Douglas DC-3	12·00	12·00
544	20l. Douglas DC-3	20·00	20·00
539/544 Set of 6		37·00	37·00

1952. Nos. 541/3 surcharged in figures.
571	0l.50 on 2l. Douglas DC-3	£160	£130
572	0l.50 on 5l. Douglas DC-3	35·00	25·00
573	2l.50 on 5l. Douglas DC-3	£250	£140
574	2l.50 on 10l. Douglas DC-3	35·00	25·00
571/574 Set of 4		£425	£300

1960. Second Anniv of Tirana-Moscow Jet Air Service.
658	1l. Tupolev Tu-104A of Aeroflot on Tirana-Moscow service	1·00	75
659	7l.50 Tupolev Tu-104A of Aeroflot on Tirana-Moscow service	3·75	1·50
660	11l.50 Tupolev Tu-104A of Aeroflot on Tirana-Moscow service	6·00	3·00
658/660 *Set of 3*		9·75	4·75

1968.
1258*	65q. Pilot, Ilyushin Il-28 and Mikoyan Gurevich MiG-17	2·50	85

1969.
1310*	40q. Leonardo da Vinci's drawing of a "helicopter"	85	20

1975.
1798	20q. Tupolev Tu-104A (?)	25	15
1799	40q. Tupolev Tu-104A (?)	40	20
1800	60q. Tupolev Tu-104A (?)	70	30
1801	90q. Tupolev Tu-104A (?)	90	40
1802	1l.20 Tupolev Tu-104A (?)	1·25	50
1803	2l.40 Tupolev Tu-104A (?)	2·40	1·00
1804	4l.05 Tupolev Tu-104A (?)	3·50	1·75
1798/1804 *Set of 7*		8·50	3·75

1992. Aircraft.
2506	30q. Lilienthal biplane glider, 1896	10	10
2507	80q. Clement Ader's Avion III, 1897	25	20
2508	90q. Wright Type A	30	25
2509	1l.20 Concorde	40	30
2510	1l.80 Tupolev Tu-144 (wrongly inscribed "Tu-114")	55	40
2511	2l.40 Dornier Do-31E (wrongly inscribed "Dernier")	75	55
2506/2511 *Set of 6*		2·10	1·60

2000. Centenary of First Zeppelin Flight.
2817	15l. Airship LZ-1 Zeppelin	15	10
2818	30l. Santos Dumont airship *Ballon No. 5*	30	15
2819	300l. Beardmore airship *R-34*	2·75	1·25
2817/2819 *Set of 3*		3·00	1·40
MS2820	300l. Count Ferdinand von Zeppelin and airships	3·40	3·40

2001.
2868*	40l. Clement Ader's *Eole* 1890	40	20
2869*	40l. Bleriot XI, 1909	40	20
2870*	40l. Lindbergh's Ryan NYP Special, *Spirit of St. Louis* 1927	40	20
2871*	40l. First flight to Tirana, 1925 (aircraft unidentified)	40	20
2872*	40l. Antonov AH-10, 1956	40	20
2873*	40l. Concorde	40	20
2874*	40l. Concorde	40	20

ALDERNEY

See under Guernsey

ALEXANDRETTA

See Hatay

ALGERIA

North Africa

1945. 100 centimes = 1 franc
1964. 100 centimes = 1 dinar

1945. No. 742 of France overprinted **RF ALGERIE**.
249	1f.50 +3f.50 Potez 63-11 bombers	1·00	4·25

1946.
254	5f. Potez 56	1·10	75
255	10f. Potez 56	35	10
256	15f. Potez 56	60	70
257a	20f. Potez 56	65	10
258	25f. Potez 56	65	20
259	40f. Potez 56	1·20	1·40
254/259 *Set of 6*		4·00	3·00

1947. No. 254 surcharged **-10%**.
265	"-10%" on 5f. Potez 56	15	55

1947. No. 255 surcharged with Cross of Lorraine and **18 Juin 1940 +10 Fr.**
283	10f. +10f. Potez 56	2·75	5·75

1948. No. 254 surcharged with Cross of Lorraine and **18 JUIN 1940+10 Fr.**
286	5f. +10f. Potez 56	2·50	5·50

1949.
289*	18f.+22f. Grumman F6F Hellcats over aircraft carrier Arromanches	7·00	18·00

1949.
291*	100f. Dewoitine D-338 trimotor	1·70	60
293*	500f. Dewoitine D-338 trimotor	8·00	3·75

1949.
298	15f. +20f. Liore et Olivier 451C	5·25	17·00

1955.
376*	200f. Sud Aviation SE 210 Caravelle	7·25	10·00

1967.
481	1d. Sud Aviation SE 210 Caravelle of Air Algerie	1·40	55
482	2d. Sud Aviation SE 210 Caravelle of Air Algerie	3·25	1·40
483	5d. Sud Aviation SE 210 Caravelle of Air Algerie	8·50	2·50
481/483 *Set of 3*		12·00	4·00

1970.
550*	30c. Douglas DC-8	55	25

1971.
581	2d. Sud Aviation SE 210 Caravelle	2·50	1·10
582	3d. Sud Aviation SE 210 Caravelle	3·75	1·60
583	4d. Sud Aviation SE 210 Caravelle	4·25	2·00
581/583 *Set of 3*		9·50	4·25

1989. Aiports.
1006	2d.90 Oran Es Senia Airport and Boeing 727	1·20	45
1007	3d.30 Tebessa Airport and Boeing 757	1·40	60
1008	5d. Tamanrasset Airport and Boeing 707	2·10	1·20
1006/1008 *Set of 3*		4·25	2·00

1989.
1013	1d. Biplane spraying crops	55	25

1991.
1056	10d. Boeing 737 of Air Algerie	2·75	1·20
1057	20d. Boeing 737 of Air Algerie	5·50	2·75
1056/1057 *Set of 2*		5·75	2·75

1993.
1129	50d. Boeing 727	5·75	2·00

1997. First Anniv of Aeropostale.
1232   5d. Beech Model 100 King Air 50   15

2000.
1311*   5d. Concorde 55   40

2006.
1529   30d. New air terminal, Algiers .... 1·80   1·30

ANDORRA

Pyrenees mountains between France and Spain

French Post Offices
100 centimes = 1 franc

1961.
F181*   2f. Sud Aviation SE 210 Caravelle .... 2·00   1·80
F182*   3f. Sud Aviation SE 210 Caravelle .... 2·20   2·10
F183*   5f. Sud Aviation SE 210 Caravelle .... 3·00   1·60
F184*   10f. Sud Aviation SE 210 Caravelle .... 5·50   4·50

1983. Bicentenary of Manned Flight.
F329   2f. Montgolfier balloon (first manned
          free flight, 1783) and Charles'
          hydrogen balloon 65   2·30

ANGOLA

South-west Africa
1938. 100 centavos = 1 angolar
1954. 100 centavos = 1 escudo
1977. 100 lweis = 1 kwanza

1938.
401*   10c. Airplane 30   30
402*   20c. Airplane 30   20
403*   50c. Airplane 30   20
404*   1a. Airplane 30   20
405*   2a. Airplane 60   20
406*   3a. Airplane 55   35
407*   5a. Airplane .... 5·25   80
408*   9a. Airplane .... 4·25   8·50
409*   10a. Airplane .... 5·75   1·10

1949.
445   1a. Boeing 377 Stratocruiser, Douglas
              DC-3 and other aircraft 50   10
446   2a. Boeing 377 Stratocruiser, Douglas
              DC-3 and other aircraft .... 1·10   10
447   3a. Boeing 377 Stratocruiser, Douglas
              DC-3 and other aircraft .... 1·40   15
448   6a. Boeing 377 Stratocruiser, Douglas
              DC-3 and other aircraft .... 2·50   50
449   9a. Boeing 377 Stratocruiser, Douglas
              DC-3 and other aircraft .... 3·50   1·20
445/449 Set of 5 .... 8·00   1·80

1962.
560*   50c. Piper PA-25 Pawnee 15   15

1963.
611   1e. Boeing 707 (top) and Lockheed
              L.1049G Super Constellation of T.A.P   85   30

1965.
633   1e.50 Boeing 707 80   10
634   2e.50 Boeing 707 85   10
635   3e. Boeing 707 .... 1·20   10
636   4e. Boeing 707 .... 1·20   15
637   4e.50 Boeing 707 85   15
638   5e. Boeing 707 85   20
639   6e. Boeing 707 .... 1·40   30
640   7e. Boeing 707 .... 2·00   30
641   8e.50 Boeing 707 .... 2·50   80
642   12e.50 Boeing 707 .... 2·50   1·10
633/642 Set of 10 .... 12·50   3·00

1965.
643   2e.50 Fokker F.27 Friendship CR-LEO of
              DETA over Luanda Airport 85   20

1970.
698*   2e.50 Fokker F.27 Friendship CR-LEO of
              DETA and Boeing 707 of T.A.P .... 1·50   65

1972.
706   1e. Fairey IIID seaplane *Santa Cruz* 25   15

1980. No. 698 overprinted **REPUBLICA POPULAR DE**.
752*   2e.50 Fokker F.27 Friendship CR-LEO of
              DETA and Boeing 707 of T.A.P 15   10

1983.
812*   3k.50 Mail being unloaded from airliner 20   15

1992.
1011*   550k. Boeing 707 of Angolan Airlines
              Express Mail Service 65   50

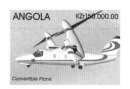

1998.
1358   150000k. Ultralight plane 70   55
1359   150000k. Gyroplane 70   55
1360   150000k. Business jet 70   55
1361   150000k. Convertible plane 70   55
1362   150000k. Chuterplane 70   55
1363   150000k. Twin-rotor craft 70   55
1364   150000k. Skycrane 70   55
1365   150000k. Concorde 70   55
1366   150000k. Flying boat 70   55
1367   200000k. Boeing 737-100 70   55
1368   200000k. Ilyushin Il-62M 70   55
1369   250000k. Pedal powered plane 70   55
1370   250000k. Sail plane 70   55
1371   250000k. Aerobatic plane 70   55
1372   250000k. Hang-gliding 70   55
1373   250000k. Balloon 70   55
1374   250000k. Glidercraft 70   55
1375   250000k. Model airplane 70   55
1376   250000k. Air racing 70   55
1377   250000k. Solar-celled plane 70   55
1358/1377 Set of 20
MS1378 Four sheets. (a) 1000000k. Boeing 777; (b)
      1000000k. Space shuttle;(c) 1000000k. Boeing
      737-200; (d) 1000000k. Boeing 747-300 .... 3·00   3·00

2003. Centenary of Powered Flight.
1670   25k. Wright Flyer .... 1·40   1·10

ANGUILLA

West Indies
100 cents = 1 dollar

1967.
24*   15c. Piper PA-23 Apache 235 N5946Y at
              Wall Blake Airport .... 2·50   20
25*   20c. Beech A90 King Air .... 1·25   2·25

1970.
94*   40c. Piper PA-23 Apache 235 at Wall Blake
              Airport .... 4·00   3·25

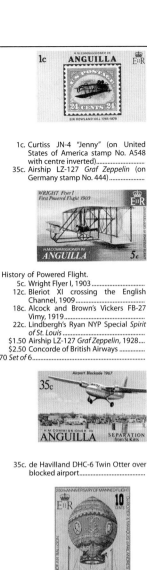

1979.
359* 1c. Curtiss JN-4 "Jenny" (on United States of America stamp No. A548 with centre inverted).............................. 10 10
361* 35c. Airship LZ-127 *Graf Zeppelin* (on Germany stamp No. 444)....................... 20 20

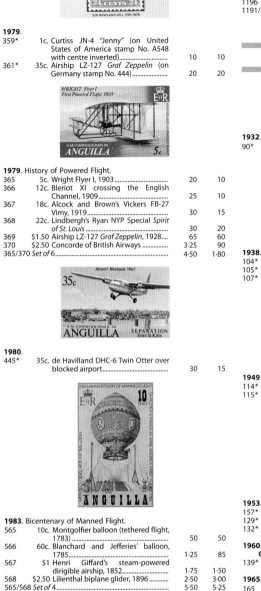

1979. History of Powered Flight.
365 5c. Wright Flyer I, 1903................. 20 10
366 12c. Bleriot XI crossing the English Channel, 1909............................ 25 10
367 18c. Alcock and Brown's Vickers FB-27 Vimy, 1919............................ 30 15
368 22c. Lindbergh's Ryan NYP Special *Spirit of St. Louis* 30 20
369 $1.50 Airship LZ-127 *Graf Zeppelin*, 1928.... 65 60
370 $2.50 Concorde of British Airways .... 3·25 90
365/370 *Set of 6* .... 4·50 1·80

1980.
445* 35c. de Havilland DHC-6 Twin Otter over blocked airport.................. 30 15

1983. Bicentenary of Manned Flight.
565 10c. Montgolfier balloon (tethered flight, 1783)........................... 50 50
566 60c. Blanchard and Jefferies' balloon, 1785................................ 1·25 85
567 $1 Henri Giffard's steam-powered dirigible airship, 1852............ 1·75 1·50
568 $2.50 Lilienthal biplane glider, 1896 .... 2·50 3·00
565/568 *Set of 4* .... 5·50 5·25
MS569 $5 Wilbur Wright in Wright Type B .... 2·75 3·50

1992.
887* $1.60 Anguilla Airport .... 4·00 3·75

1998. 80th Anniversary of the Royal Air Force.
1027 30c. Sopwith Camel & Bristol F2B............. 1·00 50
1028 $1 Supermarine Spitfire MkII, Hawker Hurricane Mk 1................... 2·00 90
1029 $1.50 Avro Lancaster.......................... 2·25 2·25
1030 $1.90 Panavia Tornado F3, Harrier GR7........ 2·75 3·00
1027/1030 *Set of 4* .... 7·25 6·00

2006. Early Airlines.
1191 30c. Cessna 402 .... 40 30
1192 40c. de Havilland Canada DHC-8 .... 45 30
1193 60c. de Havilland Canada DHC-7 .... 70 40
1194 $1 Piper Aztec .... 1·00 70
1195 $1.50 Piper Aztec .... 1·40 1·60
1196 $1.90 Piper Aztec .... 1·90 2·10
1191/1196 *Set of 6* .... 5·25 4·75

ANTIGUA

West Indies

1932. 12 pence = 1 shilling

20 shillings = 1 pound

1951. 100 cents = 1 dollar

1932.
90* 5s. Biplanes................................ £100 £130

1938.
104* 6d. Martin M-130 flying boat.................. 3·50 1·25
105* 1s. Martin M-130 flying boat.................. 6·00 2·00
107* 5s. Martin M-130 flying boat.................. 14·00 9·00

1949.
114* 2½d. Airplane................................ 40 60
115* 3d. Jet-powered Vickers Viking................. 2·00 2·50

1953.
157* 12c. Martin M-130 flying boat.................. 55 20
129* 24c. Martin M-130 flying boat.................. 2·50 15
132* $1.20 Martin M-130 flying boat.................. 3·00 70

1960. No. 157 overprinted **COMMEMORATION ANTIGUA CONSTITUTION 1960.**
139* 12c. Martin M-130 flying boat.................. 15 15

1965. No. 157 surcharged **15c.**
165 15c. on 12c. Martin M-130 flying boat 10 10

1966.
188a* 15c. Hawker Siddeley Comet 4 over Coolidge International Airport.......... 55 10

1969.
230* 4c. Vickers VC-10.......................... 10 10
231* 15c. Vickers VC-10.......................... 20 30

1970. 40th Anniv of Antiguan Air Services.
260 5c. Sikorsky S-38 flying boat NV-6778 of Pan Am............................ 50 10
261 20c. Dornier Do-X flying boat 80 10
262 35c. Hawker Siddeley H.S.748 of L.I.A.T .... 1·00 10
263 50c. Douglas C-124C Globemaster II .... 1·00 1·50
264 75c. Vickers Super VC-10 of B.O.A.C........... 1·25 2·00
260/264 *Set of 5*... 4·00 3·50

1974.
386* ½c. Westland Dragonfly helicopter 10 10
389* 5c. Concorde of British Airways 60 30
391* 35c. Sikorsky S-88 flying boat of Pan Am. 45 15
392* $1 Boeing 747-100 of B.O.A.C............... 3·50 2·50

1975. Nos. 391/2 surcharged in figures.
423* $2.50 on 35c. Sikorsky S-88 flying boat of Pan Am .... 2·00 5·50
424* $5 on $1 Boeing 747-100 of B.O.A.C........ 6·50 7·00

1976.
486A* $10 Boeing 747 over Coolidge International Airport......................... 3·50 8·00

1978. 75th Anniv of Powered Flight.
568* ½c. Wright Glider No. III, 1902.................... 10 10
569* 1c. Wright Flyer I, 1903...................... 10 10
570* 2c. Wright Flyer III on launching ramp ... 10 10
572* 50c. Wright Flyer III, 1905.................... 60 15
574* $2 Wright Type B, 1910...................... 1·00 80
MS575* $2.50 Wright Flyer I being prepared for take-off................................. 1·25 2·75

1979.
606* $2 Westland Dragonfly helicopter and Concorde .... 1·10 60

1980. No. 606 overprinted **LONDON 1980.**
650* $2 Westland Dragonfly helicopter and Concorde .... 3·25 3·00

1981. No. 486a overprinted "**INDEPENDENCE 1981**".
696B* $10 Boeing 747 over Coolidge International Airport...................... 3·25 5·50

1982. Coolidge International Airport.
738 10c. Airbus Industrie A300 over Coolidge International Airport................. 10 10
739 50c. Hawker Siddeley H.S.748 over Coolidge International Airport.......... 30 30
740 90c. de Havilland DHC-6 Twin Otter 1.00 over Coolidge International Airport.......... 60 60
741 $2.50 Britten Norman Islander over Coolidge International Airport.......... 1·75 1·75
738/741 *Set of 4* .... 2·50 2·50
MS742 $2 Boeing 747-100 over Coolidge International Airport................. 2·75 4·00
Nos. 738/42 also show various light monoplanes on the ground.

1983.
782* $3 Lockheed L-1011 TriStar 500 .... 1·00 1·50

1983.
811	30c. Dornier Do-X flying boat	1·00	30
812	50c. Supermarine S6B seaplane, 1931	1·25	60
813	60c. Curtiss F-9C Sparrowhawk biplane and airship U.S.S. Akron	1·40	85
814	$4 Hot-air balloon Pro Juventute	3·25	5·00
811/814 Set of 4		6·25	6·00
MS815 $5 Airship LZ-127 Graf Zeppelin		1·75	2·25

1984. No. 782 surcharged $2.
855*	$2 on $3 Lockheed L-1011 TriStar 500	2·75	1·25

1985.
911*	$1 Sikorsky S-61N helicopter	1·60	1·40

1985. 40th Anniv of ICAO.
934	30c. Cessna 172D Skyhawk	1·25	30
935	90c. Fokker D.VII, 1918	2·75	1·25
936	$1.50 SPAD VII, 1916	3·75	3·25
937	$3 Boeing 747-100	5·50	7·50
934/937 Set of 4		12·00	11·00
MS938 $5 de Havilland DHC-6 Twin Otter		4·50	6·50

1986.
1001*	10c. Messerschmitt Me 163B Komet	30	15

1986. No. 1001 overprinted with Halley's Comet emblem.
1048*	10c. Messerschmitt Me 163B Komet	50	10

1987.
1107*	$1.50 Cierva C.4 autogyro, 1923	1·75	2·75
1108*	$2 Curtiss NC-4 flying boat, 1919	2·00	3·00

1989. 50th Anniv of First Jet Flight.
1272	10c. Hawker Siddeley Comet 4 of B.O.A.C	90	45
1273	30c. Messerschmitt Me 262 of the Luftwaffe and Supermarine Spitfire of the R.A.F.	1·50	45
1274	40c. Boeing 707 of Pan Am	1·50	45
1275	60c. Canadair CL-13 Sabre of the Luftwaffe (inscribed "F-86")	1·90	55
1276	$1 Lockheed F-104 Starfighters of the U.S.A. F	2·25	1·10
1277	$2 Douglas DC-10 of Lufthansa	3·00	3·00
1278	$3 Boeing 747-300/400 of Japan Air Lines	3·25	4·50
1279	$4 McDonnell Douglas F-4 Phantom II.	3·25	4·50
1272/1279 Set of 8		16·00	13·50
MS1280 Two sheets. (a) $7 Grumman F-14A Tomcat; (b) $7 Concorde of British Airways Set of 2 sheets		9·50	12·00

1990.
1384*	$4 Short S.23 Empire "C" Class flying boat Centaurus of Imperial Airways.	4·00	5·50

1990.
1408*	45c. North American X-15	1·10	85
1409*	45c. Bell X-1	1·10	85

1991.
1483*	$5 Allied fighter-bombers, 1942	3·25	4·25
MS1484* Two sheets. (a) $6 Japanese aircraft, Pearl Harbor, 1941; (b) $6 Boeing B-17 Flying Fortress bombers raiding Schweinfurt Set of 2 sheets		9·00	11·00

1991.
1569*	$5 Sud Aviation SE 3160 Alouette III helicopter	3·25	4·50

1991.
1578*	$2 Lilienthal glider No. 5	3·25	2·75

1991.
1588*	$1 Modern jet fighters	2·25	1·75
1590*	$1 Mitsubishi A6M Zero-Sen fighters over Pearl City	2·25	1·75
1591*	$1 Mitsubishi A6M Zero-Sen fighters attacking ships at Pearl Harbor	2·25	1·75
1594*	$1 Mitsubishi A6M Zero-Sen fighters returning to aircraft carriers	2·25	1·75

1992.
MS1644* Two sheets. (a) $6 Montgolfier balloon (the other sheet does not show airplane). Price for 2 sheets		14·00	15·00

1992.
1673*	25c. Igor Sikorsky and Bolshoi Baltiskii (first four-engine airplane)	1·50	40

1992.
1701*	40c. Airship LZ-127 Graf Zeppelin	1·50	65
1713*	$6 Hugo von Eckener (airship pioneer).	4·50	5·50
MS1714* Four sheets. (b) $6 Airship LZ-129 Hindenburg (other sheets do not show aircraft) Price for 4 sheets		21·00	22·00

1993.
1811*	$1.50 Curtiss JN-4 "Jenny" (on United States of America stamp No. A548 with centre inverted)	1·25	1·25

1993. Aviation Anniversaries.
1848*	30c. Airship LZ-127 Graf Zeppelin	1·00	70
1850*	40c. Gloster Whittle E28/39, 1941	1·00	1·00
1851*	40c. Jean-Pierre Blanchard and his balloon at Philadelphia, 1793	1·00	1·00
1852*	$4 Curtiss JN-4 "Jenny"	3·75	4·50
1853*	$5 Airship LZ-129 Hindenburg, 1936	3·75	4·50
1854*	$5 Gloster Meteor Mk. I and German V-1 flying bomb	3·75	4·50
MS1855* Three sheets. (b) $6 Consolidated PBY-5 Catalina flying boat of 209 Squadron, R.A.F.; (c) $6 Blanchard's balloon at Philadelphia, 1793 (other sheet does not show airplane) Set of 3 sheets		16·00	18·00

1994.
1957	$1.50 Airship LZ-127 Graf Zeppelin	2·75	2·50

1994.
2010	40c. Short S.25 Sunderland	1·00	40
2011	$2 Lockheed P-38 Lightning	2·75	2·75
2012	$3 Martin B-26 Marauder	3·25	3·75
2010/2012 Set of 3		6·25	6·25
MS2013 $6 Hawker Typhoon		6·00	6·50

1995.
2112*	$1.20 Lavochkin La-G	1·40	1·25

1995.
2134*	$1.20 Curtiss P-40B	1·10	1·25
2135*	$1.20 Supply drop	1·10	1·25
2136*	$1.20 US supply plane	1·10	1·25
2137*	$1.20 Loading cow onto plane	1·10	1·25

ANTIGUA & BARBUDA

1998. Modern Aircraft.
2700*	$1.65 Lockheed Martin YF-22 Raptor..........	1·10	1·25
2701*	$1.65 Dassault Rafale BO1..........	1·10	1·25
2702*	$1.65 Mikoyan MiG-29 'Fulcrum'..........	1·10	1·25
2703*	$1.65 Dassault Mirage 2000D..........	1·10	1·25
2704*	$1.65 Rockwell B-1B Lancer..........	1·10	1·25
2705*	$1.65 Boeing (McDonnell Douglas) C-17A Globemaster III..........	1·10	1·25
2707*	$1.65 Saab JAS39 Gripen..........	1·10	1·25
2708*	$1.65 Eurofighter EF-2000 Typhoon..........	1·10	1·25
2709*	$1.65 Sukhoi Su 27 Flanker..........	1·10	1·25
2710*	$1.65 Northrop B-2A Spirit..........	1·10	1·25
2711*	$1.65 Lockheed F-117 Nighthawk..........	1·10	1·25
MS2712*	Two sheets. (a) $6 Boeing (McDonnell Douglas) F/A18 Hornet; (b) $6 Sukhoi Su-27, Su-35 Flanker-E. Set of 2 sheets..........	7·50	8·00

1998.
2715*	$1 Boeing B-29 Superfortress *Enola Gay*	80	80
2719*	$1 Messerschmitt Me 262	80	80
2720*	$1 Dr. Hans Pabst von Ohain, jet engine pioneer..........	80	80
2723*	$1 Zeppelin airship..........	80	80
2724*	$1 Count Ferdinand von Zeppelin, airship pioneer..........	80	80

1998. 80th Anniv of the Royal Air Force.
2748	$1.75 McDonnell Douglas Phantom F GR1	1·25	1·40
2749	$1.75 SEPECAT Jaguar GR1A	1·25	1·40
2750	$1.75 Panavia Tornado F3..........	1·25	1·40
2751	$1.75 McDonnell Douglas Phantom FGR2.	1·25	1·40
2748/2751	Set of 4..........	4·50	5·00
MS2752	Two sheets. (a) $6 Bristol F2B; (b) $6 Hawker Hurricane and Eurofighter EF-2000 Typhoon. Set of 2 sheets..........	8·00	8·50

2000. Centenary of First Zeppelin Flight.
3105	$3 Zeppelin LZ-1 airship, 1900..........	1·75	2·00
3106	$3 Zeppelin LZ-2 airship, 1906..........	1·75	2·00
3107	$3 Zeppelin LZ-3 airship, 1906..........	1·75	2·00
3105/3107	Set of 3..........	4·75	5·50
MS3108	$6.00 Zeppelin LZ-7 *Deutschland* 1910.......	3·25	3·50

2000. 60th Anniv of the Battle of Britain.
3220*	$1.20 Hawker Hurricane..........	1·00	1·00
3225*	$1.20 Bristol Blenheim..........	1·00	1·00
3227*	$1.20 Bristol Blenheim..........	1·00	1·00
3228*	$1.20 Heinkel He III..........	1·00	1·00
3229*	$1.20 Supermarine Spitfire..........	1·00	1·00
3231*	$1.20 Messerschmitt Bf 109..........	1·00	1·00
MS3233*	Two sheets. (a) $6 Junkers Ju Stuka (inscribed 878 in error); (b) $6 Supermarine Spitfire Set of 2 sheets..........	10·00	11·00

2002. 75th Anniv of First Solo Trans-Atlantic Flight.
3589	$2.50 Ryan NYP Special *Spirit of St. Louis*.....	1·60	1·75
3590	$2.50 Ryan NYP Special *Spirit of St. Louis*.....	1·60	1·75

3591	$2.50 Charles Lindbergh..........	1·60	1·75
3589/3591	Set of 3..........	4·25	4·75
MS3592	$6 Charles Lindbergh..........	3·25	3·50

2003. Centenary of Powered Flight.
MS3773*	$2 Wright Flyer I; $2 Cornu's helicopter; $2 Ely's biplane; $2Curtiss A-1	5·00	5·50
MS3774*	$2 Bell X-5; $2 Convair XFY-1; $2 North American X-15	5·00	5·50
MS3775*	$2 Concorde; $2 Martin X-24..........	3·25	3·50
MS3776*	Three sheets. (a) $6 Boeing 200 Monomail; (b) $6 Bell X-1; (c) $6 Grumman X-29 Set of 3 sheets..........	3·25	3·50

2004.
MS3844*	Two sheets. (a) $2 General Aircraft G.A.L. 49 Hamilcar Mk1 glider; (b) $2 Airspeed AS58 Horsa Mk1 glider Set of 2 sheets..........	9·00	9·50

2006. 50th Anniv of LIAT (Leewards Islands Air Transport).
3990	30c. Hawker Siddeley HS-748..........	25	15
3991	50c. Britten Norman BN-2 Islander..........	30	20
3992	50c. Britten Norman BN-2 Islander..........	30	20
3993	50c. Beech Model 50 Twin Bonanza.........	30	20
3994	$1.50 BAC 111 and Hawker Siddeley HS748	90	90
3995	$2.50 de Havilland Canada DHC-8..........	1·60	1·40
3990/3995	Set of 6..........	3·25	2·75
MS3996	$5 Beech Model 50 Twin Bonanza..........	2·75	3·00

2006.
4009	$2 Northrop T-38 Talon..........	1·25	1·25
4010	$2 Northrop T-38 Talon..........	1·25	1·25

2006.
4018	$3 Recovery of ASTP Apollo Command module	1·75	1·75

2007.
4115	$1.50 Concorde in flight..........	90	75
4116	$1.50 Concorde in flight..........	90	75
4117	$1.50 Concorde in flight..........	90	75
4118	$1.50 Concorde in flight..........	90	75
4119	$1.50 Concorde in flight..........	90	75
4120	$1.50 Concorde in flight..........	90	75
4121	$1.50 Concorde and London Eye..........	90	75
4122	$1.50 Concorde and Sydney Opera House	90	75
4123	$1.50 Concorde and London Eye..........	90	75
4124	$1.50 Concorde and Sydney Opera House	90	75
4125	$1.50 Concorde and London Eye..........	90	75
4126	$1.50 Concorde and Sydney Opera House	90	75
4115/4126	Set of 12..........	9·75	8·00

2007. Centenary of the Helicopter.
4127	$1.50 NH Industries NH90..........	90	75
4128	$1.50 Bolkow BO105..........	90	75
4129	$1.50 NH Industries NH90..........	90	75
4130	$1.50 Agusta (Sikorsky) AS-61..........	90	75
4131	$1.50 Bolkow BO105..........	90	75
4132	$1.50 Agusta (Sikorsky) A5-61..........	90	75
4127/4132	Set of 6..........	4·75	4·00
MS4133	$6 Bell UH-1 Iroquois (Huey)..........	3·00	3·25

ARGENTINA

South America

1928. 100 centavos = 1 peso

1985. 100 centavos = 1 austral

1992. 100 centavos = 1 peso

1928.
558*	5c. Biplane..........	1·80	75
559*	10c. Biplane..........	2·75	1·10
561*	18c. Biplane..........	5·00	3·75
567a*	36c. Biplane..........	3·00	1·50

1930. Nos. 562, 568, 571/2 and 575/6 overprinted ZEPPELIN 1er. VUELO 1930 and LZ-127 *Graf Zeppelin* airship.
587	20c. Yellow-headed Caracara (bird)	14·50	8·50
588	50c. Andean Condor..........	19·00	13·00
589	90c. Winged wheel..........	13·00	8·50
584	1p. Winged wheel..........	29·00	14·00
585	1p.80 Andean Condor..........	85·00	37·00
586	3p.60 Andean Condor..........	£225	£110

1931. No. 561 overprinted 1930 6 Septiembre 1931.
624*	18c. Biplane..........	2·75	1·60

1932. Nos. 558 and 561 overprinted GRAF ZEPPELIN 1932.
629*	5c. Biplane..........	3·25	2·10
630*	18c. Biplane..........	14·00	9·50

1940.
692*	1p.25 Douglas DC-2..........	90	10

1946.
779	15c. Airplane..........	45	15
780	25c. Airplane..........	45	15
779/780	Set of 2..........	30	10

1946.
781*	15c. Gliders (?)..........	90	30

1947.
794	15c. Savoia Marchetti S-55 flying boat (?)	45	15

1951. 10th Anniv of Aerolineas Argentinas (state airline).
827	20c. Douglas DC-3 of Aerolineas Argentinas..........	70	20

1951.
831*	20c. Douglas DC-4..........	95	20

1955. 25th Anniv of Commercial Air Services.
880   1p 50 Airliner and model airplane................   1·40   25

1958.
925*   1p. Douglas DC-6.........................   90   30

1958. 50th Anniv of Argentine Aero Club.
929   2p. Farman H.F.20 type biplane   35   20

1959. Inauguration of Comet Jet Airliner by Aerolineas Argentinas.
940   5p. Hawker Siddeley Comet 4 of
             Aerolineas Argentinas..........................   50   10

1963. Ninth World Gliding Championship.
1078   5p.60 Skylark 3 glider.........................   25   10
1079   11p. Super Albatross glider   60   35

1965.
1128*   11p. TA-05 (Douglas DC-3 fitted with
               skis)   90   25

1967. 50th Anniv of First Argentina-Uruguay Airmail Services.
1205   26p. Teodoro Fels' Bleriot XI, 1917..............   40   10

1967. Aeronautics Week.
1210   20p. Pedro Zanni and Fokker C.IV biplane
             Provincia de Buenos Aires, 1924   50   20

1968. Aeronautics Week.
1237   20p. Aaron de Anchorena and balloon
             Pampero   50   20

1969. 50th Anniv of First Argentine Airmail Service.
1263   20p. Nieuport 28 biplane, 1919   50   20

1969. Aeronautics Week.
1278   20p. Benjamin Matienzo and Nieuport 28
             biplane   90   20

1970. Aeronautics Week.
1351   26c. Jorge Newbery and Morane Saulnier
             Type L   65   25

1971. Aeronautics and Space Week.
1382   25c. Luis Candelaria and Morane Saulnier
             Type P   65   20

1972. Aeronautics Week.
1405   25c. Baron Antonio de Marchi, balloon
             and Voisin "Boxkite".....................   75   40

1973. 10th Anniv of First Argentine Flight to South Pole.
1414   50c. Douglas DC-3 transport aircraft.........   2·50   95

1974. Air Force Day.
1451   1p.20 Alberto Mascias and Bleriot XI............   1·00   20

1975. Air Force Day.
1478   6p. Eduardo Bradley and balloon   75   25

1976. 25th Anniv of Aerolineas Argentinas.
1513   30p. Airliner.....................................   2·00   25

1976. Air Force Day.
1527   15p. Teodoro Fels and Bleriot XI   65   15

1977. Air Force Day and Commemoration of 1926 Buenos Aires-
New York Flight.
1563*   70p. +35p. SPAD XIII and Boeing 707.....   1·60   1·00

1977.
1573   40p. Savoia S-16 ter flying boat, 1926   50   20

1977. 50th Anniv of Military Aviation Factory.
1574   30p. Jet fighter   40   10

1979. Air Force Day.
1644   250p. Vicente Almandos Almonacid and
              SPAD XIII...............................   1·30   35

1980. Air Force Day.
1685   500p. Francisco de Arteaga and Avro 504K   1·10   30

1981.
1701*   2000p. de Havilland DHC-6 Twin Otter
               200/300 ....   4·50   95

1981. Air Force Day.
1715	1000p. Pablo Castaibert and Bleriot XI..........	2·10	45

1985. First Airmail Flights.
1906	20p. Teodoro Fels' Bleriot XI Gnome..........	40	20
1907	40p. Junkers F-13L..........	65	35
1908	60p. Saint-Exupery's Latecoere	1·00	40
1909	80p. Airship LZ-127 *Graf Zeppelin*..........	1·30	60
1910	100p. Consolidated PBY-5A Catalina amphibian..........	1·80	70
1906/1910 Set of 5..........		4·75	2·00

1989. World Model Airplane Championships, La Cruz-Embals-Cordoba.
2156	5a. Model gliders	1·00	35
2157	5a. Rubber-powered model aircraft	1·00	35
2158	10a. Petrol-engine model aircraft	1·80	50
2156/2158 Set of 3..........		3·50	1·10

1990.
MS2207	2000a.+2000a. Marcos A. Zar and Savoia S-16 ter flying boat; 3000a.+ 3000a. Captain Antonio Parodi and biplane..........	12·50	12·00

1990. 50th Anniv of LADE (Airline).
2210	2500a. Junkers Ju 52/3m of LADE..................	2·10	1·10
2211	2500a. Grumman SA-16 Albatross flying boat of LADE..........	2·10	1·10
2212	2500a. Fokker F.27 Friendship of LADE..........	2·10	1·10
2213	2500a. Fokker F.28 Fellowship of LADE..........	2·10	1·10
2210/2213 Set of 4..........		7·50	4·00

1990.
2217*	3000a. Boeing 707..........	2·50	1·00

1991. 75th Anniv of Crossing of the Andes by Balloon.
2257	4000a. Eduardo Bradley, Angel Zuloaga and balloon *Eduardo Newbery*..........	1·80	85

1992.
2302*	38c. FMA IA 58 Pucara of the Argentinian Air Force..........	1·30	70

1993. 75th Anniv of First Flight over the Andes.
2340	80c. Luis Candelaria and Morane Saulnier Type P	1·90	95

1994.
2391*	75c. Helicopter and Raul Pateras de Pescara	2·75	1·20

1995.
MS2421*	25c. +25c. Antoine de Saint-Exupery (pioneer aviator) (other stamps in the miniature sheet do not show airplane)..........	12·50	12·00

1995.
MS2422*	1p.25+75c. Lockheed C-130 Hercules (other stamps in the miniature sheet do not show airplane)..........	14·00	14·00

1995.
2461	25c. Dirigible airship..........	1·00	65
2462	25c. Kite..........	1·00	65
2463	25c. Hot air balloon..........	1·00	65
2464	50c. Balloons..........	1·00	65
2465	50c. Paper airplane..........	2·00	1·30
2466	75c. Airplane..........	2·75	1·70
2467	75c. Helicopter..........	2·75	1·70
2468	75c. Parachute..........	2·75	1·70
2461/2468 Set of 8..........		13·50	8·75

1996.
2483	25c. +25c. Ramon Franco's Dornier Do-J Wal *Plus Ultra*..........	2·00	1·30
2484	25c. +25c. Alberto Santos-Dumont's biplane *14 bis*..........	2·00	1·30
2485	50c. +50c. Charles Lindbergh's Ryan NYP Special *Spirit of St. Louis*..........	4·00	2·50
2486	50c. +50c. Savoia Marchetti S.59..........	4·00	2·50
2483/2486 Set of 4..........		10·50	9·00

1996.
2496*	1p. Helicopter..........	3·75	2·40

1999.
2690	75c. Latecoere 25 mailplane..........	2·50	1·70
2691	75c. Parachutists..........	2·50	1·70

2000.
2750	25c. Potez 25	1·00	75
2751	50c. Latecoere 28..........	2·00	1·50

2000.
2752	25c. Potez 25	1·00	75
2753	25c. Saint-Exupery..........	1·00	75
2754	50c. Latecoere 28..........	2·00	1·50
2755	50c. Almonacid and Mermoz..........	2·00	1·50
2756	50c. Map, tail of Latecoere 25..........	2·00	1·50
2757	$1 Latecoere 25..........	4·00	3·00
2752/2757 Set of 6..........		11·00	8·00

2000.
2788*	50c. +50c. Airship *Graf Zeppelin*	4·25	3·25

2001.
2831	75c. Dornier Do-J Wal *Plus Ultra*	3·25	2·40

2001.
2870	75c. Carola Lorenzini and Focke Wulf 44-J	3·25	2·40
2871	75c. Jean Mermoz and Couzinet 70 'Arc-en-Ciel'..........	3·25	2·40

2002.
2881*	75c. Consolidated PBY-5A Catalina	3·25	2·40

2004.
MS3016* 75c. Sikorsky S-61R (other stamp in the miniature sheet does not show aircraft) .... 3·50   3·50

2007.
3224*   75c. Stylised aircraft on stamp.................... 1·60   95
3225*   75c. IAI Dagger A .... 1·60   95

2007. Centenary of Aaron de Anchorena and Jorge Newbery's Balloon Flight across the River Plate.
3274   1p. Balloon *Pampero* .... 1·80   1·20

ARMENIA

Western Asia

1992. 100 kopeks = 1 rouble

1994. 100 luna = 1 dram

1992.
261*   2r. Zvartnots Airport, Yerevan 30   30

1995. 86th Anniv of Atriom Katsian's World Record for Range and Altitude 1909.
335   90d. Antoinette.................................... 60   60

1996.
343*   90d. N. Stepanian (WWII pilot) and Ilyushin Il-2 Shturmovik 55   55

2000.
447*   110d. Mikoyan (aircraft designer) 65   65

2002.
516   350d. Antonov An-14 (?) .... 1·90   1·90

2005.
579*   350d. Mikoyan (aircraft designer) and MiG-25, MiG-19 and MiG-1 .... 1·90   1·90

ARUBA

West Indies

100 cents = 1 gulden

2002. Queen Beatrix Airport.
299   30c. Douglas DC-6, Dakota Airport, 1950   45   45
300   75c. Boeing 757, Queen Beatrix Airport, 1972.. 1·10   1·10
301   175c. Boeing 737, Queen Beatrix Airport, 2000.. 2·50   2·50

2007.
MS401* 500c. Convair CV-440 .... 4·50   4·50

ASCENSION

South Atlantic

1949. 12 pence = 1 shilling

20 shillings = 1 pound

1971. 100 pence = 1 pound

1949. As Nos. 114/15 of Antigua.
52*   3d. Airplane.................................... 1·00   2·00
53*   4d. Jet-powered Vickers Viking .... 4·00   1·50

1975. Wideawake Airfield.
187   2p. Lockheed C-141A StarLifter of the U.S.A.F. at Wideawake Airfield............ 80   65
188   5p. Lockheed C-130 Hercules of the R.A.F. at Wideawake Airfield................ 80   85
189   9p. Vickers Super VC-10 of British Caledonian............................... 80   1·40
190   24p. Lockheed C-5A Galaxy of the U.S.A.F   1·25   2·50
187/190 Set of 4 .... 3·25   4·75

1980.
267*   50p. Lockheed C-141B StarLifter of the U.S.A.F 60   90

1982. 40th Anniv of Wideawake Airfield.
318   5p. Fairey Swordfish torpedo bomber 75   35
319   10p. North American B-25C Mitchell .... 1·00   40
320   15p. Boeing EC-135C Aria of the U.S.A.F.   1·25   55
321   50p. Lockheed C-130 Hercules .... 1·75   1·10
318/321 Set of 4 .... 4·25   2·20

1983. Bicentenary of Manned Flight.
341   12p. Westland Wessex 5 helicopter of 845 Naval Air Squadron, Royal Navy........ 40   65
342   15p. Avro Vulcan B.2 of 44 Squadron, R.A.F. 40   75
343   20p. Hawker Siddeley H.S.801 Nimrod M.R.2P of 120 Squadron, R.A.F........ 40   85
344   60p. Handley Page H.P.80 Victor K2 XH-619 of 55 Squadron, R.A.F. 60   2·00
341/344 Set of 4 .... 1·60   3·75

1986.
403*   15p. Lockheed C-141B StarLifter of the U.S.A.F. (on stamp No. 267) 25   80
405*   70p. North American B-25C Mitchell (on stamp No. 319) 70   2·25
MS406* 75p. Bell 206B-Jet Ranger III helicopter........ 2·00   2·75

1990.
523*   25p. Mail being unloaded from Vickers VC-10 of the R.A.F. at Wideawake Airfield.. 95   85

1992.
579*   18p. Avro Type 685 York and nose hangar at Wideawake Airfield.................. 70   80

1992.
582   15p. Hawker Siddeley H.S.801 Nimrod M.R 2P .... 1·50   1·75
583   18p. Vickers VC-10 of the R.A.F. landing at Wideawake Airfield.................. 1·50   1·75
584   25p. Westland Wessex HU Mk 5 helicopter.................................. 2·00   2·25
585   65p. Avro Vulcan B.2 .... 3·25   4·75
582/585 Set of 4 .... 7·50   9·00
MS586 As Nos. 582/5, but with face values of 15p.+3p., 18p.+4p., 25p.+5p. and 65p.+13p.......... 4·75   6·00

1993. 75th Anniv of Royal Air Force.
595   20p. Sopwith Snipe, 1918.................. 2·00   1·75
596   25p. Supermarine Southampton I flying boat, 1925 .... 2·00   1·75
597   30p. Avro Type 652 Anson Mk I, 1936.... 2·00   1·90
598   70p. Vickers-Armstrong Wellington Mk Ic   3·25   4·50
595/598 Set of 4 .... 8·25   9·00
MS599 25p. Westland Lysander Mk I, 1938; 25p. Armstrong Whitworth Meteor N.F.11, 1948 (inscribed "Gloster Meteor"); 25p. de Havilland D.H.106 Comet 2 of the R.A.F.; 25p. Hawker Siddeley H.S.801 Nimrod M.R.2 .... 3·00   4·00

ASCENSION ISLAND

1993.
609*	20p. Lockheed L-1011 TriStar of the R.A.F. being loaded with mail at Brize Norton	75	60
610*	25p. Lockheed L-1011 TriStar of the R.A.F.	85	70
611*	30p. Mail being unloaded from Lockheed L-1011 TriStar of the R.A.F. at Wideawake Airfield	1·10	80

1995.
653*	25p. Fairey Swordfish	1·75	2·00

1997.
710*	25p. Lockheed Tristar	1·10	1·10

1998. 80th Anniv of Royal Air Force.
742	15p. Fairey Fawn	1·00	85
743	35p. Vickers Vernon	1·60	1·50
744	40p. Supermarine Spitfire F.22	1·75	1·75
745	50p. Bristol Britannia C.2	1·90	2·25
742/745 Set of 4		5·75	5·75
MS746 50p. Blackburn RT1 Kangaroo; 50p. Royal Aircraft Factory S.E.5a; 50p. Curtiss P-40M Kittyhawk III; 50p. Boeing B.17 Flying Fortress II		4·75	4·75

1999.
760	15p. Curtiss C-46 Commando	1·25	1·25
761	35p. Douglas C-47 Dakota	1·75	2·00
762	40p. Douglas C-54 Skymaster	1·75	2·00
763	50p. Consolidated B-24 Liberator Mk.V	1·75	2·00
760/763 Set of 4		5·75	6·50
MS764 $1.50 Consolidated B-24 Liberator LB-30A		8·00	8·00

2002.
846*	40p. Westland Sea King	1·25	1·40
847*	50p. Avro Vulcan at Wideawake Field	1·25	1·50

2003. Centenary of Powered Flight.
878	15p. Bleriot XI	75	75
879	20p. Vickers VC-10	80	80
880	35p. BAe Harrier FRS Mk.1	1·40	1·40
881	40p. Westland Sea King HAS Mk.4	1·50	1·50
882	50p. (space shuttle)	1·50	1·50
883	90p. Lockheed Martin F-16 Fighting Falcon	3·00	3·50
878/883 Set of 6		8·00	8·50
MS884 $1.50 Fairey Swordfish Mk.II		5·00	5·50

2007.
966	35p. Handley Page Victor K.Mk2	1·20	90
967	40p. Boeing Chinook	1·40	1·40
968	50p. Westland Sea King	1·40	1·40
969	£1·25 Vulcan XM607 taking off	4·00	4·50
966/969 Set of 4		7·25	7·50
MS970 Two sheets. (a) 40p. Vickers VC10; 50p. BAe Nimrod MR2. (b) £1·25 BAe Harrier		16·00	16·00

2008. 50th Anniv of NASA.
1004*	35p. Bell X-1E of NACA	1·10	1·20

2008. 90th Anniv of Royal Air Force.
1010	15p. Sopwith F7.1 Snipe	45	50
1011	35p. Vickers Wellington Mk	1·10	1·20
1012	40p. Supermarine Spitfire Mk.IX	1·20	1·30
1013	50p. Gloster Meteor F.IV	1·50	1·60
1014	65p. BAe Hawk	1·90	2·00
1015	90p. Eurofighter EF-2000 Typhoon	2·75	3·00
1010/1015 Set of 6		8·00	8·75

AUSTRALIA

Oceania

1929. 12 pence = 1 shilling

20 shillings = 1 pound

1966. 100 cents = 1 dollar

1929.
115	3d. de Havilland D.H.66 Hercules of Western Australian Airways	8·00	4·00

1931.
121	2d. Fokker F.VIIa/3m Southern Cross	1·00	1·00
122	3d. Fokker F.VIIa/3m Southern Cross	4·75	5·00
123	6d. Fokker F.VIIa/3m Southern Cross (purple) (air)	5·50	15·00
121/123 Set of 3		10·00	19·00

This design shows the incorrect registration "VH-USU".
No. 123 is inscribed "AIR MAIL" at left and "SERVICE" at right.

1931. As No. 123, but inscribed "AIR MAIL SERVICE" at foot.
139	6d. Fokker F.VIIa/3m 1985 Southern Cross (brown)	25·00	48·00

1931. No. 139 overprinted O.S. (but available for public use).
139a	6d. Fokker F.VIIa/3m 1985 Southern Cross (brown)		

1949.
232	3½d. Convair CV 240	40	60

1958.
301	2s. Lockheed L.1049 Super Constellation of QANTAS	75	1·00

1958.
304	8d. Sir Charles Kingsford Smith and Fokker F.VIIa/3m G-AUSU Southern Cross (shows incorrect registration "VH-USU")	60	1·00

1964.
370	5d. Maurice Guillaux's Bleriot XI	30	10
371	2s.3d. Maurice Guillaux's Bleriot XI	1·50	2·75
370/371 Set of 2		3·25	2·10

1965.
379	5d. Lawrence Hargrave and his "multi plane" seaplane, 1902	15	10

1969.
450*	5c. Ross and Keith Smith's Vickers Vimy G-EAOU, 1919	15	10
452*	5c. Captain Wrigley's Royal Aircraft Factory B.E.2E	15	10

1970.
477	6c. Boeing 707 of QANTAS and Avro 504	30	10
478	30c. Avro 504 and Boeing 707	70	1·50

1971.
489	6c. Dassault Mirage IIIO jet fighters and Airco (de Havilland) D.H.9A biplane	60	10

1973.
544*	35c. Airplane	2·25	2·75

1978.
658	18c. Harry Hawker and Sopwith Atlantic	30	50
659	18c. Bert Hinkler and Avro Type 581 Avian G-EBOV	30	50

660	18c. Sir Charles Kingsford Smith and Fokker F.VIIa/3m 1985 *Southern Cross*	30	50
661	18c. Charles Ulm and Fokker F.VIIa/3m 1985 *Southern Cross*	30	50
658/661	*Set of 4*	1·10	1·80

1978.

663	18c. Piper PA-31 Navajo of the Royal Flying Doctor Service	20	15

1980.

761	22c. Commonwealth Aircraft Factory CA-6 Wackett trainer, 1941	30	10
762	40c. Commonwealth Aircraft Factory CA-25 Winjeel trainer, 1955	50	75
763	45c. Commonwealth Aircraft Factory CA-13 Boomerang fighter, 1944	50	85
764	60c. Government Aircraft Factory N22B Nomad prototype VH-AUI, 1975	65	1·40
761/764	*Set of 4*	1·80	2·75

1981.

770	22c. Fokker F.VIIa/3m 1985 *Southern Cross* (on stamp No. 123)	15	10
771	60c. Fokker F.VIIa/3m 1985 *Southern Cross* (on stamp No. 123)	40	90

1984.

903	45c. Charles Ulm and Avro Type 618 Ten UH-*X *Faith in Australia*	75	1·25
904	45c. Fokker F.VIIa/3m 1985 *Southern Cross* (on stamp No. 139), Charles Ulm and Avro Type 618 Ten UH-*X *Faith in Australia*	75	1·25

1990.

1194*	$1.20 Hang-gliders	4·00	1·10

1990.

1242*	41c. Curtiss P-40B Tomahawk II fighters of the Royal Australian Air Force	50	40
1244*	$1 Bell Model 204 UH-18 Iroquois helicopter	1·25	1·40

1992.

1338*	45c. Kawasaki Ki-32 "Mary" bombers over Darwin, 1942	70	45
1339*	75c. Curtiss P-40E Kittyhawk I of the Royal Australian Air Force	1·25	1·50
1341*	$1.05 Douglas SBD Dauntless dive bombers and aircraft carrier	1·50	1·75

1994. Aviation Pioneers.

1475	45c. Lawrence Hargrave and boxkite	80	50
1476	45c. Ross and Keith Smith and Vickers FB27 Vimy	80	50
1477	$1.35 Ivor McIntyre, Stanley Goble and Fairey IIID	2·50	3·25
1478	$1.80 Freda Thompson and de Havilland D.H.60 Moth Major *Christopher Robin*	2·75	3·50
1475/1478	*Set of 4*	6·25	7·00

1996. Military Aviation.

1578	45c. Bristol Type 156 Beaufighter and Curtiss P-40E Kittyhawk II	1·75	1·75
1579	45c. Hawker Sea Fury and Fairey Firefly	1·75	1·75
1580	45c. Bell Kiowa	1·75	1·75
1581	45c. ASTA F/A18 Hornets	1·75	1·75
1578/1581	*Set of 4*	6·25	6·25

1997.

1698*	45c. Aerospatiale Dauphin (?)	1·25	1·00

1998. 50th Anniv of Royal Australian Navy Fleet Air Arm.

1758	45c. Sikorsky S-70 Seahawk	50	50

2001.

2089*	45c. Douglas DC-3 and Bell UH-1 Iroquois	60	45

2001.

2110*	45c. School of the Air pupil	80	75
2112*	45c. Royal Flying Doctor Service aircraft	80	75

2004.

2381*	50c. Black box flight recorder	85	70

2007. 50th Anniv of Special Air Service (SAS).

2860*	50c. CAC/Bell 206B-1 (A-17 helicopter)	70	70

2008. 150th Anniv of First Hot Air Balloon Flight in Australia.

2991	50c. Balloons over Sydney, New South Wales	75	75
2992	50c. Orange and white balloons over Mt. Feathertop, Victoria	75	75
2993	50c. Multicoloured balloons over Western MacDonnell Ranges, Northern Territories	75	75
2994	50c. Balloons over Canberra, Australia Central	75	75
2991/2994	*Set of 4*	2·75	2·75

OFFICIAL STAMPS

1931. Nos. 121/2 overprinted **O.S.**

O123*	2d. Fokker F.VIIa/3m 1985 *Southern Cross*	55·00	16·00
O124*	3d. Fokker F.VIIa/3m 1985 *Southern Cross*	£200	38·00

AUSTRALIAN ANTARCTIC TERRITORY

Antarctica

100 cents = 1 dollar

1966.

15*	20c. Bell 47G Trooper helicopter with floats	7·50	2·50

1973.

24*	5c. Sir Douglas Mawson's de Havilland D.H.60G Gipsy Moth VH-ULC, 1931	55	80
26*	8c. John Rymill's de Havilland D.H.83 Fox Moth G-ACRU, 1934	60	1·00
30*	25c. Hubert Wilkins' Lockheed Vega X-3903 *San Francisco*, 1928	55	1·00
31*	30c. Lincoln Ellsworth's Northrop Gamma *Polar Star*, 1935	55	1·00
32*	35c. Christensen's Avro Type 581 Avian LN-ASF, 1934	55	1·00
33*	50c. Admiral Richard E. Byrd's Ford 4-AT-B Trimotor NX-4542 *Floyd Bennett*	55	1·25

1979. 50th Anniv of First Flight over South Pole.

35	20c. Admiral Richard E. Byrd and Ford 4-AT-B Trimotor NX-4542 *Floyd Bennett*	25	60
36	55c. Admiral Richard E. Byrd and Ford 4-AT-B Trimotor NX-4542 *Floyd Bennett*	50	1·25

1984.

75*	85c. Pilatus PC-6 Porter at Antarctic landing strip	2·50	3·00

1988.

81*	37c. Hughes 500D helicopters	1·10	1·25

1998.

124*	$1 Eurocopter AS355 Eureuil	3·50	2·75

2001.

138*	10c. Lockheed Vega	55	65
145*	25c. Weather balloon	60	70

2005.

168	50c. Hughes 500 helicopter	1·25	1·40
169	50c. de Havilland Canada DHC-2 Beaver..	1·25	1·40
170	$1 Pilatus PC06 Porter	1·75	1·75
171	$1.45 Douglas DC-3/Dakota C-47	2·40	2·75
168/171 *Set of* 4		6·00	6·50

AUSTRIA

Central Europe

1915. 100 heller = 1 krone

1925. 100 groschen = 1 schilling

2002. 100 cents = 1 euro

1915.

246*	35h. +3h. Lohner Pfeilflieger B-1	2·20	5·00

1925.

616	2g. Pilot and Hansa Brandenburg C-I	65	1·30
617	5g. Pilot and Hansa Brandenburg C-I	35	35
618	6g. Pilot and Hansa Brandenburg C-I	1·50	1·70
619	8g. Pilot and Hansa Brandenburg C-I	1·80	2·10
620	10g. de Havilland D.H.34 (red)	2·20	3·00
621	10g. Pilot and Hansa Brandenburg C-I (orange)	2·75	2·10
622	15g. de Havilland D.H.34 (lake)	1·10	1·50
623	15g. Pilot and Hansa Brandenburg C-I (red)	90	95
624	20g. Pilot and Hansa Brandenburg C-I	16·00	8·50
625	25g. Pilot and Hansa Brandenburg C-I	6·25	9·25
626	30g. de Havilland D.H.34 (purple)	1·30	3·00
627	30g. Pilot and Hansa Brandenburg C-I (brown)	15·00	10·00
628	50g. de Havilland D.H.34 (grey)	1·90	3·25
629	50g. Pilot and Hansa Brandenburg C-I (blue)	25·00	15·00
630	80g. Pilot and Hansa Brandenburg C-I	4·50	4·25
631	1s. de Havilland D.H.34	16·00	8·50
632	2s. de Havilland D.H.34	2·75	4·25
633	3s. de Havilland D.H.34	60·00	65·00
634	5s. de Havilland D.H.34	18·00	27·00
635	10s. de Havilland D.H.34	10·50	21·00
616/635 *Set of* 20		£170	£170

1935.

763	5g. Junkers W.33	45	65
764	10g. Junkers G.24	45	50
765	15g. Junkers G.31 A-46 *Osterreich* of Osterreichische Luftverkehrs Aktien Gesellschaft	90	1·70
766	20g. Junkers F-13	50	50
767	25g. Junkers G.24	45	40
768	30g. Junkers W.33 A-100 *Faunas* of Osterreichische Luftverkehrs Aktien Gesellschaft	45	40
769	40g. Junkers Ju 52/3m	45	40
770	50g. Junkers W.33	45	75
771	60g. Junkers G.24 A-24	45	1·40
772	80g. Junkers F-13	55	1·40
773	1s. Junkers W.33	45	1·30
774	2s. Junkers W.33	3·25	6·75
775	3s. Junkers W.33	9·75	21·00
776	5s. Junkers G.24	5·25	17·00
777	10s. Glider	65·00	£110
763/777 *Set of* 15		80·00	£150

1947.

1017	50g. Airplane	30	85
1018	1s. Lockheed Constellation	35	85
1019	2s. Airplane	40	1·30
1020	3s. Airplane	3·00	5·75
1021	4s. Airspeed A.S.57 Ambassador (?)	2·40	5·75
1022	5s. Airplane	2·40	5·75
1023	10s. Glider	1·10	9·25
1017/1023 *Set of* 7		9·00	27·00

1958. Austrian Airlines Inaugural Flight, Vienna-London.

1329	4s. Vickers Viscount 800 OE-LAB of Austrian Airlines	90	35

1961. First Austrian Airmail Commemoration.

1363	5s. Hansa Brandenburg C-1	1·20	85

1968.

1521	2s. Etrich Limousine	40	35
1522	3s.50 Sud Aviation SE 210 Caravelle	70	65
1523	5s. Douglas DC-8 A-8021 of Austrian Airlines	1·30	1·00
1521/1523 *Set of* 3		2·20	1·80

1973. Austrian Aviation.

1658	2s. Douglas DC-9-30 OE-LDA of Austrian Airlines	40	25

1974.

1720*	4s. Tail of Douglas DC-9 OE-LBA of Austrian Airlines	75	50

1983. 25th Anniv of Austrian Airlines.

1958	6s. Douglas DC-9-80 Super Eighty of Austrian Airlines	85	65

1984. Bicentenary of First Balloon Flight in Austria.

2029	6s. Johann Stuwer's flight in a Montgolfier balloon, Vienna, 1784	1·00	70

1989. World Gliding Championships, Wiener Neustadt and World Paraskiing Championships, Damuls.

2187	6s. Glider and paraskier	95	65

1989.

2199	6s. +3s. Hansa Brandenburg C-1, 1918	1·50	1·40

1994.

2386	6s. Tail of Douglas DC-9	80	70

1995.

2401	7s. McDonnell Douglas MD-87	95	85

1999.

2543	32s. +16s. Vienna airport and Airbus A-340	7·50	7·25

2000. 75th Anniv of Civil Aviation at Klagenfurt Airport.
2559   7s. Junkers F13......................   1·10   1·00

2001. 75th Anniv of Salzburg Airport.
2585   14s. Salzburg airport and Fieseler Fi-156
           Storch..........................   2·30   2·10

2001. Centenary of Austrian Flying Club.
2590   7s. Air balloon................................   1·10   1·00

2003.
2697   55c. Balloon (cartoon)................................   1·00   1·00

2004.
2717   €2.65 +€1.30 Oeffag C.II.....................................   7·75   7·50

2005.
2765   265c. +130c. Junkers F13 flying boat...........   8·75   7·50

2006.
2823   265c. +130c. Airbus A310-300......................   9·00   9·00

2008. 50th Anniv of Austrian Airlines.
2913   140c. Airbus A320............................   1·60   1·60

AZERBAIJAN

Central Asia

1995. 100 qopik = 1 manat

2006. 1 manat = 100 qepik

1995. History of Airships.
249   100m. Charles's hydrogen balloon, 1783   15   15
250   150m. Tissandier Brothers' electrically-
           powered airship, 1883   30   30
251   250m. J-B Meusnier's elliptical balloon
           design, 1784..........................   50   50
252   300m. Baldwin's dirigible airship, 1904........   60   60
253   400m. U.S. Navy dirigible airship, 1917........   85   85
254   500m. Pedal-powered airship, 1909..............   1·00   1·00
249/254 *Set of* 6...   3·00   3·00
MS255 800m. First rigid dirigible airship by Hugo
     Eckener, 1924 No 249 is incorrectly dated..............   1·70   1·70

2005.
606   1000m. Ilyushin Il-2 Shturmovik........................   60   60

AZORES

Atlantic Ocean

1987. 100 centavos = 1 escudo

2002. 100 cents = 1 euro

1987.
480   25e. Curtiss NC-4 flying boat, 1919   50   10
481   57e. Dornier Do-X flying boat ....   1·80   1·00
482   74e.50 Savoia Marchetti S-55X flying boat...   2·50   95
483   125e. Charles Lindbergh's Lockheed 8 Sirius
           seaplane NR-211 *Tingmissartoq*,
           1933..........................   3·00   1·30
480/483 *Set of* 4..   7·00   3·00

1991.
523*   60e. Beech Model 18, 1947   95   45
525*   110e. British Aerospace ATP of Air Acores,
           1991................................   1·80   80

2000.
579*   140e. Zeppelin........................   1·10   60

BADEN

See under Germany (Allied Occupation)

BAHAMAS

West Indies

1948. 12 pence = 1 shilling

20 shillings = 1 pound

1966. 100 cents = 1 dollar

1948.
191*	5s. Avro Type 688 Tudor IV......................	18·00	4·50

1949. As Nos. 114/15 of Antigua.
196*	2½d. Airplane.........................	5·00	75
197*	3d. Jet-powered Vickers Viking.................	2·25	3·25

1954.
208*	6d. Avro Type 688 Tudor IV......................	2·25	20

1964. No. 208 overprinted **NEW CONSTITUTION 1964.**
235*	6d. Avro Type 688 Tudor IV......................	3·25	30

1965.
253*	6d. Nassau Airport...........................	1·25	10
258*	2s.6d. Sikorsky S-38 flying boat and Boeing 707	2·50	3·00

1966. Nos. 253 and 258 surcharged in decimal currency.
278*	8c. on 6d. Nassau Airport	20	20
284*	50c. on 2s.6d. Sikorsky S-38 flying boat and Boeing 707	1·00	1·40

1967. As Nos. 253 and 258, inscribed in decimal currency.
300*	8c. Nassau Airport...........................	25	10
306*	50c. Sikorsky S-38 flying boat and Boeing 707	2·25	1·00

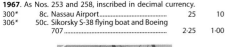

1969.
331	12c. Wings of Sikorsky S-38 flying boat.....	50	50
332	15c. Sikorsky S-38 flying boat.....................	60	1·75

1970.
350*	15c. B.A.C. One Eleven	1·50	1·75

1971.
359*	1c. Vickers Super VC-10 at airport	10	30

1980.
570*	$2 Boeing 737......................	4·25	5·50

1983.
650*	$1 Lockheed L.1329 JetStar......................	3·50	2·75

1983.
663	10c. Consolidated PBY-5 Catalina flying boat NC-77...........................	55	15
664	25c. Avro Type 688 Tudor IV G-AHNK *Star Lion* of British South American Airways...........................	75	30
665	31c. Avro Type 691 Lancastrian G-AGWH of British South American Airways....	85	45
666	35c. Consolidated Commodore flying boat of Pan Am...........................	1·00	50
663/666	*Set of 4*...........................	2·75	1·30

1985. As Nos. 663/6, but without emblem at top right.
699	10c. Consolidated PBY-5 Catalina flying boat NC-77...........................	80	50
700	25c. Avro Type 688 Tudor IV G-AHNK *Star Lion* of British South American Airways...........................	95	50
701	31c. Avro Type 691 Lancastrian G-AGWH of British South American Airways....	95	60
702	35c. Consolidated Commodore flying boat of Pan Am...........................	1·40	1·10
699/702	*Set of 4*...........................	3·75	2·50

1986.
747*	25c. Sikorsky S-38 flying boat (on stamps Nos. 331/2)...........................	2·25	50

1987.
800	15c. Boeing 737 of Bahamasair....................	3·00	1·50
801	40c. Boeing 757-200 of Eastern Airlines.....	4·00	2·25
802	45c. Airbus Industrie A300B4-200 of Pan Am...........................	4·00	2·25
803	50c. Boeing 747-200 of British Airways	4·50	4·50
800/803	*Set of 4*...........................	14·00	9·50

1987.
809*	40c. Hawker Siddeley H.S.748 of Bahamasair	2·25	2·25
810*	40c. Boeing 737 of Bahamasair and Boeing 727-200 of Pan Am....................	2·25	2·25
811*	40c. Beech 200 Super King Air....................	2·25	2·25
812*	40c. Nose of Beech A90 King Air foreground), Mooney Mk 22 Mustang and Britten Norman Islander (background)	2·25	2·25
813*	40c. Tail of Beech A90 King Air (foreground), Piper PA-31T-350 Chieftain and Bell 222 helicopter	2·25	2·25

Nos. 809/13 form a composite design showing Nassau International Airport.

1989.
868*	$1 Airplane (on stamp No. 196) and Boeing 737 of Bahamasair....................	5·50	7·00

1990.
MS876	$1 Supermarine Spitfire Mk I *Bahamas I*; $1 Hawker Hurricane Mk IIC *Bahamas V*......................	9·50	7·50

1991.
918*	60c. Lockheed WP-3D Orion of the U.S. Department of Commerce.................	2·75	4·00

1992. No. **MS876** surcharged **HURRICANE RELIEF+$1** on each stamp.
MS952	$1+$1 Supermarine Spitfire Mk I *Bahamas I*; $1 +$1 Hawker Hurricane Mk IIC *Bahamas V*.........	12·00	15·00

1993.
957	15c. Westland Wapiti IIA, 1927......................	1·75	85
958	40c. Gloster Gladiator I, 1934......................	2·25	1·00
959	55c. de Havilland D.H.100 Vampire F.3, 1946...........................	2·50	1·75
960	70c. English Electric Lightning F.3, 1962 ..	3·00	5·00
957/960	*Set of 4*...........................	8·50	7·75
MS961	60c. Avro Shackleton M.R.2, 1952; 60c. Fairey Battle, 1936; 60c. Douglas Boston III, 1942; 60c. Airco (de Havilland) D.H.9A, 1917......................	8·50	9·50

1995.
1031*	55c. Consolidated PBY-5A Catalina	2·00	1·25
1033*	70c. Consolidated B-24 Liberator................	2·50	3·75

1995.
1048*	15c. Sikorsky S-55	70	50
1050*	60c. Fokker F27 Friendship	1·50	2·00
1051*	70c. Lockheed C-130 Hercules......................	1·60	2·75

1998. 80th Anniv of Royal Air Force.
1132	15c. Handley Page HP-24 Hyderabad........	55	40
1133	55c. Hawker Demon	1·00	85
1134	60c. Gloster Meteor F8	1·10	1·25
1135	70c. Lockheed P2 Neptune	1·40	2·25
1132/1135	*Set of 4*...........................	3·75	4·25
MS1136	50c. Sopwith Camel; 50c. Short 184; 50c. Supermarine Spitfire PR19; 50c. North American B-25 Mitchell III...........................	4·00	4·25

2000. 60th Anniv of Battle of Britain.
1221	15c. Supermarine Spitfire	70	45
1222	65c. Hawker Hurricane Mk1	1·40	1·40
1223	70c. Spitfires and Heinkel He IIIs (dogfight)	1·60	1·75
1224	80c. Supermarine Spitfires	1·60	2·25
1221/1224 *Set of 4*		4·75	5·25
MS1225 $2 Presentation Spitfire		3·50	4·00

2003. Centenary of Powered Flight.
1322	15c. Piper Cub	60	30
1323	25c. de Havilland DH.82 Tiger Moth	85	55
1324	50c. Lockheed SR-71A Blackbird	1·50	1·10
1325	65c. Supermarine S.6B	1·60	1·40
1326	70c. North American P-51D Mustang *Miss America*	1·75	1·60
1327	80c. Douglas DC-3 Dakota	1·90	2·00
1322/1327 *Set of 6*		7·50	6·25

BAHAWALPUR

Indian sub-continent

12 pies = 1 anna

16 annas = 1 rupee

1947. No. 277 of India overprinted with star and crescent and line of Urdu text.
13*	14a. Armstrong Whitworth A.W.27 Ensign I	65·00

BAHRAIN

Arabian Peninsula

1938. 16 annas = 1 rupee

1957. 100 naye paise = 1 rupee

1966. 1000 fils = 1 dinar

1938. No. 258 of India overprinted **BAHRAIN**.
31*	12a. Armstrong Whitworth A.W.27 Ensign I	£130	45·00

1964.
135*	1r. Muharraq Airport	11·00	2·25
136*	2r. Muharraq Airport	11·00	2·75

1966.
143*	30f. Hawker Siddeley Comet 4 at Bahrain Airport	35	15
144*	40f. Hawker Siddeley Comet 4 at Bahrain Airport	40	15

1966.
151	10f. Hawker Siddeley Comet 4	40	10
152	20f. Hawker Siddeley Comet 4	60	10
153	40f. Hawker Siddeley Comet 4	1·70	40
154	200f. Hawker Siddeley Comet 4	8·00	3·75
151/154 *Set of 4*		9·75	4·00

1970.
175	30f. Vickers Super VC-10 of Gulf Aviation	2·75	75
176	60f. Vickers Super VC-10 of Gulf Aviation	5·00	1·70
177	120f. Vickers Super VC-10 of Gulf Aviation	9·25	5·00
175/177 *Set of 3*		15·00	6·75

1973.
196*	60f. Boeing 747-100 over Muharraq Airport	2·50	90

1974.
205	30f. Boeing 707	1·00	1·00
206	60f. Boeing 707	1·20	1·20
207	120f. Boeing 707	3·25	3·25
208	150f. Boeing 707	4·00	4·00
205/208 *Set of 4*		8·50	8·50

1976.
232	80f. Concorde of British Airways taking off from Heathrow Airport	3·50	2·50
233	80f. Concorde of British Airways landing at Bahrain Airport	3·50	2·50
234	80f. Concorde of British Airways in the air	3·50	2·50
235	80f. Concorde of British Airways on runway	3·50	2·50
232/235 *Set of 4*		12·50	9·00

1992.
453	50f. Airbus Industrie A320 over Bahrain International Airport	35	35
454	80f. Airbus Industrie A320 over Bahrain International Airport	65	65
455	150f. Airbus Industrie A320 over Bahrain International Airport	1·30	1·30
456	200f. Airbus Industrie A320 over Bahrain International Airport	1·70	1·70
453/456 *Set of 4*		3·50	3·50

1993.
465*	50f. Lockheed Martin (General Dynamics) F-16 Fighting Falcon	35	35
466*	80f. Lockheed Martin (General Dynamics) F-16 Fighting Falcon	60	60
468*	200f. Lockheed Martin (General Dynamics) F-16 Fighting Falcon	1·50	1·50

2000. 50th Anniv of Gulf Air (national airline).
660	100f. Map of Bahrain and Emblem	90	90
661	200f. Map of Bahrain and Emblem in circle	1·80	1·80
662	250f. Map of Bahrain and eagles	2·20	2·20
660/662 *Set of 3*		4·50	4·50

BANGLADESH

Indian sub-continent

100 paisa = 1 taka

1978.
121	40p. Sir Alan Cobham's de Havilland DH.50J G-EBFO	15	10
122	2t.25 Hans Bertram's Junkers W.33 seaplane D-1167 *Atlantis*	25	45
123	3t.50 Wright Flyer III	25	65
124	5t. Concorde	2·50	3·50
121/124 *Set of 4*		2·75	4·25

1980.
157*	10t. Douglas DC-9	1·25	90

1983.
218*	5t. Boeing 707	2·00	1·50

1983.
228*	2t. Zia International Airport	75	10

1989.
318*	3t. Douglas DC-10s of Bangladesh Biman at and over airport	10	10

1990.
349*	10t. Boeing 707 (on stamp No. 218)	1·75	2·50

1999.
728*	6t. Douglas DC-10 and Boeing 737	1·00	90
MS729* 25t. Douglas DC-10 and Boeing 737		3·25	3·25

OFFICIAL STAMPS

1983. No. 228 overprinted **Service**.
O43*   2t. Zia International Airport...................... 10   10

BARBADOS

West Indies

1949. 12 pence = 1 shilling
20 shillings = 1 pound
1950. 100 cents = 1 dollar

1949. As Nos. 114/15 of Antigua.
267*   1½d. Airplane.. 50   2·00
268*   3d. Jet-powered Vickers Viking............... 2·50   4·00

1970.
467* $5 Concorde over Seawell International
          Airport .... 6·50   5·50

1973. Aviation.
472   5c. Wright Type B..................................... 30   10
473   15c. de Havilland D.H.60 Cirrus Moth....... 90   10
474   25c. Lockheed 14 Super Electra PJ-AIT of
          KLM, 1939.. 1·25   20
475   50c. Vickers Super VC-10 of B.O.A.C .... 2·00   1·90
472/475 Set of 4.. 4·00   2·10

1974.
504* $1 Boeing 747... 55   1·00

1981.
688* $1 McDonnell F2H-2P Banshee
          "hurricane chaser"................................ 85   90

1983. Bicentenary of Manned Flight.
726   20c. U.S. Navy "M" Class airship M-20........ 35   15
727   40c. Douglas DC-3 CF-TOA of Trans
          Canada Airlines................................... 40   40
728   55c. Vickers Viscount 837 of B.W.I.A 40   50
729     $1 Lockheed L-1011 TriStar 500 9Y-TGJ
          Flamingo of B.W.I.A 65   2·50
726/729 Set of 4.. 1·60   3·25

1984.
MS754 $2 Jet-powered Vickers Viking (on stamp
          No. 268).. 2·50   2·50

1986.
815*   50c. Canadair DC-4M2 North Star of Trans
          Canada Airlines................................... 75   50

1986.
819*   65c. McDonnell F2H-2P Banshee
          "hurricane chaser" (on stamp
          No. 688) 90   1·00
MS821* $2 Bell Model 206L LongRanger II
          helicopter .... 10·00   12·00

1989. 50th Anniv of Commercial Aviation in Barbados.
876   25c. Hawker Siddeley H.S.748 of L.I.A.T.... 2·50   40
877   65c. Douglas DC-8-62 of Pan Am............... 3·25   1·25
878   75c. Concorde airliners of British Airways
          at Grantley Adams Airport................... 3·75   1·75
879     $2 Boeing 707-351C freighters of
          Caribbean Air Cargo .... 6·00   9·50
876/879 Set of 4.. 14·00   11·50

1992.
985*   90c. McDonnell Douglas MD-83 9Y-THM
          of B.W.I.A. over Grantley Adams
          Airport .... 3·00   2·25

1993. 75th Anniv of Royal Air Force.
991   10c. Hawker Hunter F.6, 1956.................. 75   40
992   30c. Handley Page H.P.80 Victor K2, 1965.. 1·25   40
993   70c. Hawker Typhoon IB, 1940................ 1·75   1·50
994     $3 Hawker Hurricane Mk I, 1936 .... 3·75   6·50
991/994 Set of 4.. 6·75   8·00
MS995 50c. Armstrong Whitworth Siskin IIIA,
          1925; 50c. Supermarine S6B seaplane, 1931; 50c.
          Supermarine Walrus Mk I amphibian, 1936; 50c.
          Hawker Hart, 1928............................ 2·50   2·75

1995.
1049*   35c. Avro Lancaster.............................. 90   50
1050*   55c. Supermarine Spitfire .... 1·25   75

1995.
1058   30c. Douglas C-124 Globemaster II............ 70   40
1059   45c. Westland Sea King .... 1·00   50
1060 $1.40 Westland Wessex.......................... 1·50   2·00
1061 $2 Sud Aviation SA 341 Gazelle............... 1·50   2·75
1058/1061 Set of 4.. 4·25   5·00

1996.
1089   10c. Douglas DC-10 80   30
1090   90c. Boeing 767 .... 1·75   80
1091 $1 Airbus Industrie A320 .... 1·75   1·25
1092 $1.40 Boeing 767 .... 2·25   3·50
1089/1092 Set of 4.. 6·00   5·25

1999.
1150* $1.75 Sikorsky S42 (flying boat) .... 2·00   2·25

2000.
1166* $10 Concorde over Grantley Adams
          International Airport .... 9·00   10·00

2002.
1210 $2 Lockheed. 1011 Tristar....................... 2·00   2·50

2003. Centenary of Powered Flight.
1235   10c. McDonnell F2H-2P Banshee 40   20
1236   45c. Vickers Viscount 700 70   30
1237   50c. Douglas DC9-30 80   30
1238 $1.15 Short S25 Sunderland MkII .... 1·10   70
1239 $1.40 North American P-51D Mustang ...... 1·25   1·25
1240 $2.50 Concorde .... 2·75   3·50
1235/1240 Set of 6.. 6·25   5·75

2005.
1283*   90c. Airport rescue and fire-fighting
          tender .... 1·50   75

BARBUDA

West Indies

100 cents = 1 dollar 1974.

1922. Nos. 386, 389 and 391/2 of Antigua overprinted **BARBUDA 13 JULY 1922**.
148*   ½c. Westland Dragonfly helicopter 10   10
154*   5c. Concorde of British Airways 50   15
158*   35c. Sikorsky S-38 flying boat of Pan Am... 80   1·50
160* $1 Boeing 747-100 of B.O.A.C .... 1·75   4·00

1974. Nos. 386, 389 and 391/2 of Antigua overprinted **BARBUDA 15 SEPT. 1874 G.P.U.**
149*   ½c. Westland Dragonfly helicopter 10   10
155*   5c. Concorde of British Airways 50   15
159*   35c. Sikorsky S-38 flying boat of Pan Am... 80   1·50
161* $1 Boeing 747-100 of B.O.A.C .... 1·75   4·00

1974.
179* $2.50 Britten-Norman BN-2 Islander 35   75

1974.
194* 75c. Britten-Norman BN-2 Islander 2·50 1·00

1977. No. 486 of Antigua overprinted **BARBUDA**.
322* $10 Boeing 747 over Coolidge International Airport 3·50 7·50

1977.
363* 75c. Airship LZ-1 30 30
364* 75c. German Navy airship L-31 (LZ-72) 30 30
365* 75c. Airship LZ-127 *Graf Zeppelin* in hangar 30 30
366* 75c. Gondola of military airship 30 30
371* $1.25 Lindbergh's Ryan NYP Special *Spirit of St. Louis* being fuelled 40 45
372* $1.25 Lindbergh's Ryan NYP Special *Spirit of St. Louis* leaving New York 40 45
373* $1.25 Lindbergh's Ryan NYP Special *Spirit of St. Louis* in flight 40 45
374* $1.25 Lindbergh's Ryan NYP Special *Spirit of St. Louis* arriving in France 40 45

1978. Nos. 568/70, 572, 574 and **MS**575 of Antigua overprinted **BARBUDA**.
395* ½c. Wright Glider No. III, 1902 10 10
396* 1c. Wright *Flyer I*, 1903 10 10
397* 2c. Wright *Flyer III* on launching ramp 10 10
399* 50c. Wright *Flyer III*, 1905 25 20
401* $2 Wright Type B, 1910 60 45
MS402* $2.50 Wright *Flyer I* being prepared for take-off 1·50 2·50

1978.
443* 95c. Wilbur and Orville Wright and Wright *Flyer I* 30 40
444* $1.25 Balloon *Double Eagle II* 40 45

1979. No. 606 of Antigua overprinted **BARBUDA**.
455* $2 Westland Dragonfly helicopter and Concorde 80 60

1979.
461* 75c. Nose of Boeing 747-200 25 50
463* $1.25 Douglas DC-8 25 50

1980. No. 455 further overprinted **LONDON 1980**.
497* $2 Westland Dragonfly helicopter and Concorde 2·75 1·50

1981. No. 696 of Antigua further overprinted **BARBUDA**.
597* $10 Boeing 747 over Coolidge International Airport 4·50 6·00

1983. No. 782 of Antigua overprinted **BARBUDA MAIL**.
657* $3 Lockheed L-1011 TriStar 500 1·50 3·50

1983.
663 $1 Vincenzo Lunardi's balloon over London, 1785 25 35
664 $1.50 Montgolfier balloon (first manned free flight, 1783) 40 55
665 $2.50 Blanchard and Jeffries' balloon, 1785 *Set of 3* 60 90
MS666 $5 Airship LZ-127 *Graf Zeppelin*, 1928 2·00 2·75

1983. Nos. 811/15 of Antigua overprinted **BARBUDA MAIL**.
672 30c. Dornier Do-X flying boat 1·25 35
673 50c. Supermarine S6B seaplane, 1931 1·50 60
674 60c. Curtiss F-9C Sparrowhawk biplane and airship U.S.S. *Akron* 1·75 70
675 $4 Hot-air balloon *Pro Juventute* 5·00 4·00
672/675 *Set of 4* 8·50 5·00
MS676 $5 Airship LZ-127 *Graf Zeppelin* 3·75 4·25

1985. No. 911 of Antigua overprinted **BARBUDA MAIL**.
791* $1 Sikorsky S-61N helicopter 60 60

1985. Nos. 934/8 of Antigua overprinted **BARBUDA MAIL**.
821 30c. Cessna 172D Skyhawk 2·50 75
822 90c. Fokker D.VII, 1918 3·50 1·25
823 $1.50 SPAD VII, 1916 4·25 5·50
824 $3 Boeing 747 6·00 8·50
821/824 *Set of 4* 14·50 14·50
MS825 $5 de Havilland Canada Twin Otter 3·25 3·50

1986. No. 1001 of Antigua overprinted **BARBUDA MAIL**.
887* 10c. Messerschmitt Me 163B Komet 2·50 1·00

1987. Nos. 1107/8 of Antigua overprinted **BARBUDA MAIL**.
957* $1.50 Cierva C.4 autogyro, 1923 6·50 7·00
958* $2 Curtiss NC-4 flying boat, 1919 7·00 8·00

1989. Nos. 1272/80 of Antigua overprinted **BARBUDA MAIL**.
1117 10c. Hawker Siddeley Comet 4 of B.O.A.C 3·50 2·00
1118 30c. Messerschmitt Me 262 of the Luftwaffe and Supermarine Spitfire of the R.A.F 4·50 1·50
1119 40c. Boeing 707 of Pan Am 4·75 1·25
1120 60c. Canadair CL-13 Sabre of the Luftwaffe (inscribed "F-86") 6·00 1·25
1121 $1 Lockheed F-104 Starfighters of the U.S.A.F 7·00 2·50
1122 $2 Douglas DC-10 of Lufthansa 9·00 8·00
1123 $3 Boeing 747-300/400 of Japan Air Lines 10·00 11·00
1124 $4 McDonnell Douglas F-4 Phantom II 10·00 11·00
1117/1124 *Set of 8* 49·00 35·00
MS1125 Two sheets. (a) $7 Grumman F-14A Tomcat; (b) $7 Concorde of British Airways *Set of 2 sheets* 50·00 40·00

1990. Nos. 1408/9 of Antigua overprinted **BARBUDA MAIL**.
1224* 45c. North American X-15 3·25 2·25
1225* 45c. Bell X-1 3·25 2·25

1991. No. 1384 of Antigua overprinted **BARBUDA MAIL**.
1246* $4 Short S.23 Empire "C" Class flying boat *Centaurus* of Imperial Airways 15·00 15·00

1991. Nos. 1483/4 of Antigua overprinted **BARBUDA MAIL**.
1283* $5 Allied fighter-bombers, 1942 12·00 12·00
MS1284* Two sheets. (a) $6 Japanese aircraft, Pearl Harbour, 1941; (b) $6 Boeing B-17 Flying Fortress bombers raiding Schweinfurt *Set of 2 sheets* 55·00 38·00

1992. No. 1569 of Antigua overprinted **BARBUDA MAIL**.
1341* $5 Sud Aviation SE 3160 Alouette III helicopter 10·00 12·00

1992. No. 1578 of Antigua overprinted **BARBUDA MAIL**.
1357* $2 Lilienthal glider No. 5 3·00 3·50

1992. Nos. 1588, 1590/1 and 1594 of Antigua overprinted **BARBUDA MAIL**.
1367* $1 Modern jet fighters 6·00 3·50
1369* $1 Mitsubishi A6M Zero-Sen fighters over Pearl City 6·00 3·50
1370* $1 Mitsubishi A6M Zero-Sen fighters attacking ships at Pearl Harbour 6·00 3·50
1373* $1 Mitsubishi A6M Zero-Sen fighters returning to aircraft carriers 6·00 3·50

1993. No. 1673 of Antigua overprinted **BARBUDA MAIL**.
1435* 25c. Igor Sikorsky and *Bolshoi Baltiskii* (first four-engine airplane) 3·75 80

1993. Nos. 1701 and **MS**1714 of Antigua overprinted **BARBUDA MAIL**.
1444* 40c. Airship LZ-127 *Graf Zeppelin* 3·00 1·00
MS1457* Four sheets. (b) $6 Airship LZ-129 *Hindenburg* (other sheets do not show aircraft) *Set of 4 sheets* 55·00 42·00

1995. Nos. 2010/2013 of Antigua overprinted **BARBUDA MAIL**.
1658 40c. Short S.25 Sunderland 3·50 1·25
1659 $2 Lockheed P-38 Lightning 11·00 6·00
1660 $3 Martin B-26 Marauder 11·00 7·00
1658/1660 *Set of 3* 70·00 13·00
MS1661 $6 Hawker Typhoon 19·00 18·00

1995. 50th Anniv of the end of the Second World War.
1663* $8 Heinkel He III 24·00 15·00

1997. Nos. 2112 and 2134/7 of Antigua overprinted **BARBUDA MAIL**.
1803* $1.20 Curtiss P-40 (?) 90 90
1809* $1.20 US fighter plane 90 90
1810* $1.20 Supply drop 90 90
1811* $1.20 US supply plane 90 90
1812* $1.20 Loading cow onto Douglas C-47 Skytrain 90 90

1997. No. 1663 further overprinted Golden Wedding of H.M. Queen Elizabeth II and Prince Philip 1947–1997.
1871* $8 Heinkel He III 8·00 9·00

2000. Nos. 2700/12 of Antigua overprinted **BARBUDA MAIL**.
2214* $1.65 Lockheed Martin YF-22 Raptor 1·25 1·25
2215* $1.65 Dassault Rafale BO1 1·25 1·25
2216* $1.65 Mikoyan MiG-29 "Fulcrum" 1·25 1·25
2217* $1.65 Dassault Mirage 2000D 1·25 1·25
2218* $1.65 Rockwell B-1B Lancer 1·25 1·25
2219* $1.65 Boeing (McDonnell Douglas) C-17A Globemaster III 1·25 1·25
2221* $1.65 Saab JAS39 Gripen 1·25 1·25
2222* $1.65 Eurofighter EF-2000 Typhoon 1·25 1·25
2223* $1.65 Sukhoi Su-7 Flanker 1·25 1·25
2224* $1.65 Northrop B-2A Spirit 1·25 1·25
2225* $1.65 Lockheed F-117 Nighthawk 1·25 1·25
MS2226* Two sheets. (a) $6 McDonnell Douglas F/A18 Hornet; (b) $6 Sukhoi Su-35 Flanker-E *Set of 2 sheets* 11·00 12·00

BASUTOLAND

Southern Africa
1949. 12 pence = 1 shilling
20 shillings = 1 pound
1961. 100 cents = 1 rand

1949. AS Nos. 114/15 of Antigua.
38* 1½d. Airplane 20 1·50
39* 3d. Jet-powered Vickers Viking 2·00 2·00

1954.
50* 1s.3d. de Havilland DH.106 Comet 1 22·00 6·50

1961. No. 50 surcharged in decimal currency.
65*a** 12½c. on 1s.3d. de Havilland DH.106 Comet 1 3·75 1·25

1961. As No. 50, but inscribed in decimal currency.
90* 12½c. de Havilland DH.106 Comet 1 5·00 1·50

BECHUANALAND

Southern Africa
12 pence = 1 shilling
20 shillings = 1 pound

1949. As Nos. 114/15 of Antigua.
138* 1½d. Airplane 30 1·25
139* 3d. Jet-powered Vickers Viking 1·50 2·50

BELARUS

Eastern Europe
100 kopeks = 1 rouble

1994.
76* 500r. Map and Ilyushin Il-2 Shturmovick 60 45

1995. Birth Centenary of Pavel Sukhoi (aircraft designer).
130 600r. Sukhoi Su-27 and another aircraft (possibly Su-7 swing-wing or one of its many developments) 40 30

1997.
273* 1400r. Stylized hang-glider 30 20

1999. Third Death Anniv of Wing Commander Karvat.
355 25000r. Wing Commander Karvat 1·20 95

2000. 25th Death Anniv of Pavel Sukhoi.
392	50r. Sukhoi Su-24		80	60
393	50r. Sukhoi Su-27		80	60
394	50r. Sukhoi Su-25		80	60
392/394 Set of 3			2·20	1·60
MS395 150r. Sukhoi Su-24; 150r. Sukhoi Su-25; 150r. Sukhoi Su-27			2·50	2·30

2001. 25th Death Anniv of Pavel Sukhoi.
436	250r. Tupolev ANT-25RD		1·20	95
437	250r. Tupolev ANT-37 'Rodina'		1·20	95

BELGIAN CONGO

Central Africa
100 centimes = 1 franc

1920.
87	50c. Bleriot XI		40	10
88	1f. Bleriot XI		40	10
89	2f. Bleriot XI		65	35
90	5f. Bleriot XI		1·00	50
87/90 Set of 4			2·20	95

1930.
169	15f. de Havilland D.H.66 Hercules		4·25	1·75
170	30f. de Havilland D.H.50A		5·75	3·75
169/170 Set of 2			4·25	1·75

1934.
197	50c. Fokker F.VII3m OO-AIX		60	65
198	1f. Fokker F.VII3m OO-AIX		85	30
199	1f.50 Fokker F.VII3m OO-AIX		70	15
200	3f. Fokker F.VII3m OO-AIX		30	20
201	4f.50 Fokker F.VII3m OO-AIX		90	10
202	5f. Fokker F.VII3m OO-AIX		95	10
203	15f. Fokker F.VIIb/3m OO-AIX		2·10	85
204	30f. Fokker F.VIIb/3m OO-AIX		2·50	2·40
205	50f. Fokker F.VIIb/3m OO-AIX		7·00	2·25
197/205 Set of 9			14·50	6·25

1936. No. 200 surcharged **3.50F**.
214	3f.50 on 3f. Fokker F.VIIb/3m OO-AIX		25	10

1941. No. 199 surcharged **50c**.
245*	50c. on 1f.50 Fokker F.VIIb/3m OO-AIX		90	80

BELGIUM

North-west Europe
100 centimes = 1 franc

1930.
560	50c. Fokker F.VIIa/3m I-BDEO		50	25
561	1f.50 Fokker F.VIIa/3m I-BDEO		3·00	2·50
562	2f. Fokker F.VIIa/3m I-BDEO		2·00	90
563	5f. Fokker F.VIIa/3m I-BDEO (red)		2·00	1·20
564	5f. Fokker F.VIIa/3m I-BDEO (violet)		33·00	31·00
560/564 Set of 5			36·00	32·00

1932.
621	75c. Piccard's stratosphere balloon F.N.R.S., 1931		3·00	25
622	1f.75 Piccard's stratosphere balloon F.N.R.S., 1931		17·00	2·10
623	2f.50 Piccard's stratosphere balloon F.N.R.S., 1931		20·00	14·00
621/623 Set of 3			36·00	14·50

1935. Nos. 561 and 563 surcharged.
686	1f. on 1f.50 Fokker F.VIIa/3m I-BDEO		50	50
687	4f. on 5f. Fokker F.VIIa/3m I-BDEO		9·50	8·75
686/687 Set of 2			6·75	5·25

1946.
1165	6f. Douglas DC-4 OO-DAA of SABENA		50	25
1166	8f.50 Douglas DC-4 OO-DAA of SABENA		65	45
1167	50f. Douglas DC-4 OO-DAA of SABENA		6·00	85
1168	100f. Douglas DC-4 OO-DAA of SABENA		10·00	2·10
1165/1168 Set of 4			15·00	3·25

1946.
1177	17f.50 +62f.50 Lockheed C-60 Lodestar and Boeing B-17 Flying Fortress (green)		1·60	1·00
1178	17f.50 +62f.50 Lockheed C-60 Lodestar and Boeing B-17 Flying Fortress (purple)		1·60	1·00

1946.
1193	2f. +8f. Douglas DC-4		60	60

1948.
1222*	2f.25 Douglas DC-4		1·00	60
1224*	3f. Douglas DC-4		13·00	40
1227*	6f. Douglas DC-4		25·00	50
1228*	6f.30 Douglas DC-4		3·00	2·50

1949.
1275*	50f. Douglas DC-4 and Airco (de Havilland) D.H.9 biplane		50·00	18·00

1950.
1317	7f. +3f. Sikorsky S-51 helicopter and Douglas DC-4 at Melsbroeck Airport		8·00	5·00

1951.
1368	6f. Arsenal Air 100 glider (blue)		27·00	16·00
1369	7f. Fairey Tipsy Belfair Trainer I OO-TIC (red)		27·00	16·00

Nos. 1368/9 were sold with a combined additional premium of 37f.

1951. As Nos. 1368/9, but colours changed.
1370	6f. Arsenal Air 100 glider (brown)		5·25	30
1371	7f. Fairey Tipsy Belfair Trainer I OO-TIC (green)		5·25	80

1957.
1610	4f. Sikorsky S-58 helicopter OO-SHC of SABENA		80	45

1957.
1619	5f. +2f.50 Helicopter at Antarctic base		3·50	2·50

1959.
1704	6f. Boeing 707 of SABENA		1·70	60

1960.
1726*	40c. +10c. Parachutists and Douglas DC-4		30	60
1727*	1f. +50c. Parachutists and Douglas DC-4		1·60	1·20

1960.
1740	40c. +10c. Boeing 707 airliners		20	25
1741	3f. +1f.50 Boeing 707 airliners of SABENA		2·30	1·50
1742	6f. +3f. Boeing 707 of SABENA		5·00	4·00
1740/1742 Set of 3			6·75	5·25

1963.
1861	3f. Sud Aviation SE 210 Caravelle of SABENA		30	15

1973.
2311	8f. Douglas DC-10-30CF of SABENA and Airco (de Havilland) D.H.9 O-BIEN of Syndicat National pour l'Etude des Transports Aeriens over airport		55	45

1973.
2312	10f. Ernest Tips' biplane, 1908		70	45

1975.
2404   7f. Edmond Thieffry and Handley Page
H.P.26 W.8e Hamilton O-BAHO
Princess Marie-Jose................................. 50   25

1976.
MS2435 25f.+10f. Jan Olieslagers and Bleriot XI....... 2·50   2·20

1980.
2590   9f. Fokker F.VIIa/3m (on stamp No. 564)   60   20

1983.
2758   11f. Hot-air balloon 65   15
2759   22f. Hot-air balloon .... 1·50   45
2758/2759 *Set of 2* .... 1·25   35

1993.
3190   15f. Airliners at airport .... 1·00   25

1994.
3215   13f. Hanriot HD-1 80   45
3216   15f. SPAD XIII.. 1·00   30
3217   30f. Schrenck FBA.H flying boat .... 1·70   80
3218   32f. Stampe SV-4B biplane .... 1·80   80
3215/3218 *Set of 4* .... 4·75   2·10

1998. 75th Anniv of Sabena Airlines.
3427   17f. Avro RJ85 90   65

1999.
3482*   17f. Lockheed Martin F-16 Fighting
Falcon... 90   70

2000.
3557*   17f. Lockheed L-1011 Tristar 85   60

2000.
3570   17f. +4f. Children flying kites .... 1·20   1·40

2000.
MS3613 17f. American soldiers and Boeing CH-47
Chinook (miniature sheet also contains other
stamps which do not show aircraft) .... 18·00   17·00

RAILWAY OFFICIAL STAMPS

1946. As No. 1224, but additionally inscribed "B" in oval frame.
O1242*   3f. Douglas DC-4 .... 27·00   7·75

BELIZE

Central America

100 cents = 1 dollar

1976.
440*   35c. Charles Lindbergh and Ryan NYP
Special *Spirit of St. Louis* 20   40

1979.
480*   5c. Fairchild monoplane XH-TAD 25   30

1979.
504   4c. Mortimer and Vaughan "Safety"
airplane, 1910 50   10
505   25c. Boeing 720 of Belize Airways .... 1·50   20
506   50c. Concorde.. 4·25   30
507   75c. Handley Page H.P.18 W.8b, 1922 .... 2·00   30
508   $1 Avro Type F, 1912 .... 2·00   30
509   $1.50 Samuel Cody's Michelin Cup biplane,
1910.. 2·75   30
510   $2 A.V. Roe Triplane I, 1909 .... 2·75   40
511   $3 Santos-Dumont's biplane *14 bis* ...... 2·75   45
512   $4 Wright Type A .... 3·00   65
504/512 *Set of 9* .... 19·00   2·75
MS513 Two sheets. (a) $5 Dunne D-5 biplane, 1910,
$5 Concorde (on Great Britain stamp No. 784); (b)
$10 Boeing 720 *Set of 2 sheets* .... 21·00

1983.
736   10c. Francesco de Lana-Terzi's "Aerial
Ship", 1670... 2·50   65
737   25c. Bartolomeu de Gusmao's *La
Passarola*, 1709 .... 3·25   70
738   50c. Guyton de Morveau's balloon with
oars, 1784 .... 3·50   1·00
739   85c. Airship .... 4·25   1·60
740   $1 Airship *Clement Bayard* .... 4·50   1·60
741   $1.50 Beardmore airship R-34.............. 5·00   3·25
736/741 *Set of 6*.. 21·00   7·50
MS742 Two sheets. (a) $3 Charles Green's balloon
Royal Vauxhall, 1836; (b) $3 Montgolfier balloon
(first manned free flight, 1783) *Set of 2 sheets*........ 30·00   6·00

1985.
840*   50c. Hawker Hurricane Mk I and
Supermarine Spitfires 55   85

1985. No. 840 overprinted **PRE "WORLD CUP FOOTBALL"
MEXICO 1986.**
881*   50c. Hawker Hurricane Mk I and
Supermarine Spitfires 75   90

1986.
931*   50c. Curtiss JN-4 "Jenny" (on United
States of America stamp No. A548
with centre inverted)............................... 75   80

1986. No. 931 overprinted **STOCKHOLMIA 86** and emblem.
952*   50c. Curtiss JN-4 "Jenny" (on United
States of America stamp No. A548
with centre inverted)............................... 80   1·10

1988.
1048* $2 Auster ambulance airplane, 1940...... 5·50   6·00

1990.
1086   10c. Fairey Battle of No. 12 Squadron,
R.A.F. .... 1·00   50
1087   25c. Bristol Type 152 Beaufort of No. 22
Squadron, R.A.F. .... 1·60   50
1088   60c. Bristol Type 142 Blenheim Mk IV of
No. 21 Squadron, R.A.F .... 2·00   2·00
1089   75c. Armstrong Whitworth Whitley of
No. 102 Squadron, R.A.F .... 2·00   2·00
1090 $1 Vickers-Armstrong Wellington Mk Ic
of No. 214 Squadron, R.A.F...................... 2·00   2·00
1091 $2 Handley Page Hampden of No. 83
Squadron, R.A.F. .... 2·50   3·50
1086/1091 *Set of 6*... 10·00   9·50

1993.
1138   25c. Sud Aviation SA 330E Puma
helicopter of the R.A.F. .... 1·00   60
1139   50c. Hawker Siddeley Harrier GR.3 .... 1·25   80
1140   60c. de Havilland D.H.98 Mosquito
Mk XVIII .... 1·40   1·10
1141   75c. Avro Type 683 Lancaster .... 1·40   1·10
1142 $1 Consolidated Liberator I of the R.A.F   1·60   1·40

1143	$3 Short Stirling Mk I	3·25	5·50
1138/1143	Set of 6	9·00	9·50

1995.
1185*	$1 Vickers Type 271 Wellington	1·40	1·75

2003. Centenary of Powered Flight.
1299	25c. Avro Shackleton Mk3	55	45
1300	60c. Lockheed L-749 Constellation	75	65
1301	75c. SEPECAT Jaguar GR.1	85	75
1302	$3 BAe Harrier GR.3	2·25	3·00
1299/1302	Set of 4	4·00	4·25
MS1303	$5 Ryan NYP Special *Spirit of St. Louis*	4·50	5·00

BENIN

West Africa

100 centimes = 1 franc

1977.
648	200f. Outline of Douglas DC-10	3·00	2·10

1977.
654	80f. Concorde of Air France	95	40
655	150f. Airship LZ-127 *Graf Zeppelin*	2·10	90
656	300f. Charles Lindbergh and Ryan NYP Special *Spirit of St. Louis*	3·00	1·60
657	500f. Charles Nungesser, Francois Coli and Levasseur PL-8 *L'Oiseau Blanc*	6·25	3·25
654/657	Set of 4	14·00	7·25

1977. No. 654 overprinted 1er Vol Commercial 22.11.77 Paris-New York.
678	80f. Concorde of Air France	1·70	85

1978.
688	50f. Boeing 707 and airfield under attack	1·20	45

1978.
728*	90f. Boeing 747	1·30	55

1978.
732	500f. Wilbur and Orville Wright and Wright *Flyer I*	6·00	3·00

1979.
753*	50f. Lockheed L-1011 TriStar 500	2·00	95

1979.
763	50f. Concorde	50	25
764	60f. Concorde	55	25

1980.
789	90f. Breguet 19 Super TR *Point d'Interrogation*	1·00	45
790	100f. Dieudonne Costes, Maurice Bellonte and Breguet 19 Super TR *Point d'Interrogation*	1·20	55

1983. Nos. 790 and 655 surcharged 75F.
902*	75f. on 100f. Dieudonne Costes, Maurice Bellonte and Breguet 19 Super TR *Point d'Interrogation*	3·25	65
904*	75f. on 150f. Airship LZ-127 *Graf Zeppelin*	3·25	65

1983.
914	125f. Boeing 747	1·20	60

1984. No. 914 surcharged 5f.
923*	5f. on 125f. Boeing 747	3·25	75

1984. No. 648, 656 and 732 surcharged in figures.
954*	75f. on 200f. Outline of Douglas DC-10	6·00	1·30
963*	75f. on 300f. Charles Lindbergh and Ryan NYP Special *Spirit of St. Louis*	4·50	1·30
965*	90f. on 500f. Wilbur and Orville Wright and Wright *Flyer I*	4·50	1·40

1985.
991	150f. Boeing 727	1·80	75

1986.
1035	100f. Douglas DC-10 of Air Afrique	1·00	50

1988. No. 439 of Dahomey surcharged Republique Populaire du Benin 10f.
1076*	10f. on 50f. Boeing 747	55·00	2·75

1990.
1127	150f. Balloons and airplane	1·40	65

BERMUDA

North Atlantic Ocean

1949. 12 pence = 1 shilling

20 shillings = 1 pound

1970. 100 cents = 1 dollar

1949. As Nos. 114/15 of Antigua.
130*	2½d. Airplane	30	2·00
131*	3d. Jet-powered Vickers Viking	1·75	1·25

1967.
210*	1s.6d. Vickers VC-10	25	25

1975. 50th Anniv of Air Mail Service to Bermuda.
330	5c. Short S.23 flying boat G-ADUU *Cavalier* of Imperial Airways	40	10
331	17c. U.S. Navy airship ZR-3 *Los Angeles*	1·25	85
332	20c. Lockheed L.049 Constellation of Pan Am	1·40	2·75
333	25c. Boeing 747-100 at airport	1·50	3·50
330/333	Set of 4	4·00	6·50

1980.
417*	25c. Lockheed L-1011 TriStar 500 of British Airways	30	15

1983. Bicentenary of Manned Flight.
465	12c. Curtiss N-9 seaplane	60	20
466	30c. Stinson Pilot Radio seaplane	1·25	1·25
467	40c. Short S.23 flying boat G-ADUU *Cavalier* of Imperial Airways	1·50	1·75
468	$1 U.S. Navy airship ZR-3 *Los Angeles*	2·75	5·50
465/468	Set of 4	5·50	7·75

1986.
531*	50c. Curtiss N-9 seaplane (on stamp No. 465)	2·25	1·00

1987. 50th Anniv of Inauguration of Bermuda-USA Air Service.

549	15c. Sikorsky S-42B flying boat *Bermuda Clipper* of Pan Am	2·00	15
550	40c. Short S.23 flying boat G-ADUU *Cavalier* of Imperial Airways	3·00	70
551	50c. Sikorsky S-42B flying boat *Bermuda Clipper* of Pan Am	3·25	80
552	$1.50 Short S.23 flying boat G-ADUU *Cavalier* of Imperial Airways (on ground) and Sikorsky S.42B flying boat *Bermuda Clipper* of Pan Am (in flight)	6·00	3·50
549/552 *Set of 4*		13·00	4·75

1991.

637*	55c. Boeing B-17 Flying Fortress over Kindley Airfield	2·50	1·40
638*	70c. Boeing 314A flying boat	3·00	3·50

1993. 75th Anniv of Royal Air Force.

687	25c. Consolidated PBY-5 Catalina flying boat of the R.A.F.	85	35
688	60c. Supermarine Spitfire Mk IX	2·00	2·00
689	75c. Bristol Type 156 Beaufighter Mk X	2·25	2·25
690	$2 Handley Page Halifax Mk III	3·75	6·00
687/690 *Set of 4*		8·00	9·50

1995.

731*	25c. Kite flying	55	35

1995. Military Bases.

739*	60c. Douglas C-47	1·50	1·50
740*	75c. RAF base (Darrrell's Island flying boat base)	1·75	2·00

BHUTAN

Central Asia

100 chetrum = 1 ngultrum

1967. Nos. 22/4, 41/2 and 75/9 overprinted **AIR MAIL** and Sikorsky S-55 helicopter.

107	33ch. Dancer	10	15
108	50ch. Rhododendron	25	25
109	70ch. Dancer	30	30
110	75ch. Peony	25	25
111	1n. Dancer	35	35
112	1n.50 Dhole	55	55
113	2n. Pygmy hog	80	80
114	3n. Snow leopard	1·20	1·20
115	4n. Asiatic black bear	1·80	1·80
116	5n. Takin	2·30	2·30
107/116 *Set of 10*		7·00	7·25

1967. Commemoration of the Battle of Britain.

137	45ch. Avro Type 683 Lancaster	20	20
138	2n. Supermarine Spitfire Mk IIB	45	45
139	4n. Hawker Hurricane Mk IIC	90	90
137/139 *Set of 3*		1·40	1·40

1970. Nos. 138/9 surcharged **20 CH**.

229*	20ch. on 2n. Supermarine Spitfire Mk IIB	2·75	2·75
230*	20ch. on 4n. Hawker Hurricane Mk IIC	2·75	2·75

1972. Appendix stamp (U.P.U. Headquarters Building) surcharged **90 CH**.

264*	90ch. on 2n.50 Airliner	2·75	2·75

1974.

286*	4ch. Vickers FB-27 Vimy and Concorde	10	10
290*	2n. Vickers FB-27 Vimy and Concorde	80	80

1978.

381*	20n. Lindbergh's Ryan NYP Special *Spirit of St. Louis*	4·00	4·00
382*	20n. Airship LZ-3	4·50	4·50
MS384*	Seven sheets. (e) 25n. Lindbergh's Ryan NYP Special *Spirit of St. Louis* landing at Le Bourget; (g) 25n. Airship LZ-11 *Viktoria Luise* (other sheets do not show aircraft) *Price for 7 sheets*	42·00	42·00

1978. No. 290 surcharged **25 CH**.

398*	25ch. on 2n. Vickers FB-27 Vimy and Concorde	3·00	2·50

1983. Bicentenary of Manned Flight.

506	50ch. Dornier Do-J II 10-t Wal flying boat D-AGAT *Boreas* of Lufthansa	10	10
507	3n. Savoia Marchetti S-66 flying boat I-TUTO	60	55
508	10n. Hawker Osprey biplane	2·00	1·90
509	20n. Astra airship *Ville de Paris*	4·00	3·75
506/509 *Set of 4*		6·00	5·75
MS510	25n. Henri Giffard's balloon *Le Grand Ballon Captif*, 1878	5·00	4·50

1988.

MS736*	Four sheets. (a) 25n. Concorde of British Airways (other sheets show trains) *Price for 4 sheets*	17·00	17·00

1992.

982*	1n. British Aerospace BAe 146	10	10

1992.

986*	5n. Avro RJ70	35	35

1999.

1446*	20n. North American X-15	90	90

2000. Centenary of First Zeppelin Flight.

1554	25n. LZ-1 (first flight, 1900)	1·30	1·30
1555	25n. LZ-2, 1906	1·30	1·30
1556	25n. LZ-3 over hills (first flight, 1906)	1·30	1·30
1557	25n. LZ-127 *Graf Zeppelin* (first flight, 1928)	1·30	1·30
1558	25n. LZ-129 *Hindenburg* (first flight, 1936)	1·30	1·30
1559	25n. LZ-130 *Graf Zeppelin II* (first flight, 1938)	1·30	1·30
1560	25n. LZ-1 over hill	1·30	1·30
1561	25n. LZ-2 over mountains	1·30	1·30
1562	25n. LZ-3 against sky	1·30	1·30
1563	25n. LZ-4 (first flight, 1908)	1·30	1·30
1564	25n. LZ-5 (first flight, 1909)	1·30	1·30
1565	25n. LZ-6 (formation of Deutsche Liftschiffahrts Aktien Gesallschaft DELAG)	1·30	1·30
1566	25n. LZ-1 over grassy hills	1·30	1·30
1567	25n. Z-11 *Ersatz* 1913	1·30	1·30
1568	25n. LZ-6 exiting hangar	1·30	1·30
1569	25n. LZ-10 *Schwaben* (first flight 1911)	1·30	1·30
1570	25n. LZ-7 *Deutschland*	1·30	1·30
1571	25n. LZ-11 *Viktoria Luise*	1·30	1·30
1554/1571 *Set of 18*		21·00	21·00
MS1572	Three sheets. (a) 80n. Count Ferdinand von Zeppelin wearing white cap; (b) 80n. Zeppelin wearing cap; (c) 80n. Zeppelin	12·50	12·50

2000.

1580*	25n. North American X-15	1·30	1·30

2000.

1613	25n. Laird Commercial, 1929	1·20	1·20
1614	25n. Ryan B-5 Brougham, 1927	1·20	1·20
1615	25n. Cessna AW, 1928	1·20	1·20
1616	25n. Travel Aire 4000, 1927	1·20	1·20
1617	25n. Fairchild F-71, 1927	1·20	1·20
1618	25n. Command Aire, 1928	1·20	1·20
1619	25n. Waco YMF, 1935	1·20	1·20

1620	25n. Piper J-4 Cub Coupe, 1938	1·20	1·20
1621	25n. Ryan ST-A, 1937	1·20	1·20
1622	25n. Spartan Executive, 1939	1·20	1·20
1623	25n. Luscombe 8, 1939	1·20	1·20
1624	25n. Stinson SR-5 Reliant, 1935	1·20	1·20
1625	25n. Cessna 195, 1949	1·20	1·20
1626	25n. Waco SRE, 1940	1·20	1·20
1627	25n. Erco Model 415 Ercoupe, 1948	1·20	1·20
1628	25n. Boeing Stearman Model 75, 1941	1·20	1·20
1629	25n. Beech Model 17 Staggerwing, 1944	1·20	1·20
1630	25n. Republic Seabee, 1947	1·20	1·20
1613/1630 Set of 18		19·00	19·00

MS1631 Three sheets. (a) 100n. Waco CSO, 1929; (b) 100n. Curtiss-Wright 19W, 1936; (c) 100n. Grumman G-44 Widgeon, 1941 *Set of 3 sheets* ...... 12·00 12·00

2002. 75th Anniv of First Solo Trans-Atlantic Flight.
MS1730 Two sheets. (a) 75n. Lindbergh and Ryan NYP Special *Spirit of St. Louis*; 75n. Lindbergh; (b) 90n. Lindbergh *Set of 2 sheets* ...... 5·75 5·75

APPENDIX

The following stamps have either been issued in excess of postal needs or have not been made available to the public in reasonable quantities at face value. Miniature sheets, imperforate stamps, etc are excluded from this section.

1970

New U.P.U Headquarters Building, Berne. 3ch., 10ch., 20ch., 2n.50 (airliner).

BOLIVIA

South America

1924. 100 centavos = 1 boliviano

1963. 100 centavos = 1 peso boliviano

1987. 100 centavos = 1 boliviano

1924.

170	10c. Morane Saulnier Type P	55	45
171	15c. Morane Saulnier Type P	2·10	1·70
172	25c. Morane Saulnier Type P	1·10	80
173	50c. Morane Saulnier Type P	1·80	1·40
174	1b. Morane Saulnier Type P	2·30	1·90
175	2b. Morane Saulnier Type P	4·50	4·00
176	5b. Morane Saulnier Type P	6·50	6·25
170/176 Set of 7		17·00	15·00

1930. Nos. 170/4 overprinted **CORREO AEREO R.S. 6-V-1930** or surcharged also.

228	5c. on 10c. Morane Saulnier Type P	11·30	13·00
229	10c. Morane Saulnier Type P	11·50	13·00
231	15c. Morane Saulnier Type P	11·50	13·00
232	25c. Morane Saulnier Type P	11·50	13·00
233	50c. Morane Saulnier Type P	11·50	13·00
235	1b. Morane Saulnier Type P	£225	£225

1930.

244	5c. Junkers F-13	1·90	1·10
245	15c. Junkers F-13 seaplane	1·90	1·10
246	20c. Junkers F-13 seaplane	1·50	95
247	35c. Junkers F-13	1·20	70
248	50c. Junkers F-13 seaplane	2·30	1·60
249	1b. Junkers F-13	3·50	2·40
250	2b. Junkers F-13 seaplane	4·50	3·25
251	3b. Junkers F-13	7·00	4·50
244/251 Set of 8		21·00	14·00

1935.

298	5c. Fokker Super Universal	20	20
299	10c. Fokker Super Universal	20	20
300	20c. Fokker Super Universal	20	20
301	30c. Fokker Super Universal	20	20
302	50c. Fokker Super Universal	30	20

303	1b. Fokker Super Universal	30	45
304	1½b. Fokker Super Universal	1·10	20
305	2b. Fokker Super Universal	1·10	20
306	5b. Fokker Super Universal	1·80	55
307	10b. Fokker Super Universal	3·75	1·30
298/307 Set of 10		8·25	3·25

1937. Nos. 170, 173 and 247 surcharged **Correo Aereo D.S. 25-2-37** and value in figures.

321*	5c. on 35c. Junkers F-13	45	30
325*	2b. on 50c. Morane Saulnier Type P	1·70	1·40
326*	12b. on 10c. Morane Saulnier Type P	9·00	6·50
327*	15b. on 10c. Morane Saulnier Type P	9·00	3·75

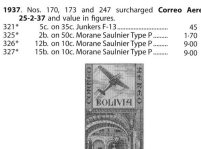

1938.

337*	20c. Junkers F-13 (?)	30	25
340*	50c. Junkers Ju 52/3m	65	25
341*	60c. Junkers F-13 (?)	65	25
343*	2b. Junkers F-13 (?)	1·60	30
345*	5b. Junkers F-13, Junkers G.24, Junkers W.34 seaplane and Junkers Ju 52/3m	2·30	55

1943.

415*	10c. Airplane	30	15
416*	20c. Airplane	35	15
417*	30c. Airplane	45	20
418*	3b. Airplane	65	30
419*	5b. Airplane	95	55

1944.

428*	1b.50 Lockheed 10 Electra	25	10
429*	2b.50 Lockheed 10 Electra	65	30

1945.

433	10c. Douglas DC-2 of Panagra	20	15
434	50c. Douglas DC-2 of Panagra	25	15
435	90c. Douglas DC-2 of Panagra	30	20
436	5b. Douglas DC-2 of Panagra	55	30
437	20b. Douglas DC-2 of Panagra	1·90	65
433/437 Set of 5		1·30	

1950. Nos. 433 and 437 surcharged **XV ANIVERSARIO PANAGRA 1935–1950** and value.

490	4b. on 10c. Douglas DC-2 of Panagra	20	10
491	10b. on 20b. Douglas DC-2 of Panagra	55	35

1950.

499	20c. Douglas DC-2 of Lloyd Aereo Boliviano	20	10
500	30c. Douglas DC-2 of Lloyd Aereo Boliviano	20	10
501	50c. Douglas DC-2 of Lloyd Aereo Boliviano	20	10
502	1b. Douglas DC-2 of Lloyd Aereo Boliviano	20	10
503	3b. Douglas DC-2 of Lloyd Aereo Boliviano	20	10
504	15b. Douglas DC-2 of Lloyd Aereo Boliviano	65	20
505	50b. Douglas DC-2 of Lloyd Aereo Boliviano	1·90	65
499/505 Set of 7		3·25	1·20

1957.

618	5b. Douglas DC-6B over control tower	55	20
620	5b. Douglas DC-6B over runway	9·50	9·50
619	10b. Douglas DC-6B airliners	45	20
620b	20b. Lockheed Constellation	55	30
618/620b Set of 4		10·00	9·25

1962.

749*	600b. Aircraft	55	20
750*	1200b. Lockheed 14 Super Electra	65	30
751*	2000b. Douglas DC-3 survey airplane (incorrect in detail)	95	55
752*	5000b. Lockheed 14 Super Electra	2·10	1·40

1973.

922	1p.40 Alberto Santos-Dumont and his biplane *14 bis*	90	40

1974.

944	3p. Morane Saulnier Type P	80	65
945	3p.80 Douglas DC-3	1·30	80
946	4p.50 Triplane trainer and Morane Saulnier MS 760 Paris I	1·30	80
947	8p. Biplane fighter	2·00	1·60
948	15p. Jet airliner	4·25	2·50
944/948 Set of 5		8·75	5·75

1975.

980*	1p.50 Douglas DC-9 of Lloyd Aereo Boliviano	70	35
981*	2p. Junkers F-13	95	45

1976.

988	3p. Douglas DC-10 of Lufthansa	1·20	45

1994.

1334	5b. Boeing 747	5·50	2·30

1995.

1356	50c. Airbus Industrie A-320	90	45

2002. 50th Anniv of Military Aviation College, Germán Busch.
1614	4b. Gates Learjet 25	3·00	2·75
1615	5b. Aerobatic airplanes	4·00	3·50
1616	6b. Helicopters	4·75	4·00
1614/1616 Set of 3		10·50	9·25

2006. Centenary of First Flight by Santos-Dumont.
1711	1b.50 Santos-Dumont's *14 bis*	90	75

2007. Heads of American Air Forces Conference.
1761	10b.50 Emblem	6·00	5·25

2007. 50th Anniv of Bolivian Air Force.
1782	7b.50 North American F-86 Sabres	4·25	3·50
1783	9b. Aircraft	5·00	4·25

BOPHUTHATSWANA

Southern Africa

100 cents = 1 rand

1978.
33*	10c. Wright *Flyer I*	1·00	1·00

1986.
179	14c. Cessna Citation II ZS-LHW of BOP Airways	25	10
180	20c. Passengers disembarking from Boeing 707	40	20
181	25c. Cessna Citation II over Mmabatho International Airport	50	35
182	30c. Cessna Citation II	60	50
179/182 Set of 4		1·60	1·00

1990.
247	21c. Sud Aviation SE 3130 Alouette II helicopter	1·40	1·10
248	21c. MBB-Kawasaki Bk-117 helicopter	1·40	1·10
249	21c. Pilatus PC-7 Turbo Trainer	1·40	1·10
250	21c. Pilatus PC-6 Turbo Porter	1·40	1·10
251	21c. CASA C-212 Aviocar	1·40	1·10
247/251 Set of 5		6·25	5·00

BOSNIA AND HERZEGOVINA

South-East Europe

B. Independent Republic

I. SARAJEVO GOVERNMENT

1997. 100 fennig = 1 mark

1997.
542*	130d. Airplane (unidentifiable)	1·60	1·60

2000. Centenary of First Zeppelin Flight.
652	1m.50 Count Ferdinand von Zeppelin and LZ-1	1·60	1·60

2003. Centenary of Powered Flight.
752	1m. Wilbur and Orville Wright and Wright *Flyer I*	1·30	1·30

II. CROATIAN POSTS

1993. 100 paras = 1 Croatian dinar

1994. 100 lipa = 1 kuna

2003. Centenary of Powered Flight.
C123	2k. Emblem (Abstract design)	4·25	4·25

III. REPUBLIKA SRPSKA

1992. 100 paras = 1 dinar

1998. 100 fennig = 1 mark

1999. Founding of Air Srpska (state airline).
S132	50f. Avions de Transport Regional ATR 72	70	70
S133	50f. Avions de Transport Regional ATR 72 above clouds	70	70
S134	75f. Avions de Transport Regional ATR 72 over beach	1·20	1·20
S135	1m.50 Avions de Transport Regional ATR 72 over lake	2·20	2·20
S132/S135 Set of 4		4·25	4·25

2002.
S250	1m. Lindbergh and Ryan NYP Special *Spirit of St. Louis*	1·40	1·40

2003.
S279	1m. Dornier Do-J Wal	1·40	1·40

2003. Centenary of Powered Flight.
S298	50f. Wright Brothers and Wright *Flyer I*	70	70
S299	1m. Ferdinand von Zeppelin and airship LZ-127 *Graf Zeppelin*	1·40	1·40

2005.
S355	1m.50 Bleriot XI	4·00	4·00

BOTSWANA

Southern Africa

1966. 100 cents = 1 rand

1976 100 thebe = 1 pula

1966.
204*	15c. Douglas DC-3 VQ-ZEA of Botswana National Airways	65	20

1974.
321*	20c. Hawker Siddeley H.S.748 of Air Botswana and de Havilland D.H.9 biplane	2·75	2·50

1980.
477*	6t. Jet-powered Vickers Viking (on Bechuanaland stamp No. 139)	50	30

1984.
562	7t. Avro 504	75	20
563	10t. Westland Wessex trimotor G-ABEC	1·00	35
564	15t. Junkers Ju 52/3m ZS-AFJ	1·40	95
565	25t. de Havilland DH.89B Dominie VP-YCJ of Rhodesia and Nyasaland Airways (inscribed "DRAGON SIX")	2·00	1·75
566	35t. Douglas DC-3 VP-YSM *Wenala* of Botswana National Airways	2·25	3·50
567	50t. Fokker F.27 Friendship A2-ADG of Air Botswana	2·50	7·00
562/567 Set of 6		9·00	12·50

1991.
719* 35t. de Havilland Canada DHC-7 .... 3·50 3·25

1994.
788* 10t. Interior of control tower, Gaborone
Airport 40 10
790* 40t. Boeing 747 .... 1·00 85
791* 50t. Control tower, Gaborone Airport....... 1·00 1·75

2000. Airborne Medical Services.
929* 35t. Cessna 208 Caravan...................... 30 10
931* 2p. Cessna 502 .... 1·25 1·40

BRAZIL

South America

1920. 1000 reis = 1 milreis

1942. 100 centavos = 1 cruzeiro

1986. 100 centavos = 1 cruzado

1990. 100 centavos = 1 cruzeiro

1994. 100 centavos = 1 real

1920.
387* 10r. Biplane... 20 15
388* 20r. Biplane... 20 15
390* 50r. Biplane (purple) 20 15
391* 50r. Biplane (green) 20 15
309* 100r. Biplane (red).................................. 3·75 45
392* 100r. Biplane (orange) 35 15
367* 100r. Biplane (green) 45 20
311* 150r. Biplane... 1·30 25
312* 200r. Biplane (blue)................................. 6·00 45
330* 200r. Biplane (red)................................... 30 10
383* 200r. Biplane (green)................................ 3·25 85

1929.
470* 200r. Santos-Dumont's airship *Ballon
No. 6*, 1901 .... 1·40 15
471* 300r. Augusto Severo's airship *Pax*, 1902... 2·00 15
472* 500r. Santos-Dumont's biplane *14 bis*........ 2·50 15
473* 1000r. Ribeiro de Barros' Savoia Marchetti
S-55C flying boat *Jahu* .... 8·50 30

1931. Nos. 470/1 surcharged **ZEPPELIN** and value.
508* 2$500 on 200r. Santos-Dumont's airship
Ballon No. 6, 1901................................. 27·00 24·00
509* 5$000 on 300r. Augusto Severo's airship
Pax, 1902 .... 35·00 32·00

1933.
530 3500r. Dornier Do-J Wal flying boat .... 6·25 1·60

1944. Air Week.
703 1cr.20 Bartolomeu de Gusmao and his
model balloon *Aerostat*, 1709............. 75 45

1946.
727* 1cr.30 Lockheed 14 Super Electra 75 75
728* 1cr.70 Lockheed 14 Super Electra 75 75
730* 2cr.20 Lockheed 14 Super Electra .... 1·10 1·10

1949. Brazilian Air Force.
789 60c. Douglas DC-3.................................... 55 10

1951. 50th Anniv of Santos-Dumont's Flight over Paris.
817 60c. Alberto Santos-Dumont, and boys
with model aircraft .... 1·00 35
818 3cr.80 Santos-Dumont's airship *Ballon No. 6*,
1901 (air).. 3·25 45

1955. Third Aeronautical Congress, Sao Paulo.
923 60c. Stylised airplane............................... 65 15

1956. 25th Anniv of National Air Mail.
940 3cr.30 Douglas DC-3.............................. 1·10 45

1956. 50th Anniv of Dumont's First Heavier-than-air Flight.
MS948a 3cr. x4 Santos-Dumont's biplane *14 bis*
(red) .... 18·00 15·00

1956. Alberto Santos-Dumont Commemoration. As No. **MS**948a
but colour changed.
949 3cr. Santos-Dumont's biplane *14 bis*
(green) .... 2·50 35
950 3cr.30 Santos-Dumont's biplane *14 bis*........ 25 10
951 4cr. Santos-Dumont's biplane *14 bis*......... 1·50 10
952 6cr.50 Santos-Dumont's biplane *14 bis*........ 25 10
953 11cr.50 Santos-Dumont's biplane *14 bis*........ 4·00 35
949/953 *Set of 5* .... 7·75 90

1958.
977 2cr.50 Airplane.................................. 75 20

1959. Aviation Week.
1012 3cr.30 Santos-Dumont's biplane *14 bis* and
airliner.. 75 20

1959. Inauguration of Caravelle Airliner by Brazilian National
Airlines.
1017 6cr.50 Sud Aviation SE 210 Caravelle............. 75 20

1965. Aviation Week.
1129 35cr. Curtiss Fledgling 70 15

1967. Aviation Week.
1190 10c. Balloon and airplane .... 1·40 55
MS1191 15c. Balloon and airplane .... 17·00 17·00

1967.
1204 5c. Aircraft and aircraft carrier 80 25

1968. Inauguration of Varig (Brazilian Airline), Brazil-Japan Air
Service. Without gum.
1216 10c. Boeing 707 .... 1·70 80

1969. Santos-Dumont's Flight (1906) Commemoration. Without gum.

1270   50c. Alberto Santos-Dumont and his
         airship *Ballon No. 6* ....   4·25   1·90

1969. Brazilian Aeronautical Industry Expansion. Without gum.

1276   50c. Embraer EMB-110 Bandeirante of
         the Brazilian Air Force ....   7·00   2·50

1971. First Flight of Embraer Xavante Jet Fighter. Without gum.

1327   40c. Embraer AT-26 Xavante and Santos-
         Dumont's biplane *14 bis*......................   4·25   1·70

1972. Without gum.

1425*   30c. Dassault Mirage IIIC ....   3·75   2·50

1973. Birth Centenary of Alberto Santos-Dumont.

1445   20c. Santos-Dumont's biplane *14 bis*..........   2·20   55
1446   70c. Alberto Santos-Dumont and his
         airship Ballon *No. 6*..............................   4·50   2·75
1447   2cr. Alberto Santos-Dumont and his
         monoplane No. 20 *Demoiselle* ....   5·25   2·75
1445/1447 *Set of 3*...   11·00   5·50

1976. Concorde's First Commercial Flight, Paris-Rio de Janeiro.

1576   5cr.20 Concorde of Air France.........................   1·30   75

1977. Aviation Anniversaries.

1683   1cr.30 Augusto Severo's airship *Pax*, 1902...   80   55
1684   1cr.30 Ribeiro de Barros' Savoia Marchetti
         S-55C flying boat *Jahu*..........................   80   55

1977.

1694*   1cr.30 Tail of Curtiss Fledgling K 263 and
         Douglas DC-3..   70   45

1977. 50th Anniv of Varig (state airline).

1697   1cr.30 Douglas DC-10 of VARIG.....................   55   30

1978. 50th Anniv of South Atlantic Flight by del Prete and Ferrarin.

1717   1cr.80 Savoia Marchetti S-64   55   30

1979.

1758*   2cr.50 Boeing 727-200..   55   30

1979. 10th Anniv of Brazilian Aircraft Industry.

1777   2cr.50 Embraer EMB-121 Xingu OP-ZCT.......   55   30

1979.

1780*   2cr.50 Douglas DC-9..   55   30

1980. 50th Anniv of *Graf Zeppelin* and First South Atlantic Air Mail Flight.

1845   4cr. Airship LZ-127 *Graf Zeppelin*................   1·00   45
1846   4cr. Latecoere 28-3 seaplane F-AJNQ
         Comte de la Vaulx ....   1·00   45

1981. 50th Anniv of National Air Mail Service.

1905   7cr. Curtiss Fledgling K 263 ....   1·00   45

1981. 75th Anniv of Santos-Dumont's First Powered Flight.

1923   60cr. Alberto Santos-Dumont and his
         biplane *14 bis* ....   2·20   65

1982.

1942   17cr. Lage HL-1...   1·60   45

1982. Aeronautical Industry Day.

1981   24cr. Embraer EMB-312 Tucano trainers....   55   25

1983.

2003   150cr. Helicopter..   4·50   1·20

1983.

MS2033 Five sheets. (a) 2000cr. Montgolfier balloon
         (first manned free flight, 1783) (other sheets
         show sporting events) *Price for 5 sheets*...................   £225   £225

1983. Brazilian Aeronautics Day.

2035   30cr. Embraer EMB-120 Brasilia.....................   50   20

1983. Bicentenary of Manned Flight.

2058   345cr. Montgolfier balloon (tethered flight,
         1783) ....   10·00   3·00

1984. 50th Anniv of First Tran-Oceanic Air Route.

2087   610cr. Dornier Do-J II 10-t Wal flying boat
         D-AKER of Lufthansa ....   2·50   1·00
2088   620cr. Dornier Do-J II 10-t Wal flying boat
         D-AKER of Lufthansa ....   2·75   1·10

1984. 50th Anniv of ICAO.

2124   120cr. Airbus Industrie A300   65   20

1985.
2174   220cr. Bell 47J Ranger helicopter.................... 60   40

1985. AM-X International (joint project by Embraer (Brazil), Alenia and Aermacchi (Italy).
2183   330cr. Aeritalia/Aermacchi AM-X.................... 45   25

1985. 50th Anniv of First Flight of Muniz M-7.
2198   500cr. Muniz M-7 biplane PP-TBV.................... 45   25

1985. 300th Birth Anniv of Bartolomeu de Gusmao (balloon pioneer).
2211   500cr. Bartolomeu de Gusmao and balloons 45   25

1986.
2265*   50c. Pilot and biplane fighter 35   25

1986. 50th Anniv of Bartolomeu de Gusmao Airport.
2266   1cz. Airship LZ-127 *Graf Zeppelin* over Bartolomeu de Gusmao Airport, Rio de Janeiro.................... 45   35

1987. Air Force Participation in Brazilian Antarctic Programme.
2269   1cz. Lockheed C-130 Hercules of the Brazilian Air Force.................... 95   25

1989.
2347*   25c. Airplane (top left) and Airbus Industrie A300.................... 85   55

1989. Aerosports and 80th Anniv of Santos-Dumont's Flight in *Demoiselle.*
2373   50c. Microlight.................... 95   80
2374   1cz.50 Santos-Dumont's monoplane No. 20 *Demoiselle* .... 3·25   2·20

1989.
2380   1cz.50 North American T-6 Texan (on photograph).................... 2·40   1·70

1990. Aeronautics Week.
2440   10cr. Embraer/FMA CBA-123 Vector.................... 85   45

1991. 50th Anniv of Aeronautics Ministry.
2465   17cr. Aeritalia/Aermacchi AM-X jet fighter and Republic P-47 Thunderbolt.................... 55   35

1991. Eighth World Free Flight Championships, Governador Valadares.
2470   36cr. Hang-gliders.................... 85   55

1992.
MS2563 1200cr. Hang-glider (sheet also contains 9000cr. design).................... 3·75   3·75

1993. 50th Anniv of Formation of 1st Fighter Group, Brazilian Expeditionary Force.
2615   42cr. Republic P-47 Thunderbolt.................... 90   55

1995.
2717   15c. Paratroopers and Lockheed C-130 Hercules.................... 80   65

1997.
2795   15c. Embraer EMB-145 Amazon AEW........ 40   25
2796   15c. AM-X International AM-X................. 40   25
2797   15c. Embraer EMB-314 Super Tucano 40   25
2798   15c. Embraer EMB-120 Brasilia................ 40   25
2799   15c. Embraer EMB-312 Tucano 40   25
2795/2799 Set of 5.................... 1·80   1·10

1998.
2957   31c. Santos-Dumont and his first balloon 'Brasil'.................... 85   75
2958   31c. Santos-Dumont and Dirigible No. 1.. 85   75

1999. 30th Anniv of the 6th Transportation Squadron.
3016   51c. Embraer EMB-110 Bandeirante......... 1·60   90

1999.
3020   1r.20 Santos-Dumont and Ballon No 3....... 3·50   1·80

2000. Women Aviators.
3060   22c. Ada Rogato.................... 50   40
3061   22c. Thereza de Marzo.................... 50   40
3062   22c. Anesia Pinheiro 50   40
3060/3062 Set of 3.................... 1·40   1·10

2000.
3099*   27c. Hang-gliding.................... 65   50

2000. Brazilian Aircraft.
3164   27c. Embraer EMB-145 Amazon AEW...... 65   50
3165   27c. Embraer EMB-314 Super Tucano 65   50
3166   27c. AM-X International AMX-T 65   50
3167   27c. Embraer ERJ-135.................... 65   50
3168   27c. Embraer ERJ-170.................... 65   50
3169   27c. Embraer ERJ-145.................... 65   50
3170   27c. Embraer ERJ-190.................... 65   50
3171   27c. Embraer EMB-145 RS/MP.................... 65   50
3172   27c. Embraer ERJ-140.................... 65   50
3173   27c. Embraer EMB-120 Brasilia.................... 65   50
3164/3173 Set of 10.................... 5·75   4·50

2001.
3198   1r.30 McDonnell Douglas DC-10 ....   3·00   2·50

2001. Commercial Aircraft.
MS3253 55c. Junkers F13; 55c Douglas DC-3/
C47; 55c. Dornier Do-J Wal; 55c. Lockheed
Constellation; 55c. Convair CV 340; 55c.
Aerospatiale Caravelle V1-R ....   6·50   6·50

2002. Smoke Air Squadron (airforce display team).
MS3291 55c. North American T6; 55c. Fouga
CM-170 Magister; 55c. Neiva T-25 Universal; 55c.
Embraer T-27 Tucano; 55c. Embraer T-27 Tucano;
55c. Embraer T-27 Tucano.............................   6·50   6·50

2002.
MS3302 1r. House of Alberto Santos-Dumont; 1r
Alberto Santos-Dumont......................   2·75   2·75

2003.
3353*   50c. Kite flying   80   70

2003.
3364   75c. Para glider ....   1·20   1·00

2004.
3405*   50c. Republic P-47 Thunderbolt   80   70

2005.
3456*   85c. Santos-Dumont's biplane *14 bis*........   1·40   1·20

2006.
3470   (1st porte) Centenary, flight of Santos-
Dumont's *14 bis*.........................   1·40   1·20

BRITISH ANTARCTIC
TERRITORY

Antarctica

1963. 12 pence = 1 shilling

20 shillings = 1 pound

1971. 100 pence = 1 pound

1963.
5*   2½d. de Havilland Canada DHC-2 Beaver
seaplane..   3·25   1·25
8*   6d. Westland Whirlwind helicopter..........   4·75   2·50
10*   1s. de Havilland Canada DHC-3 Otter....   4·25   1·50
12*   2s. 6d. Westland Whirlwind helicopter.........   22·00   13·00

1971. Nos. 5, 8, 10 and 12 surcharged in decimal currency.
28*   2½p. on 2½d. de Havilland Canada DHC-2
Beaver seaplane...........................   3·00   2·25
31*   5p. on   6d.   Westland   Whirlwind
helicopter....................................   4·75   2·50
33*   7½p. on 1s. de Havilland Canada DHC-3
Otter...   18·00   8·50
35*   15p. on   2s.6d.   Westland   Whirlwind
helicopter....................................   18·00   12·00

1973.
76*   25p. Hubert Wilkins and Lockheed Vega
X-3903 *San Francisco*....................   1·00   1·50
77b*   50p. Lincoln Ellsworth and Northrop
Gamma *Polar Star*........................   85   2·75

1983. Bicentenary of Manned Flight.
119   5p. de Havilland Canada DHC-6 Twin
Otter 200/300................................   25   30
120   13p. de Havilland Canada DHC-3 Otter....   35   45
121   17p. Consolidated   PBY-5A   Canso
amphibian...................................   45   60
122   50p. Hubert Wilkins' Lockheed Vega
X-3903 *San Francisco*....................   70   1·25
119/122 *Set of 4*...   1·60   2·30

1985.
141*   27p. de Havilland DH.83 Fox Moth   80   1·60

1988.
164*   24p. de Havilland Canada DHC-3 Otter.....   50   1·25

1991.
195*   62p. Lockheed ER-2............................   3·25   4·50

1993.
224*   20p. Westland Widgeon helicopter on
ship H.M.S. "Protector"...........................   2·75   3·00
229*   £5 Westland WG-13 Lynx helicopter ......   11·00   13·00

1994. Nos. 241/5 overprinted with Hong Kong 94 logo.
231*   24p. de Havilland Canada DHC-2 Turbo
Beaver III of British Antarctic Survey.   1·60   1·75
232*   31p. de Havilland Canada DHC-3 Otter of
British Antarctic Survey ....   1·75   1·90
233*   36p. de Havilland Canada DHC-6 Twin
Otter 200/300 of British Antarctic
Survey...   1·90   2·00
234*   62p. de Havilland Canada DHC-7 Dash
Seven of British Antarctic Survey.......   2·75   2·75
235*   72p. de Havilland Canada DHC-7 Dash
Seven of British Antarctic Survey.......   2·75   2·75
241*   24p. de Havilland Canada DHC-2 Turbo
Beaver III of British Antarctic Survey .   90   1·00
242*   31p. de Havilland Canada DHC-3 Otter of
British Antarctic Survey......................   1·00   1·10
243*   36p. de Havilland Canada DHC-6 Twin
Otter 200/300 of British Antarctic
Survey...   1·10   1·40
244*   62p. de Havilland Canada DHC-7 Dash
Seven of British Antarctic Survey.......   2·00   2·50
245*   72p. de Havilland Canada DHC-7 Dash
Seven of British Antarctic Survey.......   2·00   2·75

2000.
317* 43p. de Havilland Canada DHC-6-Twin
Otter...................................... 2·25 2·50

2000.
328* 43p. Westland Lynx helicopter.................... 3·75 3·50

2005.
405* 80p. Bell 47D helicopter........................ 3·25 3·25
406* £1 Canadian Vickers (Consolidated)
Canso...................................... 3·50 3·50

BRITISH GUIANA

South America

100 cents = 1 dollar

1949. As Nos. 114/15 of Antigua.
324* 4c. Airplane................................ 10 50
325* 6c. Jet-powered Vickers Viking............... 1·75 1·75

BRITISH HONDURAS

Central America

100 cents = 1 dollar

1938.
156* 15c. Airplane................................ 4·50 70

1949. As Nos. 114/5 of Antigua.
172* 4c. Airplane................................ 30 30
173* 5c. Jet-powered Vickers Viking............... 1·50 50

1953.
184* 10c. Stanley Field Airport.................... 10 10

1961. No. 184 overprinted **NEW CONSTITUTION 1960.**
196* 10c. Stanley Field Airport.................... 30 10

1962. No. 184 overprinted **HURRICANE HATTIE.**
199* 10c. Stanley Field Airport.................... 30 10

BRITISH INDIAN OCEAN TERRITORY

Indian Ocean

100 pence = 1 pound

1992.
124 20p. Consolidated PBY-5 Catalina of the
R.A.F.. 1·50 2·50
125 24p. Hawker Siddeley H.S.801 Nimrod
M.R.2 of the R.A.F.......................... 1·75 2·50
126 34p. Lockheed P-3 Orion..................... 2·50 3·25
127 54p. Boeing B-52 Stratofortress............. 3·00 4·50
124/127 Set of 4.................................... 7·75 11·50

1993. 75th Anniv of Royal Air Force.
136 20p. Vickers Virginia Mk X, 1925.............. 1·00 1·50
137 24p. Bristol Bulldog IIA, 1929............... 1·10 1·50
138 34p. Short S.25 Sunderland Mk III flying
boat, 1937............................... 1·25 2·00
139 54p. Bristol Type 142 Blenheim Mk IV,
1939..................................... 2·00 3·25
136/139 Set of 4.................................... 4·75 7·50
MS140 20p. Douglas DC-3 Dakota of the R.A.F.; 20p.
Gloster G.41 Javelin F.A.W.7, 1956; 20p. Blackburn
Beverley C1, 1950; 20p. Vickers VC-10 of the R.A.F
.... 7·50 8·00

1995.
169* 30p. Short S.25 Sunderland.................... 2·00 2·25

1997.
203* 24p. Aircraft carrier launching BAe
(Hawker) Sea Harrier....................... 1·50 1·60

1998. 80th Anniv of Royal Air Force.
215 26p. Blackburn Iris.......................... 1·00 1·10
216 34p. Gloster Gamecock....................... 1·25 1·40
217 60p. North American F-86 Sabre F4.......... 2·25 2·50
218 80p. Avro Type 694 Lincoln.................. 2·75 3·00
215/218 Set of 4.................................... 6·50 7·25
MS219 34p. Sopwith Baby; 34p. Martinsyde
Elephant; 34p. de Havilland DH.82 Tiger Moth;
34p. North American P-51 Mustang III........... 6·00 7·00

2003. Centenary of Powered Flight.
288 34p. Avro Type 683 Lancaster................ 1·50 1·50
289 34p. de Havilland DH.98 Mosquito........... 1·50 1·50
290 58p. Hawker Hurricane...................... 2·00 2·00
291 58p. Supermarine Spitfire.................. 2·00 2·00
292 76p. Vickers Wellington.................... 2·50 2·50
293 76p. Lockheed C-130 Hercules............... 2·50 2·50
288/293 Set of 6.................................... 11·00 11·00
MS294 26p. Boeing E-3A Sentry; 26p. Boeing B-17
Flying Fortress; 26p. Lockheed P-3 Orion; 26p.
Consolidated B-24 Liberator; 26p. Lockheed
C-141 StarLifter; 26p. Supermarine Walrus;
26p. Short S25 Sunderland; 26p. Supermarine
Stranraer; 26p. Consolidated PBY-5 Catalina; 26p.
Supermarine Sea Otter............................. 9·00 10·00

2008. 90th Anniv of Royal Air Force.
379* 27p. Avro Type 504......................... 1·00 1·00
380* 27p. Short S.25 Sunderland................. 1·00 1·00
381* 27p. de Havilland DH.98 Mosquito.......... 1·00 1·00
382* 27p. Vickers Type 1100 VC10............... 1·00 1·00
383* 54p. English Electric Canberra............ 1·60 1·60

BRITISH VIRGIN ISLANDS

West Indies

1949. 12 pence = 1 shilling

20 shillings = 1 pound

1951. 100 cents = 1 West Indian dollar

1962. 100 cents = 1 U.S. dollar

1949. As Nos. 114/15 of Antigua.
126* 2½d. Airplane.............................. 30 1·00
127* 3d. Jet-powered Vickers Viking............ 1·50 2·50

1964.
179* 2c. Cessna 172 Skyhawk seaplane
N2560Y................................... 15 30
188* 25c. Piper PA-23 Apache at Beef Island
Airfield................................. 11·00 1·75

1966.
205* 25c. Piper PA-23 Apache at Beef Island
Airfield................................. 55 10

1968. No. 188 overprinted **1968 INTERNATIONAL YEAR FOR HUMAN RIGHTS.**
225* 25c. Piper PA-23 Apache................... 30 40

1968. Opening of Beef Island Airport Extension.
228* 2c. de Havilland Canada DHC-6 Twin
Otter 100 of L.I.A.T...................... 15 1·25
229* 10c. Hawker Siddeley H.S.748 of L.I.A.T.... 20 10
230* 25c. de Havilland Canada DH.114 Heron
2 of Prinair.............................. 40 10

1982. 10th Anniv of Air BVI.
492 10c. Douglas DC-3 VP-LVI of Air BVI........ 45 15
493 15c. Britten-Norman BN-2 Islander of Air
BVI...................................... 60 20
494 60c. Hawker Siddeley H.S.748 G-ATMI of
Air BVI.................................. 1·10 75
495 75c. Nose of Douglas DC-3, Hawker
Siddeley H.S.748 and tail of Britten-
Norman BN-2 Islander, all of Air BVI... 1·25 90
492/495 Set of 4.................................... 3·00 1·80

1983. Bicentenary of Manned Flight.
513 10c. Grumman G-21 Goose amphibian
N-95467................................. 20 15
514 30c. Riley Turbo Skyliner N-582-PR of
Prinair.................................. 45 45
515 60c. Embraer EMB-110 Bandeirante VP-
LCK of L.I.A.T........................... 65 85
516 $1.25 Hawker Siddeley H.S.748 of Air BVI... 90 1·60
513/516 Set of 4.................................... 2·00 2·75

1984.
527* 25c. Boeing 747-100 of British Airways.... 45 50

1984.
MS530 $1 Boeing 747-100 of British Airways .... 2·25 2·50

1987.
665* $1.50 Piper PA-23 Apache (also on stamp
No. 188).. 7·50 11·00

1988.
676* 35c. de Havilland Canada DHC-5
Transporter .... 7·00 1·75

1994.
868* 15c. Loading disaster relief onto HS748
aircraft 35 35

1995.
906* $2 Westland Lynx AH7 helicopter .... 3·75 5·50

1998. 80th Anniv of Royal Air Force.
990 20c. Fairey IIIF 60 40
991 35c. Supermarine Scapa..................... 85 50
992 50c. Westland Sea King H.A.R............. 1·40 1·10
993 $1.50 BAe Harrier GR7......................... 2·50 3·25
990/993 Set of 4 .... 4·75 4·75
MS994 75c. Curtiss H.16; 75c. Curtiss JN-4A 'Jenny';
75c. Bell P-39 Airacobra; 75c. Boulton-Paul P.82
Defiant... 6·50 7·00

2003. Centenary of Powered Flight.
1132 15c. Douglas DC-4............................... 70 40
1133 20c. Boeing Stearman Kaydet 75 40
1134 35c. North American B-25J Mitchell .... 1·00 50
1135 40c. McDonnell Douglas F-4B Phantom .. 1·10 55
1136 70c. Boeing CH-47 Chinook................ 2·00 1·50
1137 $2 Boeing (McDonnell Hughes/
Douglas) AH-64 Apache................. 4·25 4·75
1132/1137 Set of 6 .... 8·75 7·25

BRUNEI

South-east Asia

100 cents = 1 dollar

1949. As Nos. 114/15 of Antigua.
96* 8c. Airplane .... 1·00 1·50
97* 15c. Jet-powered Vickers Viking................. 3·50 1·50

1971.
179* 15c. Bell Model 205 UH-1H Iroquois
helicopter .... 1·75 70

1972. Opening of RAF Museum, Hendon.
200 25c. Blackburn Beverley C1 .... 1·75 1·25
201 75c. Blackburn Beverley C1 .... 3·25 4·75

1974. Inauguration of Brunei International Airport.
234 50c. Douglas DC-9 at Brunei International
Airport .... 1·25 1·00
235 75c. Douglas DC-9 over Brunei
International Airport .... 1·50 1·50

1975. Inauguration of Royal Brunei Airlines.
241 12c. Boeing 737 over Brunei International
Airport and tail of Boeing 737 of
Royal Brunei Airlines........................ 1·00 25
242 35c. Boeing 737 of Royal Brunei Airlines.. 1·75 1·50
243 75c. Boeing 737 of Royal Brunei Airlines.. 2·50 3·50
241/243 Set of 3 .... 4·75 4·75

1986.
388* 10c. Bell Model 205 UH-1H Iroquois
helicopter .... 4·25 4·25
390* 50c. MBB-Bolkow Bo 105L helicopter........ 6·00 6·00

1992.
508* 25c. Brunei International Airport .... 1·90 2·00

1994. 20th Anniv of Royal Brunei Airlines.
537 10c. Fokker F-27 Friendship .... 1·00 45

538 20c. Boeing 757 on runway.................. 1·50 45
539 $1 Boeing 757 in the air .... 3·50 4·50
537/539 Set of 3 .... 5·50 4·75

1999.
607* 60c. Modern telecommunications and
Boeing 757 .... 1·25 1·00

2000.
628* 20c. Ship and Boeing 757 .... 75 75

2000.
634* 30c. Boeing 757, Royal Brunei Airlines...... 1·00 1·00

2006.
718* 100s. Stylised airliner............................ 1·10 1·10

BULGARIA

South-east Europe

100 stotinki = 1 lev

1927. Nos. 267a, 268 and 273/4 overprinted with Albatros biplane
or surcharged also.
281 1l. on 6l. Lion emblem............................. 2·20 2·10
282 2l. King Boris III..................................... 2·20 2·10
283 4l. Harvesters...................................... 3·25 2·10
284 10l. Lion emblem..................................... 85·00 50·00
281/284 Set of 4 .... 85·00 50·00

1932.
323 18l. Airplane.. 1·40 70
324 24l. Airplane.. 95 45
325 28l. Airplane.. 50 35
323/325 Set of 3 .... 2·50 1·40

1940.

434	1l.	Airplane	20	15
435	2l.	Heinkel He 111C (?) LZ-PIA	2·50	15
436	4l.	Heinkel He 111C (?) LZ-PIA	20	15
437	6l.	Armstrong Whitworth A.W.27 Ensign (?)	40	20
438	10l.	Heinkel He 111C (?) LZ-PIA	75	30
439	12l.	Potez 56 (?)	1·00	50
440	16l.	Hirtenburg HV 15 (?)	1·60	80
441	19l.	Potez 56 (?)	1·70	1·00
442	30l.	Airplane (registration LZ-HET)	2·50	1·50
443	45l.	Airplane	6·75	3·75
444	70l.	Heinkel He 111C (?) LZ-PIA	5·25	4·00
445	100l.	Airplane (registration LZ-ILA)	21·00	14·00
434/445 Set of 12			39·00	24·00

1945. Nos. 457, 459 and as No. P540, but in yellow, overprinted with airplane or surcharged also. Nos. 542/5 are imperforate.

540	1l.	Heinkel He 111H overprint (King Boris III)	20	15
541	4l.	Heinkel He 111H overprint (King Boris III)	20	15
542	10l.	on 100l. Arado Ar 240 overprint (Lion emblem)	30	15
543	45l.	on 100l. Arado 240 overprint (Lion emblem)	40	20
544	75l.	on 100l. Arado Ar 240 overprint (Lion emblem)	1·00	60
545	100l.	Arado Ar 240 overprint (Lion emblem)	1·30	90
540/545 Set of 6			3·00	1·90

1946.

615*	6l.	Junkers Ju 87B "Stuka" dive bomber.	20	15

1947.

649	70l. +30l.	Lisunov Li-2 (?)	2·10	2·00

1947. Imperf.

671*	40l.	Airplane	1·60	1·50

1948.

706	50l.	Petlyakov Pe-2 bomber	2·10	2·00

1949.

748	50l.	Lisunov Li-2	5·75	5·00

1949.

763*	60l.	Airplane	4·75	4·00

1951.

841*	40l.	Ilyushin Il-12	2·50	2·00

1954.

935	8s.	Yakovlev Yak-16 (?)	20	15
936	12s.	Yakovlev Yak-16 (?)	20	15
937	16s.	Yakovlev Yak-16 (?)	20	15
938	20s.	Yakovlev Yak-16 (?)	20	15
939	28s.	Yakovlev Yak-16 (?)	40	20
940	44s.	Yakovlev Yak-16 (?)	50	20
941	60s.	Yakovlev Yak-16 (?)	85	30
942	80s.	Yakovlev Yak-16 (?)	95	40
943	1l.	Yakovlev Yak-16 (?)	3·00	85
944	4l.	Yakovlev Yak-16 (?)	5·25	2·40
935/944 Set of 10			10·50	4·50

1956. 30th Anniv of Gliding Club.

1036	44s.	Glider being launched	40	20
1037	60s.	Glider over hangar	50	30
1038	80s.	Glider and light airplane	1·50	95
1036/1038 Set of 3			2·20	1·30

1957. 10th Anniv of Balkanair (Bulgarian Airline).

1055	80s.	Lisunov Li-2 LZ-TUA of TABSO	1·50	50

1957.

1067*	44s.	Polikarpov Po-2 biplane	70	30

1959.

1177	1l.	Tupolev Tu-104A of Aeroflot	4·00	4·00

1962. 13th Anniv of TABSO Airline.

1336	13s.	Ilyushin Il-18 of TABSO	1·50	50

1964.

1474	20s.	Airliner	1·60	1·10

1964.

1492	5s.	Sud Aviation SE 210 Caravelle	55	25
1493	13s.	Tupolev Tu-104A	1·30	65

1965.

1525	13s.	Ilyushin Il-18	1·90	1·10

1965.

1569*	5s.	Model airplane	30	20

1965. Bulgarian Civil Aviation.

1572	1s.	Junkers Ju 52/3m	20	15
1573	2s.	Ilyushin Il-14M	20	15
1574	3s.	Mil Mi-4 helicopter	20	15
1575	5s.	Tupolev Tu-104A	35	20
1576	13s.	Ilyushin Il-18	1·10	45
1577	20s.	Tupolev Tu-114	1·90	80
1572/1577 Set of 6			3·50	1·70

1969.

1876*	10s.	Montgolfier balloon (first manned free flight, 1783) and Henri Giffard's steam-powered dirigible airship, 1852	35	20
1877*	13s.	Early flying machines	65	35
1878*	20s.	Airplane	1·10	45

1971.

2083*	2s.	Stylised jet airliner	20	15

1977. 30th Anniv of Balkanair (Bulgarian Airline).

2590	35s.	Tupolev Tu-154	1·70	85

1977.

2605	25s.	Balloon over Plovdiv, 1892	95	55

1979.
2738* 2s. Tupolev Tu-154.............................. 20 15

1980. 15th World Parachute Championships, Kazanluk.
2870 13s. Parachute descent.................................. 35 20
2871 25s. Parachutist in free fall 75 35

1980. Bulgarian Armed Forces.
2881 3s. Yakovlev Yak-24 helicopter 10 10
2882 5s. Mikoyan Gurevich MiG-21.................. 20 15
2883 8s. Mil Mi-24 helicopter 35 20
2881/2883 Set of 3 .... 60 40

1981.
2951 5s. Deutsche Flugzeugwerke D.F.W. C.V.
biplane B-BATA............................... 20 15
2952 12s. LAS-7 monoplane............................. 30 15
2953 25s. LAS-8 monoplane LZ-BKP 75 45
2954 35s. DAR-1 biplane B-BIKM 95 55
2955 45s. DAR-3 biplane................................. 1·10 85
2956 55s. DAR-9 biplane LZ-BCK .... 1·40 1·10
2951/2956 Set of 6 .... 4·25 3·00

1984. 40th Anniv of ICAO.
3203 42s. Tupolev Tu-154 of Balkanair 95 55

1987. 40th Anniv of Balkanair (Bulgarian Airline).
3454 25s. Mil Mi-8 helicopter, Tupolev Tu-154
and Antonov An-12 .... 55 20

1988.
3582* 25s. Biplane..................................... 55 20

1989.
3626 42s. Nadar taking photograph from his
balloon *Le Geant*, 1863, and airship
LZ-127 *Graf Zeppelin*.......................... 1·10 45

1989. 82nd International Airsports Federation General Conference,
Varna.
3651* 5s. Gliders.. 10 10
3652* 13s. Hang-glider 35 20

1990.
3705 5s. Airbus Industrie A310 (inscribed
"A300").. 10 10
3706 10s. Tupolev Tu-204............................. 20 10
3707 25s. Concorde 55 35
3708 30s. Douglas DC-9................................ 60 45
3709 42s. Ilyushin Il-86 .... 75 55
3710 60s. Boeing 747-300/400....................... 1·30 90
3705/3710 Set of 6 .... 3·25 2·20

1995.
4031 3l. Polikarpov Po-2............................. 45 20
4032 5l. Lisunov Li-2.................................. 75 35
4033 7l. Junkers Ju52................................. 1·10 55
4034 10l. Focke Wulf FW58........................... 1·60 90
4031/4034 Set of 4 .... 3·50 1·80

1997. 50th Anniv of Civil Aviation.
4147 120l. Anniversary emblem............................ 35 20

1998.
4206 80l. Focke Wulf FW61, 1937................... 20 10
4207 100l. Sikorsky R-4, 1943......................... 35 15
4208 120l. Mil Mi-V12, 1970........................... 45 20
4209 200l. McDonnell Douglas MD-900, 1995... 65 35
4206/4209 Set of 4 .... 1·50 75

2000.
4320* 60st. Antoine de Saint-Exupery (pioneer
aviator) .... 1·60 45

2000. Centenary of First Zeppelin Flight.
4321 10st. *La Jeune* (Lebardy-Juillot airship)....... 25 10

4322 18st. LZ-13 *Hansa* Zeppelin......................... 35 15
4323 20st. N-1 *Norge* airship 55 20
4324 60st. *Graf Zeppelin*............................. 1·60 65
4321/4324 Set of 4 .... 2·50 1·00

2006.
MS4614 55st. New airport terminal, Sofia, and
Boeing 737... 1·00 1·00

2007. Military Aircraft.
4626 10st. DAR-3 Garvan II, 1937 .... 20 10
4627 35st. DAR-9 Siniger, 1939......................... 55 45
4628 55st. Kaproni Bulgarski KB-6 Papagal,
1939... 85 65
4629 1l. Kaproni Bulgarski KB-11A Fanzan ..... 1·60 1·50
4626/4629 Set of 4 .... 3·00 2·40

2008. History of Military Aviation. Pilots Birth Anniversaries.
4667 55st. Captain Dimiter Spissarevski (90th
anniv)... 85 65
4668 1l. General Stoyan Stoyanov (95th
anniv)... 1·60 1·50

BURKINA FASO

West Africa
100 centimes = 1 franc

1985.
782* 45f. Bleriot XI 60 10
783* 50f. Breguet 14T biplane.......................... 60 10

1985.
785* 500f. Airbus Industrie A300 (air) .... 4·25 1·30
787* 600f. Airbus Industrie A300 .... 5·25 1·70
MS788* 1000f. Louis Bleriot and Bleriot XI................ 8·50 3·50

1985.
835* 40f. Sikorsky S-55 helicopter...................... 1·70 35

1985.
839*   250f. Boeing 707 ....   3·50   1·50

BURUNDI

Central Africa

100 centimes = 1 franc

1967. Opening of Bujumbura Airport.
325   10f. Boeing 707 of Air Congo......................   40   10
326   14f. Boeing 727-100 of SABENA   65   20
327   17f. Vickers Super VC-10 of East African
              Airways...   95   20
328   26f. Boeing 727-100 of SABENA ....   1·60   30
325/328 *Set of 4*..   3·25   75

1974.
978*   14f. Tail of Boeing 720B ....   1·25   70
979*   14f. Boeing 720B ....   1·25   70
986*   31f. Tail of Boeing 720B (air)......................   2·75   1·10
987*   31f. Boeing 720B ....   2·75   1·10

1979.
1350*   60f. Boeing 720B (on stamps Nos. 986/7)   6·75   3·00

1984.
1439*   65f. Boeing 720B (on stamps Nos. 978/9)   18·00   11·50

1987.
1473*   5f. Airplane...   55   55

1995.
1603*   250f. Air Burundi Beech King Air...................   1·40   1·40

CAICOS ISLANDS

West Indies

100 cents = 1 dollar

1983.

20*	95c. Boeing 707 at Providenciales Airport	5·50	3·00

1984. No. 20 overprinted **UNIVERSAL POSTAL UNION 1874–1984** and emblem.

55*	95c. Boeing 707 at Providenciales Airport	1·00	1·25

1985. 40th Anniv of ICAO.

78	35c. Douglas DC-3 of Air Caicos	3·00	55
79	75c. Convair CV 440 Metropolitan of Air Caicos	4·00	1·40
80	90c. Britten Norman Islander of Turks and Caicos National Airlines	4·00	1·60
78/80 *Set of 3*		10·00	3·25
MS81 $2.20 Hang-glider		3·00	3·25

CAMBODIA

South-east Asia

1954. 100 cents = 1 piastre

1955. 100 cents = 1 riel

1954.

41*	2p.50 Sud Ouest SO.30P Bretagne	2·50	2·10
43*	4p. Sud Ouest SO.30P Bretagne	3·25	2·75
45*	5p. Sud Ouest SO.30P Bretagne	3·50	2·50
47*	10p. Sud Ouest SO.30P Bretagne	4·00	2·75
48*	15p. Sud Ouest SO.30P Bretagne	5·00	5·00

1962.

132*	6r. Tupolev Tu-104A on airstrip at Phnom Penh	1·00	35

1964. Eighth Anniv of Royal Air Cambodia.

174	1r.50 Airline emblem	25	20
175	3r. Airline emblem	45	30
176	7r.50 Airline emblem	90	45
174/176 *Set of 3*		1·40	85

1991.

1171	5r. Douglas DC-10-30	15	10
1172	25r. McDonnell Douglas MD-11	20	10

1173	70r. Ilyushin Il-96-300	30	10
1174	100r. Airbus Industrie A310	40	10
1175	200r. Yakovlev Yak-42	80	20
1176	400r. Tupolev Tu-154	1·50	20
1177	1000r. Douglas DC-9	3·75	20
1171/1177 *Set of 7*		6·50	90

1992.

1231*	80r. Sikorsky S.55 helicopter	30	10
1233*	1500r. Parachutists	4·75	35
MS1234 1000r. Da Vinci drawing, Flying Man		4·75	90

1992.

1235*	5r. Cierva and Cierva C4 autogiro	20	10

1992.

1264	5r. Bellanca Pacemaker,1930	20	10
1265	15r. Canadair CL-215, 1965	20	10
1266	80r. Grumman G-21 Goose	30	10
1267	400r. Short SA6 Sealand	1·30	30
1268	1500r. Short S.23 Empire C-Class, 1936	4·50	35
1264/1268 *Set of 5*		5·75	85
MS1269 1000r. Grumman G-44 Widgeon		4·50	90

1993.

1277*	200r. Dassault Mirage III	65	20

1993. 120th Birth Anniv of Alberto Santos-Dumont (aviator).

1312	150r. Santos-Dumont and *Ballon No. 6*	55	10
1313	200r. *14 bis* biplane 1906	65	20
1314	250r. *Demoiselle* monoplane, 1909	75	20
1315	500r. Embraer EMB-201A Ipanema	2·00	20
1316	900r. Embraer EMB-111 Bandeirante Patrulha	3·00	30
1312/1316 *Set of 5*		6·25	90

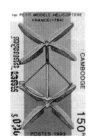

1993.

1329	150r. First helicopter model, France, 1784	55	10
1330	200r. Model of steam helicopter, 1863	65	20
1331	250r. New York-Atlanta-Miami autogyro flight, 1927 by Pitcairn autogyro	75	20
1332	500r. Vought Sikorsky VS-316A helicopter, 1943	1·70	20
1333	900r. Dassault Balzac V001 (French vertical take-off jet)	3·00	30
1329/1333 *Set of 5*		6·00	90
MS1334 1000r. Cierva's C4 autogyro		4·75	90

1994

1408	150r. Sikorsky S-42	55	10
1409	200r. Vought-Sikorsky VS-300A	65	20
1410	250r. Sikorsky S-37	75	20
1411	500r. Sikorsky S-35	2·00	20
1412	900r. Sikorsky, S-43	3·00	30
1408/1412 *Set of 5*		6·25	90
MS1413 1500r. Sikorsky *'Ilya Muromets'*		4·50	90

1995.

1469	100r. Bristol Type 142 Blenheim Mk II	20	10
1470	200r. North American B-25B Mitchell	75	20
1471	300r. Avro Type 652 Anson Mk I	1·10	20
1472	600r. Avro Type 679 Manchester	1·70	20
1473	800r. Consolidated B-24 Liberator	2·10	30
1469/1473 *Set of 5*		5·25	90
MS1474 1000r. Boeing B-17 Flying Fortress		3·25	90

1996.

1545	100r. Douglas M-2, 1926	30	10
1546	200r. Pitcairn PS-5, Mailwing, 1926	45	10
1547	300r. Boeing 40-B, 1928	75	20
1548	500r. Potez 25, 1925	1·30	20
1549	900r. Stearman C-3MB 1927	2·30	20
1550	1000r. Airco (de Havilland) DH.4, 1918	2·75	20
1545/1550 *Set of 6*		7·00	90
MS1551 1500r. Standar JR-1B, 1918		4·75	90

1996.

1598	200r. MD Helicopters MD500	75	10
1599	300r. Float helicopter	1·40	20
1600	500r. Helicopter	2·10	30
1601	900r. Helicopter	3·75	35
1598/1601 *Set of 4*		7·25	85
MS1602 10000r. MD500 helicopters		4·75	90

CAMEROUN

West Africa

100 centimes = 1 franc

1941.

190c	25c. Sikorsky S-43 amphibian	65	5·00
190d	50c. Sikorsky S-43 amphibian	65	5·00
190e	1f. Sikorsky S-43 amphibian	2·50	5·00
190f	2f. Sikorsky S-43 amphibian	1·50	3·50
190g	3f. Sikorsky S-43 amphibian	1·70	3·75
190h	4f. Sikorsky S-43 amphibian	1·20	3·75
190i	6f. Sikorsky S-43 amphibian	1·50	3·25
190j	7f. Sikorsky S-43 amphibian	1·40	3·25
190k	10f. Sikorsky S-43 amphibian	7·25	11·50
190l	20f. Sikorsky S-43 amphibian	3·75	5·75
190m	50f. Latecoere 631 flying boat	4·25	5·75
190c/190m *Set of 11*		24·00	50·00

1942.
207*	1f. Fairey FC-1 airliner	1·30	3·75
208*	1f.50 Fairey FC-1 airliner	2·00	4·50
209*	5f. Fairey FC-1 airliner	1·20	4·50
210*	10f. Fairey FC-1 airliner	1·10	4·75
211*	25f. Fairey FC-1 airliner	1·90	4·75
212*	50f. Fairey FC-1 airliner	2·75	3·25
213*	100f. Fairey FC-1 airliner	2·25	3·00

1946.
252*	100f. Dewoitine D-333 trimotor	2·50	2·50

1949.
254	25f. Lockheed Constellation	5·25	4·75

1953.
261*	100f. Airplane	11·00	1·50
262a*	500f. Sud Ouest SO.95 Corse II	20·00	16·00

1954.
264	15f. Bomber	6·25	4·75

1961. Nos. 261 and 262a surcharged **REPUBLIQUE FEDERALE** and value in sterling.
295*	5s. on 100f. Airplane	10·00	9·50
297*	£1 on 500f. Sud Ouest SO.95 Corse II	34·00	32·00

1962. Foundation of Air Afrique Airline.
307	25f. Boeing 707 airliners of Air Afrique	1·00	50

1966.
435*	100f. Dassault MD-315 Flamant	2·75	1·20

1966. Inauguration of Douglas DC-8 Air Service.
438	25f. Douglas DC-8F Jet Trader of Air Afrique	80	45

1969. 10th Anniv of Aerial Navigation Security Agency for Africa and Madagascar (ASECNA).
552	100f. Airliner over airport	1·80	85

1974.
730*	200f. Lockheed Constellation (on stamp No. 254)	2·75	1·70

1976. Concorde's First Commercial Flight, Paris-Rio de Janeiro.
768	500f. Concorde of Air France	5·25	2·75

1977. History of Aviation.
794	50f. Jean Mermoz and Latecoere 28-3 seaplane F-AJNQ *Comte de la Vaulx*	95	40
795	60f. Antoine de Saint-Exupery and Latecoere 26	95	55
796	80f. Maryse Bastie and Caudron C-635 Simoun F-ANXH	1·20	55
797	100f. Sikorsky S-43 amphibian F-AOUM of Air France	1·60	80
798	300f. Concorde of Air France	5·25	2·50
799	500f. Charles Lindbergh and Ryan NYP Special *Spirit of St. Louis*	7·75	4·50
794/799	Set of 6	16·00	8·25

1977. Nos. 798 and 768 overprinted **PREMIER VOL PARIS-NEW YORK FIRST FLIGHT PARIS-NEW YORK 22 nov. 1977–22nd Nov. 1977.**
820	300f. Concorde of Air France	3·25	1·60
821	500f. Concorde of Air France	5·00	2·50

1979.
871	500f. Ben Abruzzo, Max Anderson, Larry Newman and balloon *Double Eagle II*	5·25	2·00
872	500f. Balloon *Double Eagle II*	5·25	2·00
871/872	Set of 2	8·00	2·75

1981. 10th Anniv of Cameroun Airlines.
900*	200f. Boeing 747-100 *Mount Cameroun* of Camair	2·00	75
901*	300f. Douglas DC-8 airliners at Douala International Airport	3·00	1·10

1984. 40th Anniv of ICAO.
1030*	300f. Boeing 747 of Camair	2·75	1·40

1986.
1099*	500f. Jean Mermoz and Couzinet 70 F-AMBV *Arc en Ciel*	3·50	1·50

CANADA

North America

100 cents = 1 dollar

1928.
274	5c. Fairchild FC-2W	6·50	4·25

1932. No. 274 surcharged 6.
313	6c. on 5c. Fairchild FC-2W	3·00	2·50

1938.
371	6c. Fairchild 45-80 Sekani seaplane	13·00	1·50

1942.
399*	6c. Pilots and North American AT-6 Harvard trainers	26·00	9·50
400*	7c. Pilots and North American AT-6 Harvard trainers	4·00	20

1951.
438*	7c. Canadair DC-4M North Star CF-TFB	50	1·25

1959. 50th Anniv of First Flight of *Silver Dart*.
509	5c. John McCurdy's biplane *Silver Dart*, 1909, and Avro (Canada) CF-105 Arrow jet fighters	30	10

1963.
540*	7c. Douglas DC-9 over Uplands Airport, Ottawa	35	70
540a*	8c. Douglas DC-9 over Uplands Airport, Ottawa	50	30

1964. No. 540 surcharged **8.**
556	8c. on 7c. Douglas DC-9 over Uplands Airport, Ottawa	15	15

1969. 50th Anniv of First Non-stop Trans-Atlantic Flight.
636	15c. Alcock and Brown's Vickers FB-27 Vimy, 1919	40	55

1979. Canadian Aircraft (1st series). Flying Boats.
966	17c. Canadair CL-215 fire-fighting amphibian	25	20
967	17c. Curtiss HS-2L flying boat of Ontario Provincial Air Services	25	20
968	35c. Vickers Vedette flying boat	65	65
969	35c. Consolidated PBY-5A Canso amphibian	65	65
966/969 Set of 4		1·60	1·50

1980. Canadian Aircraft (2nd series).
996	17c. Avro (Canada) CF-100 Canuck Mk 5..	40	20
997	17c. Avro Type 683 Lancaster	40	20
998	35c. Curtiss JN-4 Canuck biplane	60	65
999	35c. Hawker Hurricane Mk I	60	65
996/999 Set of 4		1·80	1·50

1981. Canadian Aircraft (3rd series).
1026	17c. de Havilland DH.82C Tiger Moth	20	15
1027	17c. Canadair CL-41 Tutor jet trainer	20	15
1028	35c. Avro (Canada) CF-102 jet airliner CF-EJD-X	35	40
1029	35c. de Havilland Canada DHC-7	35	40
1026/1029 Set of 4		1·00	1·00

1982. Canadian Aircraft (4th series).
1050	30c. Fairchild FC-2W1 G-CAIP with skis	35	20
1051	30c. de Havilland Canada DHC-2 Beaver seaplane CF-FHG of Norcanair	35	20
1052	60c. Fokker Super Universal seaplane G-CASK of Western Canada Airways.	65	85
1053	60c. Noorduyn Norseman CF-SAM with skis	65	85
1050/1053 Set of 4		1·80	1·90

1986.
1205*	34c. Anti-gravity flying suit and Supermarine Spitfire	1·10	1·75
1206*	34c. Variable pitch propeller and Avro 504	1·10	1·75

1987. 50th Anniv of Air Canada.
1251	36c. Boeing 767-200 of Air Canada	1·00	35

1989.
1348*	38c. Pilot and North American AT-6 Harvard trainers	1·10	1·25

1991.
1441*	40c. Sud Aviation SA 341 Gazelle helicopter	2·00	1·75
1444*	40c. Boeing-Vertol CH-147 Chinook helicopter	2·00	1·75

1991.
1458*	40c. Model airplane	1·75	1·25

1992.
1522*	42c. Consolidated Liberator bombers of the R.A.F	1·60	1·90

1993.
1577*	43c. Avro Type 683 Lancaster being loaded with bombs	1·50	1·75

1994.
1609*	43c. Nieuport 17	1·00	1·25

1994. 50th Anniv of Second World War.
1623	43c. Hawker Typhoons	1·75	1·75

1995. 50th Anniv of Second World War.
1628*	43c. Parachute drop	2·00	1·75

1995.
1659*	45c. de Havilland Canada DHC-2 Beaver..	1·00	1·25

1996.
1678*	45c. Canadair Challenger 601-3R	75	1·00

1999. 75th Anniv Canadian Air Force.
1920	46c. de Havilland Mosquito F.B.V1	65	70
1921	46c. Sopwith F.1 Camel	65	70
1922	46c. de Havilland Canada DHC-3 Otter.....	65	70
1923	46c. de Havilland Canada CC-108 Caribou (DHC-4A)	65	70
1924	46c. Canadair CL-28 Argus Mk 2	65	70
1925	46c. Canadair (North American) F-86 Sabre 6	65	70
1926	46c. McDonnell Douglas CF-18 Hornet	65	70
1927	46c. Sopwith 5 F.1 Dolphin	65	70
1928	46c. Armstrong Whitworth Siskin IIIA	65	70
1929	46c. Canadian Vickers (Northrop) Delta II	65	70
1930	46c. Sikorsky CH-124A Sea King	65	70
1931	46c. Vickers Wellington Mk II	65	70
1932	46c. Avro Type 652 Anson Mk I	65	70
1933	46c. Canadair (Lockheed) CF-104G Starfighter	65	70
1934	46c. Burgess-Dunne	65	70
1935	46c. Avro 504K	65	70
1920/1935 Set of 16		9·25	10·00

1999. 50th Anniv of Canadian International Air Show.
1936	46c. Fokker DR-1	75	75
1937	46c. H-101 Salto glider	75	75
1938	46c. de Havilland DH-100 Vampire Mk III.	75	75
1939	46c. Stearman A-75	75	75
1936/1939 Set of 4		2·75	2·75

Nos. 1936/9 form a composite design which includes a nine-plane Snowbird formation of Canadair CT114 Tutor in the background.

2005.
MS2357	50c. Crashed aircraft; 50c. Helicopter and float plane (miniature sheet contains other stamps that do not show aircraft)	4·50	4·50

2006.
2403	51c. Canadair CT-114 Tutor	60	50
2404	51c. Canadair CT-114 Tutor	60	50

SPECIAL DELIVERY STAMPS

1927.
S5	20c. Biplanes	11·00	10·00

1942.
S13*	16c. Lockheed L.18 Lodestar	6·00	45
S14*	17c. Lockheed L.18 Lodestar	4·50	55

Nos. S13/14 show the incorrect registration "CF-BAF".

1946.
S16*   17c. Canadair DC-4M North Star CF-TOM
        of Trans Canada Airlines...................... 4·50   6·50

CANAL ZONE

Central America

100 cents = 1 dollar

1931.
126	4c. Fokker F.10A Super Trimotor..............	55	55
127	5c. Fokker F.10A Super Trimotor..............	45	35
128	6c. Fokker F.10A Super Trimotor..............	55	30
129	10c. Fokker F.10A Super Trimotor..............	70	30
130	15c. Fokker F.10A Super Trimotor..............	90	30
131	20c. Fokker F.10A Super Trimotor..............	1·40	30
132	30c. Fokker F.10A Super Trimotor..............	2·50	80
133	40c. Fokker F.10A Super Trimotor..............	2·50	85
134	$1 Fokker F.10A Super Trimotor..............	6·50	1·50
126/134 *Set of 9*........		14·50	4·75

1939.
143*	5c. Douglas DC-3................	3·00	1·80
144*	10c. Douglas DC-3 and Sikorsky S-42A flying boat..............	2·50	1·60
145*	15c. Sikorsky S-42A flying boat...........	3·75	90
146*	25c. Sikorsky S-42A flying boat...........	11·00	6·50
147*	30c. Sikorsky S-42A flying boat...........	11·00	4·75
148*	$1 Sikorsky S-42A flying boat...........	30·00	16·00

OFFICIAL STAMPS

1941. Nos. 127/34 overprinted **OFFICIAL PANAMA CANAL.**
O167	5c. Fokker F.10A Super Trimotor..............	4·50	1·50
O168	6c. Fokker F.10A Super Trimotor..............	10·50	4·75
O169	10c. Fokker F.10A Super Trimotor..............	9·00	3·50
O170	15c. Fokker F.10A Super Trimotor..............	12·50	4·25
O171	20c. Fokker F.10A Super Trimotor..............	12·50	6·50
O172	30c. Fokker F.10A Super Trimotor..............	15·00	8·50
O173	40c. Fokker F.10A Super Trimotor..............	14·50	7·50
O174	$1 Fokker F.10A Super Trimotor..............	17·00	10·00
O167/O174 *Set of 8*......		85·00	42·00

CAPE JUBY

North-west Africa

100 centimos = 1 peseta

1938. Nos. 203, 205/9 and 211 of Spanish Morocco overprinted **CABO JUBY.**
95*	5c. Airplane............	10	10
97*	25c. Savoia Marchetti S-74.............	10	10
98*	40c. Savoia Marchetti S-74.............	1·50	1·50
99*	50c. Airplane............	10	10
100*	75c. Airplane............	10	15
101*	1p. Savoia Marchetti S-74.............	10	15
103*	2p. Junkers Ju 52/3m.............	2·10	2·10

1942. As Nos. 258/62 of Spanish Morocco (without **Z** overprint), inscribed "CABO JUBY".
125	5c. Junkers Ju 52/3m...........	10	10
126	10c. Junkers Ju 52/3m...........	10	10
127	15c. Junkers Ju 52/3m...........	10	10
128	90c. Junkers Ju 52/3m EC-AAX...........	35	35
129	5p. Junkers Ju 52/3m...........	1·30	1·30
125/129 *Set of 5*...........		1·80	1·80

CAPE VERDE ISLANDS

Atlantic Ocean

100 centavos = 1 escudo

1938. As Nos. 401/9 of Angola.
307*	10c. Airplane...........	65	50
308*	20c. Airplane...........	65	50
309*	50c. Airplane...........	65	50
310*	1e. Airplane...........	65	50
311*	2e. Airplane...........	1·50	80
312*	3e. Airplane...........	2·00	1·40
313*	5e. Airplane...........	5·75	2·00
314*	9e. Airplane...........	9·50	3·50
315*	10e. Airplane...........	10·50	4·50

1963. 10th Anniv of T.A.P. Airline. As No. 611 of Angola.
391   2e.50 Boeing 707 and Lockheed L.1049G
        Super Constellation of T.A.P................ 90   60

1969.
419   30c. Fairey IIID seaplane *Lusitania* 15   15

1972. 50th Anniv of First Flight Lisbon-Rio de Janeiro.
427   3e.50 Fairey IIID seaplane *Lusitania* 50   25

1978. No. 419 surcharged **3$00.**
455   3e. on 30c. Fairey IIID seaplane *Lusitania*   15   10

1984. 40th Anniv of ICAO.
552	50c. Auster D.5/160 Husky CR-CAP	10	10
553	2e. de Havilland DH.104 Dove	10	10
554	10e. Hawker Siddeley H.S.748	25	15
555	13e. de Havilland DH.89A Dragon Rapide	25	15
556	20e. de Havilland Canada Twin Otter ...	50	30
557	50e. Britten-Norman BN-2 Islander	1·10	65
552/557 *Set of 6*...........		2·10	1·30

1989.
623   30e. Hot-air balloon *Pro Juventute* 45   25

1999. 30th Anniv of Concorde.
827	30e. Concorde in flight.......	35	15
828	50e. Concorde at airport........	60	30

1999.
833*   50e. Paper airplanes................ 60   30

2003. 75th Anniv of First Postal Hydroplane Base.
908	10e. CAMS 51-F...........	15	10
909	42e. Paulin Paris (pilot)...........	50	25
910	60e. CAMS 51-F...........	75	30
908/910 *Set of 3*.........		1·30	60
MS911 100e. CAMS 51-F................		1·20	1·20

CAYMAN ISLANDS

West Indies

1949. 12 pence = 1 shilling

20 shillings = 1 pound

1969. 100 cents = 1 Jamaican dollar

1949. As Nos. 114/15 of Antigua.
131*	2½d. Airplane............	30	1·00
132*	3d. Jet-powered Vickers Viking.............	1·50	2·25

1950.
143*   9d. Consolidated   PBY-5A   Catalina
        amphibian VP-JAO .... 11·00   2·00

1953. As No. 143, but with portrait of Queen Elizabeth II.
157*   9d. Consolidated   PBY-5A   Catalina
        amphibian VP-JAO .... 7·50   30

1966. Opening of Cayman Jet Service.
203	1s. B.A.C. One Eleven 200/400.............	35	30
204	1s. 9d. B.A.C. One Eleven 200/400.............	40	35

1979. 25th Anniv of Owen Roberts Airfield.
477	3c. Lockheed L.18 Lodestar VP-JAN over Owen Roberts Airfield	30	15
478	5c. Consolidated PBY-5A Catalina amphibian VP-JAU.............	30	15
479	10c. Vickers Viking 1B VP-TAV of British South American Airways over Owen Roberts Airfield	35	15
480	15c. B.A.C. One Eleven 475 VR-CAL of Cayman Airways at Owen Roberts Airfield	65	25
481	20c. Piper PA-31-T Cheyenne II, Bell 47G Trooper helicopter VR-CAI and tail of Hawker Siddeley H.S.125 executive jet	75	35
482	30c. B.A.C. One Eleven 475 VR-CAL of Cayman Airways over Owen Roberts Airfield	1·00	50
477/482 *Set of 6*............		3·00	1·40

1983. Bicentenary of Manned Flight.
578	3c. Cessna 188 Ag Wagon VR-CAX	60	50
579	10c. Consolidated PBY-5A Catalina amphibian VP-BAO.............	65	50
580	20c. Boeing 727-200 of Cayman Airways.	1·25	1·50
581	40c. Hawker Siddeley H.S.748 of Cayman Airways.............	1·75	3·75
578/581 *Set of 4*...........		3·75	5·50

1986.
634*   50c. Westland WG-13 Lynx helicopter ...... 1·60   2·00

1987.
650*   35c. Paragliding.............. 2·50   2·00

1988.
672* 50c. Boeing 727 of Cayman Airways.......... 4·50 3·25

1989.
680* $1 B.A.C. One Eleven 200/400 (on stamp No. 203) and Shorts 330 of Cayman Airways...................................... 8·00 9·50

1991.
720* $1 Lockheed WP-3D Orion of the U.S. Department of Commerce................... 5·00 8·00

1993.
764* 30c. Boeing 737 airliners of Cayman Airways... 1·75 1·90

1995. 50th Anniv of End of Second World War.
808* $1 US Navy L-3 airship .... 3·75 6·00

1996.
825* 20c. Boeing 737-200............................ 1·25 55

1998. 80th Anniv of Royal Air Force.
859 10c. Hawker Horsley 60 70
860 20c. Fairey Hendon 75 80
861 25c. Hawker Siddeley Gnat 85 90
862 30c. Hawker Siddeley Dominie .... 95 1·00
859/862 Set of 4....................................... 2·75 3·00
MS863 40c. Airco (de Havilland) D.H.9; 60c. SPAD S.XII Scout; 80c. Airspeed Oxford; $1 Martin Baltimore .... 5·50 6·50

2001.
967* $1 Consolidated PBY-5 Catalina .... 2·50 1·75
969* $10 Boeing 767................................ 17·00 19·00

2002.
983* 30c. Boeing 737-200.. 1·25 70

2002. 50th Anniv of Cayman Islands Aviation.
1000 15c. Consolidated PBY-5 Catalina.............. 90 70
1001 20c. Grand Cayman Airport, 1952. Shows Bell 47 helicopter, Piper PA-31T Cheyenne and tail of Hawker 1000... 1·00 70
1002 25c. Cayman Brac Airways AC 50 .... 1·10 70
1003 30c. Consolidated PBY5 Catalina .... 1·25 70
1004 40c. British Airways Aerospatiale/BAe Concorde.. 1·75 1·25
1005 $1.30. Island Air de Havilland Canada DHC-6 Twin Otter .... 3·75 4·75
1000/1005 Set of 6................................ 8·75 8·00

CENTRAL AFRICAN EMPIRE

Central Africa

100 centimes = 1 franc

1977.
509 40f. Airship LZ-127 *Graf Zeppelin* (on Italy stamp No. 372)............................. 85 25
510 60f. Airship LZ-127 *Graf Zeppelin* (on Russia stamp No. 574)....................... 1·00 45
511 100f. Airship LZ-127 *Graf Zeppelin* (on Germany stamp No. 471)................. 1·40 40
512 200f. Airship LZ-127 *Graf Zeppelin* (on Germany stamp No. 511)................. 2·50 75
513 300f. Airship LZ-127 *Graf Zeppelin* (on Germany stamp No. 443)................. 3·75 1·00
509/513 Set of 5 .... 8·50 2·50
MS514 500f. Airship LZ-127 *Graf Zeppelin* (on United States of America stamp No. A688)............... 5·50 2·20

1977. History of Aviation.
515 50f. Charles Lindbergh and Ryan NYP Special *Spirit of St. Louis*....................... 50 25
516 60f. Alberto Santos-Dumont and his biplane *14 bis* 75 25
517 100f. Louis Bleriot and Bleriot XI............. 1·40 45
518 200f. Roald Amundsen and Dornier Do-J Wal flying boat N-24.......................... 2·10 60
519 300f. Concorde .... 4·00 1·40
515/519 Set of 5 .... 8·00 2·75
MS520 500f. Lindbergh's Ryan NYP Special *Spirit of St. Louis*.............................. 5·00 1·80

1978.
560* 100f. Mail balloon, Paris, 1870 .... 1·00 40
561* 200f. Latecoere 28-3 seaplane F-AJNQ *Comte de la Vaulx* and Concorde...... 1·80 70
MS562* 500f. Airship.......................... 6·75 1·90

1978. Aviation Pioneers.
586 40f. Clement Ader and his *Avion III* 50 25
587 50f. Wilbur and Orville Wright and Wright Glider No. III 50 25
588 60f. John Alcock, Arthur Whitten Brown and their Vickers FB-27 Vimy, 1919 ... 60 40
589 100f. Sir Alan Cobham and his de Havilland DH.50 G-EBFO .... 1·20 40
590 150f. Dr. Claude Dornier and Dornier Gs 1 flying boat .... 1·80 70
586/590 Set of 5 .... 4·25 1·80
MS591 500f. Wilbur and Orville Wright and Wright Type A .... 5·50 1·80

1978.
622* 200f. Mail balloon, Paris, 1870 .... 1·70 70

1979.
635* 100f. Dornier Do-X flying boat .... 1·30 45

CENTRAL AFRICAN REPUBLIC

Central Africa

100 centimes = 1 franc

1962. Foundation of Air Afrique Airline. As No. 307 of Cameroun.
24 50f. Boeing 707 airliners of Air Afrique 95 70

1966. Inauguration of Douglas DC-8 Air Services. As No. 438 of Cameroun.
112 25f. Douglas DC-8F Jet Trader of Air Afrique.. 85 45

1967. No. 112 with first digit of face value obliterated.
127* 5f. on 25f. Douglas DC-8F Jet Trader of Air Afrique 45 25

1967.
128 100f. Douglas DC-8 of Air Afrique over Bangui M'Poko Airport .... 2·30 1·10

1967. Aircraft.
145 1f. Douglas DC-3 *St. Sylvestre* of Air Bangui 10 10
146 2f. Beech A55 Baron of Air Bangui.......... 10 10
147 5f. Douglas DC-4 of Air Afrique 30 10
148 100f. Potez 25 TOE biplane (air).................. 2·00 85
149 200f. Junkers Ju 52/3m.......................... 4·75 1·80
150 500f. Sud Aviation SE 210 Caravelle 11R of U.T.A.. 12·50 4·75
145/150 Set of 6 .... 18·00 7·00

1968. Nos. 148/9 with last digit of face value obliterated.
165* 10f. on 100f. Potez 25 TOE biplane 30 10
166* 20f. on 200f. Junkers Ju 52/3m................. 45 30

1969. 10th Anniv of Aerial Navigation Security Agency for Africa and Madagascar (ASECNA). As No. 552 of Cameroun.
202 100f. Airliner over airport .... 1·80 85

1972.
290*   50f. Douglas DC-3 of Air Bangui   80   70

1974.
360   100f. Douglas DC-8 ....   1·50   85

1976.
432   100f. Airliner ....   1·60   90

1980.
MS713 500f. Concorde ....   5·25   1·70

1981.
753*   150f. Boeing 747 SCA of NASA carrying
       Space Shuttle *Enterprise* ....   1·40   45

1982.
831*   5f. Astra Torres AT-16 airship, 1919   10   10
834*   110f. Vickers Valentia biplane, 1928 ....   1·30   45

1983. Bicentenary of Manned Flight.
930   65f. Robert Brothers' and Colin Hullin's
       balloon, 1784   85   25
931   130f. John Wise's balloon *Atlantic*, 1859 ......   1·40   35

---

932   350f. Balloon *Ville d'Orleans*, Paris, 1870 ......   3·75   1·10
933   400f. Modern advertising balloon ....   4·25   1·40
930/933 *Set of 1* 9 25   2 75
MS934 500f. Montgolfier balloon (tethered flight,
       1783) ....   6·00   1·60

1983. Bicentenary of Manned Flight.
963   50f. Joseph Montgolfier and unmanned
       balloon, 1783   45   10
964   100f. Blanchard and Jeffries' balloon, 1785 .....   1·00   25
965   200f. Joseph   Gay-Lussac   making
       4000-metre balloon ascent, 1804 ......   2·20   65
966   300f. Henri Giffard and his steam-powered
       dirigible airship, 1852 ....   3·00   1·00
967   400f. Alberto Santos-Dumont and his
       airship *Ballon No. 6*, Paris, 1901 (air)..   4·00   1·30
968   500f. A. Caquot and captive observation
       balloon, 1914 ....   5·00   1·70
963/968 *Set of 6* ....   14·00   4·50
MS969 600f. Jacques Charles and his hydrogen
       balloon, 1783, and Tissandier Brothers' airship,
       1883 ....   6·00   1·60

1984.
1032*   70f. Auguste Piccard, his stratosphere
       balloon *F.N.R.S.*, 1931, and North
       American X-15   70   25

1984.
1060*   90f. Auguste Piccard and his stratosphere
       balloon *F.N.R.S.*, 1931   95   30
1062*   200f. Louis Bleriot and Bleriot XI ....   2·30   60

1986. 25th Anniv of Air Afrique.
1229   200f. Douglas DC-10 of Air Afrique ....   1·80   85

1990.
1414*   250f. Concorde ....   2·40   70

1992. 75th Death Anniv of Ferdinand von Zeppelin.
1428*   80f. Count Ferdinand von Zeppelin   80   20

CEYLON

Indian Ocean

100 cents = 1 rupee

1949.
410   5c. Douglas DC-4   75   10
411   15c. Douglas DC-3 ....   1·10   2·75
412   25c. Short S.25 Sandringham flying boat   1·10   1·10
410/412 *Set of 3* ....   2·75   3·50

1950.
417*   75c. Douglas DC-4 *Ratamalana* of Air
       Ceylon ....   7·50   20

1957.
442*   4c. Douglas DC-4   75   50
443*   10c. Douglas DC-4   75   10

1958.
460a*   75c. Douglas DC-4 *Ratamalana* of Air
       Ceylon ....   9·00   2·25

1963. 25th Anniv of Airmail Services.
474   50c. de Havilland DH.85 Leopard Moth
       and Hawker Siddeley Comet 4 of
       B.O.A.C.   50   50

1968. Opening of Colombo Airport.
539   60c. Vickers Super VC-10 over Colombo
       Airport ....   1·00   10

CHAD

Central Africa

100 centimes = 1 franc

1962. Foundation of Air Afrique Airline. As No. 307 of Cameroun.
87   25f. Boeing 707 airliners of Air Afrique ....   1·00   40

1963.
107   100f. Holste MH 1521 Broussard................... 3·75   1·80

1966. Inauguration of Douglas DC-8 Air Service. As No. 438 of Cameroun.
161   30f. Douglas DC-8F Jet Trader of Air Afrique......................... 90   40

1967. First Anniv of Air Chad Airline.
180   25f. Dagnaux's Breguet 19A2 biplane 90   40
181   30f. Latecoere 631 flying boat................... 1·10   55
182   50f. Douglas DC-3 of Air Chad................. 2·10   1·20
183   100f. Piper PA-32 Cherokee Six of Air Chad................... 3·75   1·60
180/183 Set of 4................... 7·00   3·50

1969. 10th Anniv of Aerial Navigation Security Agency for Africa and Madagascar (ASECNA). As No. 552 of Cameroun.
294   30f. Airliner over airport......................... 90   50

1970. Air Afrique Douglas DC-8 *Fort Lamy.*
309   30f. Douglas DC-8-63 *Fort Lamy* of Air Afrique......................... 1·20   60

1974.
412*   100f. Douglas DC-8................... 2·20   75

1976. Concorde's First Commercial Flight.
465   250f. Concorde of Air France................... 6·50   3·75

1977. Zeppelin Flights.
481   100f. Airship LZ-129 *Hindenburg* (on Germany stamp No. 603)................... 2·10   1·70
482   125f. Airship LZ-127 *Graf Zeppelin* (on Germany stamp No. 469) (air) .... 2·00   60
483   150f. Airship LZ-127 *Graf Zeppelin* (on Germany stamp No. 512)................... 3·25   75
484   175f. Airship LZ-127 *Graf Zeppelin* (on Germany stamp No. 444)................... 3·75   90
485   200f. Airship LZ-127 *Graf Zeppelin* (on United States of America stamp No. A689)................... 4·00   1·40
481/485 Set of 5 4................... 13·50   4·75
MS486 500f. Airship LZ-127 *Graf Zeppelin* (on United States of America stamp No. A689)................... 8·75   2·75

1977. Concorde and Lindbergh Commemorations.
501   100f. Concorde................... 2·30   1·20

---

502   120f. Charles Lindbergh and Ryan NYP Special *Spirit of St. Louis*................... 1·40   75
503   150f. Charles Lindbergh and Ryan NYP Special *Spirit of St. Louis*................... 1·80   1·10
504   200f. Charles Lindbergh and Ryan NYP Special *Spirit of St. Louis*................... 2·40   1·20
505   300f. Charles Lindbergh and Ryan NYP Special *Spirit of St. Louis*................... 3·50   1·80
501/505 Set of 5................... 10·50   5·50

1977. No. 501 overprinted **PARIS NEW-YORK 22.11.77.**
516   100f. Concorde................... 3·50   1·80

1978. History of Aviation.
529   40f. Antoine de Saint-Exupery and Latecoere 28-3 seaplane F-AJNQ *Comte de la Vaulx*................... 75   30
530   50f. Wilbur and Orville Wright and Wright *Flyer I*................... 90   50
531   80f. Hugo Junkers and Junkers J.1............ 1·20   65
532   100f. General Italo Balbo and Savoia Marchetti S-55A flying boat................ 1·70   85
533   120f. Concorde................... 2·00   1·00
529/533 Set of 5................... 5·75   3·00
MS534 500f. Wilbur and Orville Wright and Wright Type B................... 7·50   2·75

1978.
553*   60f. Sikorsky S-55 helicopter................... 3·00   1·70

1980. 20th Anniv of African Air Safety Organisation (ASECNA).
589   15f. Concorde................... 15   10
590   30f. Concorde................... 35   15
591   60f. Concorde................... 65   30
589/591 Set of 3................... 1·00   50

1983. Balloons.
652   100f. Charles' hydrogen balloon, 1783 85   25
653   200f. Jean-Pierre Blanchard's balloon flight, Berlin, 1788................... 1·80   50
654   300f. Charles Green's balloon *Royal Vauxhall* over London, 1836 (inscribed "1837")................... 2·40   80
655   400f. Advertising airship *Musketier*............ 3·00   1·00
652/655 Set of 4................... 7·25   2·30
MS656 500f. Montgolfier balloon (first manned free flight, 1783)................... 6·50   2·30

1983. Bicentenary of Manned Flight.
664   25f. Joseph and Etienne Montgolfier and balloon *Le Martial*, 1783................... 35   10
665   45f. Jean-Francois Pilatre de Rozier and Montgolfier balloon (tethered flight, 1783)................... 75   25

---

666   50f. Andre Jacques Garnerin's parachute descent from a balloon, 1797 75   30
667   60f. Jean-Pierre Blanchard and his propeller-driven balloon, 1784........... 85   70
668   80f. Henri Giffard and his steam-powered dirigible airship, 1852 (air)................... 1·10   40
669   250f. Count Ferdinand von Zeppelin and airship LZ-1, 1900................... 3·25   1·10
664/669 Set of 6................... 6·25   2·50
MS670 300f. Montgolfier balloon *Le Flesselles*, 1784................... 6·25   1·90

1984.
730   50f. Boeing 747-100................... 55   10
731   60f. Boeing 747-100................... 75   15
732   70f. Boeing 747-100................... 90   30
733   125f. Boeing 747-100 (air)................... 1·50   35
734   250f. Boeing 747-100................... 2·75   1·10
730/734 Set of 5................... 5·75   1·80

1984.
742*   300f. Airship LZ-127 *Graf Zeppelin*................ 4·75   1·40
744*   400f. Bloch 120 (air) .... 4·75   1·90
745*   500f. Douglas DC-8 of Air Afrique at N'Djamena Airport................... 5·75   2·30

1985.
778*   200f. Fokker F.27 Friendship 500................... 3·00   2·30

1985.
782*   60f. Louis Bleriot and Bleriot XI................... 1·00   30

1985. 25th Anniv of African Air Safety Organisation (ASECNA).
799   70f. Fokker F.27 Friendship 500 and Farman M.F.11 Type 14 "Shorthorn"..   90   45
800   110f. Fokker F.27 Friendship 500 and Lindbergh's Ryan NYP Special *Spirit of St. Louis*................... 1·50   65
801   250f. Fokker F.27 Friendship 500 and Farman M.F.11 Type 14 "Shorthorn"..   2·75   1·60
799/801 Set of 3................... 4·75   2·40

1985.
809*   250f. Boeing 747-100................... 4·00   2·50

1987. Nos. 669 and 734 surcharged with new values.
824* 100f. on 250f. Count Ferdinand von
Zeppelin and airship LZ-1, 1900........
828* 170f. on 250f. Boeing 747-100....................

APPENDIX

The following stamps have either been issued in excess of postal needs or have not been made available to the public in reasonable quantities at face value. Miniature sheets, imperforate stamps, etc are excluded from this section.

1973.
Aircraft. 5f., 25f., 70f., 150f., 200f.

1983.
Bicentenary of Manned Flight. Embossed on gold foil. 1500f.

CHAMBA

Indian sub-continent

12 pies = 1 anna

16 annas = 1 rupee

1938. No. 258 of India overprinted **CHAMBA STATE**.
93* 12a. Armstrong Whitworth A.W.27 Ensign I   18·00   65·00

1942. No. 277 of India overprinted **CHAMBA**.
120* 14a. Armstrong Whitworth A.W.27 Ensign I   14·00   3·00

CHILE

South America

1931. 100 centavos = 1 peso

1960. 10 milesimos = 1 centesimo

100 centesimos = 1 escudo

1975. 100 centavos = 1 peso

1931.
223	5c. Fokker Super Universal of L.A.N	35	20
224	10c. Fokker Super Universal of L.A.N	35	20
225	20c. Fokker Super Universal of L.A.N	35	20
226a	50c. Fokker Super Universal of L.A.N. (sepia)	1·10	20
227	50c. Ford 4-AT Trimotor of L.A.N. over Los Cerrillos Airport (blue)	1·70	65
228	1p. Fokker Super Universal of L.A.N	65	30
229	2p. Fokker Super Universal of L.A.N	1·40	30
230	5p. Ford 4-AT Trimotor of L.A.N. over Los Cerrillos Airport	3·50	20
223/230 *Set of 8*		7·25	2·20

1934.
236*	10c. Fokker Super Universal	35	10
237*	15c. Fokker Super Universal	55	30
238*	20c. Fokker Super Universal	35	10
239*	30c. Junkers G.24	35	10
239a*	40c. Junkers G.24	20	15
240*	50c. Junkers G.24	35	10
244*	1p. Fokker Super Universal	35	10
245*	2p. Fokker Super Universal	35	10
360*	3p. Stinson Faucett F.19 seaplane	20	10
361*	4p. Stinson Faucett F.19 seaplane	20	10
248*	5p. Stinson Faucett F.19 seaplane	35	10
249*	6p. Northrop Alpha monoplane	55	10
250*	8p. Northrop Alpha monoplane	55	30
251*	10p. Northrop Alpha monoplane	65	30
252*	20p. Stylised Dornier Wal flying boat	90	30
253*	30p. Stylised Dornier Wal flying boat	1·00	55

1940. Nos. 225, 229 and 230 surcharged with winged device and value.
282	80c. on 20c. Fokker Super Universal of L.A.N.	75	20
283	1p.60 on 5p. Ford 4-AT Trimotor of L.A.N. over Los Cerrillos Airport	4·75	1·60
284	5p.10 on 2p. Fokker Super Universal of L.A.N	3·75	1·80
282/284 *Set of 3*		8·25	3·25

1941.
290	10c. Cessna C.34 (?) (olive)	35	20
291	10c. Cessna C.34 (?) (mauve)	35	10
316	10c. Cessna C.34 (?) (blue)	20	10
292	20c. Potez 56 (red)	35	20
318	20c. Potez 56 (green)	20	10
294	20c. Potez 56 (brown)	20	10
295	30c. Douglas DC-2	35	20
295a	30c. Douglas DC-2 (olive)	20	10
296	40c. Douglas DC-2 (brown)	35	10
297	40c. Douglas DC-2 (blue)	20	10
324	50c. Cessna C.34 (red)	20	10
325	50c. Cessna C.34 (orange)	20	10
299a	60c. Potez 56 (green)	20	10
326	60c. Potez 56 (orange)	20	10
300	70c. Douglas DC-2	65	30
301	80c. Douglas DC-2 (blue)	3·25	55
302	80c. Douglas DC-2 (brown)	20	20
303a	90c. Lockheed L.18 Lodestar	35	20
304	1p. Sikorsky S-43 amphibian (blue)	65	30
304a	1p. Sikorsky S-43 amphibian (green and blue)	35	10
305	1p.60 Douglas DC-4	35	20
306	1p.80 Douglas DC-4	35	10
307	2p. Douglas DC-2 (lake)	90	30
308	2p. Douglas DC-2 (brown)	65	20
309	3p. Douglas DC-2 (green)	1·30	65
310a	3p. Douglas DC-2 (violet and yellow)	2·75	45
334	3p. Douglas DC-2 (violet and orange)	90	20
311	4p. Northrop Delta I (violet and brown)	2·00	1·10
335	4p. Northrop Delta I (green)	90	45
336a	5p. Douglas DC-4 (brown)	35	10
336	5p. Douglas DC-4 (red)	75	30
314	10p. Sikorsky S-42 flying boat (green and blue)	10·50	6·50
337	10p. Sikorsky S-42 flying boat (blue)	90	45

1949.
384	2p. Aircraft and badge of L.A.N	65	45

1950.
393*	5p. Douglas DC-6B	35	20
394*	10p. Douglas DC-6B	90	55

1950.
395	20c. Douglas DC-2	35	10
396	40c. Martin 2-0-2	35	10
404c	60c. Martin 2-0-2	45	10
398	1p. Martin 4-0-4	10	15
399	2p. Martin 2-0-2	35	10
404f	3p. Martin 4-0-4	20	10
401	4p. Martin 4-0-4	35	10
402	5p. Martin 2-0-2	35	10
403	10p. Martin 2-0-2	45	10
480	20p. Martin 4-0-4	45	20
481	50p. Douglas DC-6B	45	20
482	100p. Douglas DC-6B	45	20
483	200p. Douglas DC-6B	65	20

1951. No. 303a surcharged **UN PESO**.
407	1p. on 90c. Lockheed L.18 Lodestar	35	20

1952. No. 302 surcharged **40 Centavos**.
411	40c. on 80c. Douglas DC-2 (olive)	35	20

1954. 25th Anniv of L.A.N.-Chile (national airline).
427	3p. Biplane and silhouette of airplane	35	10

1955.
441a	100p. de Havilland DH.106 Comet 1	65	20
441b	200p. Morane Saulnier MS 760 Paris I	75	20
441c	500p. Douglas DC-6B	1·30	30
441a/441c *Set of 3*		2·40	65

1956.
451	1p. de Havilland DH.112 Venom FB.4	35	10
452	2p. Bell 47G Trooper helicopter	20	10
455	5p. Douglas DC-6B	20	10
456	10p. Douglas DC-6B	20	10
456a	20p. de Havilland DH.112 Venom FB.4	20	10
456b	50p. Douglas DC-2	20	10
451/456b *Set of 6*		1·25	55

1960.
497	1m. Martin 2-0-2	20	20
498	2m. Martin 2-0-2	20	10
499	3m. Martin 4-0-4	20	10
500	4m. Martin 4-0-4	20	10
501	5m. Martin 4-0-4	20	10
502	1c. Martin 2-0-2	20	10
503	2c. Martin 4-0-4	45	10
504	5c. Douglas DC-6B	2·75	10
505	10c. Douglas DC-6B	45	10
506	20c. Douglas DC-6B	55	10
497/506 *Set of 10*		5·00	1·10

1961. As Nos. 441a/c and 455/6b, but inscribed in revalued currency.
524	5m. Douglas DC-6B	20	10
525	1c. Douglas DC-6B	20	10
526	2c. de Havilland DH.112 Venom FB.4	20	10
527	5c. Douglas DC-2	20	10
528	10c. de Havilland DH.106 Comet 1	90	10
529	20c. Morane Saulnier MS 760 Paris I	1·10	10
530	50c. Douglas DC-6B	20	10
524/530 *Set of 7*		2·75	65

1971. First Trans-Andes Flight (1918) Commemoration.
677	1E.15 Dagoberto Godoy and Bristol M.1C monoplane	35	10

1972. First Air Service, Santiago-Easter Island-Tahiti.
684	2E.35 Boeing 707	35	20

1977.
785*	2p. Police helicopter	55	30

1980. 50th Anniv of Chilean Air Force.
844	3p.50 Bell Model 205 UH-1H Iroquois helicopter fitted with skis	75	30
845	3p.50 Consolidated PBY-5A Catalina Skua amphibian	75	30
846	3p.50 Northrop F-5E Tiger II jet fighter	75	30
844/846 *Set of 3*		2·00	80

1981. First Anniv of Lieutenant Marsh Antarctic Air Base.
873 3p.50 Cargo being unloaded from Lockheed C-130 Hercules of the Chilean Air Force at Lieutenant Marsh Antarctic Air Force Base.......... 1·10 30

1982. American Air Forces Co-operation System.
916 4p.50 Dassault Mirage IIIC..................... 55 20

1984. Third International Aeronautical Fair.
966 9p. Chilean-built Piper PA-28R Pillan .... 1·30 20

1987.
1104* 50p. MBB-Bolkow Bo 105 helicopters........ 1·20 55

1988. Fida 88. Fifth International Air Fair.
1146 60p. Silhouettes of Leonardo da Vinci's drawing of a glider, Wright *Flyer I*, Junkers Ju 52/3m, de Havilland DH.100 Vampire and Grumman F-14 Tomcat.............. 1·30 90

1988. Birth Centenary of Commodore Arturo Merino Benitez (aviation pioneer).
1157 35p. Arturo Merino Benitez, de Havilland DH.60G Gipsy Moth biplane, Boeing 767 airliner and Dassault Mirage 50 jet fighter................ 1·20 35

1988. 70th Anniv of First National Airmail Service.
1186 150p. Bleriot XI.................... 2·50 1·50

1989.
1248* 45p. Aerospatiale SA.365 Dauphin 2 helicopter....................... 85 35

1990. Chilean Air Force Airplanes.
1279 40p. Vickers Wibault biplane I No. 10 of the Chilean Air Force................ 65 35
1280 40p. Curtiss O1E Falcon No. 3 of the Chilean Air Force................ 65 35
1281 40p. Pitts S-2A No. 1 of the Falcons aerobatics team 65 35
1282 40p. Extra 33 No. 2 of the Falcons aerobatics team (inscribed "EXTRA 300")................ 65 35
1279/1282 *Set of 4*.................. 2·30 1·30

1990.
1288* 50p. Helicopter on Antarctic supply ship *Piloto Pardo*...................... 65 35

1990.
1338* 250p. Bell 206 JetRanger helicopters .... 4·00 1·80

1991.
1354 150p. Voisin "Boxkite"..................... 2·40 1·30
1355 150p. Royal Aircraft Factory S.E.5A.............. 2·40 1·30
1356 150p. Morane Saulnier MS 35 .... 2·40 1·30
1357 150p. Consolidated PBY-5A/OA-10 Catalina amphibian............. 2·40 1·30
1354/1357 *Set of 4*................... 8·75 4·75

1992. Fidae 1992 International Air and Space Fair.
1435 60p. Stylised jet fighter 80 35

1992.
1453* 200p. Boeing 737................... 2·40 1·10

1993. Aviation and Space.
1503 100p. Douglas B-26 Invader.............. 1·10 45
1504 100p. Dassault Mirage 5OCN Pantera .... 1·10 45
1505 100p. Sanchez Besa biplane............. 1·10 45
1506 100p. Bell 47 D1 helicopter............ 1·10 45
1503/1506 *Set of 4*................. 4·00 1·60

1994. International Air and Space Fair.
1554 300p. Sukhoi Su-30 Flanker.............. 2·75 2·40
1555 300p. Vought Sikorsky OS2U3 Kingfisher... 2·75 2·40
1556 300p. Lockheed F-117 Nighthawk.......... 2·75 2·40
1557 300p. Northrop F-5E Tigre (Tiger) III.......... 2·75 2·40
1554/1557 *Set of 4*................ 10·00 8·75

1996.
1653 400p. Embraer EMB-145.................. 4·25 1·80
1654 400p. Dassault Mirage M5M Elkan .... 4·25 1·80
1655 400p. de Havilland Canada DHC-6 Twin Otter...................... 4·25 1·80
1656 400p. Saab JAS-39 Gripen .... 4·25 1·80
1653/1656 *Set of 4*................. 15·00 6·50

2001. Chilean Airforce.
1985 260p. Lockheed C-130 Hercules..................... 1·70 1·50
1986 260p. Extra-300..................... 1·70 1·50
1987 260p. North American AT-6 Texan .... 1·70 1·50
1988 260p. Consolidated PBY-5A/OA-10 Catalina 1·70 1·50
1985/1988 *Set of 4*................. 6·00 5·50

2001.
1999* 490p. Bell UH-1 Iroquois helicopter............. 3·25 3·00

2002.
2040 250p. Eurocopter (MBB) BO105..................... 1·90 1·70

2003. Centenary of Powered Flight.
2083 200p. Bristol M1C and Wright Flyer.............. 1·30 1·20

2005. 75th Anniv of National Air Force.
2094 230p. Lockheed Martin F-16 Fighting Falcon................... 1·50 1·30

2008.
MS2202 250p. Helicopter; 250p. Supply aircraft; 250p. Light aircraft (other stamps on the sheet do not show aircraft)................. 7·50 7·75

CHINA

Eastern Asia

Chinese Republic

100 cents = 1 dollar (yuan)

1921. Tail fin showing Republican striped emblem.
352	15c. Curtiss JN-4 "Jenny"	28·00	30·00
353	30c. Curtiss JN-4 "Jenny"	28·00	30·00
354	45c. Curtiss JN-4 "Jenny"	28·00	20·00
355	60c. Curtiss JN-4 "Jenny"	33·00	35·00
356	90c. Curtiss JN-4 "Jenny"	45·00	48·00
352/356 Set of 5		£150	£150

1929. As Nos. 352/6, but with tail fin showing Nationalist "sun" emblem.
384a	15c. Curtiss JN-4 "Jenny"	3·00	55
385	30c. Curtiss JN-4 "Jenny"	7·00	2·50
386	45c. Curtiss JN-4 "Jenny"	14·00	6·50
387	60c. Curtiss JN-4 "Jenny"	17·00	8·50
388	90c. Curtiss JN-4 "Jenny"	14·00	14·50
384a/388 Set of 5		50·00	29·00

1932.
422	15c. Junkers F-13	35	40
556	25c. Junkers F-13	40	55
557	30c. Junkers F-13	40	55
558	45c. Junkers F-13	40	85
559	50c. Junkers F-13	40	55
560	60c. Junkers F-13	40	80
561	90c. Junkers F-13	40	85
562	$1 Junkers F-13	55	65
563	$2 Junkers F-13	1·40	1·40
564	$5 Junkers F-13	1·10	1·10
422/564 Set of 10		5·25	7·00

1946. Nos. 422, 556/7 and 563/4 surcharged with new value in frame and row of Chinese characters.
820	$23 on 30c. Junkers F-13	20	85
821	$53 on 15c. Junkers F-13	20	85
822	$73 on 25c. Junkers F-13	20	1·00
823	$100 on $2 Junkers F-13	20	30
824	$200 on $5 Junkers F-13	20	30
820/824 Set of 5		90	3·00

1946.
905	$27 Douglas DC-4	30	1·00

1947.
985*	$100 Aircraft	30	70
988*	$400 Airplane	30	70
989*	$500 Airplane	30	70

1948. Perforated or imperforate.
1001	$5,000 Airplane (on stamp No. 989) (red)	70	2·50
1002	$5,000 Airplane (on stamp No. 989) (green)	70	2·50

1948. Nos. 556/7, 560/2 and 905 surcharged with new value in frame and horizontal or vertical row of Chinese characters.
1022*	$10,000 on 30c. Junkers F-13	20	60
1028*	$10,000 on $27 Douglas DC-4	35	1·30
1023*	$20,000 on 25c. Junkers F-13	20	60
1024*	$50,000 on 90c. Junkers F-13	20	80
1025*	$50,000 on 60c. Junkers F-13	20	80
1026*	$50,000 on $1 Junkers F-13	20	70

1949. Revenue stamps surcharged with new value between two rows of Chinese characters.
1136	50c. on $20 Airplane	20	45
1137	$1 on $15 Airplane	20	6·50
1127	$2 on $50 Airplane	20	95
1144	$3 on $50 Airplane	20	60
1138	$5 on $500 Airplane	20	35
1129	$10 on $30 Airplane	20	45
1140	$15 on $30 Airplane	20	35
1141	$25 on $20 Airplane	20	35
1145	$50 on $50 Airplane	20	35
1147	$50 on $300 Airplane	20	45
1130	$80 on $50 Airplane	20	95
1146	$100 on $50 Airplane	40	2·00
1124	$200 on $50 Airplane	60	75
1142	$200 on $500 Airplane	40	40
1125	$300 on $50 Airplane	85	95
1143	$500 on $15 Airplane	1·00	3·00
1134	$500 on $30 Airplane	50	2·10
1135	$1,000 on $50 Airplane	8·25	7·00
1148	$1,000 on $100 Airplane	2·30	4·00
1126	$1,500 on $50 Airplane	1·00	2·75
1151	$2,000 on $300 Airplane	40	55

1949. Revenue stamps surcharged as Nos. 1122/51 but key pattern inverted at top and bottom.
1183	$50 on $10 Airplane	8·75	11·50
1184	$100 on $10 Airplane	2·00	13·50
1185	$500 on $10 Airplane	1·25	5·00
1186	$1,000 on $10 Airplane	1·00	7·75
1187	$5,000 on $20 Airplane	25·00	19·00
1188	$10,000 on $20 Airplane	14·50	11·50
1189	$50,000 on $20 Airplane	17·00	19·00
1190	$100,000 on $20 Airplane	21·00	19·00
1191	$500,000 on $20 Airplane	£300	£190
1192	$2,000,000 on $20 Airplane	£750	£275
1193	$5,000,000 on $20 Airplane	£1300	£550
1183/1193 Set of 11		£2250	£1000

1949. No value indicated (sold at airmail rate). Perforated or rouletted.
1212A*	(–) Douglas DC-4	6·50	17·00

1949. Revenue stamps overprinted with two rows of Chinese characters, for type of service shown.
1232	$10 Airplane (express letter)	23·00	29·00
1233	$30 Airplane (domestic letter)	95·00	90·00
1234	$50 Airplane (registered letter)	25·00	25·00
1235	$100 Airplane (air mail)	45·00	60·00
1236	$200 Airplane (domestic letter)	15·00	9·75
1237	$200 Airplane (domestic letter)	18·00	16·00
1232/1237 Set of 6		£200	£200

1949. Revenue stamps surcharged in figures below two rows of Chinese characters. On Nos. 1312/13 the key pattern is inverted at top and bottom.
1312	1c. on $20 Airplane	55·00	55·00
1284	1c. on $5,000 Airplane	5·00	4·25
1285	4c. on $100 Airplane	3·00	2·20
1286	4c. on $3,000 Airplane	3·00	1·10
1313	10c. on $20 Airplane	55·00	55·00
1287	10c. on $50 Airplane	4·50	1·80
1288	10c. on $1,000 Airplane	4·75	2·00
1289	20c. on $1,000 Airplane	5·00	2·50
1290	50c. on $30 Airplane	15·00	4·25
1291	50c. on $50 Airplane	22·00	1·80
1292	$1 on $50 Airplane	16·00	21·00
1284/1313 Set of 11		£170	£140

SINKIANG

用貼省新限

1942. Nos. 422 and 556/64 of Chinese Republic overprinted with one row of Chinese characters.
187	15c. Junkers F-13	5·25	6·50
197	25c. Junkers F-13	4·50	7·75
198	30c. Junkers F-13	5·00	8·25
190	45c. Junkers F-13	7·75	13·00
199	50c. Junkers F-13	6·50	9·75
192	60c. Junkers F-13	7·75	16·00
193	90c. Junkers F-13	42·00	60·00
194	$1 Junkers F-13	8·50	14·00
200	$2 Junkers F-13	31·00	31·00
201	$5 Junkers F-13	31·00	31·00
187/201 Set of 10		£130	£180

COMMUNIST CHINA

100 cents = 1 yuan

NORTH CHINA PEOPLE'S POST

1949.
NC349	$50 Airplane	1·90	3·25
NC350	$100 Airplane	30	90
NC351	$200 Airplane	65	90
NC352	$300 Airplane	8·25	2·10
NC353	$400 Airplane	8·25	2·10
NC354	$500 Airplane	8·25	1·10
NC355	$700 Airplane	3·00	3·25
NC349/NC355 Set of 7		28·00	12·00

NORTH EAST CHINA PEOPLE'S POST

1950.
NE298	$2,500 Airliner	11·00	8·75
NE299	$5,000 Airliner	11·00	8·75

CHINESE PEOPLE'S REPUBLIC

1949. 100 cents = 1 yuan

1950. 100 fen = 1 yuan

1950. No. 1212 of Chinese Republic (perforated or rouletted) surcharged with Chinese characters and **300** in frame.
1429*	$300 on (–) Douglas DC-4	35	90

1950. As Nos. NE298/9, but without the four Chinese characters at right.
1469	$400 Airliner	10·50	4·00
1470	$800 Airliner	10·50	4·00

1951.
1488	$1,000 Ilyushin Il-18 with piston engines	25	50
1489	$3,000 Ilyushin Il-18 with piston engines	35	30
1490	$5,000 Ilyushin Il-18 with piston engines	30	30
1491	$10,000 Ilyushin Il-18 with piston engines	50	50
1492	$30,000 Ilyushin Il-18 with piston engines	6·75	2·50
1488/1492 Set of 5		7·25	3·75

1951. No. 1212 of Chinese Republic (perforated or rouletted) surcharged with Chinese characters and **10** in frame.
1501	$10 on (–) Douglas DC-4	65	65

1952.
1564*	$800 Pilot, Ilyushin Il-4 DB-3 bomber and Mikoyan Gurevich MiG-15 jet fighters	35	15

1957.
1727	16f. Lisunov Li-2 at Peking Airport	10·50	35
1728	28f. Lisunov Li-2	10·50	35
1729	35f. Lisunov Li-2	10·50	2·40
1730	52f. Lisunov Li-2	10·50	85
1727/1730 Set of 4		3·75	3·50

1958. Aviation Sports.
1799	4f. Children with model aircraft	85	25
1800	8f. Gliders	85	25
1801	10f. Airplane and parachutists	85	25
1802	20f. Yakovlev Yak-18U trainers	1·50	25
1799/1802 Set of 4		3·75	90

1959. Inauguration of Peking Airport.
1821   8f. Airplane over Peking Airport..............   8·75   1·10
1822   10f. Ilyushin Il-14P at Peking Airport ....   8·75   50

1979.
2889*   8f. Antonov An-2 biplane spraying
     crops..   80   45
2891*   8f. Jet fighter   80   45

1979.
2894*   8f. Children with model aircraft   65   50

1980.
2972*   10f. Antonov An-2 biplane   85   40

1980.
2978*   10f. Tupolev Tu-154...............................   3·00   1·80

1980. Peking International Airport.
2993   8f. Ilyushin Il-86, other airliners and
     plan of airport buildings......................   1·30   80
2994   10f. Airplane and runway.......................   1·80   1·30

1986.
3424*   8f. Mil Mi-8 helicopters......................   20   20

1987.
3510*   30f. Pilot and jet fighters ....   1·40   75

1989.
3647   20f. Jettison of fuel tank   25   15

1995.
4016*   60f. Airplane....................................   25   15

1996. Chinese Aircraft.
4086   20f. Shenyang F-8   15   10
4087   50f. Nanchang A-5   25   15
4088   50f. Xian Y-7   25   15
4089   100f. Harbin Y-12   35   35
4086/4089 *Set of 4*   90   70

1996.
4151*   10f. Airplane....................................   15   10

1996.
4170   60f. Boeing 747 taking off, Kai Tak
     Airport   25   15

1997.
4213*   50f. Shenyang J-8 11B   20   10
4215*   200f. Jet fighters   60   45

1998.
4287   150f. Sanya Phoenix International Airport   50   35

1998.
4351   200f. Macao Airport...........................   65   45

2000.
4551   2y.80 Harbin Y-12   85   60

2003. Centenary of Powered Flight.
4827   80f. Concorde, Bell X-1 and Wright Flyer.   20   15
4828   2y. Nanchang Q-5   65   50

2006.
5144   1y.20 Tail of airplane   20   10

TAIWAN

100 cents = 1 yuan

用貼灣臺限

1949. No. 1212 of Chinese Republic (rouletted) overprinted with five Chinese characters.
87*   (–) Douglas DC-4 ....   5·00   2·50

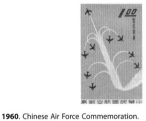

1954. 15th Anniv of Air Force Day. Without gum.
190* $1 Douglas DC-6............................   13·50   1·00
191* $1.60 Republic F-84G Thunderjet...............   12·00   55

1956. No. 1212 of Chinese Republic (perforated or rouletted) surcharged 3 below two Chinese characters.
242   3c. on (–) Douglas DC-4 ....   1·00   25

1960. Chinese Air Force Commemoration.
344    $1 North American F-86D Sabre jet fighters of the Thunder Tiger Aerobatic Squadron in "bomb burst" manoeuvre...............................   5·25   45
345    $2 North American F-86D Sabre jet fighters of the Thunder Tiger Aerobatic Squadron in "loop" manoeuvre...............................   4·75   35
346    $5 North American F-86D Sabre jet fighters of the Thunder Tiger Aerobatic Squadron in diamond formation...............................   7·25   55
344/346 *Set of 3*...............................   16·00   1·20

1961. 40th Anniv of Chinese Civil Air Service.
407    $10 Convair 880 and biplane.............   3·75   1·40

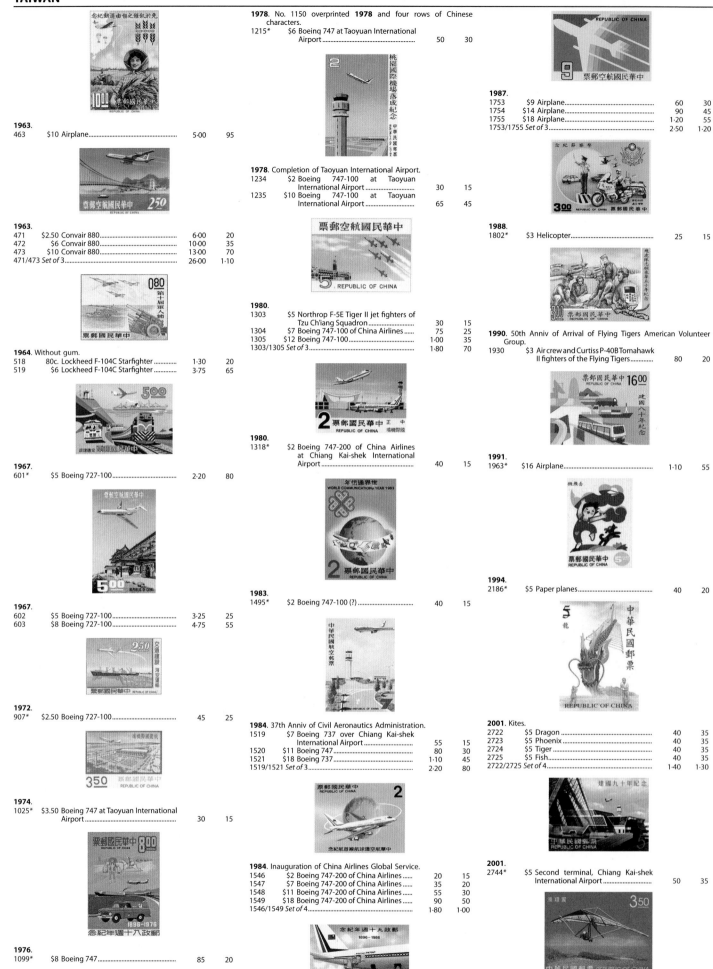

1963.
463    $10 Airplane.................................   5·00   95

1963.
471    $2.50 Convair 880.........................   6·00   20
472    $6 Convair 880..............................   10·00   35
473    $10 Convair 880.............................   13·00   70
471/473 Set of 3..................................   26·00   1·10

1964. Without gum.
518   80c. Lockheed F-104C Starfighter.............   1·30   20
519    $6 Lockheed F-104C Starfighter..............   3·75   65

1967.
601* $5 Boeing 727-100.........................   2·20   80

1967.
602    $5 Boeing 727-100.........................   3·25   25
603    $8 Boeing 727-100.........................   4·75   55

1972.
907* $2.50 Boeing 727-100.....................   45   25

1974.
1025* $3.50 Boeing 747 at Taoyuan International
       Airport...   30   15

1976.
1099* $8 Boeing 747..............................   85   20

1976. As No. 1025, but changed face value.
1122f* $6 Boeing 747 at Taoyuan International
       Airport...   35   20

1977. As No. 1122f, but face value in double-lined figures.
1150* $6 Boeing 747 at Taoyuan International
       Airport...   30   20

1978. No. 1150 overprinted **1978** and four rows of Chinese characters.
1215* $6 Boeing 747 at Taoyuan International
       Airport...   50   30

1978. Completion of Taoyuan International Airport.
1234 $2 Boeing 747-100 at Taoyuan
       International Airport......................   30   15
1235 $10 Boeing 747-100 at Taoyuan
       International Airport......................   65   45

1980.
1303 $5 Northrop F-5E Tiger II jet fighters of
       Tzu Ch'iang Squadron....................   30   15
1304 $7 Boeing 747-100 of China Airlines......   75   25
1305 $12 Boeing 747-100.......................   1·00   35
1303/1305 Set of 3..............................   1·80   70

1980.
1318* $2 Boeing 747-200 of China Airlines
       at Chiang Kai-shek International
       Airport...   40   15

1983.
1495* $2 Boeing 747-100 (?)....................   40   15

1984. 37th Anniv of Civil Aeronautics Administration.
1519 $7 Boeing 737 over Chiang Kai-shek
       International Airport......................   55   15
1520 $11 Boeing 747.............................   80   30
1521 $18 Boeing 737.............................   1·10   45
1519/1521 Set of 3..............................   2·20   80

1984. Inauguration of China Airlines Global Service.
1546 $2 Boeing 747-200 of China Airlines......   20   15
1547 $7 Boeing 747-200 of China Airlines......   35   20
1548 $11 Boeing 747-200 of China Airlines......   55   30
1549 $18 Boeing 747-200 of China Airlines......   90   50
1546/1549 Set of 4..............................   1·80   1·00

1986.
1645* $2 Mail being unloaded from Boeing
       747 of China Airlines....................   25   15

1987.
1753 $9 Airplane................................   60   30
1754 $14 Airplane...............................   90   45
1755 $18 Airplane...............................   1·20   55
1753/1755 Set of 3..............................   2·50   1·20

1988.
1802* $3 Helicopter..............................   25   15

1990. 50th Anniv of Arrival of Flying Tigers American Volunteer Group.
1930 $3 Air crew and Curtiss P-40B Tomahawk
       II fighters of the Flying Tigers.............   80   20

1991.
1963* $16 Airplane...............................   1·10   55

1994.
2186* $5 Paper planes...........................   40   20

2001. Kites.
2722 $5 Dragon.................................   40   35
2723 $5 Phoenix................................   40   35
2724 $5 Tiger...................................   40   35
2725 $5 Fish....................................   40   35
2722/2725 Set of 4..............................   1·40   1·30

2001.
2744* $5 Second terminal, Chiang Kai-shek
       International Airport......................   50   35

2006.
3159 $3.50 Hang gliding........................   20   15
3160   £3.50 Paragliding.........................   20   15
3161 $12 Microlight............................   75   60
3162 $15 Parasailing...........................   95   75
3159/3162 Set of 4..............................   1·90   1·50

CHRISTMAS ISLAND

Indian Ocean

100 cents = 1 dollar

1983.
177*   85c. Boeing 727.................................   1·50   1·75

1988.
258* $1 Hunting P. 66 Pembroke.....................   1·75   1·25

1990.
297*   65c. Aero Commander 1121 Jet Commander ....   3·75   1·50

1995.
407*   45c. de Havilland DH.98 Mosquito............   95   95

COCOS (KEELING) ISLANDS

Indian Ocean

1963. 12 pence = 1 shilling

20 shillings = 1 pound

1966. 100 cents = 1 dollar

1963.
2*   5d. Lockheed L.1049G Super Constellation...................................   1·50   80

1981. Aircraft.
65   22c. Consolidated PBY-5 Catalina flying boat NC-777 *Guba*   25   25
66   22c. Consolidated B-24 Liberator (in air) and Avro Type 691 Lancastrian VH-EAS of QANTAS.............................   25   25
67   22c. Douglas DC-4 (in air) and Lockheed Constellation of QANTAS   25   25
68   22c. Lockheed L.188 Electra of QANTAS...   25   25
69   22c. Boeing 727-100 of Ansett Airways (in air) and Boeing 727-100 of Trans Australian Airways................................   25   25
65/69 *Set of 5* ....   1·10   1·10

1984.
120*   55c. West Island airstrip.............................   85   60

1987.
166*   75c. Boeing 727-100 at airport ....   1·50   1·75

1988.
187*   65c. Lockheed L.1049G Super Constellation (on stamp No. 2)..........   1·90   2·50

1989. 50th Anniv of First Indian Ocean Aerial Survey.
208*   70c. Consolidated PBY-5 Catalina flying boat NC-777 *Guba* and crew ....   1·75   2·50
209* $1 Consolidated PBY-5 Catalina flying boat NC-777 *Guba* ....   2·00   2·50

1992.
270   45c. Supermarine Spitfires at island airstrip......................................   2·50   1·40
271   85c. Mitsubishi A6M Zero-Sen ....   3·75   3·75
272    $1.20 Short S.25 Sunderland flying boat of the R.A.F.................................   4·75   5·00
270/272 *Set of 3*.......................................   10·00   9·00

1993. Air-Sea Rescue.
290*   85c. Israeli Aircraft Industry Westwind Seascan ....   3·50   3·75

COLOMBIA

South America

100 centavos = 1 peso

1932. Overprinted **CORREO AEREO**.
422*   1p. Dornier Wal flying boat ....   19·00   15·00
423*   2p. Dornier Wal flying boat ....   50·00   45·00
424*   3p. Dornier Wal flying boat ....   £100   85·00
425*   5p. Dornier Wal flying boat £170   £180

1945. 25th Anniv of First Airmail Service in America.
634*   30c. Junkers F-13 seaplane *Tolima* ....   4·75   1·80

1954.
824   2c. Lockheed Constellation   20   20

1954.
825   5c. Lockheed Constellation (brown frame)...   10   10
826   5c. Lockheed Constellation (violet frame)...   10   10

1955.
849   10c. Lockheed Constellation   35   20

1955.
864*   1p. Airplane..   22·00   10·50
865*   2p. Airplane..   15·00   8·00

1955.
868   20c. Lockheed Constellation   20   10

1956.
905*   20c. Airplane...   20   10

1959. Various issues overprinted **UNIFICADO** within outline of airplane.
968   5c. brown (Loyola) (No. 903)......................   45   45
969   5c. orange (farm) (No. 911)......................   45   45
970   5c. red (St. Vincent de Paul) (No. 926)   65   85
971   10c. red (Falls) (No. 772)............................   45   65
972   10c. red (Monastery) (No. 789)..................   35   20
973   15c. red (Gen. Reyes) (No. 921)   35   20
974   20c. brown (mountains) (No. 792).............   35   20
975   20c. brown (cadet school) (No. 922).........   35   20
976   20c. brown (fencer) (No. 932)....................   35   20
977   25c. blue (Sanctuary of the Rocks) (No. 793)..   35   20
978   25c. purple (Sanctuary of the Rocks) (No. 794)..   35   20
979   25c. grey (Father Almanza) (No. 941)........   35   20
980   25c. red (Msr. Carrasquilla) (No. 947)........   35   20
981   30c. brown (Galeras Volcano) (No. 795)....   35   20
982   50c. on 60c. sepia (fountain) (No. 960)......   45   30
983   1p. blue (Msr. Carrasquilla) (No. 948)........   1·20   30
984   1p.20 multicoloured ("Miss Universe") (No. 953)...   1·80   1·30
985   2p. black and green (Pastelillo Fort) (No. 801)..   2·40   30
986   3p. black and red (Popayan) (No. 802) ....   6·50   95
987   5p. green and brown (Sanctuary of the Rocks) (No. 803)..............................   8·75   1·80
988   10p. olive and red (map) (No. 804).............   11·00   3·75
968/988 *Set of 21* ....   24·00   12·00

1959.
994*	50c. Junkers F-13 seaplane *Colombia*........	1·70	85
995*	1p.20 Lockheed L.1049 Super Constellation	3·50	2·10

1959. 40th Anniv of Avianca (Colombian National Airline).
998	35c. Junkers F-13 seaplane *Colombia* and Lockheed L.1049 Super Constellation........................	65	20
999	60c. Junkers F-13 seaplane *Colombia* and Lockheed L.1049 Super Constellation........................	1·10	1·10
MS1000	1p.x2 Junkers F-13 seaplane *Colombia* and Lockheed L.1049 Super Constellation	17·00	17·00
MS1001	1p.50×2 Junkers F-13 seaplane *Colombia* and Lockheed L.1049 Super Constellation ("EXTRA RAPIDO")....................	17·00	17·00

1960.
1002	35c. Eldorado Airport, Bogota	90	30
1003	60c. Eldorado Airport, Bogota	1·00	65
1004	1p. Eldorado Airport, Bogota ("EXTRA RAPIDO")....................	1·80	95
1002/1004 *Set of 3*....................		3·25	1·70

1961. Various stamps overprinted **Aereo** or **AEREO** and Boeing 720B airliner or surcharged also.
1077	5c. Flower (No. 1011).....................	35	10
1078	5c. Sloth (No. 1005).....................	35	10
1079	10c. on 20c. Spider monkey (No. 1007)	35	10
1077/1079 *Set of 3*.....................		85	25

1961.
1085*	35c. Boeing 720B.....................	75	30

1965. History of Colombian Aviation.
1159	5c. Junkers F-13 seaplane *Colombia*........	35	10
1160	10c. Dornier Do-J Wal flying boat...............	35	10
1161	20c. Dornier Do-B Merkur seaplane (inscribed "Mercur")........................	35	10
1162	50c. Ford 5-AT Trimotor........................	35	10
1163	60c. de Havilland DH.60G Gipsy Moth......	55	30
1164	1p. Douglas DC-4 HK-138 of Aviacion Colombiana........................	1·10	30
1165	1p.40 Douglas DC-3 HK-159 of Aviacion Colombiana........................	1·30	30
1166	2p.80 Lockheed L.1049G Super Constellation of Aviacion Colombiana (wrongly dated "1951")	2·40	1·10
1167	3p. Boeing 720B of Avianca	3·50	1·50
1159/1167 *Set of 9*.....................		9·25	3·50

1969. 50th Anniv of First Colombian Airmail Flight.
1240	1p. Junkers F-13 seaplane	35	10
1241	1p.50 Boeing 720B of Avianca	55	20
MS1242	5p. Junkers F-13 seaplane; 5p. Boeing 720B of Avianca. Imperforate.....................	6·00	6·50

1969. 50th Anniv of Avianca.
1249	2p. Junkers F-13 seaplane	55	20
1250	3p.50 Boeing 720B of Avianca	1·10	45
MS1251	3p.50 Junkers F-13 seaplane; 5p. Boeing 720B of Avianca. Imperforate.....................	6·00	6·50

1976. Inauguration of Avianca Jumbo Jet Service.
1403	2p. Boeing 747-200 of Avianca	30	10

1977. No. 1403 surcharged **$3.00.**
1414*	3p. on 2p. Boeing 747-200 of Avianca.....	20	10

1982. American Air Forces Co-operation.
1667	18p. Biplane........................	75	20

1985. Birth Centenary of Gonzalo Mejia (airport architect).
1717	12p. Farman F.40 type biplane	55	30

1985.
1728	15p. Airplane at Medellin Airport................	35	10

1989.
1847	130p. Boeing 767 of Avianca........................	1·50	45

1991.
1913	80p. Police helicopter........................	60	45

1992.
1941	110p. McDonnell Douglas MD-83 of Avianca........................	95	55

1994. 75th Anniv of First Airmail Flight.
2013	270p. Curtiss JN-4 Jenny........................	1·90	1·20

1995. 75th Anniv of Compania Colombiana de Navagacion Aerea (private air company contracted to carry mail).
2028	330p. Biplane (unidentifiable).....................	2·40	1·50

1997.
2130*	500p. Guillermo Misas (aviation pioneer)...	2·75	1·40

SPECIAL DELIVERY STAMPS

1963.
E1143	50c. Boeing 720B........................	35	10

1966. History of Colombian Aviation.
E1168	80c. Boeing 727-100........................	75	30

1994. 75th Anniv of Colombian Air Force.
E2004	300p. Caudron G-IV........................	2·10	1·30

COMORO ISLANDS

Indian Ocean
100 centimes = 1 franc

1950.
13*	50f. Airplane........................	3·00	2·50
14*	100f. Airplane........................	2·75	4·25

1954. As No. 264 of Cameroun.
17	15f. Bomber........................	15·00	46·00

1969. First Flight of Concorde.
83	100f. Concorde of Air France........................	10·00	27·00

1972. Inauguration of New Airport, Moroni.
119* 100f. Moroni Airport.................................. 4·00 4·50

1975. Inauguration of Direct Moroni-Hahaya-Paris Air Service.
162 135f. Boeing 707.................................. 10·50 9·75

1976.
188* 200f. Airship LZ-127 *Graf Zeppelin* and
Concorde.. 2·20 90
189* 400f. Jet airliner.. 4·00 2·10

1977.
221 20f. Henri Giffard's steam-powered
dirigible airship, 1852................. 30 10
222 25f. Santos-Dumont's airship *Ballon
No. 6*, 1901................................. 35 10
223 50f. Russian airship *Astra*, 1914.................. 75 25
224 75f. Beardmore airship R-34................. 1·00 30
225 200f. U.S. Navy airship ZR-3 *Los Angeles*
(air)... 2·30 80
226 500f. Airship LZ-129 *Hindenburg*.................. 5·75 1·90
221/226 *Set of 6*.................................. 9·50 3·00
MS227 500f. Airship LZ-127 *Graf Zeppelin*.................. 5·50 2·10

1977. No. 188 overprinted **Paris-New-York-22 nov. 1977.**
270 200f. Airship LZ-127 *Graf Zeppelin* and
Concorde.. 4·25 2·75

1978.
304* 200f. Dupuy de Lome's airship, 1872........... 1·90 65

1978.
311* 100f. Stylised airliner................................. 1·00 30

1979. History of Aviation. Overprinted **REPUBLIQUE FEDERALE DES COMORES** or surcharged also.
364 30f. Otto Lilienthal and Lilienthal biplane
glider.. 45 45
365 50f. Wilbur and Orville Wright and Wright
Flyer I... 65 65
366 50f. on 75f. Louis Bleriot and Bleriot XI 75 75
367 100f. Claude Dornier and Dornier Do-J Wal
flying boat N-24 (inscribed "WALL").. 1·40 1·30

368 200f. Charles Lindbergh and Ryan NYP
Special *Spirit of St. Louis* (air)............... 2·20 2·10
364/368 *Set of 5*.................................. 5·00 4·75

1980.
424* 260f. Concorde.. 2·75 1·20

1980. 50th Anniv of First South Atlantic Flight.
430 200f. J. Dabry, L. Gimie, Jean Mermoz and
Latecoere 28-3 seaplane F-AJNQ
Comte de la Vaulx............................ 3·75 2·10

1981. No. 430 surcharged **30F.**
435* 30f. on 200f. J. Dabry, L. Gimie, Jean
Mermoz and Latecoere 28-3
seaplane F-AJNQ *Comte de la Vaulx*.. 70 70

1981.
MS451 500f. Boeing 747 SCA of NASA carrying
Space Shuttle.................................. 4·50 1·60

1981. No. 424 surcharged **50F.**
468* 50f. on 260f. Concorde.................................. 1·20 1·10

1983. Bicentenary of Manned Flight.
505 100f. Montgolfier balloon (tethered flight,
1783).. 1·20 45
506 200f. Vincenzo Lunardi's balloon (flight
from London to Ware, 1784)................. 1·80 70
507 300f. Blanchard and Jeffries' balloon,
1785... 3·00 95
508 400f. Henri Giffard's steam-powered
dirigible airship, 1852................. 4·25 1·40
505/508 *Set of 4*.................................. 9·25 3·25
MS509 500f. Mail balloon, Paris, 1870................. 5·50 1·70

1985. Nos. **MS**451, **MS**509 and three other miniature sheets not showing aircraft overprinted.
MS554 Five sheets. (a) 500f. Boeing 747 SCA of NASA
carrying Space Shuttle (overprinted **MOPHILA
'85 HAMBOURG**); (d) 500f. Mail balloon, Paris,
1870 (overprinted **ROME** and "Italia 85" stamp
exhibition emblem) *Set of 5 sheets*............... 6·75 3·00

1985.
578 25f. Wright Type A 30 10
579 75f. Wright Type A 80 40
580 125f. Wright Type A .... 1·30 50
581 500f. Wright Type A .... 4·50 2·30
578/581 *Set of 4*.................................. 6·25 3·00

1985. 50th Anniv of UTA (Union des Transports Aeriennes).
587 25f. Sikorsky S-43 amphibian F-AOUL...... 25 10
588 75f. Douglas DC-9.................................. 65 30
589 100f. Douglas DC-4, Douglas DC-6, Nord
2501 Noratlas and de Havilland
DH.114 Heron 2............................ 1·00 55
590 125f. Boeing 747-200F freighter being
loaded with cargo........................ 1·30 70
591 1000f. Latecoere 28 F-ANNF, Sikorsky S-43
amphibian F-AOUK, Douglas DC-10
and Boeing 747-200, all of U.T.A ...... 11·00 5·50
587/591 *Set of 5*.................................. 13·00 6·50

1987. Aviation.
624 200f. Didier Daurat, Raymond Vanier and
Caudron C-635 Simoun F-ANRI *Air
Bleu*.. 2·00 80
625 300f. Letord 4 Lorraine .... 2·75 1·10
626 500f. Morane Saulnier Type H.................. 4·75 1·90
627 1000f. Henri Pecquet flying Humber
Sommer biplane.......................... 9·50 3·25
624/627 *Set of 4*.................................. 17·00 6·25

1988. Aviation Pioneers.
669 100f. Alberto Santos-Dumont and his
biplane *14 bis*............................ 1·20 45
670 150f. Wilbur and Orville Wright and Wright
Type A.. 1·70 60
671 200f. Louis Bleriot and Bleriot XI.................. 2·00 80
672 300f. Henri Farman and Farman Voisin
No. 1 bis..................................... 2·75 1·50
673 500f. Gabriel and Charles Voisin and Voisin
"Boxkite".................................... 4·75 2·40
674 800f. Roland Garros and Morane Saulnier
Type I.. 7·50 3·00
669/674 *Set of 6*.................................. 18·00 8·00

1989. No. 671 surcharged.
732* 150f. on 200f. Louis Bleriot and Bleriot XI.. 1·40 55

1990.
733* 5f. Moroni Airport................................. 10 10
734* 10f. Moroni Airport................................. 10 10
735* 25f. Moroni Airport................................. 10 10

1990.
755* 375f. Concorde.. 3·75 1·00

1991.
775* 375f. Supermarine Spitfire and two
Messerschmitt Bf 109 fighters .... 3·50 75
776* 450f. Hawker Hurricane Mk I and
Messerschmitt Bf 109 (air)............... 4·50 1·00
MS778* 1000f. Yakovlev Yak-9 fighters of the
Normandy-Niemen Squadron................. 10·50 2·30

1991.
788*   500f. Airship LZ-127 *Graf Zeppelin* and
         Zeppelin-Staaken E4/20 airliner......... 5·00 1·00

APPENDIX

The following stamps have either been issued in excess of postal needs or have not been made available to the public in reasonable quantities at face value. Miniature sheets, imperforate stamps, etc are excluded from this section.

1975.

No. 162 surcharged **ETAT COMORIEN 100F.** 100f. on 135f. Boeing 707.

CONGO (BRAZZAVILLE)

Central Africa

100 centimes = 1 franc

1961. As No. 307 of Cameroun.
12   50f. Boeing 707 airliners of Air Afrique .... 1·50 80

1966. As No. 438 of Cameroun.
103   30f. Douglas DC-8F Jet Trader of Air
        Afrique...................................... 75 25

1967. 30th Anniv of Aeromaritime Airmail Link.
139   30f. Sikorsky S-43 amphibian 75 45

1969. As No. 552 of Cameroun.
195   100f. Airliner over airport .... 2·00 90

1970. History of Flight and Space Travel.
250*   45f. Lilienthal biplane glider (wrongly
        dated "1891")........................... 85 30
251*   50f. Lindbergh's Ryan NYP *Special Spirit
        of St. Louis*............................. 90 45

1973.
359   50f. Holste MH 1521 Broussard................. 1·50 70

1975.
452   40f. Balloon from *Five Weeks in a Balloon*
        by Jules Verne.......................... 1·50 60
453   50f. Balloon from the film *Around the
        World in Eighty Days*................... 1·80 1·10

1975.
495*   95f. Clement Ader and his *Avion III* .... 1·70 80

1977. History of the Zeppelin.
567   40f. Airship LZ-10 *Schwaben*, 1911 .... 50 25
568   60f. Airship LZ-11 *Viktoria Luise*, 1913....... 75 45
569   100f. Airship LZ-120 *Bodensee*, 1920......... 1·10 45
570   200f. Airship LZ-127 *Graf Zeppelin*............. 2·00 70
571   300f. Airship LZ-130 *Graf Zeppelin* II .... 3·50 1·00
567/571 *Set of 5* .... 7·00 2·50
MS572 500f. Airship LZ-127 *Graf Zeppelin*.............. 6·75 2·20

1977. Aviation History.
583   60f. Traian Vuia and Vuia No. 1, 1906 .... 55 25
584   75f. Louis Bleriot and Bleriot XI................ 70 25
585   100f. Roland Garros and Morane Saulnier
        Type I................................. 95 55
586   200f. Charles Lindbergh and Ryan NYP
        Special *Spirit of St. Louis*............... 2·20 70
587   300f. Tupolev Tu-144........................ 3·00 90
583/587 *Set of 5* .... 6·75 2·40
MS588 500f. Charles Lindbergh and Ryan NYP
        Special *Spirit of St. Louis*.............. 5·75 2·10

1979.
669*   150f. Concorde................................. 2·75 1·90

1979.
673*   300f. Alcock and Brown's Vickers FB-27
        Vimy, 1919 (on aerial post label)........ 3·00 95
MS674* 500f. Concorde .... 6·00 2·40

1979. 20th Anniv of ASECNA (African Air Safety Organisation).
702   100f. Douglas DC-10 .... 1·10 60

1982. 50th Anniv of Amelia Earhart's Transatlantic Flight.
884   150f. Amelia Earhart and Lockheed Vega
        5B NR-7952 *Friendship*, 1932 .... 1·80 90

1983. Bicentenary of Manned Flight.
913   100f. Montgolfier balloon (first manned
        free flight, 1783)...................... 1·50 25
914   200f. Montgolfier balloon *Le Flesselles*,
        1784................................... 2·50 60
915   300f. Auguste Piccard's stratosphere
        balloon *F.N.R.S.*, 1931.................... 3·25 85
916   400f. Modern hot-air balloon................. 4·50 1·20
913/916 *Set of 4* .... 10·50 2·50
MS917 500f. Balloon *Ville d'Orleans*, Paris, 1870......... 5·75 1·80

1985. No. MS917 and three other miniature sheets not showing aircraft overprinted.
MS984 Four sheets. (d) 500f. Mail balloon *Ville
        d'Orleans*, Paris, 1870 (overprinted **MOPHILA '85
        HAMBOURG**) *Price for 4 sheets*................... 5·50 5·50

1985.
1005*   250f. Fokker F.28 Fellowship and de
        Havilland Canada Twin Otter at
        Mavalhaya Airport...................... 2·75 2·00

1986. 25th Anniv of Air Afrique.
1049   200f. Douglas DC-10 of Air Afrique............. 2·10 95

1988.
1133*   60f. Jet fighters representing an antiviral
        drug................................... 45 25

1991.
1199*   60f. Hot-air balloon 55 40

1991.
1268*   75f. Airship LZ-127 *Graf Zeppelin*............. 85 45

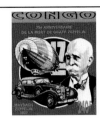

1992.
1303* 240f. Count Ferdinand von Zeppelin and airship LZ-127 *Graf Zeppelin* .... 3·00 85

POSTAGE DUE STAMPS

1961.
D20* 50c. Holste MH 1521 Broussard.......... 10 10
D29* 25f. Seaplane.......... 1·60 1·50
D30* 25f. Boeing 707.......... 1·60 1·50

CONGO (KINSHASA)

Central Africa

1963. 100 centimes = 1 franc

1967. 100 sengi = 1 (li)kuta

100 (ma)kuta = 1 zaire

1963.
460 2f. Boeing 707.......... 1·40 1·00
461 4f. Boeing 707.......... 10 10
462 7f. Boeing 707.......... 20 10
463 20f. Boeing 707.......... 30 15
460/463 *Set of 4*.......... 1·80 1·20

1963. Air Congo Commemoration.
501 2f. Boeing 707 of Air Congo over N'Djili Airport.......... 10 10
502 5f. Tail of Boeing 707 of Air Congo and control tower.......... 10 10
503 6f. Boeing 707 of Air Congo over N'Djili Airport.......... 90 40
504 7f. Tail of Boeing 707 of Air Congo and control tower.......... 10 10
505 30f. Boeing 707 of Air Congo over N'Djili Airport.......... 25 15
506 50f. Tail of Boeing 707 of Air Congo and control tower.......... 40 25
501/506 *Set of 6*.......... 1·70 1·00

1963. Nos. 460/3 overprinted 10 DECEMBRE 1948 10 DECEMBRE 1963 15e anniversaire DROITS DE L'HOMME.
507 2f. Boeing 707.......... 10 10
508 4f. Boeing 707.......... 10 10
509 7f. Boeing 707.......... 20 20
510 20f. Boeing 707.......... 20 20
507/510 *Set of 4*.......... 55 55

1967. First Flight by Air Congo BAC One-Eleven. No. 504 surcharged 1er VOL BAC ONE ELEVEN 14/5/67 and value.
644 9.6k. on 7f. Boeing 707 of Air Congo and control tower.......... 70 20

COOK ISLANDS

South Pacific

1949. 12 pence = 1 shilling

20 shillings = 1 pound

1967. 100 cents = 1 dollar

1949.
154* 5d. Douglas DC-3 at Rarotonga Airfield . 6·00 1·50

1960. No. 154 surcharged 1/6.
162 1s.6d. on 5d. Douglas DC-3 at Rarotonga Airfield.......... 75 40

1966. Nos. 134, 165 and 167/73 overprinted Airmail and Douglas DC-3 airplane or surcharged also.
185 6d. Hibiscus.......... 1·25 20
186 7d. on 8d. Tuna.......... 2·00 25
187 10d. on 3d. Frangipani.......... 1·00 15
188 1s. Oranges.......... 1·00 15
189 1s.6d. Queen Elizabeth II.......... 1·50 1·25
190 2s.3d. on 3s. Administration Centre.......... 1·00 65
191 5s. Rarotonga.......... 1·75 1·50
192 10s. on 2s. Island scene.......... 1·75 14·00
193 £1 Arms overprinted COOK ISLANDS.......... 13·00 17·00
185/193 *Set of 9*.......... 22·00 32·00

1967. Face value in both decimal currency and sterling.
225* 18c. (1s.9d) Douglas DC-3.......... 1·40 30

1972.
389* 30c. Sikorsky S-61B SH-3 Sea King helicopter.......... 1·00 40

1972. No. 389 surcharged HURRICANE RELIEF Plus 2c.
398* 30c. +2c. Sikorsky S-61B SH-3 Sea King helicopter.......... 25 15

1974.
496* 25c. Douglas DC-3 at old landing strip, Rarotonga.......... 35 40

1979.
641* 50c. Balloon *Le Neptune*, Paris, 1870.......... 25 25
642* 50c. Junkers F-13.......... 25 25
643* 50c. Airship LZ-127 *Graf Zeppelin*.......... 25 25
644* 50c. Concorde.......... 25 25

1980. Nos. 641/4 overprinted ZEAPEX STAMP EXHIBITION-AUCKLAND 1980 and New Zealand stamp.
695* 50c. Balloon *Le Neptune*, Paris, 1870.......... 60 35
696* 50c. Junkers F-13.......... 60 35
697* 50c. Airship LZ-127 *Graf Zeppelin*.......... 60 35
698* 50c. Concorde.......... 60 35

1983.
864* 60c. Rarotonga Airport.......... 70 50

1984. Bicentenary (1983) of Manned Flight.
939 36c. Montgolfier balloon (first manned free flight, 1783)......... 50 50
940 48c. Adorne's balloon *Aerostat*, 1784......... 60 60
941 60c. Engraving of a "sail steered" balloon, 1789......... 75 90
942 72c. Pierre Testu-Brissy's balloon ascent on horseback, 1798......... 90 1·25
943 96c. Eugene Godard's quintuple "acrobatic" balloon, 1850......... 1·00 1·60
939/943 *Set of 5*......... 3·50 4·25
MS944 $2.50 Blanchard and Jeffries' balloon, 1785.. 1·50 2·25
MS945 As Nos. 939/43, but each with a charity premium of 5c......... 1·50 2·25

OFFICIAL STAMPS
1985. No. 864 surcharged 75c O.H.M.S.
O48* 75c. on 60c. Rarotonga Airport.......... 3·00 1·00

COSTA RICA

Central America

100 centimos = 1 colon

1926.
164 20c. Curtiss JN-4 "Jenny"......... 2·75 60

1928. No. 144 surcharged LINDBERGH ENERO 1928 10 10 and airplane.
169 10c. on 12c. *Santa Maria* (ship)......... 4·75 4·75

1930. No. O178 surcharged CORREO 1930 AEREO, Bleriot XI airplane and value.
177 8c. on 1col. Arms......... 70 60
178 20c. on 1col. Arms......... 1·00 65
179 40c. on 1col. Arms......... 2·10 1·60
180 1col. on 1col. Arms......... 3·00 2·00
177/180 *Set of 4*......... 6·00 4·25

1934.
198* 5c. Ryan B-5 Brougham over landing ground, San Jose (green)......... 20 20
507* 5c. Ryan B-5 Brougham over landing ground, San Jose (deep blue)......... 40 20
508* 5c. Ryan B-5 Brougham over landing ground, San Jose (pale blue)......... 40 20
199* 10c. Ryan B-5 Brougham over landing ground, San Jose (red)......... 20 20
509* 10c. Ryan B-5 Brougham over landing ground, San Jose (green)......... 40 20
510* 10c. Ryan B-5 Brougham over landing ground, San Jose (turquoise)......... 40 20
200* 15c. Ryan B-5 Brougham over landing ground, San Jose (brown)......... 40 20
511* 15c. Ryan B-5 Brougham over landing ground, San Jose (red)......... 50 20
201* 20c. Ryan B-5 Brougham over landing ground, San Jose......... 40 20
202* 25c. Ryan B-5 Brougham over landing ground, San Jose......... 55 20
512* 35c. Ryan B-5 Brougham over landing ground, San Jose......... 1·30 20
203* 40c. Ryan B-5 Brougham over landing ground, San Jose......... 1·70 20
204* 50c. Ryan B-5 Brougham over landing ground, San Jose......... 70 20
205* 60c. Ryan B-5 Brougham over landing ground, San Jose......... 1·40 20
206* 75c. Ryan B-5 Brougham over landing ground, San Jose......... 2·75 50

1937.
228 1c. Ryan B-5 Brougham......... 40 35
229 2c. Ryan B-5 Brougham......... 40 35
230 3c. Ryan B-5 Brougham......... 40 35
228/230 *Set of 3*......... 1·10 95

1937.
238* 2c. Airplane......... 15 10
239* 5c. Airplane......... 20 10
240* 20c. Airplane......... 30 10
241* 1col.40 Airplane......... 2·40 2·40

1938.

244*	1c. Douglas DC-3	10	10
245*	3c. Douglas DC-3	10	10
246*	10c. Douglas DC-3	30	10
247*	75c. Douglas DC-3	2·40	1·80

1940. Opening of San Jose Airport.

249	5c. La Sabana Airport, San Jose	20	20
250	10c. La Sabana Airport, San Jose	20	20
251	25c. La Sabana Airport, San Jose	20	20
252	35c. La Sabana Airport, San Jose	20	20
253	60c. La Sabana Airport, San Jose	40	40
254	85c. La Sabana Airport, San Jose	1·20	1·00
255	2col.35 La Sabana Airport, San Jose	6·00	5·75
249/255 *Set of 7*		7·50	7·25

1940. Overprinted **DIA PAN-AMERICANO DE LA SALUD 2 DICIEMBRE 1940.**

266*	10c. Douglas DC-3	20	20
267*	15c. Douglas DC-3	20	20
268*	25c. Douglas DC-3	45	40
269*	35c. Douglas DC-3	65	55
270*	60c. Douglas DC-3	1·00	80
271*	75c. Douglas DC-3	2·50	2·20
272*	1col.35 Douglas DC-3	8·00	6·25
273*	5col. Douglas DC-3	42·00	42·00
274*	10col. Douglas DC-3	£140	£110

1941. Nos. 201 and 206 surcharged **MAYO 1941 TRATADO LIMITROFE COSTA RICA-PANAMA** and value.

300*	5c. on 20c. Ryan B-5 Brougham over landing ground, San Jose	10	10
301*	15c. on 20c. Ryan B-5 Brougham over landing ground, San Jose	10	10
302*	40c. on 75c. Ryan B-5 Brougham over landing ground, San Jose	35	10

1945. Nos. O211/19 further overprinted **1945** in frame.

389*	5c. Ryan B-5 Brougham over landing ground, San Jose	75	70
390*	10c. Ryan B-5 Brougham over landing ground, San Jose	75	75
391*	15c. Ryan B-5 Brougham over landing ground, San Jose	75	75
392*	20c. Ryan B-5 Brougham over landing ground, San Jose	55	50
393*	25c. Ryan B-5 Brougham over landing ground, San Jose	75	75
394*	40c. Ryan B-5 Brougham over landing ground, San Jose	45	45
395*	50c. Ryan B-5 Brougham over landing ground, San Jose	75	75
396*	60c. Ryan B-5 Brougham over landing ground, San Jose	1·40	1·20
397*	75c. Ryan B-5 Brougham over landing ground, San Jose	1·10	1·00

1961.

626*	85c. Douglas DC-6	70	55

1965.

715*	1col. Douglas DC-8	40	25

1976. 30th Anniv of LACSA Airline.

1052	1col. Boeing 727-200 of Lineas Aereas Costarricenses	25	15
1053	1col.20 Boeing 727-200 of Lineas Aereas Costarricenses	40	20
1054	3col. Boeing 727-200 of Lineas Aereas Costarricenses	1·10	70
1052/1054 *Set of 3*		1·60	95

1980.

1205*	1col.30 Juan Santamaria International Airport	40	15

1986. 40th Anniv of LACSA (national airline).

1439	1col. Airplane	50	15
1440	7col. Airplane	3·50	30
1441	16col. Airplane	8·00	75
1439/1441 *Set of 3*		11·00	1·10

1988. Airmail Pioneers.

1478	10col. Roman Macaya and Curtiss 50 Robin 4C-1A	50	15

1996. 50th Anniv of LACSA (national airline).

1599	5col. Douglas DC-3	25	25
1600	10col. Curtiss C-46 Commando	25	25
1601	20col. Beech Model 18	40	40
1602	30col. Douglas DC-6B	65	65
1603	35col. BAC One-Eleven	75	75
1604	40col. Convair CV 440 Metropolitan	90	90
1605	45col. Lockheed L.188 Electra	95	95
1606	50col. Boeing 727-200	1·10	1·10
1607	55col. Douglas DC-8	1·20	1·20
1608	60col. Airbus Industrie Airbus A320	1·30	1·30
1599/1608 *Set of 10*		7·00	7·00

2003. 75th Anniv of Charles Lindbergh's Arrival in Costa Rica.

1754	110col. Lindbergh and Ryan NYP Special *Spirit of St Louis*	2·10	1·60

EXPRESS DELIVERY STAMPS

1976.

E1031	1col. Concorde	50	40
E1135	2col. Concorde (buff and mauve slipstream)	80	45
E1136	2col. Concorde (blue and light blue slipstream)	75	45
E1137	4col. Concorde	65	40
E1031/E1137 *Set of 4*		2·40	1·50

OFFICIAL STAMPS

1934. Nos. 198, 199, 200 and 201/6 overprinted **OFICIAL.**

O211*	5c. Ryan B-5 Brougham over landing ground, San Jose (green)	20	20
O212*	10c. Ryan B-5 Brougham over landing ground, San Jose (red)	20	20
O213*	15c. Ryan B-5 Brougham over landing ground, San Jose (brown)	45	45
O214*	20c. Ryan B-5 Brougham over landing ground, San Jose	75	75
O215*	25c. Ryan B-5 Brougham over landing ground, San Jose	75	75
O216*	40c. Ryan B-5 Brougham over landing ground, San Jose	90	75
O217*	50c. Ryan B-5 Brougham over landing ground, San Jose	90	75
O218*	60c. Ryan B-5 Brougham over landing ground, San Jose	1·10	90
O219*	75c. Ryan B-5 Brougham over landing ground, San Jose	1·10	90

CROATIA

South-east Europe

1942. 100 banicas = 1 kuna

1991. 100 paras = 1 dinar

1942. Aviation Fund.

55	2k. +2k. Glider	1·10	1·60
56	2k.50 +2k.50 Glider	1·60	1·80
57	3k. +3k. Model glider	2·00	2·20
58	4k. +4k. Seaplane glider	2·75	3·25
55/58 *Set of 4*		6·75	8·00
MS58a	2k.+8k. Glider; 3k.+12k. Model glider	65·00	65·00

The miniature sheet exists perforated or imperforate.

1943.

86*	2k. +1k. Heinkel He 111H bomber	35	45

1991.

154*	1d. Sud Aviation SE 210 Caravelle	35	35
156*	3d. Sud Aviation SE 210 Caravelle	35	35

2008.

939*	5k. Aircraft (embossed on stamp)	4·00	4·00

CUBA

West Indies

100 centavos = 1 peso

1927.

353	5c. Philadelphia Navy Yard PN-9 flying boat	3·50	1·70

1928. No. 353 overprinted **LINDBERGH FEBRERO 1928.**

364	5c. Philadelphia Navy Yard PN-9 flying boat	3·50	1·50

1931.

376	5c. Fokker F.10A Super Trimotor	50	15
377	8c. Fokker F.10A Super Trimotor	3·25	1·00
378	10c. Fokker F.10A Super Trimotor	50	15
379	15c. Fokker F.10A Super Trimotor	1·10	30

380	20c. Fokker F.10A Super Trimotor		1·10	15
381	30c. Fokker F.10A Super Trimotor		1·70	20
382	40c. Fokker F.10A Super Trimotor		3·75	45
383	50c. Fokker F.10A-Super Trimotor		4·25	50
384	1p. Fokker F.10A Super Trimotor		6·75	1·10
376/384 *Set of 9*			21·00	3·50

1931.

385	5c. Ford "Tin Goose"		40	15
386	10c. Ford "Tin Goose"		40	15
387	20c. Ford "Tin Goose" (red)		3·00	90
388	20c. Ford "Tin Goose" (pink)		1·80	50
389	50c. Ford "Tin Goose" (blue)		5·00	95
390	50c. Ford "Tin Goose" (turquoise)		2·50	1·00
385/390 *Set of 6*			12·00	3·25

1935. No. 378 surcharged **PRIMER TREN AEREO INTERNACIONAL 1935 O'Meara y du Pont+10 cts.** Perforated or imperforate.

400	10c. +10c. Fokker F.10A Super Trimotor		4·25	4·25

1936.

410*	10c. U.S. Navy airship ZR-5 *Macon*		1·00	45
411*	20c. Breguet Super Bidon *Cuatro Vientos*.		3·50	2·00

1938. No. 353 overprinted **1913 1938 ROSILLO Key West-Habana.**

426	5c. Philadelphia Navy Yard PN-9 flying boat		3·50	2·10

1939. No. 386 overprinted **EXPERIMENTO DEL COHETE Postal ANO DE 1939.**

433	10c. Ford "Tin Goose"		40·00	7·75

1952.

605	8c. Curtiss A-1 seaplane and route map		1·40	55
606	25c. Agustin Parla Orduna and Curtiss A-1 seaplane		4·00	1·70

1953.

666	8c. Lockheed Constellation		1·10	20
667	15c. Lockheed Constellation		2·10	65
668	2p. Lockheed Constellation (brown and green)		25·00	9·25
670	2p. Lockheed Constellation (myrtle and blue)		48·00	16·00
669	5p. Lockheed Constellation (brown and blue)		18·00	6·50
671	5p. Lockheed Constellation (myrtle and red)		39·00	15·00
666/671 *Set of 6*			£120	43·00

1953.

675*	25c. Lockheed Constellation		3·25	1·10

1954.

698	5c. Lockheed Constellation		40	15
699	8c. Lockheed Constellation		1·10	50
700	10c. Lockheed Constellation		1·10	50
701	15c. Lockheed Constellation		2·50	50
702	20c. Lockheed Constellation		1·10	15
703	25c. Lockheed Constellation		80	15
704a	30c. Lockheed Constellation		3·00	1·00
705	40c. Lockheed Constellation		4·25	1·20
706	45c. Lockheed Constellation		3·50	2·00
707	50c. Lockheed Constellation		3·50	1·30
708	1p. Lockheed Constellation		9·25	2·75
698/708 *Set of 11*			27·00	9·25

1955.

748	8c. Wright *Flyer I*		1·20	60
749	12c. Lindbergh's Ryan NYP Special *Spirit of St. Louis*		2·75	85
750	24c. Airship LZ-127 *Graf Zeppelin*		8·50	3·25
751	30c. Lockheed L.1049 Super Constellation		7·25	4·25
752	50c. Convair TF-102A Delta Dagger		9·75	5·00
748/752 *Set of 5*			27·00	12·50

1957. 30th Anniv of Inauguration of Air Mail Service between Havana and Key West, Florida.

841	12c. Fokker F.7 Trimotor *General New* of Pan Am		2·50	1·00

1960. Nos. 382 and 706 surcharged **12c.**

942*	12c. on 40c. Fokker F.10A Super Trimotor		2·30	85
943*	12c. on 45c. Lockheed Constellation		2·30	85

1960. 80th Anniv of National Airmail Service.

960	8c. Ford "Tin Goose"		4·25	2·50

1961. Nos. 667 and 380 surcharged **HABILITADO PARA 8 cts.**

992	8c. on 15c. Lockheed Constellation		95	50
993	8c. on 20c. Fokker F.10A Super Trimotor		95	50

1962.

1030c*	10c. Model airplane		80	30

1964.

1151*	50c. Ford "Tin Goose" (on stamp No. 433)		10·50	3·00

1964. As No. 1151, but colours changed, overprinted **VOSJOD-I octubre 12 1964 PRIMERA TRIPULACION DEL ESPACIO** and rocket.

1153	50c. Ford "Tin Goose" (on stamp No. 433)		4·75	1·80

1965.

1217*	13c. Fokker F.10A Super Trimotor (on stamp No. 400) and airplane towing mail-carrying gliders		2·50	70

1965. Matias Perez (pioneer balloonist) Commemoration.

1232	3c. Matias Perez and balloon		1·80	1·20
1233	13c. Matias Perez and balloon		2·75	1·20

1965.

1317*	20c. Ilyushin Il-18 of Cubana		3·00	1·10

1966.

1321*	10c. Mikoyan Gurevich MiG-21		1·80	50

1968. 35th Anniv of Seville–Camaguey Flight by Barberan and Collar.

1580*	13c. Breguet Super Bidon *Cuatro Vientos*.		2·10	50

1968.

1618*	3c. Antonov An-2 biplane spraying crops		15	10

1970. Aviation Pioneers.

1752	3c. Jose Domingo Blino and balloon		80	15
1753	13c. Adolfo Teodore and balloon, 1830		2·75	70

1970.

1776*	2c. Antonov An-2 biplane spraying sugar crop		15	10

1971. 35th Anniv of Camaguey-Seville Flight by Menendez Pelaez.

1818*	13c. Antonio Menendez Pelaez's Lockheed 8A Sirius, 1936		2·40	25

1972. First Anniv of Havana-Santiago de Chile Air Service.

1938	25c. Ilyushin Il-18		2·50	85

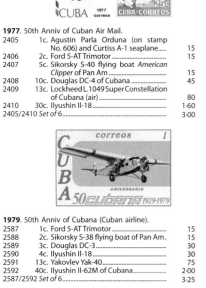

1974. 10th Anniv of Civil Aeronautical Institute.
2157*	1c. Model airplane	25	10
2159*	8c. Glider	35	15
2160*	10c. Antonov An-2 biplane spraying crops	1·10	40
2161*	13c. Ilyushin Il-62M of Cubana	1·70	40

1976.
2289*	13c. Stylised fighter aircraft	80	25

1976.
2310*	30c. Tupolev Tu-144	2·10	60

1977. 50th Anniv of Cuban Air Mail.
2405	1c. Agustin Parla Orduna (on stamp No. 606) and Curtiss A-1 seaplane	15	10
2406	2c. Ford 5-AT Trimotor	15	10
2407	5c. Sikorsky S-40 flying boat *American Clipper* of Pan Am	15	10
2408	10c. Douglas DC-4 of Cubana	45	15
2409	13c. Lockheed L.1049 Super Constellation of Cubana (air)	80	15
2410	30c. Ilyushin Il-18	1·60	70
2405/2410	*Set of 6*	3·00	1·20

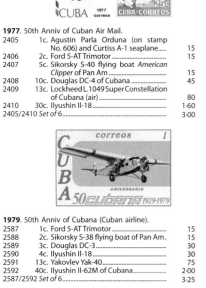

1979. 50th Anniv of Cubana (Cuban airline).
2587	1c. Ford 5-AT Trimotor	15	10
2588	2c. Sikorsky S-38 flying boat of Pan Am.	15	10
2589	3c. Douglas DC-3	30	10
2590	4c. Ilyushin Il-18	30	10
2591	13c. Yakovlev Yak-40	75	25
2592	40c. Ilyushin Il-62M of Cubana	2·00	50
2587/2592	*Set of 6*	3·25	1·00

1981.
2712*	3c. Mikoyan-Gurovich MiG-21	15	10

1982.
2794*	8c. Tupolev Tu-154	30	10

1983. Bicentenary of Manned Flight.
2882	1c. Charles' hydrogen balloon, 1783	15	10
2883	3c. Montgolfier balloon (first manned free flight, 1783)	15	10
2884	5c. Montgolfier balloon *Le Gustave*, 1784	15	10
2885	7c. Eugene Godard's quintuple "acrobatic" balloon, 1850	30	10
2886	30c. Montgolfier balloon (unmanned flight, 1783)	1·80	70
2887	50c. Charles Green's balloon *Royal Vauxhall*, 1836	2·00	95
2882/2887	*Set of 6*	4·00	1·80
MS2888	1p. Jose Domingo Blino and balloon	4·00	4·00

1983. 50th Death Anniv of Alberto Santos-Dumont.
MS2903	1p. Santos-Dumont's biplane *14 bis*	4·50	4·50

1986.
3187	5c. Tupolev Tu-154	50	25

1988. Cuban Airlines Transatlantic Flights.
3339	2c. Douglas DC-4	10	10
3340	4c. Ilyushin Il-18M	10	10
3341	5c. Ilyushin Il-62M	15	10
3342	10c. Ilyushin Il-18	25	15
3343	30c. Ilyushin Il-62M	85	25
3344	50c. Ilyushin Il-62M	1·50	50
3339/3344	*Set of 6*	2·75	1·10

1990.
3523*	50c. Mural showing de Havilland DH.106 Comet 1	1·50	40

1991. Airships.
3632	5c. Jean-Baptiste Meusnier and his dirigible balloon design, 1784	20	10
3633	10c. Henri Giffard and his steam-powered dirigible airship, 1852	40	20
3634	20c. Paul Hanlein and his airship, 1872	75	40
3635	30c. Karl Wolfert and his airship *Deutschland*	1·00	60
3636	50c. David Schwartz and his aluminium airship, 1897	1·80	1·00

3637	1p. Count Ferdinand von Zeppelin and airship LZ-127 *Graf Zeppelin* (inscribed "LZ-129 *Hindenburg*")	3·50	2·00
3632/3637	*Set of 6*	7·00	3·75

1993.
3827	30c. Unidentified aircraft	1·10	50

No. 3827 commemorates the flight from Seville to Cuba in 1933, which was undertaken in a Breguet 19 Super Bidon, built under licence by CASA in Spain.

1994.
3932	65c. Douglas DC-3	2·20	1·00

1995. World War II Combat Airplane.
3974	10c. Supermarine Spitfire	35	10
3975	15c. Ilyushin Il-2	35	20
3976	65c. Curtiss P-40	1·60	95
3977	75c. Messerschmitt Me-109	1·80	1·20
3978	85c. Morane Saulnier 406	2·20	1·30
3974/3978	*Set of 5*	5·75	3·50

1996.
4058*	15c. Cierva C 4 Autogyro	35	20
4059*	65c. Junkers Ju52/3m	1·70	95
4060*	75c. CASA 201 Alcotan	2·00	1·20
4061*	85c. CASA C-212 Aviocar	2·30	1·30
4058/4061	*Set of 4*	5·75	3·25

1997.
4161*	65c. Fokker F.10A Super Trimotor	2·20	1·20

1999. 75th Anniv of Cubana (national airline).
4380	15c. Fokker F.27 Friendship	40	20
4381	15c. Douglas DC-10	40	30
4382	65c. Airbus Industrie A320	1·90	95
4383	75c. Douglas DC-3	2·10	1·20
4380/4383	*Set of 4*	4·25	2·40

2000.
4409*	90c. Boeing XP-15	2·30	1·50

2000. Airship Development and Pioneers.

4418	10c. Henri Giffard and steam-powered dirigible airship	30	20
4419	15c. Albert and Gaston Tissander and airship	45	30
4420	50c. Charles Renard, Arthur Krebs and *La France* airship	1·40	85
4421	65c. Pierre and Paul Lebaudy and airship	1·80	1·20
4422	75c. August von Perseval and airship	2·10	1·40
4418/4422	*Set of 5*	5·50	3·50
MS4423	1p. Ferdinand von Zeppelin and Zeppelin LZ-1	3·00	2·20

2002.

| 4591 | 65c. Mikoyan-Gurevich MiG 21 | 1·90 | 95 |

2003.

| 4658* | 65c. Airplanes | 2·10 | 1·10 |

2003. Centenary of Powered Flight.

4707	5c. Wright Bros. and Wright Flyer 1903	20	10
4708	15c. Pitcairn PA-5, 1928	40	20
4709	65c. Stearman C-3MB, 1927	1·80	95
4710	75c. Douglas M-2, 1926	2·10	1·10
4707/4710	*Set of 4*	4·00	2·10

2004. 75th Anniv of Cubana (national airline).

4771	15c. Lockheed Constellation	40	20
4772	65c. Ilyushin Il. 62M	1·80	95
4773	75c. Airbus Industrie Airbus A330	2·10	1·10
4771/4773	*Set of 3*	3·75	2·00

2006.

4961	10c. Granville Gee Bee R2	30	15
4962	15c. Comte AC-4 Gentleman	40	20
4963	15c. Bücker Bü-131 Jungmann	40	20
4964	50c. North American Mustang TF-51	1·70	85
4965	75c. Supermarine Spitfire	2·40	1·40
4966	85c. Lavochkin La-9 (inscribed, Lavochkine)	2·50	1·50
4961/4966	*Set of 6*	7·00	3·75
MS4967	1p. Bücker Bü-131 Jungmann (diff. to SG4963)	2·50	1·90

EXPRESS MAIL STAMPS

1914.

| E352 | 10c. Bleriot XI | 12·50 | 20 |

1945.

| E485 | 10c. Douglas DC-3 | 3·75 | 50 |

1960. Nos. 388 and 390 surcharged **HABILITADO ENTREGA ESPECIAL 10 C.**

| E961 | 10c. on 20c. Ford "Tin Goose" | 2·40 | 50 |
| E962 | 10c. on 50c. Ford "Tin Goose" | 2·40 | 50 |

CURACAO

West Indies

100 cents = 1 gulden

1942.

201*	10c. Douglas DC-2 of KLM	35	35
202*	15c. Fokker F.XX PH-AIZ *Zilvermeeuw*	45	35
204*	25c. Douglas DC-2 of KLM	50	35
205*	30c. Douglas DC-2 of KLM	55	55
206*	35c. Douglas DC-2 of KLM	90	55
207*	40c. Fokker F.XX PH-AIZ *Zilvermeeuw*	1·10	55
209*	50c. Douglas DC-2 of KLM	1·60	35
210*	60c. Douglas DC-2 of KLM	1·60	90
211*	70c. Douglas DC-2 of KLM	2·00	90
212*	1g.40 Fokker F.XX PH-AIZ *Zilvermeeuw*	11·00	1·75
214*	5g. Douglas DC-2 of KLM	27·00	13·00
215*	10g. Douglas DC-2 of KLM	35·00	20·00

1943. Nos. 212 and 214/15 surcharged **Voor Krijgsgevangenen** and value.

220*	40c. +50c. on 1g.40 Fokker F.XX PH-AIZ *Zilvermeeuw*	6·25	4·75
222*	50c. +75c. on 5g. Douglas DC-2 of KLM	6·25	4·50
223*	60c. +100c. on 10g. Douglas DC-2 of KLM	6·25	4·75

1947.

275*	1g.50 Douglas DC-2	2·00	80
276*	2g.50 Douglas DC-2	13·50	3·50
277*	5g. Douglas DC-2	21·00	7·00
278*	7g.50 Douglas DC-2	65·00	55·00
279*	10g. Douglas DC-2	50·00	17·00
280*	15g. Douglas DC-2	80·00	65·00
281*	25g. Douglas DC-2	75·00	55·00

CYPRUS

Mediterranean

1949. 40 paras = 1 piastre

180 piastres = 1 pound

1955. 1000 mils = 1 pound

1983. 100 cents = 1 pound

1949. As Nos. 114/15 of Antigua.

| 168* | 1½pi. Airplane | 60 | 1·25 |
| 169* | 2pi. Jet-powered Vickers Viking | 1·50 | 1·50 |

1967.

| 311* | 50m. Hawker Siddeley Comet 4 (shown with Cyprus Airways markings) at Nicosia Airport | 15 | 10 |

1973. 25th Anniv of Cyprus Airways.

| 414* | 50m. Airline emblem | 20 | 10 |

1976.

| 458* | 60m. BAC One-Eleven | 30 | 55 |

1978.

| 514* | 125m. Wilbur and Orville Wright and Wright *Flyer I* | 35 | 80 |

1988.

| 721* | 18c. Boeing 737 of Cyprus Airways | 2·50 | 3·00 |

1994. 50th Anniv of ICAO.

| 859 | 30c. Boeing 737 | 2·00 | 2·00 |

1999.

| 976* | 15c. Paper airplanes | 1·00 | 50 |

TURKISH CYPRIOT POSTS

1978. 100 kurus = 1 lira

2005. 100 yeni kurus = 1 yeni lira

1978.

| 67* | 650k. Boeing 720 at Ercan Airport | 50 | 35 |

1986.

| 199* | 100l. Airliner at Kyrenia Airport | 3·25 | 4·25 |

1992.

| 344* | 1000l. Airliner over runway | 2·00 | 2·00 |

2005.
618*   50yhr. Ercan Airport and Boeing 737............   95   1·10

CYRENAICA

North Africa

100 centesimi = 1 lira

1932. Nos. 116/18 of Tripolitania overprinted **Cirenaica.**
91   50c. Marina Fiat MF.5 flying boat   65   30
92   60c. Marina Fiat MF.5 flying boat ....   4·00   8·00
93   80c. Marina Fiat MF.5 flying boat ....   4·00   11·50
91/93 Set of 3..   7·75   18·00

1932. Nos. 116 and 118 of Tripolitania overprinted **CIRENAICA.**
94   50c. Marina Fiat MF.5 flying boat ....   1·00   1·00
95   80c. Marina Fiat MF.5 flying boat ....   5·25   12·00

1932.
96   50c. Airplane...   3·25   10
97   75c. Airplane...   5·00   5·00
98   80c. Airplane...   5·00   10·00
99   1l. Caproni Ca 101 ....   1·60   10
100   2l. Caproni Ca 101 ....   2·00   5·00
101   5l. Caproni Ca 101 ....   3·75   10·00
96/101 Set of 6...   19·00   27·00

1933.
102   3l. Airship LZ-127 *Graf Zeppelin*................   5·75   55·00
103   5l. Airship LZ-127 *Graf Zeppelin*................   5·75   55·00
104   10l. Airship LZ-127 *Graf Zeppelin*..............   5·75   £110
105   12l. Airship LZ-127 *Graf Zeppelin*..............   5·75   £120
106   15l. Airship LZ-127 *Graf Zeppelin*..............   5·75   £120
107   20l. Airship LZ-127 *Graf Zeppelin*..............   5·75   £140
102/107 Set of 6...   31·00   £550

1933.
108   19l.75 Savoia Marchetti S-55X flying boats.   11·50   £300
109   44l.75 Savoia Marchetti S-55X flying boats.   11·50   £300

1934. No. 101, in some instances with colour changed, overprinted **1934-XII PRIMO VOLO DIRETTO ROMA = BUENOS-AYRES TRIMOTORE "LOMBARDI-MAZZOTTI"** and Savoia Marchetti S-71 airplane or surcharged also.
110   2l. on 5l. Caproni Ca 101 ....   2·00   32·00
111   3l. on 5l. Caproni Ca 101 ....   2·00   32·00
112   5l. Caproni Ca 101 ....   2·00   35·00
113   10l. on 5l. Caproni Ca 101 ....   2·25   35·00
110/113 Set of 4...   7·50   £120

1934.
120*   25c. Caproni Ca 101 ....   2·75   9·00
121*   50c. Caproni Ca 101 ....   2·75   7·50
122*   75c. Caproni Ca 101 ....   2·75   7·50
123*   80c. Caproni Ca 101 ....   2·75   9·00
124*   1l. Caproni Ca 101 ....   2·75   10·00
125*   2l. Caproni Ca 101 ....   2·75   16·00

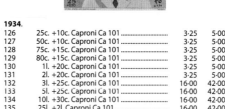

1934.
126   25c. +10c. Caproni Ca 101 ....   3·25   5·00
127   50c. +10c. Caproni Ca 101 ....   3·25   5·00
128   75c. +15c. Caproni Ca 101 ....   3·25   5·00
129   80c. +15c. Caproni Ca 101 ....   3·25   5·00
130   1l. +20c. Caproni Ca 101 ....   3·25   5·00
131   2l. +20c. Caproni Ca 101 ....   3·25   5·00
132   3l. +25c. Caproni Ca 101 ....   16·00   42·00
133   5l. +25c. Caproni Ca 101 ....   16·00   42·00
134   10l. +30c. Caproni Ca 101 ....   16·00   42·00
135   25l. +2l. Caproni Ca 101 ....   16·00   42·00
126/135 Set of 10...   75·00   £180

OFFICIAL AIR STAMP

1934. As No. 135, but colour changed, overprinted with crown and **SERVIZIO DI STATO.**
O136   25l. +2l. Caproni Ca 10l.............................   £1600   £1100

CZECHOSLOVAKIA

Central Europe

100 haleru = 1 koruna

1920. Nos. 13 and 36/7 surcharged with biplane and value. Imperforate or perforated.
215   14k. on 200h. Hradcany, Prague...................   15·00   25·00
216   24k. on 500h. Hradcany, Prague...................   38·00   38·00
220   28k. on 1000h. Hradcany, Prague ....   38·00   32·00
215/220 Set of 3...   80·00   85·00

1922. Nos. 205, 209 and 212 surcharged with biplane and value.
224   50 on 100h. Allegorical figure....................   1·50   2·25
225   100 on 200h. Allegorical figure..................   3·75   3·75
226   250 on 400h. Allegorical figure..................   6·00   8·00
224/226 Set of 3...   10·00   12·50

1930.
394   30h. Fokker F.IXD...   10   10
309   50h. Fokker F.IXD...   10   20
310   1k. Fokker F.IXD..   25   30
311   2k. Smolik S.19...   45   70
312   3k. Smolik S.19...   1·40   95
313   4k. Smolik S.19...   85   90
314   5k. Smolik S.19...   2·75   1·90
315   10k. Fokker F.IXD...   4·00   5·25
316   20k. Fokker F.IXD...   5·00   5·00

1945.
433*   50h. Staff Captain Alois Vasatko and Supermarine Spitfire   10   10
441*   5k. Staff Captain Alois Vasatko and Supermarine Spitfire   10   10

1946. First Prague-New York Flight.
468b   24k. Lockheed L.049 Constellation (blue on buff)   90   85

1946.
469   1k.50 Captain F. Novak and Westland Lysander Mk 1   15   10
470   5k.50 Captain F. Novak and Westland Lysander Mk 1   35   15
471   9k. Captain F. Novak and Westland Lysander Mk 1   60   20
472   10k. Lockheed L.049 Constellation............   50   35
473   16k. Captain F. Novak and Westland Lysander Mk 1   80   30
474   20k. Lockheed L.049 Constellation............   80   50
475   24k. Lockheed L.049 Constellation (as No. 468b) (red)..   1·00   75
476   50k. Lockheed L.049 Constellation............   2·00   1·25
469/476 Set of 8...   5·50   3·25

1947.
487   1k.20 Douglas DC-4   10   10
488   2k.40 Douglas DC-4   10   10
489   4k. Douglas DC-4   50   20
487/489 Set of 3...   65   35

1949.
547*   13k. Douglas DC-2 of C.S.A............................   1·60   40

1949. Nos. 469/76 surcharged in figures.
559   1k. on 1k.50 Captain F. Novak and Westland Lysander Mk 1   15   10
560   3k. on 5k.50 Captain F. Novak and Westland Lysander Mk 1   25   10
561   6k. on 9k. Captain F. Novak and Westland Lysander Mk 1   40   10
562   7k.50 on 16k. Captain F. Novak and Westland Lysander Mk 1   50   25
563   8k. on 10k. Lockheed L.049 Constellation..   50   55
564   12k.50 on 20k. Lockheed L.049 Constellation..   90   45
565   15k. on 24k. Lockheed L.049 Constellation..   2·25   75
566   30k. on 50k. Lockheed L.049 Constellation..   1·75   75
559/566 Set of 8...   6·00   2·75

1951.
621   6k. Ilyushin Il-12 ....   2·25   75
622   10k. Ilyushin Il-12 ....   2·25   95
623   15k. Ilyushin Il-12 ....   5·50   75
624   20k. Ilyushin Il-12 ....   7·00   2·25
621/624 Set of 4...   15·00   4·25

1951.
663*   5k. Pilots and aircraft..................................   1·60   60

1953.
807*   1k. Lisunov Li-2 of C.S.A ....   1·60   90

1955.
898*   60h. Yakovlev Yak-25 jet fighters ....   1·75   1·25

1957. Opening of Czechoslovak Airlines.
1000   75h. Tupolev Tu-104A OK-LDA of C.S.A.....   80   10
1001   2k.35 Tupolev Tu-104A OK-LDA of C.S.A.....   95   10

1959. 50th Anniv of First Flight by Jan Kaspar.
1118	1k. Bleriot XI monoplanes at Czech air school	15	10
1119	1k.80 Jan Kaspar and Bleriot XI	75	10

1960. First World Aviation Aerobatic Championships, Bratislava.
1178	60h. Zlin Z-226 Trener 6 OK-JFA	90	25

1960.
1183	1k.60 Ilyushin Il-18B	2·50	1·40
1184	2k.80 Mil Mi-4 helicopter	4·00	2·00

1963. 40th Anniv of Ceskoslovenske Aerolinte CSA (Czech airline).
1361	80h. Tupolev Tu-104A of C.S.A	80	20
1362	1k.80 Ilyushin Il-18B of C.S.A	1·50	45

1966.
1601	60h. Mikoyan Gurevich MiG-21D	35	10

1967.
1689	30h. Letov L-200A Morava	15	10
1690	60h. Hawker Siddeley Trident 1E	25	20
1691	1k. Sud Aviation SE 210 Super Caravelle 12	25	20
1692	1k.40 Vickers 953 Vanguard	35	25
1693	1k.60 Boeing 707	35	35
1694	2k. Douglas DC-8	55	25
1695	5k. Tupolev Tu-134	2·50	2·10
1689/1695 Set of 7		4·00	3·00

1967. Czech Aircraft.
1706	30h. Letov L-13 glider	15	10
1707	60h. Letov L-40 Meta Sokol OK-NMD	20	10
1708	80h. Letov L-200 Morava OK-RHA	20	10
1709	1k. Letov Z-37 Cmelak crop sprayer OK-60	45	10
1710	1k.60 Zlin Z-526 Trener Master OK-PNB	55	10
1711	2k. Aero L-29 Delfin jet trainer	1·75	65
1706/1711 Set of 6		3·00	1·00

1968.
1718	60h. Charles' hydrogen balloon	45	15
1719	1k. William Samuel Henson's *Aerial Steam Carriage*, 1842	70	25
1720	2k. Airship	80	55
1718/1720 Set of 3		1·80	85

1969.
1840*	3k. J.F. Kennedy Airport, New York	2·40	1·10

1973. 50th Anniv of Ceskoslovenske Aerolinte CSA (Czech airline).
2128	30h. Tupolev Tu-104A of C.S.A	10	10
2129	60h. Ilyushin Il-62 of C.S.A	15	10
2130	1k.40 Tupolev Tu-134A of C.S.A	40	10
2131	1k.90 Ilyushin Il-18 of C.S.A	55	20
2132	2k.40 Ilyushin Il-14P of C.S.A	2·75	60
2133	3k.60 Tupolev Tu-154 of C.S.A	70	25
2128/2133 Set of 6		4·25	1·20

1974.
2188*	1k. Ilyushin Il-14M	60	10

1976.
2286*	60h. Ilyushin Il-62 Classic	35	10

1977. Early Aviation.
2358	60h. Airship LZ-5, 1909, and airship LZ-127 *Graf Zeppelin*, 1927	15	10
2359	1k. Clement Ader's monoplane *Eole*, 1890, Etrich Holubice, 1909, and Dunne D-8, 1914	30	10
2360	1k.60 Blanchard and Jeffries' balloon, 1785	40	15
2361	2k. Lilienthal biplane glider, 1896	50	15
2362	4k.40 Jan Kaspar's Bleriot XI	3·50	85
2358/2362 Set of 5		4·25	1·20

1983.
2671*	3k.60 Aero A-10, 1922	1·00	50

1983. 60th Anniv of Ceskoslovenske Aerolinte CSA (Czech airline).
2692	50h. Ilyushin Il-62M	15	10
2693	1k. Ilyushin Il-62M	30	10
2694	4k. Ilyushin Il-62M and Aero A-14, 1923	1·90	85
2692/2694 Set of 3		2·10	95

1985.
2772*	2k. Avia B-534	70	25

1986.
2818	4k. Zlin Z-50LS	70	40

1986. 50th Anniv of Prague-Moscow Air Service.
2829	50h. Airspeed A.S.6 Envoy II (on ground) and Ilyushin Il-86 of C.S.A	10	10

1992.
3091*	2k. Supermarine Spitfires	20	10

CZECH REPUBLIC

Central Europe
100 haleru = 1 koruna

1996. Biplanes.
144	7k. Letov S-1	55	15
145	8k. Aero A-11	65	20
146	10k. Avia BH-21	80	35
144/146 Set of 3		1·80	65

DAHOMEY

West Africa

100 centimes = 1 franc

1940.
117	1f.90 Twin-engine airliner	1·60	4·00
118	2f.90 Twin-engine airliner	1·10	4·75
119	4f.50 Twin-engine airliner	1·40	4·50
120	4f.90 Twin-engine airliner	1·20	4·25
121	6f.90 Twin-engine airliner	90	4·50
117/121 *Set of 5*		5·50	20·00

1942.
143k	50f. Twin-engine airliner	5·00	7·75

1962. Foundation of Air Afrique Airline. As No. 307 of Cameroun.
163	25f. Boeing 707 airliners of Air Afrique	95	45

1963.
194	100f. Boeing 707 of Air Afrique	2·40	60
195	200f. Boeing 707 of Air Afrique	4·25	1·60
196	300f. Boeing 707 of Air Afrique over Cotonou Airport	6·25	2·50
197	500f. Boeing 707 of Air Afrique	11·00	3·25
194/197 *Set of 4*		22·00	7·25

1966. Inauguration of Douglas DC-8F Air Service. As No. 438 of Cameroun.
258	30f. Douglas DC-8F Jet Trader of Air Afrique	80	45

1970. 10th Anniv of Aerial Navigation Security Agency for Africa and Madagascar. As No. 552 of Cameroun.
401	40f. Airliner over airport	1·00	30

1971.
439*	50f. Boeing 747	1·40	70

1972. Birth Centenary of Louis Bleriot (pioneer airman).
471	100f. Louis Bleriot and Bleriot XI	3·25	1·60

1974.
552*	65f. Concorde	1·40	80

PARCEL POST STAMPS
1967. Nos. 194/7 surcharged **COLIS POSTAUX** and value.
P278*	200f. on 200f. Boeing 707 of Air Afrique	6·50	4·50
P279*	300f. on 100f. Boeing 707 of Air Afrique	6·50	5·25

58

P280*	500f. on 300f. Boeing 707 of Air Afrique over Cotonou Airport	13·50	9·75
P281*	1000f. on 500f. Boeing 707 of Air Afrique	27·00	£110

POSTAGE DUE STAMP

1967.
D316*	30f. Douglas DC-8-10/50CF	1·20	1·20

DANZIG

Baltic

1920. 100 pfennig = 1 mark

1923. 100 pfennig = 1 Danzig gulden

1920. No. 144a of Germany overprinted Danzig and further surcharged with L.V.G. Schneider biplane and value in figures.
41*	40 on 40pf. Allegorical figure	1·20	3·00
42*	60 on 40pf. Allegorical figure	1·20	3·00

1921.
57	40pf. Sablatnig PIII	25	45
58	60pf. Sablatnig PIII	25	45
59	1m. Sablatnig PIII	25	45
60	2m. Sablatnig PIII	1·30	2·20
116	5m. Sablatnig PIII	45	90
117	10m. Sablatnig PIII	45	90
118	20m. Sablatnig PIII	45	90
119	25m. Sablatnig PIII	35	60
120	50m. Sablatnig PIII	35	60
121	100m. Sablatnig PIII	35	60
122	250m. Sablatnig PIII	35	1·30
123	500m. Sablatnig PIII	35	60
57/123 *Set of 12*		3·00	6·00

1923.
162	250,000m. Etrich/Rumpler Taube	25	1·10
163	500,000m. Etrich/Rumpler Taube	25	1·10

1923. Design as Nos. 162/3, surcharged with numeral and **Millionen**.
164	2M. on 100,000m. Etrich/Rumpler Taube	25	1·10
165	5M. on 50,000m. Etrich/Rumpler Taube	25	1·10

1924.
195	10pf. Etrich/Rumpler Taube	22·00	4·00
196	20pf. Etrich/Rumpler Taube	2·20	1·60
197	40pf. Etrich/Rumpler Taube	3·00	1·80
198	1g. Etrich/Rumpler Taube	3·00	1·80
199	2½g. Stylised airplane	18·00	37·00
195/199 *Set of 5*		43·00	42·00

1935.
233*	10pf. Junkers F-13	1·80	90
234*	15pf. Junkers F-13	1·80	1·30
235*	25pf. Junkers F-13	1·80	1·80
236*	50pf. Junkers F-13	7·00	10·50

1937.
MS252*	50pf. Junkers F-13	3·50	70·00

DENMARK

Northern Europe

100 ore = 1 krone

1925.
224	10ore. Airplane	28·00	34·00
225	15ore. Airplane	55·00	55·00
226	25ore. Airplane	39·00	55·00
227	50ore. Airplane	£110	£120
228	1k. Airplane	£110	£120
224/228 *Set of 5*		£300	£350

1934.
287	10ore. Fokker F.VIIa	85	1·10
288	15ore. Fokker F.VIIa	3·25	4·50
289	20ore. Fokker F.VIIa	3·75	5·00
290	50ore. Fokker F.VIIa	3·75	5·00
291	1k. Fokker F.VIIa	13·00	17·00
287/291 *Set of 5*		22·00	29·00

1943. 25th Anniv of DDL Danish Airlines.
337	20ore. Focke Wulf Fw 200 Condor of Det Danske Luftfartselskab	30	20

1956. 50th Anniv of First Flight by J.C.H. Ellehammer.
406	30ore. Ellehammer II, 1906	45	20

1961. 10th Anniv of Scandinavian Airlines System (SAS).
431	60ore. Douglas DC-8 of Scandinavian Airlines System	75	35

1974.
594*	90ore. Johan Colding's mail balloon, 1808	35	25

1981. History of Aviation.
711	1k. Ellehammer II, 1906	55	40
712	1k.30 Captain A.P. Botved's Fokker C.VE biplane R-1, 1926	80	55
713	1k.60 Hojriis Hillig's Bellanca J-300 Special NR-797W *Liberty*, 1931	55	20
714	2k.30 Douglas DC-7C "Seven Seas", 1957	80	60
711/714 *Set of 4*		2·40	1·60

1986.
MS817 380ore. Friedrichshafen FF-49 seaplane
(sheet contains three other designs)......... 7·00 7·00

1991.
967* 4k.75 Douglas DC-3 of Det Danske
Luftfartselskab........................ 1·50 95

1994.
1024* 3k.75 Weather balloon.................... 1·30 30

1995.
1049* 8k.75 Lockheed C-130 Hercules............... 2·50 1·90

1996.
1065* 8k.75 Church dome as hot-air balloon........ 2·50 1·90

1999.
1167 4k.25 Lockheed Martin F-16 Fighting
Falcon........................ 1·30 1·10

2000. 50th Anniv of Royal Danish Air Force.
1217 9k.75 Lockheed C-130 Hercules............ 2·50 2·10
MS1218 9k.75 Lockheed C-130 Hercules............ 3·00 3·00

2006.
1472 4k.50 Ellehammer......................... 1·70 90
1473 4k.75 Kramme and Zeuthen KZ-II, 1946..... 1·80 1·00
1474 5k.50 Kramme and Zeuthen KZ-IV, 1944 .... 2·50 1·70
1475 13k. Kramme and Zeuthen KZ-VII Lark,
1947................................ 6·00 3·50
1472/1475 *Set of 4*...................... 11·00 6·50

2007.
1489 13k.50 de Havilland Canada DHC-6 Twin
Otter........................ 5·50 3·75

DJIBOUTI REPUBLIC

East Africa

100 centimes = 1 franc

1977. No. 678 of French Territory of the Afars and the Issas
overprinted **REPUBLIQUE DE DJIBOUTI.**
703* 500f. Outline of airliner over Djibouti
Airport...................... 13·50 12·50

1978. Djibouti Aero Club.
721 60f. Marcel Brochet MB 101 F-BGUE .... 1·30 75
722 85f. de Havilland D.H.82A Tiger Moth
F-OBKK........................ 1·90 1·00
723 200f. Morane Saulnier MS 892 Rallye
Commodore F-BODG................. 4·00 2·00
721/723 *Set of 3*...................... 6·50 3·50

1979.
755 30f. Sud Aviation SE 3130 Alouette II
helicopter of Air Djibouti.............. 1·20 55
756 90f. de Havilland DHC-6 Twin Otter 100
of Air Djibouti .... 2·75 1·00

1979. 75th Anniv of Powered Flight.
760 140f. Junkers Ju 52/3m, 1942, and
Dewoitine D-338 trimotor F-AOBF,
1935........................ 3·25 1·10
761 250f. Potez 63-11 bomber, 1941, and
Supermarine Spitfire Mk VII, 1942 ..... 4·75 2·20
762 500f. Concorde, 1969, and Sikorsky S-40
flying boat *American Clipper* of Pan
Am, 1931................... 10·50 3·75
760/762 *Set of 3*..................... 17·00 6·25

1979.
764* 80f. Douglas DC-8-60 "Super Sixty"........... 3·50 1·70

1980.
778* 90f. Morane Saulnier MS 892 Rallye
Commodore F-BODG............ 2·20 90

1980. Foundation of Air Djibouti.
782 400f. Boeing 737 of Air Djibouti over
Djibouti Airport................. 8·75 2·75

1980. 80th Anniv of First Zeppelin Flight.
797 100f. Airship LZ-127 *Graf Zeppelin*, 1928..... 2·75 80
798 150f. Count Ferdinand von Zeppelin and
airship LZ-3 .... 3·50 1·10

1981.
804 100f. Concorde........................ 3·25 1·00

1982.
855* 55f. Boeing 727-100 of Air Djibouti............ 1·50 70

1983. Bicentenary of Manned Flight.
870 35f. Montgolfier balloon (tethered flight,
1783)........................ 95 30
871 45f. Henri Giffard's balloon *Le Grand
Ballon Captif*, 1878................. 1·50 55
872 120f. Balloon *Double Eagle II*, 1978......... 3·00 1·30
870/872 *Set of 3*..................... 5·00 1·90

1983. 50th Anniv of Air France.

875	25f. Bloch 220 Gascogne of Air France.....	50	30
876	100f. Douglas DC-4 F-BELP of Air France ...	2·00	1·20
877	175f. Boeing 747-200 of Air France.............	3·50	1·30
875/877 Set of 3..		5·50	2·50

1983. 50th Anniv of Air France.

MS889 250f. Concorde of Air France and Saint-
Exupery's biplane .... 27·00 27·00

1984. Microlight Aircraft.

906	65f. Microlight G-MBYI	1·30	45
907	85f. Powered hang-glider *Jules*	1·70	55
908	100f. Microlight...	2·50	80
906/908 Set of 3..		5·00	1·60

1984. 75th Anniv of Louis Bleriot's Cross-Channel Flight.

925	40f. Louis Bleriot and working drawing of Bleriot XI	85	50
926	75f. Louis Bleriot, Britten Norman Islander and Bleriot XI.....................	1·50	1·00
927	90f. Louis Bleriot and Boeing 727 of Air Djibouti	1·80	1·20
925/927 Set of 3..		3·75	2·40

1984.

931* 100f. Canadair CL-215 fire-fighting
amphibian... 3·00 1·40

1987. Flight Anniversaries and Events.

994	55f. Amiot 370..	1·30	45
995	80f. Charles Lindbergh and Ryan NYP Special *Spirit of St. Louis*..................	1·60	65
996	120f. Dick Rutan, Jeana Yeager and *Voyager*, 1986................................	2·50	1·10
994/996 Set of 3..		4·75	2·00

1988. No. 994 surcharged **PARIS-DJIBOUTI-ST DENIS DE LA REUNION RALLYE ROLAND GARROS 70 F.**

1022 70f. on 55f. Amiot 370................................. 2·20 1·10

1988. 40th Anniv of Michel Lafoux Air Club.

1026 145f. de Havilland DH.82 Tiger Moth and
Socata TB-10 Tobago F-GDGY............. 2·00 1·10

DOMINICA

West Indies

100 cents = 1 dollar

1949. As Nos. 114/15 of Antigua.

114*	5c. Airplane..	20	15
115*	6c. Jet-powered Vickers Viking.................	1·25	2·75

1969.

259* 8c. Hawker Siddeley H.S.748................... 30 20

1969.

288* $1.20 Hawker Siddeley H.S.748 at Melville
Hall Airport .... 1·25 1·75

1974.

442* $2 Boeing 747-100 and Airco (de
Havilland) DH.4 biplane (inscribed
"DE HAVILAND")................................. 80 1·00

MS443* $2.40 Boeing 747-100 and de Havilland
D.H.4 biplane (sheet contains one other design).. 1·00 1·40

1978. Aviation Anniversaries.

604*	6c. Charles Lindbergh and Ryan NYP Special *Spirit of St. Louis*...................	20	60
605*	10c. Lindbergh's Ryan NYP Special *Spirit of St. Louis* taking off.....................	25	10
607*	20c. Lindbergh's Ryan NYP Special *Spirit of St. Louis* landing in Paris	45	10
608*	40c. Airship LZ-1, 1900.............................	55	20
609*	60c. Count Ferdinand von Zeppelin and airship LZ-2, 1906............................	65	30
610*	$3 Airship LZ-127 *Graf Zeppelin*, 1928....	1·40	2·25

MS611* 50c Lindbergh's Ryan NYP Special *Spirit of
St. Louis*; $2 Airship LZ-127 *Graf Zeppelin* .. 1·60 1·10

1978. 75th Anniv of First Powered Flight.

616	30c. Wright *Flyer III* being moved from hangar	15	15
617	40c. Wright Type A in Europe, 1908	20	20
618	60c. Wright *Flyer I* gliding near ground.....	25	30
619	$2 Wright *Flyer I* taking off	85	1·25
616/619 Set of 4..		1·30	1·70

MS620 $3 Wilbur and Orville Wright and Wright
Flyer I.. 1·00 1·00

1981.

MS750* $5 Westland HU Mk 5 Wessex helicopter XV
732 of the Queen's Flight .... 1·00 90

1983.

849* 60c. Boeing 707....................................... 25 35

1983. Bicentenary of Manned Flight.

853	45c. Short-Mayo composite (Short S.20 seaplane G-ADHJ *Mercury* and Short S.21 flying boat G-ADHK *Maia*)..........	50	30
854	60c. Macchi M.39 Schneider Trophy seaplane..	60	65
855	90c. Fairey Swordfish torpedo bomber L9781...	70	1·50
856	$4 Airship LZ-3..	1·25	4·75
853/856 Set of 4..		2·75	6·50

MS857 $5 Balloon *Double Eagle II*....................... 1·25 2·75

1984. 40th Anniv of ICAO.

923	30c. Hawker Siddeley H.S.748 of Montserrat Aviation Services	1·00	50
924	60c. de Havilland Canada DHC-6 Twin Otter 100 of Montserrat Aviation Services	1·75	50
925	$1 Britten Norman Islander of Montserrat Aviation Services.............	2·00	1·60
926	$3 de Havilland Canada DHC-6 Twin Otter (inscribed "CASA")...................	3·00	6·50
923/926 Set of 4..		7·00	8·25

MS927 $5 Boeing 747-200 of Montserrat Aviation
Services .... 2·50 3·50

1986.

994* 10c. Bell X-1... 45 50

1986. No. 994 overprinted with Halley's Comet emblem.

1033* 10c. Bell X-1... 20 15

1989.

1297*	60c. Curtiss JN-4 "Jenny" (also on United States of America stamp No. A548 with centre inverted)..............................	90	80
1298*	60c. Airship U.S.S. *Shenandoah* in hangar at Lakehurst, New Jersey	90	80
1299*	60c. Lindbergh's Ryan NYP Special *Spirit of St. Louis*	90	80
1306*	60c. Grumman TBF Avenger.......................	90	80

1991. 50th Anniv of Japanese Attack on Pearl Harbour.

1470*	10c. Aichi D3A "Val" bomber on Japanese aircraft carrier *Akagi*..........................	65	50
1471*	15c. Consolidated PBY-5 Catalina flying boat	70	40
1472*	45c. Mitsubishi A6M Zero-Sen	95	35
1473*	60c. Mitsubishi A6M Zero-Sen	1·25	50
1475*	$2 Aircraft attacking U.S.S. *Nevada*	1·75	1·75
1477*	$5 Mitsubishi A6M Zero-Sen	2·50	3·00

MS1478 Two sheets. (a) $6 Mitsubishi A6M Zero-
Sen over anchorage; (b) $6 Mitsubishi A6M Zero-
Sen over Hickham Field *Set of 2 sheets* .... 8·00 8·50

1992.
1641*	25c. Airship LZ-127 *Graf Zeppelin*	75	40

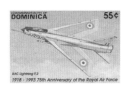

1993. Aviation Anniversaries.
1723*	55c. English Electric Lightning F.2	2·25	50
1724*	65c. Airship LZ-127 *Graf Zeppelin*	2·25	65
1725*	$1 Boeing 314A flying boat	2·50	1·10
1727*	$4 Airship LZ-11 *Viktoria Luise*	4·00	4·50
1728*	$5 Supermarine Spitfire	4·00	4·50
MS1729*Three sheets. (c) $6 Jean-Pierre Blanchard's balloon, 1793 (other sheets do not show aircraft) *Set of 3 sheets*		13·00	13·00

1994.
1880	65c. Waco CG-4A gliders	85	45
1881	$2 Airspeed Horsa glider	1·75	1·75
1882	$3 Airspeed Horsa	2·00	2·25
1880/1882 *Set of 3*		4·25	4·00
MS1883 $6 Hadrian glider (UK name for US built Waco CG-4A)		3·25	3·75

1995.
1961*	$2 Republic P-47 Thunderbolt	1·25	1·25
1963*	$2 Messerschmitt Me163 and Boeing B-17	1·25	1·25

1995.
1971*	$2 Mitsubishi A6M Zero-Sen	1·50	1·25
1972*	$2 Aichi D3A 'Val'	1·50	1·25
1973*	$2 Nakajima B5N 'Kate'	1·50	1·25
MS1977 $6 Mitsubishi AGM Zero-Sen		4·50	4·50

1996.
2198*	$1 Grumman Goose	1·00	80

1998.
2488	20c. Lockheed Jetstar II	65	50
2489	25c. Antonov An 225	65	50
2490	55c. de Havilland Canada DHC-8 Dash-8.	75	35
2491	65c. Beech Model 99 Airliner	75	40
2492	90c. Avions de Transport Régional ATR72	80	50
2493	$1 Lockheed SR-71 Blackbird	80	75
2494	$1 Northrop B-2A Spirit	80	75
2495	$1 Northrop YF-23	80	75
2496	$1 Grumman F-14A Tomcat	80	75
2497	$1 Boeing (McDonnell Douglas) F-15 Eagle	80	75
2498	$1 Mikoyan MiG 29 Fulcrum	80	75
2499	$1 Europa X5	80	75
2500	$1 Camion	80	75
2501	$1 E 400	80	75
2502	$1 Canadair (now Bombardier) CL-215 .	80	75
2503	$1 Piper PA-46 Malibu Meridian	80	75
2504	$1 Beech Model 390 Premier	80	75
2505	$1 Lockheed F-22 Raptor	80	75
2506	$1 Piper Seneca V	80	75

2507	$1 Canadair (now Bombardier) CL-215 .	80	75
2508	$1 Vantase	80	75
2509	$2 Hansa HFB 320	14·00	1·40
2488/2509 *Set of 23*		27·00	14·00
MS2510 (a) $6 Boeing (McDonnell Douglas); (b) $6 Cessna 206 seaplane *Set of 2 sheets*		8·50	9·00

1998. 80th Anniv of Royal Air Force.
2526	$2 Hawker Siddeley (BAe) Nimrod MR2P	1·50	1·60
2527	$2 Lockheed C-130 Hercules	1·50	1·60
2538	$2 Panavia Tornado GR1	1·50	1·60
2529	$2 Lockheed C-130 Hercules (landing)..	1·50	1·60
2526/2529 *Set of 4*		5·50	5·75
MS2530 (a) $5 Bristol F2B; (b) $6 Hawker Hart and Eurofighter EF-2000 Typhoon *Set of 2 sheets*		7·50	8·50
No. 2529 is inscribed Panavia Tornado GR1 in error.			

1999.
2734*	55c. Douglas C-47 Skytrain	60	55

2000. Centenary of First Zeppelin Flight.
2858	$1.65 Count Ferdinand von Zeppelin	1·00	1·00
2859	$1.65 LZ-1 at Lake Constance, 1900	1·00	1·00
2860	$1.65 LZ-10 *Schwaben*, 1911	1·00	1·00
2861	$1.65 LZ-6 & LZ-7 *Deutschland* in hangar ...	1·00	1·00
2862	$1.65 LZ-4 at Luneville	1·00	1·00
2863	$1.65 LZ-11 *Viktoria-Luise*	1·00	1·00
2858/2863 *Set of 6*		5·50	5·50
MS2864 $6 As No. 2859		4·00	4·25

2002. 75th Anniv of First Solo Trans-Atlantic Flight.
3231	$3 Lindbergh and Ryan NYP Special, *Spirit of St Louis*	1·90	1·90
3232	$3 Charles and Anne Lindbergh	1·90	1·90
MS3233 $6 Lindbergh and Ryan NYP Special, *Spirit of St Louis*		4·50	4·75

2003. Centenary of Powered Flight.
MS3330* $6 Westland Wallace over Mount Everest (1933)		3·00	3·25

2007.
3543	$1 Concorde 001 F-WTSS (French prototype)	70	50
3544	$2 Concorde 001 F-WTSS (French prototype)	1·10	1·10

DOMINICAN REPUBLIC

West Indies

100 centavos = 1 peso

1928.
256	10c. Lindbergh's Ryan NYP Special *Spirit of St. Louis* (deep blue)	5·25	2·75
280	10c. Lindbergh's Ryan NYP Special *Spirit of St. Louis* (pale blue)	1·80	60
271	10c. Lindbergh's Ryan NYP Special *Spirit of St. Louis* (yellow)	3·50	3·50
272	15c. Lindbergh's Ryan NYP Special *Spirit of St. Louis* (red)	6·75	4·75
281	15c. Lindbergh's Ryan NYP Special *Spirit of St. Louis* (turquoise)	3·25	1·00
273	20c. Lindbergh's Ryan NYP Special *Spirit of St. Louis* (green)	3·25	85
282	20c. Lindbergh's Ryan NYP Special *Spirit of St. Louis* (brown)	3·50	85
274	30c. Lindbergh's Ryan NYP Special *Spirit of St. Louis* (violet)	6·75	5·75
283	30c. Lindbergh's Ryan NYP Special *Spirit of St. Louis* (brown)	6·25	1·80

1931. As Nos. 286/7 (imperforate or perforated), surcharged **HABILITADO PARA CORREO AEREO**, premium and airplane.
288A	5c. +5c. Hurricane damage (blue and red)	6·75	6·75
289A	5c. +5c. Hurricane damage (black and red)	27·00	31·00
290A	10c. +10c. Hurricane damage (yellow and red)	5·25	5·25
291A	10c. +10c. Hurricane damage (black and red)	27·00	31·00
288A/291A *Set of 4*		60·00	65·00

1931.
300	10c. Fokker F.10A Super Trimotor (red)	3·50	50
301	10c. Fokker F.10A Super Trimotor (blue)	1·70	50
302	10c. Fokker F.10A Super Trimotor (green)	6·25	2·75
303	15c. Fokker F.10A Super Trimotor	2·75	50
304	20c. Fokker F.10A Super Trimotor	6·25	2·30
306	30c. Fokker F.10A Super Trimotor	2·50	30
307	50c. Fokker F.10A Super Trimotor	6·25	60
308	1p. Fokker F.10A Super Trimotor	10·50	2·50
300/308 *Set of 8*		36·00	9·00

1933.
331	10c. Fokker Super Universal	3·50	50

1934.
338*	10c. Ford "Tin Goose"	3·00	50

1935.
351	10c. Airplane	1·60	40

1936.
358	10c. Fokker F.10A Super Trimotor	2·50	40

1937.
384   10c. Martin M-130 flying boat and San Pedro Macoris terminal .... 1·00   20

1937. Pan American Goodwill Flight.
386*	15c. Junkers F-13	1·40	95
387*	20c. Junkers F-13	1·40	1·20
388*	25c. Junkers F-13	2·00	1·20
389*	30c. Junkers F-13	1·70	1·20
390*	50c. Junkers F-13	3·50	1·80
391*	75c. Junkers F-13	10·50	10·50

1938.
404   10c. Martin M-130 flying boat..................... 1·20   20

1939.
422*   10c. Airplane.. 1·80   85

1941.
458   10c. Douglas DC-4................................. 50   20

1942.
477	3c. Ryan B-5 Brougham	4·25	70
478	15c. Ryan B-5 Brougham	11·50	5·75

1943.
503	10c. Douglas DC-3	40	20
504	20c. Douglas DC-3	40	20
505	25c. Douglas DC-3	5·75	3·25
503/505 *Set of 3*		6·00	3·25

1944.
523	9c. Douglas DC-3	20	20
524	13c. Douglas DC-3	30	20
525	25c. Douglas DC-3	50	20
526	30c. Douglas DC-3	1·00	95
523/526 *Set of 4*		1·80	1·40

1948.
562*	37c. Douglas DC-3	2·10	1·00
563*	1p. Douglas DC-3	5·75	2·10

1950.
597*   12c. Airplane.. 85   20

1953.
610*	12c. Douglas DC-6	30	20
611*	14c. Douglas DC-6	20	20
612*	20c. Douglas DC-6	70	60
613*	23c. Douglas DC-6	40	40
614*	25c. Douglas DC-6	95	70
615*	29c. Douglas DC-6	70	60
616*	1p. Douglas DC-6	2·00	1·30

1956. Third Caribbean Region Aerial Navigation Conference.
660	1c. Punta Caucedo Airport	20	10
661	2c. Punta Caucedo Airport	20	10
662	11c. Punta Caucedo Airport (air)	50	10
660/662 *Set of 3*		80	25

1960. Dominican Civil Aviation.
798   13c. Douglas DC-4 *San Cristobal* of Dominicana 30   20

1965.
951*   10c. Douglas DC-8................................. 40   20

1969.
1053*   10c. Douglas DC-8 at Airport of the Americas, Santo Domingo 30   20

1974.
1200*   33c. Boeing 727-200 of Dominicana.......... 2·10   75

1978. 50th Anniv of First Dominican Airmail Stamp.
1320   10c. Lindbergh's Ryan NYP Special *Spirit of St. Louis* (on stamp No. 256) 45   20

1978. 75th Anniv of First Powered Flight.
1331	7c. Boeing 707 and nose of Douglas DC-6 over outline of Wright *Flyer I*	20	20
1332	10c. Wilbur and Orville Wright and Wright Glider No. I.......................	55	20
1333	13c. Diagram of airflow over a wing	75	30
1334	45c. Outline of Wright *Flyer I*	2·10	1·40
1331/1334 *Set of 4*		3·25	1·90

1987. 50th Anniv Pan-American Flight for Columbus Lighthouse Fund, 1937.
1697	25c. Major Frank Feliz Miranda and Curtiss-Wright CW-19, 1937...............	60	30
MS1698	2p. Junkers F-13 (on stamp No. 391)............	8·25	6·50

1987.
1700*   50c. Passengers disembarking from Boeing 727.. 1·50   60

1995.
1900*	5p. Barahona Airport	3·75	1·80
1901*	6p. G. Luperon Airport	4·75	2·10
1902*	13p. Las Americas Airport	10·00	4·75

1995. 50th Anniv of Dominican Air Force (1st issue).
1923	2p. Vought 02U Corsair	1·00	85
1924	2p. Stearman Pt-17 Kaydett	1·00	85
1925	2p. North American T-6 Texan	1·00	85
1926	2p. Consolidated PBY-5 Catalina	1·00	85
1927	2p. Bristol Type 156 Beaufighter	1·00	85
1928	2p. de Havilland DH.98 Mosquito	1·00	85
1929	2p. Lockheed P-38 Lightning	1·00	85
1930	2p. North American P-51 Mustang	1·00	85
1931	2p. Boeing B-17 Flying Fortress	1·00	85
1932	2p. Republic P-47 Thunderbolt	1·00	85
1933	2p. de Havilland DH.100 Vampire FB Mk50	1·00	85
1934	2p. Curtiss C-46 Commando *1	1·00	85
1935	2p. Douglas B-26 Invader	1·00	85
1936	2p. Douglas C-47 Skytrain	1·00	85
1937	2p. North American T-28D Trojan	1·00	85
1938	2p. Lockheed T-33A Silver Star	1·00	85
1939	2p. Cessna T-41D	1·00	85
1940	2p. Beech T-34 Mentor	1·00	85
1941	2p. Cessna O-2A Super Skymaster	1·00	85
1942	2p. Cessna A-37B Dragonfly	1·00	85
1923/1942 *Set of 20*		18·00	15·00

No. 1934 is wrongly inscribed Commander and No. 1935 is wrongly inscribed Boeing.

1996. 50th Anniv of Dominican Air Force (2nd issue).
1958	3p. Sikorsky S-55	1·70	85
1959	3p. Sud Aviation Alouette II	1·70	85
1960	3p. Sud Aviation Alouette III	1·70	85
1961	3p. Boeing (McDonnell Douglas Hughes) OH-6AQ Cayuse	1·70	85
1962	3p. Bell 205 A-1	1·70	85
1963	3p. Aerospatiale SA.365 Dauphin 2	1·70	85
1958/1963 *Set of 6*		9·25	4·50

1997. 50th Anniv of Dominican Air Force (3rd issue).
2026	3p. Air Force Badge	1·80	1·80
2027	3p. Air Command North	1·80	1·80
2028	3p. Air Command	1·80	1·80
2029	3p. Rescue	1·80	1·80
2030	3p. Maintenance Command	1·80	1·80
2031	3p. Combat Squadron	1·80	1·80
2026/2031 *Set of 6*		9·75	9·75

1998. 50th Anniv of Dominican Air Force (4th issue).
2040	3p. General Frank Felix Miranda	1·80	1·80
2041	3p. Curtiss-Wright CW19R	1·80	1·80
2042	3p. Colonel Ernesto Tejeda	1·80	1·80
2043	3p. Tejeda (different portrait)	1·80	1·80
2044	3p. Miranda (different portrait)	1·80	1·80
2040/2044 *Set of 5*		8·00	8·00

EXPRESS DELIVERY STAMPS

1920.
E232	10c. Biplane	6·75	1·40

DUBAI

Arabian Peninsula

100 dirhams = 1 riyal

1969.
319*	35d. de Havilland DH.66 Hercules of Imperial Airways, 1930	35	25
321*	1r. Armstrong Whitworth A.W Atalanta G-ABTI of Imperial Airways, (inscribed "ATLANTA")	85	25
323*	3r. Short S.25 Sunderland flying boat of B.O.A.C., 1943	1·80	40
MS324	1r.25 Vickers Super VC-10	4·25	4·25

1969.
345*	1r. Sikorsky S-55 helicopter	3·50	15

1970.
349*	60d. Handley Page H.P.67 Hastings Met.1 of 202 Squadron, R.A.F	40	25

1970.
367*	1r. Vickers Super VC-10 over Dubai International Airport	1·80	35

1971. Opening of Dubai International Airport.
372	1r. Vickers Super VC-10 over Dubai International Airport	3·00	1·70
373	1r.25 Dubai International Airport	3·75	2·10

1972.
391*	5r. Supermarine Spitfire	4·50	2·20

EAST GERMANY

See under Germany (Democratic Republic)

ECUADOR

South America
1929. 100 centavos = 1 sucre
2000. 100 cents = 1 dollar (US)

1929.
458	2c. Ryan B-5 Brougham	35	20
459	5c. Ryan B-5 Brougham	35	20
460	10c. Ryan B-5 Brougham	35	10
461	20c. Ryan B-5 Brougham	65	10
462	50c. Ryan B-5 Brougham	1·20	65
463	1s. Ryan B-5 Brougham (blue)	3·75	3·25
467	1s. Ryan B-5 Brougham (red)	4·50	65
709	1s. Ryan B-5 Brougham (green)	55	30
464	5s. Ryan B-5 Brougham (yellow)	15·00	13·00
468	5s. Ryan B-5 Brougham (olive)	5·50	5·00
710	5s. Ryan B-5 Brougham (violet)	1·20	30
465	10s. Ryan B-5 Brougham (red)	85·00	70·00
469	10s. Ryan B-5 Brougham (black)	19·00	6·50
711	10s. Ryan B-5 Brougham (blue)	2·75	45

1930. Nos. O475/7 further overprinted **MENDEZ BOGOTA-QUITO Junio 4 de 1930.**
470	1s. Ryan B-5 Brougham (red)	28·00	27·00
471	5s. Ryan B-5 Brougham (olive)	28·00	27·00
472	10s. Ryan B-5 Brougham (black)	28·00	27·00
470/472 Set of 3		75·00	75·00

1930.
478*	16c. Airplane	55	30

1933. No. 478 surcharged **10 DIEZ CENTAVOS.**
489*	10c. on 16c. Airplane	55	20

1935. Nos. O470, O474, O476 and O477 further overprinted **INAUGURACION MONUMENTO A BOLIVAR QUITO, 24 DE JULIO DE 1935** or surcharged also.
513*	50c. Ryan B-5 Brougham (green)	10·50	6·50
514*	50c. Ryan B-5 Brougham (brown)	10·50	6·50
515*	$1 on 5s. Ryan B-5 Brougham (olive)	10·50	6·50
516*	$2 on 10s. Ryan B-5 Brougham (black)	10·50	6·50

1936.
546*	70c. Martin M-130 flying boat	75	75
547*	1s. Martin M-130 flying boat	3·50	3·50

1937. No. 548 is surcharged **5 5 POSTAL ADICIONAL.**
548	5c. on 10c. Airplane	90	30
549	10c. Airplane	65	30

1938.
581*	1s. Airplane	55	10

1939.
594	1s. Ryan B-5 Brougham	20	20
595	2s. Ryan B-5 Brougham	55	20
596	5s. Ryan B-5 Brougham	1·40	20
594/596 Set of 3		1·90	55

1941.
637	20c. Fighter aircraft	40	15

1948. 25th Anniv of First Ecuadorian Postal Flight.
842	30c. Hanriot HD-1 *Telegrafo 1*	35	30
843	40c. Hanriot HD-1 *Telegrafo 1*	35	30
844	60c. Hanriot HD-1 *Telegrafo 1*	35	30
845	1s. Hanriot HD-1 *Telegrafo 1*	35	30
846	3s. Hanriot HD-1 *Telegrafo 1*	1·10	55
847	5s. Hanriot HD-1 *Telegrafo 1*	1·20	55
848	60c. Elia Liut and Hanriot HD-1 *Telegrafo 1* (air)	45	30
849	1s. Elia Liut and Hanriot HD-1 *Telegrafo 1*	45	45
850	1s.30 Elia Liut and Hanriot HD-1 *Telegrafo 1*	45	45
851	1s.90 Elia Liut and Hanriot HD-1 *Telegrafo 1*	45	45
852	2s. Elia Liut and Hanriot HD-1 *Telegrafo 1*	65	45
853	5s. Elia Liut and Hanriot HD-1 *Telegrafo 1*	1·20	75
842/853 Set of 12		6·50	4·75

1948.
860*	50c. Airplane	55	30
861*	70c. Airplane	55	30
862*	3s. Airplane	1·00	65
863*	5s. Airplane	1·40	85
864*	10s. Airplane	2·75	1·10

1954.
1009*	80c. Airliner	45	30

1954.
1015*	60c. Douglas DC-4	35	30
1016*	70c. Douglas DC-4	35	30
1017*	90c. Douglas DC-4	35	30
1018*	1s. Douglas DC-4	35	30
1019*	2s. Douglas DC-4	45	30
1020*	3s. Douglas DC-4	75	30

1955. Birth Centenary of Jose Abel Castillo (pioneer aviator).
1037*	60c. Jose Abel Castillo and Hanriot HD-1 *Telegrafo 1*	75	20
1038*	90c. Jose Abel Castillo and Hanriot HD-1 *Telegrafo 1*	75	20
1039*	1s. Jose Abel Castillo and Hanriot HD-1 *Telegrafo 1*	90	20
1040*	2s. Jose Abel Castillo and Hanriot HD-1 *Telegrafo 1*	1·10	30
1041*	5s. Jose Abel Castillo and Hanriot HD-1 *Telegrafo 1*	2·20	85

1955. No. 710 surcharged **1 SUCRE.**
1042	1s. on 5s. Ryan B-5 Brougham (violet)	45	30

1958.
1118*	2s. Elia Liut and Hanriot HD-1 *Telegrafo 1* (on stamp No. 851)	75	45

1960.
1164*	1s. Quito Airport	20	20

1960.
1183*	5s. El Coca Airport	65	55

1961.
1192*	80c. Martin M-130 flying boat (on stamp No. 547)	20	20

1963.
1230	2s. Boeing 707	45	30
1231	4s.20 Boeing 707	75	55

1963. Inauguration of Simon Bolivar Airport, Guayaquil.
1244	60c. Simon Bolivar Airport, Guayaquil	10	10
1245	70c. Simon Bolivar Airport, Guayaquil	20	10
1246	5s. Simon Bolivar Airport, Guayaquil	75	55
1244/1246 Set of 3		95	70

1964. No. 1164 surcharged **0,80.**
1261*	80c. on 1s. Quito Airport	35	20

1965.
1294*	60c. Piper PA-14 Vagabond N-5156-H	1·10	30

1975.
1582	2s. SEPECAT Jaguar EB	45	30

1976. 23rd Anniv of TAME Airline.
1617*	3s. Douglas DC-3 and Lockheed L.188 Electra of TAME	55	30

1976. 50th Anniv of Lufthansa Airline.
1643 10s. Dornier Do-J II 10-t Wal flying boat and Douglas DC-10, both of Lufthansa.................................. 1·70 75

1978.
1702 6s. Gates Learjet survey airplane.............. 90 45
1703 7s.60 Gates Learjet survey airplane (air)..... 1·40 75
MS1704 10s. Gates Learjet survey airplane .... 2·20 2·20

1981. 50th Anniv of Flight of Ecuador 1 from San Diego to Quito.
1849 2s. Theodore E. Gildred and Ryan B-5 Brougham *Ecuador 1* 35 20

1984. Bicentenary (1983) of Manned Flight.
1910 3s. Montgolfier balloon (first manned free flight, 1783)........................ 20 10
1911 6s. Charles' hydrogen balloon, 1783 .... 55 30
MS1912 20s. Airship LZ-127 *Graf Zeppelin* and Montgolfier balloon.......................... 2·20 1·30

1985. 65th Anniv of Ecuadorian Air Force.
1948* 10s. Israeli Aircraft Industry Kfir-C2 of the Ecuador Air Force 55 30

PRIMER CONGRESO ECUATORIANO DE FILATELIA 08251

1985.
MS1958 5s. Bleriot XI (sheet also includes three other 5s designs).................................... 1·30 1·30

1988. 60th Anniv of Avianca National Airline.
2017* 10s. Junkers F-13 seaplane 35 30
2018* 20s. Dornier Wal Flying boat 35 30
2019* 30s. Ford Tri-motor "Tin Goose"................. 45 30
2020* 40s. Boeing 247D................................. 55 30
2021* 50s. Boeing 720-059D............................ 65 45
2022* 100s. Douglas DC-3.............................. 1·50 65
2023* 200s. Boeing 727-200............................ 2·75 1·50
2024* 300s. Sikorsky S-38 flying boat............. 4·75 2·10

1994.
2207 600s. Cessna 441 Conquest....................... 1·10 70
2208 600s. Cessna 441 Conquest....................... 1·10 70

1995. 75th Anniv of Ecuadorian Air Force.
2233 1000s. Sepecat Jaguar and Dassault Mirage F1s.. 2·40 1·40

1996. 50th Anniv of the International Civil Aviation Organisation.
2257 2000s. Pitts Special................................ 4·25 2·40

1997. 66th Anniv of Ecuador Flying Club.
2289 2600s. Emblem (no airplane) .... 7·00 4·75

2002.
2567 40c. Paragliding................................. 4·00 2·75
2568 40c. Paragliding................................. 4·00 2·75

2004. 50th Anniv of Ecuador Military Aviation.
2724 40c. Aerospatiale SA330 Puma helicopter 2·50 1·70
2725 40c. Soldiers and Aerospatiale SA330 Puma helicopter......................... 2·50 1·70
2756 40c. Emblem.................................... 2·50 1·70
2727 40c. Walker and GAF Nomad (?) .... 2·50 1·70
2724/2727 *Set of 4*............................... 9·00 6·00

2005.
2809 $1.25 Mirage F1-JA................................ 7·00 4·75
2810 $1.25 Cessna A-37B.............................. 7·00 4·75
2811 $1.25 IAI Kfir C2................................. 7·00 4·75
2812 $1.25 Colonel Carlos Uscateguis.............. 7·00 4·75
2809/2812 *Set of 4*.............................. 25·00 17·00

2005. 85th Anniv of First Posts and Telegraphs Flight.
2813 25c. Hanriot HD-1 *Telegrafo 1*, tail............. 2·00 1·30
2814 $1 Hanriot HD-1 *Telegrafo 1*, nose........... 6·00 4·00

2006.
2936* 40c. Douglas C-47................................ 2·50 1·70
2938* 80c. Parachutist................................. 4·25 2·75

OFFICIAL STAMPS
1929. Nos. 458/69 overprinted **OFICIAL**.
O466 2c. Ryan B-5 Brougham 75 75
O467 5c. Ryan B-5 Brougham 75 75
O468 10c. Ryan B-5 Brougham 75 75
O469 20c. Ryan B-5 Brougham 75 75
O470 50c. Ryan B-5 Brougham (green) .... 2·40 2·30
O474 50c. Ryan B-5 Brougham (brown) .... 2·20 2·10
O471 1s. Ryan B-5 Brougham (blue) .... 2·40 2·30
O475 1s. Ryan B-5 Brougham (red) .... 2·75 2·75
O472 5s. Ryan B-5 Brougham (yellow) .... 11·00 9·00
O476 5s. Ryan B-5 Brougham (olive) .... 6·50 6·50
O473 10s. Ryan B-5 Brougham (red) .... £130 90·00
O477 10s. Ryan B-5 Brougham (black) .... 13·00 13·00

EGYPT

North Africa

1000 milliemes = 100 piastres = 1 pound

1926.
132 27m. de Havilland DH.34 of Imperial Airways (violet)............................. 13·50 14·00
133 27m. de Havilland DH.34 of Imperial Airways (brown)............................. 4·75 1·90

1931. No. 133 surcharged **GRAF ZEPPELIN AVRIL 1931** and value, in French and Arabic.
185 50m. on 27m. de Havilland DH.34 of Imperial Airways .... 42·00 42·00
186 100m. on 27m. de Havilland DH.34 of Imperial Airways .... 42·00 47·00

1933.
193 1m. Handley Page H.P.42.......................... 15 35
194 2m. Handley Page H.P.42 (black and grey) .. 75 1·10
195 2m. Handley Page H.P.42 (black and orange)............................ 3·50 2·30
196 3m. Handley Page H.P.42........................ 50 25
197 4m. Handley Page H.P.42........................ 95 80
198 5m. Handley Page H.P.42 (black and brown)............................. 70 15
199 6m. Handley Page H.P.42........................ 1·40 1·10
200 7m. Handley Page H.P.42........................ 1·10 80
201 8m. Handley Page H.P.42........................ 60 20
202 9m. Handley Page H.P.42........................ 2·00 1·10
203 10m. Handley Page H.P.42 (brown and violet)............................ 50 55
204 20m. Handley Page H.P.42........................ 60 15
205 30m. Handley Page H.P.42 (brown and blue) .... 1·50 15
206 40m. Handley Page H.P.42........................ 13·50 45
207 50m. Handley Page H.P.42........................ 12·00 15
208 60m. Handley Page H.P.42........................ 5·25 75
209 70m. Handley Page H.P.42........................ 3·25 70
210 80m. Handley Page H.P.42........................ 3·25 75
211 90m. Handley Page H.P.42........................ 4·00 75
212 100m. Handley Page H.P.42....................... 7·75 45
213 200m. Handley Page H.P.42....................... 10·50 1·00
193/213 *Set of 21*.............................. 65·00 12·50

1933. International Aviation Congress, Cairo.
214 5m. Armstrong Whitworth A.W.15 Atalanta G-ABPI of Imperial Airways 4·25 2·50

215	10m. Armstrong Whitworth A.W.15 Atalanta G-ABPI of Imperial Airways	13·00	8·00
216	13m. Dornier Do-X flying boat	14·50	10·50
217	15m. Dornier Do-X flying boat	14·50	9·50
218	30m. Airship LZ-127 *Graf Zeppelin*	18·00	12·00
214/218 *Set of 5*		60·00	38·00

1941. As Nos. 193/213, but colours changed and new value.

285	5m. Handley Page H.P.42 (brown)	30	25
286	10m. Handley Page H.P.42 (violet)	40	25
287a	25m. Handley Page H.P.42	50	25
288	30m. Handley Page H.P.42 (green)	55	25
285/288 *Set of 4*		1·60	90

1946. Cairo Aviation Congress. No. 288 overprinted **Le Caire 1946** and Arabic characters.

314	30m. Handley Page H.P.42	30	20

1947.

322	2m. Douglas DC-3 Dakota of R.A.F. Transport Command	15	45
323	3m. Douglas DC-3 Dakota of R.A.F. Transport Command	15	50
324	5m. Douglas DC-3 Dakota of R.A.F. Transport Command	15	15
325	7m. Douglas DC-3 Dakota of R.A.F. Transport Command	30	20
326	8m. Douglas DC-3 Dakota of R.A.F. Transport Command	30	45
327	10m. Douglas DC-3 Dakota of R.A.F. Transport Command	30	20
328	20m. Douglas DC-3 Dakota of R.A.F. Transport Command	50	20
329	30m. Douglas DC-3 Dakota of R.A.F. Transport Command	60	20
330	40m. Douglas DC-3 Dakota of R.A.F. Transport Command	95	25
331	50m. Douglas DC-3 Dakota of R.A.F. Transport Command	1·10	30
332	100m. Douglas DC-3 Dakota of R.A.F. Transport Command	2·20	40
333	200m. Douglas DC-3 Dakota of R.A.F. Transport Command	5·00	1·70
322/333 *Set of 12*		10·50	4·50

1948. Nos. 332/3 surcharged **S.A.I.D.E. 23-8-1948** and value, in English and Arabic.

349	13m. on 100m. Douglas DC-3 Dakota of R.A.F. Transport Command	50	50
350	22m. on 200m. Douglas DC-3 Dakota of R.A.F. Transport Command	60	75

1952. Nos. 322/33 overprinted with two lines of Arabic text.

392*	2m. Douglas DC-3 Dakota of R.A.F. Transport Command	25	20
393*	3m. Douglas DC-3 Dakota of R.A.F. Transport Command	85	80
394*	5m. Douglas DC-3 Dakota of R.A.F. Transport Command	35	30
395*	7m. Douglas DC-3 Dakota of R.A.F. Transport Command	55	30
396*	8m. Douglas DC-3 Dakota of R.A.F. Transport Command	1·20	95
397*	10m. Douglas DC-3 Dakota of R.A.F. Transport Command	70	80
398*	20m. Douglas DC-3 Dakota of R.A.F. Transport Command	2·50	1·90
399*	30m. Douglas DC-3 Dakota of R.A.F. Transport Command	1·10	1·10
400*	40m. Douglas DC-3 Dakota of R.A.F. Transport Command	3·00	1·60
401*	50m. Douglas DC-3 Dakota of R.A.F. Transport Command	1·80	1·90
402*	100m. Douglas DC-3 Dakota of R.A.F. Transport Command	4·25	2·50
403*	200m. Douglas DC-3 Dakota of R.A.F. Transport Command	9·00	4·25

1953.

433	5m. Douglas DC-3 Dakota of R.A.F. Transport Command	35	50
434	15m. Douglas DC-3 Dakota of R.A.F. Transport Command	85	65

1953. Nos. 322/33 with three bars overprinted on king's portrait.

455*	2m. Douglas DC-3 Dakota of R.A.F. Transport Command	1·50	1·60
456*	3m. Douglas DC-3 Dakota of R.A.F. Transport Command	1·20	2·20
457*	5m. Douglas DC-3 Dakota of R.A.F. Transport Command	80	1·10
458*	7m. Douglas DC-3 Dakota of R.A.F. Transport Command	30	35
459*	8m. Douglas DC-3 Dakota of R.A.F. Transport Command	1·00	1·50
460*	10m. Douglas DC-3 Dakota of R.A.F. Transport Command	34·00	47·00
461*	20m. Douglas DC-3 Dakota of R.A.F. Transport Command	1·20	45
462*	30m. Douglas DC-3 Dakota of R.A.F. Transport Command	1·60	95
463*	40m. Douglas DC-3 Dakota of R.A.F. Transport Command	1·70	1·10
464*	50m. Douglas DC-3 Dakota of R.A.F. Transport Command	3·00	1·50
465*	100m. Douglas DC-3 Dakota of R.A.F. Transport Command	4·50	3·00
466*	200m. Douglas DC-3 Dakota of R.A.F. Transport Command	55·00	75·00

1953. Nos. 392/403 with three bars overprinted on king's portrait.

480*	2m. Douglas DC-3 Dakota of R.A.F. Transport Command	45	30
481*	3m. Douglas DC-3 Dakota of R.A.F. Transport Command	85	70
482*	5m. Douglas DC-3 Dakota of R.A.F. Transport Command	25	25
483*	7m. Douglas DC-3 Dakota of R.A.F. Transport Command	17·00	18·00
484*	8m. Douglas DC-3 Dakota of R.A.F. Transport Command	50	1·40
485*	10m. Douglas DC-3 Dakota of R.A.F. Transport Command	45	95
486*	20m. Douglas DC-3 Dakota of R.A.F. Transport Command	65·00	80·00
487*	30m. Douglas DC-3 Dakota of R.A.F. Transport Command	1·00	95
488*	40m. Douglas DC-3 Dakota of R.A.F. Transport Command	65·00	80·00
489*	50m. Douglas DC-3 Dakota of R.A.F. Transport Command	2·30	1·20
490*	100m. Douglas DC-3 Dakota of R.A.F. Transport Command	3·75	3·00
491*	200m. Douglas DC-3 Dakota of R.A.F. Transport Command	7·00	7·25

1957. 25th Anniv of Egyptian Civil Airlines MISRAIR and Air Force.

545	10m. Vickers Viscount 700 SU-AIE of Misrair	45	45
546	10m. Ilyushin Il-28 bomber and two Mikoyan Gurevich MiG-17 jet fighters	45	45

1959.

MS601	50m. Airliner	10·50	10·50

1959.

620	5m. Boeing B-17 Flying Fortress	25	20
621	15m. Boeing B-17 Flying Fortress	25	25
758	50m. Airplane	1·50	60
622	60m. Douglas DC-6B	60	40
759	80m. Douglas DC-6B	1·90	90
623	90m. Airplane	1·30	80
761	115m. Airplane	2·10	80
762	140m. Airplane	2·20	1·30

1962. Silver Jubilee of UAR Air Force College.

729	10m. Al Kahira jet trainer and de Havilland DH.82 Tiger Moth biplane	30	20

1963.

741	20m. Douglas DC-6	40	20
742	30m. Boeing 707 over Cairo International Airport	50	30
743	40m. Boeing 707	75	60
741/743 *Set of 3*		1·50	1·00

1966.

872*	115m. +55m. de Havilland DH.34 of Imperial Airways (on stamp No. 132) and jet airplane	3·00	2·50

1966.

892	20m. Boeing 727-100	75	35

1967.

910	20m. Hawker Siddeley Comet 4 at Cairo Airport	65	30

1968. First United Arab Airlines Boeing Flight, Cairo to London.

965	55m. Boeing 707 of United Arab Airlines	1·00	55

1969. Inauguration of Ilyushin Il-18 Aircraft by United Arab Airlines.

976	55m. Ilyushin Il-18 of United Arab Airlines	80	55

1970.

1059	80m. McDonnell Douglas F-4D Phantom II	1·10	75

1972. International Aerospace Education Conference, Cairo.

1148	30m. Glider	1·00	40

1973. Attack on Libyan Airliner over Sinai.

1197	110m. Boeing 727	4·25	1·40

1978. 75th Anniv of First Powered Flight.

1377	140m. Wright Type A	1·50	95

1982. 50th Anniv of Egyptair (state airline).
1478 23p. de Havilland DH.86B Dragon Express of Misr Airwork (left) and Boeing 737 of Egyptair........................ 2·10 1·40

1982.
1493 3p. Avro Type 618 Ten and Lockheed Martin (General Dynamics) F-16 Fighting Falcon........................ 50 15

1986. 18th Anniv of General Assembly of African Airlines Association.
1629 15p. Boeing 707........................ 85 40

1994. 50th Anniv of Signing of International Civil Aviation Agreement.
1929 80p. Emblem........................ 50 40

2005. Aircraft Training Programme.
2418 30p. Nanchang K-8........................ 10 10
2419 150p. Karakorum 8........................ 30 20

2007. 75th Anniv of Egyptair Airlines.
2466 30p. de Havilland DH.86 and emblem...... 25 15
2467 150p. Boeing 767, de Havilland DH.86 and emblem........................ 75 45

2007. 75th Anniv of National Air Force.
2474* 30p. Lockheed Martin F-16 Fighting Falcon and de Havilland DH.82 Tiger Moth........................ 25 15

EGYPTIAN OCCUPATION OF PALESTINE

Western Asia

1000 milliemes = 100 piastres = 1 pound

1948. Nos. 322/33 of Egypt overprinted **PALESTINE** in English and Arabic.
20* 2m. Douglas DC-3 Dakota of R.A.F. Transport Command........................ 25 25

21* 3m. Douglas DC-3 Dakota of R.A.F. Transport Command........................ 25 25
22* 5m. Douglas DC-3 Dakota of R.A.F. Transport Command........................ 25 25
23* 7m. Douglas DC-3 Dakota of R.A.F. Transport Command........................ 45 45
24* 8m. Douglas DC-3 Dakota of R.A.F. Transport Command........................ 45 45
25* 10m. Douglas DC-3 Dakota of R.A.F. Transport Command........................ 55 55
26* 20m. Douglas DC-3 Dakota of R.A.F. Transport Command........................ 90 90
27* 30m. Douglas DC-3 Dakota of R.A.F. Transport Command........................ 1·80 1·80
28* 40m. Douglas DC-3 Dakota of R.A.F. Transport Command........................ 1·40 1·40
29* 50m. Douglas DC-3 Dakota of R.A.F. Transport Command........................ 1·80 1·80
30* 100m. Douglas DC-3 Dakota of R.A.F. Transport Command........................ 3·50 3·50
31* 200m. Douglas DC-3 Dakota of R.A.F. Transport Command........................ 9·00 9·00

1953. Nos. 20/31 with three bars overprinted on king's portrait.
51* 2m. Douglas DC-3 Dakota of R.A.F. Transport Command........................ 45 45
52* 3m. Douglas DC-3 Dakota of R.A.F. Transport Command........................ 45 45
53* 5m. Douglas DC-3 Dakota of R.A.F. Transport Command........................ 8·50 9·50
54* 7m. Douglas DC-3 Dakota of R.A.F. Transport Command........................ 45 65
55* 8m. Douglas DC-3 Dakota of R.A.F. Transport Command........................ 1·40 1·10
56* 10m. Douglas DC-3 Dakota of R.A.F. Transport Command........................ 1·40 1·10
57* 20m. Douglas DC-3 Dakota of R.A.F. Transport Command........................ 1·40 1·10
58* 30m. Douglas DC-3 Dakota of R.A.F. Transport Command........................ 1·40 1·10
59* 40m. Douglas DC-3 Dakota of R.A.F. Transport Command........................ 4·00 4·00
60* 50m. Douglas DC-3 Dakota of R.A.F. Transport Command........................ 13·50 13·50
61* 100m. Douglas DC-3 Dakota of R.A.F. Transport Command........................ 49·00 55·00
62* 200m. Douglas DC-3 Dakota of R.A.F. Transport Command........................ 5·50 5·50

1953. Nos. 480/2, 485 and 489/90 of Egypt additionally overprinted **PALESTINE** in English and Arabic.
63* 2m. Douglas DC-3 Dakota of R.A.F. Transport Command........................ 45 45
64* 3m. Douglas DC-3 Dakota of R.A.F. Transport Command........................ 9·00 9·00
65* 5m. Douglas DC-3 Dakota of R.A.F. Transport Command........................ 1·70 1·90
66* 10m. Douglas DC-3 Dakota of R.A.F. Transport Command........................ 16·00 17·00
67* 50m. Douglas DC-3 Dakota of R.A.F. Transport Command........................ 4·50 6·00
68* 100m. Douglas DC-3 Dakota of R.A.F. Transport Command........................ 32·00 32·00

1955. Nos. 433/4 of Egypt overprinted **PALESTINE** in English and Arabic.
86a* 5m. Douglas DC-3 Dakota of R.A.F. Transport Command........................ 3·25 4·25
86b* 15m. Douglas DC-3 Dakota of R.A.F. Transport Command........................ 4·00 5·00

1963. As Nos. 758 and 760/2 of Egypt, but additionally inscribed "PALESTINE" in English and Arabic.
133 50m. Airplane........................ 70 70
134 80m. Douglas DC-6B........................ 1·10 1·10
135 115m. Airplane........................ 1·80 1·80
136 140m. Airplane........................ 2·30 2·30
133/136 Set of 4........................ 5·25 5·25

EL SALVADOR

Central America

100 centavos = 1 colon

1930.
775 15c. Curtiss JN-4 "Jenny"........................ 35 15
776 20c. Curtiss JN-4 "Jenny"........................ 35 15
777 25c. Curtiss JN-4 "Jenny"........................ 35 15
778 40c. Curtiss JN-4 "Jenny"........................ 35 15
775/778 Set of 4........................ 1·30 55

1931. No. 759 overprinted with Curtiss JN-4 "Jenny" biplane.
787 1col. Arms........................ 4·25 2·75

1933.
810 15c. Ford "Tin Goose"........................ 1·90 1·70
811 20c. Ford "Tin Goose"........................ 2·75 2·40
812 25c. Ford "Tin Goose"........................ 2·75 2·40
813 40c. Ford "Tin Goose"........................ 2·75 2·40
814 1col. Ford "Tin Goose"........................ 2·75 2·40
810/814 Set of 5........................ 11·50 10·00

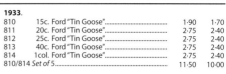

1934.
823 25c. Biplane........................ 55 25
824 30c. Biplane........................ 85 40
825 1col. Biplane........................ 2·20 90
823/825 Set of 3........................ 3·25 1·40

1935.
831* 15c. Airplane........................ 4·25 4·00
832* 25c. Airplane........................ 4·25 4·00
833* 30c. Airplane........................ 4·00 3·00
834* 55c. Airplane........................ 23·00 15·00
835* 1col. Airplane........................ 15·00 14·00

1935. Nos. 831/5 overprinted **HABILITADO**.
841* 15c. Airplane........................ 4·25 2·40
842* 25c. Airplane........................ 4·25 2·40
843* 30c. Airplane........................ 4·25 2·40
844* 55c. Airplane........................ 31·00 24·00
845* 1col. Airplane........................ 14·00 10·00

1935.
858* 10c. Fokker Super Universal........................ 1·10 90
859* 15c. Fokker Super Universal........................ 1·10 90
860* 20c. Fokker Super Universal........................ 1·10 90
861* 25c. Fokker Super Universal........................ 1·10 90
862* 30c. Fokker Super Universal........................ 1·10 90

1937. No. 844 surcharged **30** in frame.
873 30c. on 55c. Airplane........................ 2·75 1·00

1937.
874 15c. Douglas DC-3........................ 30 20
875 20c. Douglas DC-3........................ 30 20
876 25c. Douglas DC-3........................ 30 20
877 30c. Douglas DC-3........................ 25 10
878 40c. Douglas DC-3........................ 30 40
879 1col. Douglas DC-3........................ 1·30 40
880 5col. Douglas DC-3........................ 4·25 3·00
874/880 Set of 7........................ 6·25 4·00

1938.
887* 30c. Douglas DC-3........................ 85 65

1939.

901	15c. Douglas DC-3	40	25
902	30c. Douglas DC-3	40	25
903	40c. Douglas DC-3	55	40
901/903 *Set of 3*		1·20	80

1940.

910	30c. Douglas DC-3	40	25
911	80c. Douglas DC-3	75	50

1943. Nos. 901/3 surcharged in figures 10 mm high.

925	15 on 15c. Douglas DC-3	40	25
926	20 on 30c. Douglas DC-3	55	40
927	25 on 40c. Douglas DC-3	1·00	65
925/927 *Set of 3*		1·80	1·20

1944. Nos. 901/3 surcharged in figures 6 mm high.

928	15 on 15c. Douglas DC-3	40	25
929	20 on 30c. Douglas DC-3	55	40
930	25 on 40c. Douglas DC-3	1·10	40
928/930 *Set of 3*		1·80	95

1970.

1325*	20c. Republic P-47 Thunderbolt	25	15

1981. 50th Anniv of TACA (National Airline).

1683	15c. Boeing 737 of TACA at El Salvador Airport	15	10
1684	25c. Boeing 737 of TACA at El Salvador Airport	25	15
1685	75c. Boeing 737 of TACA at El Salvador Airport	60	40
1683/1685 *Set of 3*		90	60

1983. 50th Anniv of Air Force.

1780*	10c. Juan Ramon Munes and biplane	15	10
1782*	10c. Belisario Salazar and biplane	15	10

1984.

1849*	70c. El Salvador International Airport	55	30

1989.

2056*	20c. Douglas DC-9	20	15

1998. Modernisation of El Salvador International Airport.

2402	10col. El Salvador International Airport	4·50	3·00

1998. 75th Anniv of El Salvador Air Force.

2429	1col.50 Douglas C-47 T	70	55
2430	1col.50 TH 300 helicopter	70	55
2431	1col.50 Bell UH-1H Iroquois	70	55
2432	1col.50 Cessna A-37B Dragonfly	70	55
2429/2432 *Set of 4*		2·50	2·00

2004. Centenary of Powered Flight.

2665	1col.50 Wilbur and Orville Wright and Flyer .	70	45
2666	1col.50 Alberto Santos-Dumont and *14 bis*...	70	45
2667	1col.50 Louis Bleriot and Bleriot XI	70	45
2668	1col.50 Glen Curtiss and Curtiss JN-4D Jenny	70	45
2669	1col.50 Hugo Junkers and Junkers J1	70	45
2670	4col. Charles Lindbergh and Ryan NYP Special *Spirit of St Louis*	2·20	1·60
2671	4col. Amelia Earhart and Lockheed Electra 10*1	2·20	1·60
2672	4col. Captain Charles 'Chuck' Yeager & Bell X-1	2·20	1·60
2673	4col. Robert White and North American X-15	2·20	1·60
2674	4col. Dick Rutan, Jeanna Yeager and Rutan Voyager	2·20	1·60
2665/2674 *Set of 10*		13·00	9·25

No. 2671 is wrongly inscribed Lockheed Vega. No. 2673 is wrongly inscribed Withe.

2006. 75th Anniv of TACA.

2735	5col. Stinson SM-1 Detroiter	2·30	2·10
2736	5col. Airbus Industries Airbus A-319	2·30	2·10

EQUATORIAL GUINEA

West Africa

100 centimos = 1 ekuele (plural: bikuele)

APPENDIX

The following stamps have either been issued in excess of postal needs or have not been made available to the public in reasonable quantities at face value. Miniature sheets, imperforate stamps, etc are excluded from this section.

1974.

Centenary of U.P.U. (1st issue). Postage 1e.50 (airship). Air 30c. (biplane).

1976.

Apollo-Soyuz Project, Concorde, and Telephone Centenary. 5e., 50e.

1977.

World War Air Aces. Postage 5c., 10c., 15c., 20c., 25c., 30c., 35c., 40c., 45c., 50c., 55c., 60c., 1e., 2e. Air 10e., 70e.

1979.

Wright Brothers. 1e., 3e., 5e., 8e., 15e., 60e., 100e.

ERITREA

North-east Africa

100 centesimi = 1 lira

1934.

222*	25c. Caproni Ca 101	2·75	9·00
223*	50c. Caproni Ca 101	2·75	7·25
224*	75c. Caproni Ca 101	2·75	7·25
225*	80c. Savoia Marchetti S-66 flying boat	2·75	9·00
226*	1l. Savoia Marchetti S-66 flying boat	2·75	9·75
227*	2l. Savoia Marchetti S-66 flying boat	2·75	16·00

1934. Rome-Mogadiscio Flight.

228	25c. +10c. Caproni Ca 101	3·25	5·00
229	50c. +10c. Caproni Ca 101	3·25	5·00
230	75c. +15c. Caproni Ca 101	3·25	5·00
231	80c. +15c. Caproni Ca 101	3·25	5·00
232	1l. +20c. Caproni Ca 101	3·25	5·00
233	2l. +20c. Caproni Ca 101	3·25	5·00
234	3l. +25c. Caproni Ca 101	16·00	40·00
235	5l. +25c. Caproni Ca 101	16·00	40·00
236	10l. +30c. Caproni Ca 101	16·00	40·00
237	25l. +2l. Caproni Ca 101	16·00	40·00
228/237 *Set of 10*		75·00	£170

1936.

238	25c. Macchi Castoldi MC-94 flying boat ...	85	2·25
239	50c. Caproni Ca 101	50	10
240	60c. Savoia Marchetti S-74	1·40	5·25
241	75c. Savoia Marchetti S-73	1·25	1·00
242	1l. Caproni Ca 101	10	10
243	1l.50 Macchi Castoldi MC-94 flying boat ...	80	35
244	2l. Caproni Ca 101	1·00	2·00
245	3l. Caproni Ca 101	18·00	8·75
246	5l. Savoia Marchetti S-74	6·50	4·00
247	10l. Savoia Marchetti S-73	16·00	8·75
238/247 *Set of 10*		42·00	29·00

OFFICIAL AIR STAMP

1934. As No. 237, but colour changed, overprinted with crown and **SERVIZIO DI STATO**.

O238	25l. +2l. Caproni Ca 101	£1600

ESTONIA

North-eastern Europe

100 penni = 1 Estonian mark

1920. Imperforate.

15	5m. L.V.G. Schneider biplane	5·00	6·00

1923. No. 15 overprinted **1923** or surcharged **15 Marka** also.

44	5m. L.V.G. Schneider biplane	10·50	34·00
45	15m. on 5m. L.V.G. Schneider biplane	16·00	30·00

1923. No. 15 surcharged **1923** and value across pairs of stamps.

46	10m. on 5m. L.V.G. Schneider biplane	13·00	38·00
47	20m. on 5m. L.V.G. Schneider biplane	25·00	37·00
48	45m. on 5m. L.V.G. Schneider biplane	90·00	£200
46/48 *Set of 3*		£120	£250

Prices are for unsevered pairs.

1924. Perforated or imperforate.

51B	5m. Sablatnig PIII	1·40	4·25
52B	10m. Sablatnig PIII	1·40	4·25
53B	15m. Junkers F-13 with floats	1·40	8·50
54B	20m. Junkers F-13 with wheels	1·40	4·25
55B	45m. Junkers F-13 with skis	1·40	17·00
51B/55B Set of 5		6·25	34·00

2002.

422	6k. Oppelennuk PTO-4	85	80

ETHIOPIA

East Africa

1929. 16 mehaleks = 1 thaler

1936. 100 centimes = 1 thaler

1936. 100 centisimi = 1 lira

1946. 100 cents = 1 Ethiopian dollar

1976. 100 cents = 1 birr

1929. Arrival of the First Airplane of the Ethiopian Government. Overprinted with Amharic text and airplane.

238	⅛m. Emperor Haile Selassie	1·40	1·90
239	¼m. Empress Zauditu	1·40	1·90
240	½m. Emperor Haile Selassie	1·50	2·00
241	1m. Empress Zauditu	1·50	2·00
242	2m. Emperor Haile Selassie	1·50	2·00
243	4m. Empress Zauditu	1·50	2·00
244	8m. Emperor Haile Selassie	1·50	2·00
245	1t. Empress Zauditu	2·00	3·25
246	2t. Emperor Haile Selassie	3·25	4·25
247	3t. Empress Zauditu	3·25	4·25
238/247 Set of 10		17·00	23·00

1931.

296	1g. Potez 25A2	30	50
297	2g. Potez 25A2	30	50
298	4g. Potez 25A2	45	65
299	8g. Potez 25A2	1·00	1·10
300	1t. Potez 25A2	1·60	1·60
301	2t. Potez 25A2	4·00	5·25
302	3t. Potez 25A2	6·00	7·25
296/302 Set of 7		12·50	15·00

1947.

363*	$1 Douglas DC-3	10·00	12·00
364*	$2 Douglas DC-3	20·00	23·00

1947.

378*	8c. Douglas DC-3	15	10
379*	10c. Douglas DC-3	25	10
379a*	25c. Douglas DC-3	50	20
380*	30c. Douglas DC-3	75	25
380a*	35c. Douglas DC-3	1·00	40
380b*	65c. Douglas DC-3	75	35
381*	70c. Douglas DC-3	1·75	40
382*	$1 Douglas DC-3	2·75	65
383*	$3 Douglas DC-3	8·25	4·00
384*	$5 Douglas DC-3	13·00	6·50
385*	$10 Douglas DC-3	24·00	16·00

1955. 10th Anniv of Ethiopian Airlines.

462	10c. Convair CV 240 of Ethiopian Airlines	75	25
463	15c. Convair CV 240 of Ethiopian Airlines	1·10	85
464	20c. Convair CV 240 of Ethiopian Airlines	1·50	90
462/464 Set of 3		3·00	1·80

1959. 30th Anniv of Airmail Service in Ethiopia. Nos. 378/81 overprinted **30th Airmail Ann. 1929–1959.**

491	8c. Douglas DC-3	40	25
492	10c. Douglas DC-3	50	40
493	25c. Douglas DC-3	65	50
494	30c. Douglas DC-3	1·10	65
495	35c. Douglas DC-3	1·50	1·00
496	65c. Douglas DC-3	2·00	1·10
497	70c. Douglas DC-3	2·25	1·25
491/497 Set of 7		7·50	4·75

1965.

626*	$5 Boeing 720B of Ethiopian Airlines	9·00	4·25

1971. 25th Anniv of Ethiopian Airlines.

775*	5c. Tail of Boeing 707 of Ethiopian Airlines	10	10
777*	20c. Nose of Boeing 707 and control tower	40	40

1976.

1012*	5c. Cessna 170A dropping relief supplies	10	10

1986. 40th Anniv of Ethiopian Airlines.

1353*	10c. Nose of Boeing 767	15	10
1354*	20c. Douglas DC-3	20	10
1357*	1b. Boeing 727 of Ethiopian Airlines	1·60	1·60

1987.

1387*	1b. Boeing 727 of Ethiopian Airlines at Bahir Dar Airport	1·50	1·50

1988.

1404*	10c. Mikoyan Gurevich MiG-23	20	10
1407*	55c. Mikoyan Gurevich MiG-21	40	45

2006. 60th Anniv of Ethiopian Airlines.

1950	15c. Douglas C-47A Dakota III, 1946	10	10
1951	40c. Douglas DC-6B Super Cloudmaster, 1958	10	10
1952	45c. Boeing 720-060B, 1962	10	10
1953	1b. Boeing 767-300ER, 2003	15	10
1954	2b. Boeing 787 Dreamliner, 2009	25	15
1950/1954 Set of 5		65	50

FALKLAND ISLANDS

South Atlantic

1949. 12 pence = 1 shilling

20 shillings = 1 pound

1971. 100 pence = 1 pound

1949. As Nos. 114/15 of Antigua.

168*	1d. Airplane	1·75	1·00
169*	3d. Jet-powered Vickers Viking	5·00	2·75

1952.

177*	4d. Auster Autocrat VP-FAB	11·00	1·50

1969. 21st Anniv of Government Air Service.

246*	2d. de Havilland Canada DHC-2 Beaver seaplane VP-FAE	50	30
247*	6d. Noorduyn Norseman V seaplane	50	35
248*	1s. Auster Autocrat VP-FAA	50	35

1974.

302*	8p. Farman H.F.III biplane (in air) and Aeronautical Syndicate Valkyrie A	30	55
303*	16p. Biplane being launched by catapult from the liner *Ile de France*	35	75

1978. 26th Anniv of First Direct Flight, Southampton-Port Stanley.

346	11p. Short Hythe flying boat	3·25	2·50
347	33p. Short Hythe flying boat	3·75	3·00

1979. Opening of Port Stanley Airport.

360	3p. Britten-Norman BN-2 Islander	40	20
361	11p. Fokker F.27 Friendship	70	60
362	15p. Fokker F.28 Fellowship	75	60
363	25p. Britten-Norman BN-2 Islander (left), Fokker F.27 Friendship (top), Fokker F.28 Fellowship (right) and Cessna 172 Skyhawk	1·25	80
360/363 *Set of 4*		2·75	2·00

1979.

368*	3p. de Havilland Canada DHC-2 Beaver seaplane	20	20

1983.

456*	17p. Hawker Siddeley Harrier	35	70
457*	50p. Westland Sea King helicopter, and Hawker Siddeley Sea Harriers on aircraft carrier H.M.S. *Hermes*	75	1·40

1983. Bicentenary of Manned Flight.

463	5p. Britten-Norman BN-2 Islander VP-FAY of the Falkland Islands Government Air Service	15	20
464	13p. de Havilland Canada DHC-2 Beaver seaplane VP-FAE	25	35
465	17p. Noorduyn Norseman V seaplane VP-FAD	30	40
466	50p. Auster Autocrat VP-FAA	70	1·00
463/466 *Set of 4*		1·30	1·80

1984.

488	22p. Lockheed C-130 Hercules	55	75

1985. Opening of Mount Pleasant Airport.

502*	22p. Mount Pleasant Airport under construction	80	75
503*	27p. Mount Pleasant Airport	1·00	80
504*	54p. Lockheed L-1011 TriStar 500	1·25	1·75

1987.

542*	58p. Lockheed L-1011 TriStar at Mount Pleasant Airport	2·75	4·00

1990. Presentation Spitfires.

601	12p. Supermarine Spitfire Mk I *Falkland Islands I* of 92 Squadron, R.A.F.	65	45
602	26p. Supermarine Spitfire Mk I *Falkland Islands VII* of 611 Squadron, R.A.F.	1·25	80
603	31p. Supermarine Spitfire Mk I *Falkland Islands I* of 92 Squadron, R.A.F	1·25	1·10
604	62p. Supermarine Spitfires of 92 Squadron, R. A. F.	1·75	2·50
601/604 *Set of 4*		4·50	4·25
MS605 £1 Supermarine Spitfire Mk I *Falkland Islands I* of 92 Squadron, R.A.F.		4·00	2·50

1993. 75th Anniv of Royal Air Force.

676	15p. Avro Vulcan B.1A	75	1·00
677	15p. Lockheed C-130K Hercules of the R. A. F.	75	1·00
678	15p. Boeing-Vertol CH-47 Chinook helicopter of the R.A.F.	75	1·00
679	15p. Lockheed L-1011 TriStar 500 of the R. A. F.	75	1·00
676/679 *Set of 4*		2·75	3·50
MS680 36p. Hawker Siddeley Andover CC.2 of the Queen's Flight; 36p. Westland Wessex HC.2 helicopter; 36p. Panavia Tornado F Mk 3; 36p. McDonnell Douglas F-4M Phantom II of the R. A. F.		3·75	4·75

1993.

684*	72p. Britten-Norman BN-2 Islander of the Falkland Islands Government Air Service	2·25	5·00

1994.

719*	17p. Lockheed L-1011 TriStar	85	70
721*	40p. Pilatus Britten-Norman BN-2 Islander	2·00	2·00

1996.

760*	73p. Westland Sea King	4·00	4·50

1996.

767*	40p. Noorduyn Norseman V	1·75	1·50
769*	76p. de Havilland Canada DHC-2 Beaver	2·75	2·75

1998. 50th Anniv of Falkland Islands Government Air Service.

823	17p. Auster J-5 Autocar	2·75	60
824	£1 de Havilland Canada DHC-2 Beaver	6·25	6·50

1999. First Flight over Falkland Islands, 1931.

841*	40p. CAMS 37	2·75	2·75
MS842* £1 CAMS 37		6·50	6·50

2002.

930*	45p. BAe Harrier	2·00	2·25
931*	45p. Lockheed L-1011 TriStar	2·00	2·25

2002.

945*	22p. Westland Sea King	2·50	2·00

2005.

1015*	24p. Supermarine Walrus	1·40	1·60
1016*	24p. Supermarine Spitfire X4616 (presented to No 92 Squadron, 1940)	1·40	1·60

2007.
MS1076 60p. Avro Type 698 Vulcan prototype VX770; 60p. Avro Type 698 Vulcan XM 597 on 'Black Buck' raid; 60p. Avro Type 698 Vulcan XM 607 'Black Buck 1'; 60p. Avro Type 689 Vulcan XH 558 (Vulcan to the Sky project) .... 7·75 7·75

2008.
1096	1p.	Taylorcraft Auster Mk5	10	10
1097	2p.	Boeing 747-300	15	15
1098	5p.	de Havilland Canada DHC-6 Twin Otter	20	20
1099	10p.	Lockheed C-130 Hercules	35	35
1100	27p.	de Havilland Canada DHC-2 Beaver..	1·50	1·50
1101	55p.	Airbus A320	1·90	1·90
1102	65p.	Lockheed L-1011–385-3 TriStar C2..	2·25	2·50
1103	90p.	Avro Type 698 Vulcan B2	3·25	3·25
1104	£1	Britten-Norman BN-2 Islander	3·25	3·25
1105	£2	Panavia Tornado F.3	5·50	6·50
1106	£3	de Havilland Canada DHC-7-110 Dash 7	7·50	8·00
1107	£5	BAe Sea Harrier	12·00	13·00
1096/1107	*Set of 12*		34·00	37·00

MS1108 10p. Lockheed C-130 Hercules; 65p. Lockheed L-1011–385-3 TriStar C2; 90p. Avro Type 698 Vulcan B2; £2 Panavia Tornado F.3.......... 9·00 10·00

FALKLAND ISLANDS DEPENDENCIES

South Atlantic
1949. 12 pence = 1 shilling
20 shillings = 1 pound
1971. 100 pence = 1 pound

1949. As Nos. 114/15 of Antigua.
G21*	1d.	Airplane	1·00	2·50
G22*	2d.	Jet-powered Vickers Viking	5·00	3·75

1983. Bicentenary of Manned Flight.
113	5p.	Westland Whirlwind helicopter	25	35
114	13p.	Westland AS-1 Wasp helicopter	35	60
115	17p.	Vickers Supermarine Walrus II flying boat	35	60
116	50p.	Auster Autocrat seaplane	70	1·25
113/116	*Set of 4*		1·50	2·50

FAROE ISLANDS

North Atlantic
100 ore = 1 krone

1985. Aircraft.
122	300ore.	Douglas DC-3 of Faroe Airways	2·75	2·50
123	300ore.	Fokker F.27 Friendship of Flugfelag Islands (front view)	2·75	2·50
124	300ore.	Boeing 737 Special of Maersk Air (nose at left)	2·75	2·50
125	300ore.	Beech 50 Twin Bonanza LM-IKB of Bjorum Fly (nose at right)	2·75	2·50
126	300ore.	Bell 212 helicopter Snipan	2·75	2·50
123/126	*Set of 5*		12·50	11·50

FERNANDO POO

Off West Africa
100 centimos = 1 peseta

1962.
252*	35c.	Stylised airliner	65	90

FEZZAN

North Africa
100 centimes = 1 franc

1948.
38	100f.	Douglas C-47B Skytrain at Fezzan Airfield	2·50	18·00
39	200f.	Airplane	5·00	25·00

1951.
71*	100f.	Twin-engine airliner	14·00	32·00
72*	200f.	Three-engine airliner	16·00	38·00

FIJI

South Pacific
1949. 12 pence = 1 shilling
20 shillings = 1 pound
1969. 100 cents = 1 dollar

1949. As Nos. 114/15 of Antigua.
272*	2d.	Airplane	30	75
273*	3d.	Jet-powered Vickers Viking	2·00	3·75

1954.
320*	2s.6d.	Hawker Siddeley Comet 4 (right) and Boeing 707 at Nadi Airport	2·75	1·00

1964. 25th Anniv of First Fiji-Tonga Airmail Service.
338	3d.	Short S.30 modified "G" Class flying boat ZK-AMA *Aotearoa* of Tasman Empire Airways	40	10
339	6d.	de Havilland DH.114 Heron 2 VQ-FAB of Fiji Airways and Short S.30 modified "G" Class flying boat	70	1·00
340	1s.	Short S.30 modified "G" Class flying boat ZK-AMA *Aotearoa* of Tasman Empire Airways	70	1·00
338/340	*Set of 3*		1·60	1·90

1968. 40th Anniv of Kingsford Smith's Pacific Flight via Fiji.
367	2d.	Simmonds Spartan seaplane VQ-FAA	15	10
368	6d.	Hawker Siddeley H.S.748 VQ-FAL of Fiji Airways	15	10
369	1s.	Fokker F.VIIa/3m *Southern Cross*	20	10
370	2s.	Lockheed Model 8D Altair VH-USB *Lady Southern Cross*	30	15
367/370	*Set of 4*		70	40

1969.
415*	8c.	Short S.25 Sunderland flying boat	15	10

1974.
498*	50c.	B.A.C. One Eleven 200/400 of Air Pacific	35	2·50

1976. 25th Anniv of Air Services.
532	4c.	de Havilland Australia DHA.3 Drover 1 VQ-FAP of Fiji Airways	40	20
533	15c.	B.A.C. One Eleven 200/400 DQ-FBO of Air Pacific at Nadi Airport	75	1·50
534	25c.	Hawker Siddeley H.S.748 VQ-FBN of Fiji Airways	80	1·50
535	30c.	Britten-Norman BN-2A Mk III "long nose" Trislander DD-FCC of Air Pacific	90	3·50
532/535	*Set of 4*		2·50	6·00

1978. Aviation Anniversaries.
552	4c.	Fokker F.VIIa/3m *Southern Cross* (incorrectly inscribed "Fokker FVIIB-3M")	30	10
553	15c.	Fokker F.VIIa/3m *Southern Cross* (incorrectly inscribed "Fokker FVIIB-3M")	50	30
554	25c.	Wright *Flyer I*	60	60
555	30c.	Bristol F28 "Brisfit"	60	1·25
552/555	*Set of 4*		1·80	2·00

1981. World War II Aircraft.
624	6c.	Bell P-39 Airacobra fighters	1·10	10
625	18c.	Consolidated PBY-5 Catalina flying boat	1·90	40
626	35c.	Curtiss P-40E Warhawk fighters of the U.S. Army Air Corps	2·50	95
627	60c.	Short Singapore III flying boat	3·00	6·00
624/627	*Set of 4*		7·75	6·75

1983. Bicentenary of Manned Flight.
659*	8c.	Montgolfier balloon (first manned free flight, 1783)	25	10
660*	20c.	Wright *Flyer I*	35	30
661*	25c.	Douglas Super DC-3	40	40
662*	40c.	de Havilland DH.106 Comet 1	60	60
663*	50c.	Boeing 747	70	70

1984.
686*	40c.	Boeing 737 of Air Pacific	1·75	1·25

1991. 40th Anniv of Air Pacific.
839	54c.	de Havilland DH.89 Dragon Rapide of Fiji Airways	1·75	1·00
840	75c.	Douglas DC-3 DQ-FBF of Air Pacific..	2·25	2·25
841	96c.	Avions de Transport Régional ATR 42 DQ-FEP of Air Pacific	2·50	3·25
842	$1.40	Boeing 767 DQ-FDM of Air Pacific.....	3·50	5·00
839/842	*Set of 4*		9·00	10·50

1993. 75th Anniv of Royal Air Force.
873	59c. Gloster Gauntlet II, 1928	1·40	75
874	77c. Armstrong Whitworth Whitley Mk V, 1939	1·60	1·40
875	83c. Bristol F2B "Brisfit", 1917	1·75	1·60
876	$2 Hawker Tempest Mk V, 1944	3·00	4·00
873/876	*Set of 4*	7·00	7·00
MS877	$1 Vickers Vildebeest III, 1933; $1 Handley Page Hampden, 1936; $1 Vickers FB-27 Vimy, 1919; $1 British Aerospace Hawk T.1, 1973	6·50	6·50

1994. No. **MS**877 overprinted with Hong Kong 94 logo on each stamp.
MS888*	$1 Vickers Vildebeest III 1933; $1 Handley Page Hampden, 1936; $1 Vickers FB-27 Vimy, 1919; $1 British Aerospace Hawk T.1, 1973	4·50	6·00

1995.
907*	13c. Mitsubishi A6M Zero-Sen (crashed)	60	20
908*	63c. Aeronica L-3 Grasshopper	1·75	1·50

1995.
933*	$2 Boeing 747 *Island of Viti Levu*	3·25	5·00

1996. 50th Anniv of Nadi International Airport.
965	31c. Supermarine Channel Mk II Flying Boat GNZA1 *Barrie Round* (first seaplane in Fiji, 1921)	65	30
966	44c. Nadi airport in 1946	80	50
967	63c. Arrival of Boeing 707, 1959	1·25	1·00
968	87c. Airport entrance	1·40	1·50
969	$1 Control Tower	1·60	1·75
970	$2 Diagram of Global Positioning System	2·75	5·00
965/970	*Set of 6*	7·50	9·00

1998. 80th Anniv of the Royal Air Force.
1016	44c. Airship R-34	70	30
1017	63c. Handley Page H.P.50 Heyford	1·00	60
1018	87c. Supermarine Swift FR.5	1·40	1·00
1019	£2 Westland Whirlwind	2·25	3·00
1016/1019	*Set of 4*	4·75	4·50
MS1020	$1 Sopwith Dolphin; $1 Avro 504K; $1 Vickers Type 284 Warwick; $1 Short SC.5 Belfast	3·75	4·50

No. 1019, Westland also produced a helicopter called Whirlwind.

2001. 50th Anniv of Air Pacific.
1149	89c. de Havilland Australia DHA.3 Drover	1·40	1·60
1150	96c. Hawker Siddeley (BAe/Avro) 748	1·60	1·75
1151	$1 Douglas DC-10	1·60	1·75
1152	$2 Boeing 747-200	2·00	2·25
1149/1152	*Set of 4*	6·00	6·50

2005.
1273*	83c. Yokosuka E14Y Glen	1·00	1·00
1279*	83c. Avro Type 683 Lancaster (Dambusters raid)	1·00	1·00

FINLAND

Northern Europe

100 pennia = 1 markka

1938.
328*	2m. Junkers Ju 52/3m of Aero O/Y	1·80	90

1944.
395*	4m.50 +1m. Airplane	65	3·50

1944. 20th Anniv of Air Mail Service.
397	3m.50 Douglas DC-2	45	90

1950.
488	300m. Douglas DC-6 (face value "300 mk").	11·00	5·50

1958. As No. 488, but face value shown as "300".
585	300m. Douglas DC-6	33·00	1·10

1958.
593	34m. Convair CV 340 OH-LRD of Finnair	90	80
594	45m. Convair CV 340 OH-LRD of Finnair	1·80	1·70

1959. No. 593 surcharged **45**.
600	45m. on 34m. Convair CV 340 OH-LRD of Finnair	1·80	3·75

1962.
646	30m. Hunting P. 66 Pembroke	90	75

1963. As Nos. 585 and 593/4, but inscribed in revalued currency.
678*	45p. Convair CV 340 OH-LRD of Finnair	1·30	35
678a*	57p. Convair CV 340 OH-LRD of Finnair	2·00	1·00
679*	3m. Douglas DC-6 (face value "3,00")	18·00	55

1963. 40 Years of Finnish Civil Aviation.
688	35p. Convair CV 440 Metropolitan of Finnair	70	65
689	40p. Sud Aviation SE 210 Caravelle of Finnair 1966	70	50
714*	35p. +5p. Sud Aviation SE 3130 Alouette II helicopter	70	1·10

1966.
714*	35p. +5p. Sud Aviation SE 3130 Alouette II helicopter	70	1·10

1969.
761	25p. Douglas DC-8-62F over Helsinki Airport	90	90

1973. 50th Anniv of Finnair (airline) and Regular Air Services in Finland.
846	60p. Douglas DC-10-30 of Finnair	90	40

1976. 15th World Gliding Championship, Rayskala.
891	80p. Glider	80	35

1987.
1117*	2m.30 Douglas DC-10	85	75

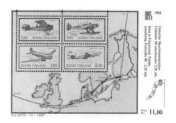

1988.
1139*	1m.80 Tail and fuselage of airplane	70	30
1140*	1m.80 Nose and wing of airplane	70	30

1988.
MS1152	1m.80 Breguet 14 biplane with skis; 1m.80 Junkers F-13; 1m.80 Douglas DC-3; 2m.40 Douglas DC-10.30 (sold at 11m.)	10·50	10·00

2003. Centenary of Powered Flight and 80th Anniv of Finnair.
1700	65c. Aerospatiale Super Caravelle	1·20	90
1701	65c. Airbus Industries Airbus A320	1·20	90
1702	65c. Junkers Ju52/3m	1·20	90
1703	65c. Douglas DC-3	1·20	90
1700/1703	*Set of 4*	4·25	3·25

2008.
MS1897* 75c. Airplane towing heart (other stamps
in the miniature sheet do not show aircraft)......... 12·00   11·00

FRANCE

Western Europe
1927. 100 centimes = 1 franc
2002. 100 cents = 1 euro

1927. First International Display of Aviation and Naviagation,
Marseilles. Overprinted with Bleriot XI airplane and **Poste
Aerienne.**
455   2f. Ornamental design....................... £160   £160
456   5f. Ornamental design....................... £160   £160

1927.
458   90c. Lindbergh's Ryan NYP Special *Spirit
          of St. Louis*..............................
                                                    1·10   1·00
459   1f.50 Lindbergh's Ryan NYP Special *Spirit
          of St. Louis*..............................
                                                    3·50   1·10

1930.
483   1f.50 Farman F.190 (red).................... 20·00   2·30
484   1f.50 Farman F.190 (blue)................... 18·00   1·20

1934. 25th Anniv of Channel Flight.
523   2f.25 Bleriot XI............................. 18·00   5·25

1936.
534   85c. Caudron C-635 Simoun................. 2·50   1·60
535   1f.50 Caudron C-635 Simoun............... 8·25   3·75
536   2f.25 Caudron C-635 Simoun............... 17·00   5·25
537   2f.50 Caudron C-635 Simoun............... 28·00   6·50
538   3f. Caudron C-635 Simoun.................. 22·00   1·10
539   3f.50 Caudron C-635 Simoun............... 55·00   19·00
540   50f. Caudron C-635 Simoun................. £700   £275
534/540 *Set of 7*................................. £750   £275

1936.
541   50f. Caudron C-635 Simoun................. £550   £250

1936.
546   75c. Jean-Francois Pilatre de Rozier and
          Montgolfier balloon (first manned
          free flight, 1783)........................ 16·00   2·20

1936. 100th Flight between France and South America.
553   1f.50 Airplane.............................. 13·50   3·00
554   10f. Latecoere 300 flying boat.............. £250   £100

1938. Clement Ader (air pioneer) Commemoration.
612a   50f. Clement Ader and his *Avion III*...... 90·00   65·00

1940. No. 612a surcharged **20f.**
689*   20f. on 50f. Clement Ader and his *Avion
          III*...................................... 31·00   38·00

1942. Air Force Dependants Relief Fund.
742   1f.50 +3f.50 Potez 63-11 bombers............ 1·10   2·00

1946.
967   40f. Lockheed 14 Super Electra.............. 55   25
968   50f. Sud Ouest SO.30P Bretagne.............. 55   20
969   100f. Sud Ouest SO.95 Corse II.............. 7·75   65
970   200f. Sud Ouest SO.30P Bretagne............. 5·25   90
967/970 *Set of 4*................................. 12·50   1·80

1948. Airmen.
1026   40f. +10f. Clement Ader's *Avion III* and
          Douglas DB-7............................ 1·30   1·40
1024   50f. +30f. Antoine de Saint-Exupery and
          Douglas DB-7............................ 2·75   3·25
1025   100f. +70f. Jean Dagnaux and Douglas
          DB-7.................................... 3·25   3·75
1026/1025 *Set of 3*............................... 6·50   7·50

1954.
1194   100f. Dassault Mystere IVA................. 3·00   15
1195   200f. Nord 2501 Noratlas................... 10·50   20
1196   500f. Fouga CM-170 Magister................ £140   10·00
1197   1000f. Breguet Br 763 Provence............. £110   13·50
1194/1197 *Set of 4*.............................. £225   21·00

1955.
1245   12f. +3f. Balloon *Armand Barbes*, Paris,
          1870.................................... 4·50   4·25

1955. Maryse Bastie (airwoman) Commemoration.
1252   50f. Maryse Bastie and Caudron C-635
          Simoun F-ANXH........................... 7·50   4·25

1957.
1318   300f. Morane Saulnier MS-760 Paris I...... 5·50   2·75
1319   500f. Sud Aviation SE 210 Caravelle....... 28·00   3·00
1320   1000f. Sud Aviation SE 3130 Alouette II
          helicopter............................. 50·00   19·00
1318/1320 *Set of 3*.............................. 75·00   22·00

1957.
1327*   30f. Etienne Oehmichen and his
          helicopter No. 2, 1922................. 1·90   2·20

1959.
1416   20f. +5f. Douglas DC-3..................... 50   50

1959. Goujon and Rozanoff (test pilots) Commemoration.
1427   20f. C. Goujon, C. Rozanoff and jet
          airplane................................ 50   45

1960. As Nos. 1195, 1318/20 and new design, each inscribed in
revalued currency.
1457   2f. Nord 2501 Noratlas..................... 2·20   20
1457b   2f. Dassault Breguet Mystere Falcon...... 1·50   30
1458   3f. Morane Saulnier MS-760 Paris I........ 1·60   15
1459   5f. Sud Aviation SE 210 Caravelle......... 3·00   45
1460   10f. Sud Aviation SE 3130 Alouette II
          helicopter............................. 13·00   1·90
1457/1460 *Set of 5*.............................. 19·00   2·75

1960.
1501   15c. Morane Saulnier Type L............... 25   35

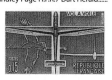

1961. Opening of New Installations at Orly Airport.
1514   50c. Orly Airport, Paris.................. 35   35

1961.
1550*   1f. Handley Page H.P.R.7 Dart Herald...... 50   15

1962. Civil and Sports Aviation.
1572   15c. Gliders.............................. 45   40
1573   20c. Jodel DR 1050 Ambassadeur and
          early airplane.......................... 45   40

1964. As No. 1416, but additionally inscribed "25E ANNIVERSAIRE".
1644   25c. Douglas DC-3......................... 20   15

1967. 40th Anniv of Trans-Atlantic Flight Attempt by Nungesser and Coli.

| 1750 | 40c. Charles Nungesser, Francois Coli and Levasseur PL-8 *L'Oiseau Blanc* | 40 | 25 |

1968. 50th Anniv of First Internal Air Mail Service.

| 1800 | 25c. Letord 4 Lorraine bomber | 40 | 35 |

1968.

| 1806 | 40c. Nord 2501 Noratlas and Sud Aviation SE 3130 Alouette II helicopter | 35 | 35 |

1969. First Flight of Concorde.

| 1823 | 1f. Concorde | 1·20 | 80 |

1969.

| 1838* | 45c. Pilot, mechanic and Yakovlev Yak-9 fighters of the Normandy-Niemen Squadron | 1·10 | 65 |

1970.

| 1856 | 45c. Sud Aviation SE 3130 Alouette II helicopter | 1·30 | 45 |

1970. Aviation Pioneers.

1890	5f. Didier Daurat, Raymond Vanier and Douglas DC-4	1·70	20
1891	10f. Helene Boucher, Maryse Hilsz, de Havilland DH.60G Gipsy Moth F-AJOE and Caudron monoplane	6·25	30
1892	15f. Paul Codos, Henri Guillaumet, Latecoere 521 flying boat *Lieutenant de Vaisseau Paris* and wreck of Potez 25A2	9·00	80
1893	20f. Jean Mermoz, Antoine de Saint-Exupery and Concorde	9·00	85
1890/1893 *Set of 4*		23·00	1·90

1971. Centenary of Paris Balloon Post.

| 1907 | 95c. Balloon *Ville d'Orleans*, Paris, 1870 | 70 | 60 |

1971.

| 1916* | 50c. +10c. Henri Farman and Farman Voisin *No. 1 bis* | 65 | 75 |

1972.

| 1953* | 50c. +10c. Louis Bleriot and Bleriot XI | 85 | 65 |

1973.

| 1991* | 50c. +10c. Alberto Santos-Dumont and his airships *Ballon No. 6, Ballon No. 14* and biplane *14 bis* | 85 | 95 |

1973.

| 1999* | 3f. Airbus Industrie A300B2-100 | 1·40 | 1·00 |

1974. Opening of Charles de Gaulle Airport, Roissy.

| 2032 | 60c. Concorde over Charles de Gaulle Airport | 35 | 35 |

1975. Development of Gazelle Helicopter.

| 2082 | 1f.30 Sud Aviation SA 341 Gazelle helicopter | 70 | 50 |

1976. Concorde's First Commercial Flight, Paris to Rio de Janeiro.

| 2101 | 1f.70 Concorde | 65 | 45 |

1976.

| 2106* | 2f.20 Concorde | 1·00 | 85 |

1977. 50th Anniv of North Atlantic Flights.

| 2194 | 1f.90 Lindbergh's Ryan NYP Special *Spirit of St. Louis* and Nungesser and Coli's Levasseur PL-8 *L'Oiseau Blanc* | 85 | 50 |

1978. 65th Anniv of First Airmail Flight, Villacoublay to Pauillac.

| 2280 | 1f.50 Morane Saulnier Type H | 1·00 | 35 |

1979.

| 2316* | 1f.20 Caudron C.635 monoplanes | 65 | 25 |

1979. International Aeronautics and Space Exhibition, Le Bourget.

| 2322 | 1f.70 Concorde and buildings at Le Bourget Airport | 90 | 60 |

1980. 50th Anniv of First Non-stop Paris to New York Flight.

| 2376 | 2f.50 Breguet 19 Super TR *Point d'Interrogation* | 80 | 40 |

1981. 34th International Aeronautics and Space Exhibition.

| 2419 | 2f. Dassault Mirage 2000 | 1·40 | 40 |

1981. Costes and Le Brix (pilots of first non-stop South Atlantic Flight) Commemoration.

| 2429 | 10f. Dieudonne Costes, Joseph Le Brix and Breguet 19 Super TR *Nungesser et Coli* | 3·50 | 30 |

1982.

| 2524 | 1f.90 Tail of Airbus Industrie A300 at Basle-Mulhouse Airport | 80 | 40 |

1982.

| 2549* | 1f.60 +30c. Balloon from *Five Weeks in a Balloon* by Jules Verne | 85 | 70 |

1982. 46th Anniv of Disappearance of *Croix du Sud*.

| 2552 | 1f.60 Latecoere 300 flying boat F-AKGF *Croix du Sud* | 60 | 60 |

1983. Bicentenary of Manned Flight.
2576   2f. Montgolfier balloon (first manned
          free flight, 1783) 80   65
2577   3f. Charles' hydrogen balloon, 1783 ...... 1·20   85

1983. 50th Anniv of Air France.
2591   3f.45 Air France colours and emblem .... 1·30   65

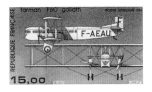

1984.
2614a   15f. Farman F.60 Goliath F-AEAU of
          Lignes Aeriennes Farman .... 5·25   45
2614ba   20f. CAMS 53 flying boat F-AIZA .... 6·25   60
2614ca   30f. Wibault 283 trimotor F-AMTS .... 10·50   4·50
2614d   50f. Dewoitine D-338 trimotor F-ARIA ..... 14·50   6·25
2614/2614d Set of 4 .... 33·00 10·50

1985. 36th International Aeronautics and Space Exhibition, Le
Bourget.
2685   10f. Falcon/Mystere .... 5·25   1·80

1986.
2706*   1f.80 +40c. Henri Fabre and seaplane
          Hydravion 90   85

1988. 2nd Death Anniv of Marcel Dassault (aircraft engineer).
2797   3f.60 Marcel Dassault, Dassault Mirage
          4000 (top), Dassault Breguet
          Falcon/Mystere 50 (foot), Second
          World War fighter (right), Dassault
          Mirage III (centre) .... 1·40   50

1988. Birth Centenary of Roland Garros (aviator).
2846   2f. Roland Garros' Bleriot XI 85   30

1990. 90th Birth Anniv of Max Hymans (civil aviation pioneer).
2965   2f.30 Max Hymans, Sud Est SE 161
          Languedoc, Lockheed Constellation
          and Douglas DC-3 80   35

1992. 80th Anniv of Nancy-Luneville Air Mail Service.
3100   2f.50 Farman H.F.16 type biplane and
          Boeing 737-500 80   40

1996.
3356   3f. +60c. Hot air balloon .... 1·00   1·00

1997.
3456   20f. Breguet 14 .... 6·25   1·20

1998.
3510   30f. Potez 25 .... 11·00 7·25

1999.
3579   15f. Airbus Industries Airbus A300-B4 ...... 5·25   3·00

2000.
3636   50f. Couzinet 70 Arc en Ciel .... 13·50 7·25

2000.
MS3654 3f. Lindbergh and Ryan NYP Special Spirit
of St Louis (other stamps in the miniature sheet
do not show aircraft) .... 9·75   8·75

2000. Birth Centenary of Antoine de Saint-Exupery (pioneer
aviator).
3674   3f. Antoine de Saint-Exupery and
          Caudron C.690 90   35

2000.
3694   3f. +60c. Toy airplane .... 1·30   1·00

2001.
3739   4f.50 Airship .... 1·20   70

2002.
MS3814 46c. Aerospatiale/BAe Concorde (other
stamps in the miniature sheet do not show
aircraft) .... 10·50 10·50

2002. 30th Anniv of First Flight of Airbus A300.
3864   €3 Airbus Industries Airbus A300-B1 ...... 5·25   2·75

2003.
3895   50c. Aircraft carrier and Dassault
          Rafale M .... 1·10   45

2003. Third Death Anniv of Jaqueline Auriol.
3912   €4 Dassault Mirage III .... 7·00   3·50

2004.
3972   50c. Douglas C-47 Skytrain 90   45

2004. 40th Death Anniv of Marie Marvingt.
3991   €5 Marie Marvingt and Bleriot XI .... 8·75   4·50

2005. 30th Death Anniv of Adrienne Boland (first woman to fly over the Andes).
4134	€2 Adrienne Boland and Caudron G3	3·25	3·00

2006.
4201	€3 Airbus Industries Airbus A380	9·00	9·00

2006. Aviation sans Frontieres.
4223	54c. Cessna 208 Caravan.................................	1·75	85

2006. Flying Machines.
4228	54c. Helicopter (Gustave de Ponton d'Amecourt 1863).................	1·75	85
4229	54c. *Demoiselle* (Alberto Santos-Dumont, 1908)....................	1·75	85
4230	54c. Flying boat (Jean-Marie le Bris, 1856)	1·75	85
4231	54c. *Avion III* (Clement Ader,1897)	1·75	85
4232	54c. *Hydravion* (Henri Fabre, 1910)............	1·75	85
4233	54c. Balloon with oars (Jean-Pierre Blanchard, 1784).................	1·75	85
4228/4233 *Set of 6*..		9·50	4·50

2007. Centenary of the Helicopter.
4268	€3 Eurocopter EC130.......................	9·00	4·00

FREE FRENCH FORCES IN THE LEVANT

Middle East

100 centimes = 1 franc

1942. Nos. 269/70 of Syria surcharged **LIGNES AERIENNES F.A.F.L.**, Cross of Lorraine and value.
4	4f. on 50p. Potez 29-4.........................	6·00	12·50
5	6f.50 on 50p. Potez 29-4.....................	5·75	9·00
6	8f. on 50p. Potez 29-4.........................	5·25	9·00
7	10f. on 100p. Potez 29-4.....................	5·50	14·50
4/7 *Set of 4*...		20·00	40·00

1943. No. 12 surcharged **4F** and airplane.
22	4f. on 3f. Camels and ruins of Palmyra ...	1·60	3·25

FRENCH EQUATORIAL AFRICA

Central Africa

100 centimes = 1 franc

1937.
75*	1f.50 Latecoere 300 flying boat....................	75	4·50
76*	2f. Latecoere 300 flying boat.....................	2·50	1·75
77*	2f.50 Latecoere 300 flying boat....................	60	50
78*	3f.75 Latecoere 300 flying boat....................	2·50	3·25
79*	4f.50 Savoia Marchetti S-73	2·75	2·30
80*	6f.50 Savoia Marchetti S-73	3·25	4·50
81*	8f.50 Savoia Marchetti S-73	3·25	5·00
82*	10f.75 Savoia Marchetti S-73	3·00	5·25

1940. Nos. 75 and 77/82 overprinted **Afrique Francaise Libre** or surcharged also.
155*	1f.50 Latecoere 300 flying boat.................	£140	£150
156*	2f.50 Latecoere 300 flying boat.................	1·60	1·70
157*	3f.75 Latecoere 300 flying boat.................	£160	£160
158*	4f.50 Savoia Marchetti S-73	1·20	2·00
159*	6f.50 Savoia Marchetti S-73	1·90	5·00
160*	8f. 50 Savoia Marchetti S-73	1·80	4·50
161*	10f. on 2f.50 Latecoere 300 flying boat....	65·00	70·00
162*	50f. on 10f.75 Savoia Marchetti S-73........	4·75	19·00

1941. As Nos. 207/13 of Cameroun.
178*	1f. Fairey FC-1 airliner..........................	70	3·25
179*	1f.50 Fairey FC-1 airliner......................	1·30	4·75
180*	5f. Fairey FC-1 airliner..........................	1·60	4·25
181*	10f. Fairey FC-1 airliner........................	2·30	2·30
182*	25f. Fairey FC-1 airliner........................	2·00	4·75
183*	50f. Fairey FC-1 airliner........................	2·30	3·75
184*	100f. Fairey FC-1 airliner......................	2·00	2·75

1943. No. 82 surcharged **Afrique Francaise Combattante+200 fr.** and cross.
192*	10f.75 +200f. Savoia Marchetti S-73..............	£120	£130

1947.
254*	50f. Savoia Marchetti S.M.75......................	3·50	2·00
255*	100f. Caudron C-445 Goeland	5·75	2·50
256*	200f. Savoia Marchetti S.M.75......................	8·25	5·00

1949. As No. 254 of Cameroun.
267	25f. Lockheed Constellation	4·00	25·00

1954. As No. 264 of Cameroun.
277	15f. Bomber...	6·25	3·25

FRENCH GUIANA

South America

100 centimes = 1 franc

1933.
164	50c. Flying boat	1·20	75
165	1f. Flying boat	25	65
166	1f.50 Flying boat	20	75
167	2f. Flying boat	60	60
168	3f. Flying boat	1·30	3·00
169	5f. Flying boat	60	1·30
170	10f. Flying boat	55	1·80
171	20f. Flying boat	65	1·00
164/171 *Set of 8*......................................		4·75	8·75

1945. As Nos. 207/13 of Cameroun.
215	50f. Fairey FC-1 airliner........................	65	3·00
216	100f. Fairey FC-1 airliner......................	95	5·25

1947.
242*	100f. Airplane..	14·50	34·00
243*	200f. Sud Ouest SO.95 Corse II......................	30·00	55·00

FRENCH GUINEA

West Africa

100 centimes = 1 franc

1940. As Nos. 117/21 of Dahomey.
173	1f.90 Twin-engine airliner	1·30	3·50

174	2f.90 Twin-engine airliner	60	3·25
175	4f.50 Twin-engine airliner	1·30	5·25
176	4f.90 Twin-engine airliner	1·50	5·50
177	6f.90 Twin-engine airliner	1·60	5·50
173/177 *Set of 5*......................................		5·75	21·00

1942. As No. 143k of Dahomey.
187	50f. Twin-engine airliner	1·70	7·25

FRENCH INDIAN SETTLEMENTS

East coast of Indian sub-continent

24 caches = 1 fanon

8 fanons = 1 rupee

1942. As Nos. 207/13 of Cameroun.
243*	4f. Fairey FC-1 airliner..........................	85	4·25
244*	1r. Fairey FC-1 airliner..........................	1·20	5·00
245*	2r. Fairey FC-1 airliner..........................	1·40	5·50
246*	5r. Fairey FC-1 airliner..........................	1·40	5·75
247*	8r. Fairey FC-1 airliner..........................	2·50	7·50
248*	10r. Fairey FC-1 airliner........................	2·75	7·00

1948.
281*	1r. Douglas DC-4	5·50	8·75

1949. As No. 254 of Cameroun.
284	6f. Lockheed Constellation	2·75	19·00

1954. As No. 264 of Cameroun.
287	1f. Bomber...	10·00	14·50

FRENCH MOROCCO

North-west Africa

100 centimes = 1 franc

1922.
112	5c. Breguet 14T biplane	70	1·60
113	25c. Breguet 14T biplane	90	1·40
114	50c. Breguet 14T biplane	80	35
115	75c. Breguet 14T biplane (blue)	75·00	8·75
116	75c. Breguet 14T biplane (green)...............	1·20	70
117	80c. Breguet 14T biplane	40	70
118	1f. Breguet 14T biplane	1·20	30
119	1f.40 Breguet 14T biplane	70	2·50
120	1f.90 Breguet 14T biplane	2·30	6·25
121	2f. Breguet 14T biplane	2·30	1·70
122	3f. Breguet 14T biplane	1·50	2·00
112/122 *Set of 11*		80·00	24·00

1931. Nos. 119/20 surcharged.
167	1f. on 1f.40 Breguet 14T biplane	1·00	55
168	1f.50 on 1f.90 Breguet 14T biplane.............	2·30	3·25

1939.
253*	1f.90 Dewoitine D-338 trimotor..................	40	1·80
254*	2f. Dewoitine D-338 trimotor..................	40	70
255*	3f. Dewoitine D-338 trimotor..................	35	20
257*	10f. Dewoitine D-338 trimotor..................	90	1·80

1944.
283	50c. Sud Est SE 161 Languedoc....................	70	1·10
284	2f. Sud Est SE 161 Languedoc....................	45	80
285	5f. Sud Est SE 161 Languedoc....................	40	55
286	10f. Sud Est SE 161 Languedoc....................	50	25
287	50f. Sud Est SE 161 Languedoc....................	65	3·25
288	100f. Sud Est SE 161 Languedoc....................	4·50	22·00
283/288 *Set of 6*......................................		6·50	25·00

1944. Design as Nos. 283/8, surcharged **ENTR'AIDE FRANCAISE +98F50.**
289   1f.50 +98f.50 Sud Est SE 161 Languedoc   1·60   6·50

1945.
290   50f. Potez 56 ....   1·60   3·75

1946. No. 285 surcharged **+5F 18 Juin 1940 18 Juin 1946.**
311   5f.+5f. Sud Est SE 161 Languedoc ....   1·20   4·00

1947.
338*   9f. Sud Est SE 161 Languedoc ....   1·20   10
339*   40f. Sud Est SE 161 Languedoc ....   1·20   30
340*   50f. Sud Est SE 161 Languedoc ....   1·40   15

1947.
345*   9f. +16f. Sud Est SE 161 Languedoc ....   2·50   6·50
346*   20f. +35f. Sud Est SE 161 Languedoc ....   1·50   5·75

1948.
349   6f. +34f. Sud Est SE 161 Languedoc ....   1·60   6·25
350   9f. +51f. Sud Est SE 161 Languedoc ....   1·40   5·75

1950. 25th Anniv of First Mail Flight from Casablanca to Dakar.
374   15f. +10f. Breguet 14T biplane ....   1·40   6·00

1950.
385*   10f. +10f. Lockheed Constellation ....   1·50   6·00
386*   15f. +15f. Lockheed Constellation ....   2·00   6·00

1951.
393*   50f. Airplane ....   1·80   7·50

1951.
397*   50f. Lockheed Constellation   90   4·25

1952.
409   15f. +5f. Breguet 14T biplane (on stamp
    No. 115) and Douglas DC-4 ....   3·75   12·50

1952.
414   10f. Lockheed Constellation ....   2·30   1·50
415   40f. Lockheed Constellation ....   1·90   15
416   100f. Lockheed Constellation ....   2·75   40
417   200f. Lockheed Constellation ....   3·75   3·50
414/417 Set of 4 ....   9·75   5·00

1955.
465   100f. Sud Est SE 161 Languedoc ....   2·75   30
466   200f. Sud Est SE 161 Languedoc ....   4·75   55
467   500f. Sud Est SE 161 Languedoc ....   5·00   2·75
465/467 Set of 3 ....   11·00   3·25

FRENCH POLYNESIA

South Pacific
100 centimes = 1 franc

1960. Inauguration of Papeete Airport.
19   13f. Douglas DC-8 over Papeete Airport .   3·00   2·75

1969. First Flight of Concorde. As No. 83 of Comoro Islands.
93   40f. Concorde of Air France ....   60·00   55·00

1971.
133*   20f. Paragliding ....   8·00   8·50

1973. Inauguration of Air France Round-the-World Service via Tahiti.
167   80f. Airplane ....   18·00   55·00

1973. Inauguration of Douglas DC-10 Service.
168   20f. Douglas DC-10 F-BTDA of U.T.A. over
    Papeete Airport ....   26·00   14·00

1975. 50 Years of Tahitian Aviation.
195*   75f. Tourville's flying boat ....   20·00   24·00
196*   100f. Boeing 707 ....   24·00   32·00

1975.
204   100f. Boeing 737 ....   19·00   22·00

1976. Concorde's First Commercial Flight.
210   100f. Concorde ....   40·00   40·00

1977. 50th Anniv of Lindbergh's Transatlantic Flight.
257   28f. Charles Lindbergh and Ryan NYP
    Special *Spirit of St. Louis* ....   13·50   9·25

1979.
312   24f. Short S.25 Sandringham 7 Bermuda
    flying boat F-OBIP of Resau Aerien
    Interinsulaire ....   3·25   2·00
313   40f. Douglas DC-4 F-BELH of Air France...   4·75   4·00
314   60f. Britten-Norman BN-2 Islander of Air
    Tahiti ....   5·25   4·25
315   80f. Fokker/Fairchild F.27A Friendship
    F-OCWZ ....   6·75   5·00
316   120f. Douglas DC-8 of U.T.A. ....   8·25   4·50
312/316 Set of 5 ....   25·00   18·00

1980. Aircraft (2nd series).
335   15f. Consolidated PBY-5A Catalina
    amphibian of TRAPAS ....   2·50   4·00
336   26f. de Havilland Canada DHC-6 Twin
    Otter 200/300 *Maui* ....   2·75   2·30
337   30f. CAMS 55 flying boat ....   2·50   2·50
338   50f. Douglas DC-6 of Transports Aeriens
    Intercontinentaux ....   5·25   4·25
335/338 Set of 4 ....   11·50   11·50

1992.
636*   6f. Sikorsky S-61N helicopter ....   2·75   2·75

1993. 50th Anniv of Bora-Bora Airfield.
675 120f. Pilot, Lockheed P-38 Lightning and airstrip at Bora Bora .... 4·75 4·25

1998. Aviation.
816 70f. Grumman Widgeon * .... 2·30 1·90
817 70f. Fairchild Hiller FH-227.................... 2·30 1·90
818 85f. de Havilland Canada DHC-6 Twin Otter .... 2·50 2·00
819 85f. Avions de Transport Régional ATR 42-500.. 2·50 2·00
816/819 Set of 4 .... 8·75 7·00
No. 816 is wrongly inscribed Grumann.

2004.
978 500f. Airplane tail fins, poss. Airbus .... 6·50 3·25

2005. Aviation.
1004 60f. Douglas DC-8 (first jet airplane in Tahiti, 1961) 80 40
1005 60f. Boeing 707 (first foreign flight, 1963) .. 80 40
1006 100f. Air Tahiti Nui Airbus A340-300 (first Tahitian airline 2000) .... 1·30 65
1007 100f. Boeing 707 (first Air France flight to Tahiti, 1973) .... 1·30 65
1004/1007 Set of 4 .... 3·75 1·90

FRENCH SOMALI COAST

East Africa

100 centimes = 1 franc

1941. As Nos. 207/13 of Cameroun, but inscribed "DJIBOUTI".
295 1f. Fairey FC-1 airliner........................ 55 45
296 1f.50 Fairey FC-1 airliner.................... 75 2·50
297 5f. Fairey FC-1 airliner........................ 55 1·40
298 10f. Fairey FC-1 airliner...................... 1·00 2·30
299 25f. Fairey FC-1 airliner...................... 1·00 5·75
300 50f. Fairey FC-1 airliner...................... 75 4·50
301 100f. Fairey FC-1 airliner.................... 1·10 2·50
295/301 Set of 7 .... 5·25 17·00

1949. As No. 254 of Cameroun.
425 30f. Lockheed Constellation .... 2·00 36·00

1954. As No. 264 of Cameroun.
428 15f. Bomber... 6·00 16·00

1956.
430* 500f. Airliner................................. 32·00 55·00

1958.
447* 100f. Airplane.................................. 7·75 6·00

FRENCH SOUTHERN AND ANTARCTIC TERRITORIES

Antarctica and nearby islands

100 centimes = 1 franc

1963.
36 20f. Weather balloon .... 50·00 55·00

1969. As No. 1806 of France.
52 25f. Nord 2501 Noratlas and Sud Aviation SE 3130 Alouette II helicopter............ 20·00 45·00

1969. As No. 83 of Comoro Islands.
53 85f. Concorde of Air France .... 46·00 60·00

1976.
108* 4f. Sud Aviation SE 3130 Alouette II helicopter .... 9·00 7·75

1979.
134* 50c. Sikorsky S-58 helicopters, Sud Aviation SE 3160 Alouette III helicopters and helicopter carrier *Jeanne d'Arc* .... 3·00 4·00

1981.
158 55c. Sud Aviation SE 3130 Alouette II helicopter................................... 1·90 4·25
159 65c. Sud Aviation SE 3130 Alouette II helicopter................................... 1·90 4·25

1982.
168 5f. Seaplane on ice patrol ship *Commandant Charcot* .... 3·75 7·75

1984. Bicentenary of Manned Flight.
190 3f.50 Charles' hydrogen balloon, 1783, Henri Giffard's steam-powered dirigible airship, 1852, unmanned Montgolfier balloon, Dupuy de Lome's airship, 1872, and stratosphere balloon............................. 1·20 5·50
191 7f.80 Montgolfier balloon (first manned free flight, 1783), Renard and Krebs' airship *La France*, 1884, balloon *Zodiac* YZ ST, other airships and balloons .... 2·00 9·00

1986.
218 14f. IAI Aravo.................................. 3·50 18·00

1992.
302 22f. Montgolfier balloon (first manned free flight, 1783)............................ 16·00 18·00

1992. Completion of Landing Strip at Dumont D'Urville Research Station, Adelie Land.
305 25f.70 Landing strip on Adelie Land............. 18·00 13·00

1993. Inauguration of Landing Strip, Adelie Land.
320 30f. Lockheed C-130 Hercules over landing strip on Adelie Land.............. 12·00 5·50

2001.
459* 5f.20 Weather balloon .... 1·70 1·70
461* 5f.20 Helicopter.......................... 1·70 1·70
467* 5f.20 Helicopter.......................... 1·70 1·70

2004.
522 90c. de Havilland Canada DHC-7 Twin Otter... 1·30 70

FRENCH SUDAN

West Africa

100 centimes = 1 franc

1940. As Nos. 117/21 of Dahomey.
208 1f.90 Twin-engine airliner .... 1·10 4·25
209 2f.90 Twin-engine airliner .... 1·00 3·75
210 4f.50 Twin-engine airliner .... 1·30 3·50
211 4f.90 Twin-engine airliner .... 1·50 2·50
212 6f.90 Twin-engine airliner .... 1·50 3·75
208/212 Set of 5 .... 5·50 16·00

1942. As No. 143k of Dahomey.
223 50f. Twin-engine airliner .... 2·30 5·50

FRENCH TERRITORY OF THE AFARS AND THE ISSAS

East Africa

100 centimes = 1 franc

1968.
530* 85f. Djibouti Airport .... 8·25 8·25

1969. First Flight of Concorde. As No. 83 of Comoro Islands.
534 100f. Concorde of Air France .... 34·00 29·00

1969.
536* 50f. Sud Aviation SE 3130 Alouette II helicopter spraying crops .... 5·75 3·50
537* 55f. Piper PA-18-A Super Cub spraying crops .... 6·25 4·75

1973.
658* 50f. Clement Ader and his *Avion III* .... 5·50 3·50
607* 100f. Henri Farman and Farman Voisin *No. 1 bis* .... 7·50 4·25

1977. Inauguration of Djibouti Airport.
678 500f. Outline of Boeing 747 over Djibouti Airport .... 27·00 21·00

FRENCH WEST AFRICA

West Africa

100 centimes = 1 franc

1945. As Nos. 207/13 of Cameroun.
24 5f.50 Fairey FC-1 airliner .... 90 2·50
25 50f. Fairey FC-1 airliner 70 35
26 100f. Fairey FC-1 airliner .... 85 1·20
24/26 *Set of 3* .... 2·20 3·50

1947.
54* 50f. Caudron C-445 Goeland .... 4·50 1·50
56* 200f. Outline of airplane .... 5·50 3·25

1949. As No. 254 of Cameroun.
69 25f. Lockheed Constellation .... 1·30 10

1951.
77* 100f. Lockheed Constellation .... 5·00 90
78* 200f. Lockheed Constellation .... 17·00 2·75
79* 500f. Douglas DC-4 .... 21·00 6·25

1954. As no. 264 of Cameroun.
81 15f. Bomber.. 5·25 2·75

1958.
99* 20f. Lockheed L.1049G Super Constellation (lower left) and Douglas DC-6 (left) .... 2·30 3·00

FUJEIRA

Arabian Peninsula

100 dirhams = 1 riyal

APPENDIX

The following stamps have either been issued in excess of postal needs or have not been made available to the public in reasonable quantities at face value. Miniature sheets, imperforate stamps, etc are excluded from this section.

1969.
"Apollo" Space Flights. 2r.50 (helicopter).
Space Flight of "Apollo 10". Overprinted on 1969 Appendix issue. 2r.50.
Moon Landing. Overprinted on 1969 Appendix issue. 2r.50.
First Man on the Moon. Overprinted on 1969 Appendix issue. 2r.50.

1970.
Exploration of the Moon. 5r (helicopter).
Space Flight of "Apollo 13". Overprinted on 1970 Appendix issue. 5r.

1971.
Space Exploration. 40d. (balloon), 60d. (Lilienthal glider), 1r. (Sopwith Camel), 2r. (Avro Vulcan), 5r. (helicopter).

GABON

West Africa

100 centimes = 1 franc

1962. Air Afrique Airline. As No. 307 of Cameroun.

184	500f. Boeing 707 airliners of Air Afrique....	12·00	7·50

1962. Evolution of Air Transport.

189*	10f. Breguet 14 biplane	60	25
190*	20f. de Havilland D.H.89 Dragon Rapide of Trans Gabon	1·00	45
191*	60f. Sud Aviation SE 210 Caravelle	2·20	1·00

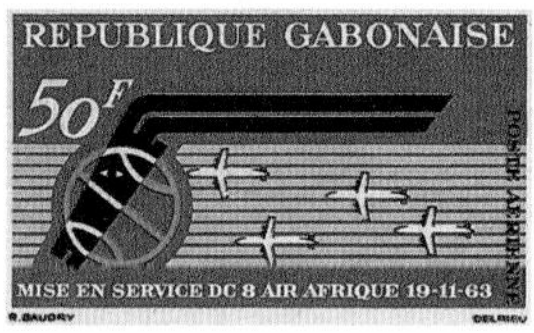

1963. First Anniv of Air Afrique and Inauguration of DC-8 Service.

202	50f. Emblem	1·30	80

1966. Inauguration of Douglas DC-8F Service. As No. 438 of Cameroun.

268	30f. Douglas DC-8F Jet Trader of Air Afrique	85	50

1966.

273	200f. Douglas DC-8 over Libreville Airport, with two Piper PA-23 Apache 235 monoplanes (left) and Douglas DC-3 on the ground	4·25	1·60

1966.

274	30f. Sikorsky S-43 amphibian	1·90	70

1967.

284	30f. Airliner	1·00	45

1967. Famous Aircraft.

288	200f. Farman F.190	4·25	1·60
289	300f. de Havilland DH.114 Heron 2	7·75	2·10
290	500f. Potez 56	13·00	5·25
288/290	*Set of 3*	23·00	8·00

1967. ICAO Commemoration.

292	100f. Airliners and flight paths	2·20	1·10

1969.

359*	15f. Boeing 707 of the Red Cross	65	35

1970. History of Flight.

383*	100f. Leonardo da Vinci's design for a pair of wings	1·80	75

1970. 10th Anniv (1969) of Aerial Navigation Security Agency for Africa and Madagascar. As No. 552 of Cameroun.

394	100f. Airliner over airport	4·50	1·80

1971.

410	15f. Douglas DC-10	45	25
411	25f. Sud Aviation SE210 Caravelle	60	25
412	40f. Boeing 707	1·00	40
413	55f. Douglas DC-8	1·50	55
414	75f. Sud Aviation SE 3130 Alouette II helicopter	2·50	80
415	120f. Boeing 727-200	3·00	1·10
410/415	*Set of 6*	8·25	3·00

1972. No. 289 surcharged **VISITE OFFICIELLE GRAND MAITRE ORDRE SOUVERAIN DE MALTE 3 MARS 1972 50F** and Maltese Cross.

448	50f. on 300f. de Havilland D.H.114 Heron 2	95	40

1973. Libreville-Paris Air Service by Air Afrique Douglas DC-10 Libreville.

487	40f. Douglas DC-10-30 over Libreville Airport	2·00	1·00

1973. History of Flight.

488	1f. Montgolfier balloon (first manned free flight, 1783)	30	10
489	2f. Santos-Dumont's airship *Ballon No. 6*, 1901	30	10
490	3f. Chanute's glider, 1896	30	10
491	4f. Clement Ader's *Avion III*, 1897	60	15
492	5f. Bleriot XI, 1909	95	35
493	10f. Fabre's seaplane *Hydravion*, 1910 (purple and blue)	1·10	35
493a	10f. Fabre's seaplane *Hydravion*, 1910 (blue)	2·40	1·10
488/493a	*Set of 7*	5·25	2·00

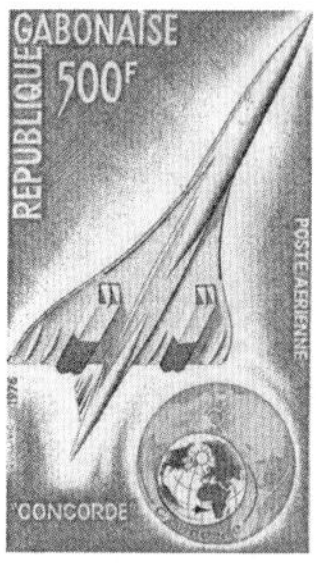

1975.

565	500f. Concorde of Air France	10·00	6·00

1975. Concorde's First Commercial Flight. No. 565 surcharged **1000F 21 Janv. 1976 1er Vol Commercial de CONCORDE**.

566	1000f. on 500f. Concorde of Air France	18·00	11·50

1977. First Air Gabon Intercontinental Air Service.

609	60f. Boeing 747 of Air Gabon	1·00	50

1977. 50th Anniv of Lindbergh's Transatlantic Flight.

628	500f. Charles Lindbergh and Ryan NYP Special *Spirit of St. Louis*	1·00	35

1977. First Commercial Paris-New York Flight by Concorde. No. 565 overprinted **PARIS NEW-YORK PREMIER VOL 22.11.77.**

631	500f. Concorde of Air France	10·00	6·50

1978.

641	500f. Boeing 747	6·25	2·50

1978. 75th Anniv of First Powered Flight.

680	380f. Wilbur and Orville Wright and Wright *Flyer I*	4·50	1·80

1979. Aviation History.
699* 250f. Louis Bleriot and Bleriot XI .... 3·00 1·80

1980. Aviation Anniversaries.
723 165f. Dieudonne Costes, Maurice Bellonte and Breguet 19 Super TR *Point d'Interrogation* .... 1·60 80
724 1000f. Jean Mermoz and Latecoere seaplane 28-3 *Comte de la Vaulx* .... 10·00 5·00

1983. Balloon Anniversaries.
857 100f. Balloon *Double Eagle II* .... 1·00 50
858 125f. Montgolfier balloon and modern hot-air balloons .... 1·30 75
859 350f. Jean-Francois Pilatre de Rozier and Montgolfier balloon (first manned free flight, 1783) .... 3·75 2·00
857/859 *Set of 3* .... 5·50 3·00

1984.
876 125f. Sikorsky S-43 amphibian (on stamp No. 274) and Boeing 747-200 of Air Gabon .... 1·50 55
877 225f. L.V.G. Schneider biplane (on Germany stamp No. 112) and Douglas DC-10 of Lufthansa .... 2·50 1·10

1984. Paris-Libreville Air Rally.
885 500f. Robin DR 400/120 Dauphin (foreground) and Piper PA-32 Cherokee Six .... 4·50 2·40

1984.
MS894 1000f. Sikorsky S-43 amphibian of Aeromaritime .... 20·00 20·00

1993.
1172 100f. Making model airplane .... 1·00 65

GAMBIA

West Africa
1949. 12 pence = 1 shilling
20 shillings = 1 pound
1971. 100 bututs = 1 dalasi

1949. As Nos. 114/15 of Antigua.
166* 1½d. Airplane .... 30 1·50
167* 3d. Jet-powered Vickers Viking .... 1·25 2·00

1969. 35th Anniv of Pioneer Air Service.
259 2d. Dornier Do-J II 10-t Wal flying boat of Lufthansa being launched from catapult ship *Westfalen* 50 20
260 1s. Dornier Do-J II 10-t Wal flying boat D-AGAT *Boreas* of Lufthansa 50 20
261 1s. 6d. Airship LZ-127 *Graf Zeppelin* .... 60 1·60
259/261 *Set of 3* .... 1·40 1·75

1979.
426* 50b. Sikorsky S-61B SH-3 Sea King helicopter 30 40
No. 426 also exists self-adhesive from stamp booklets.

1982.
483* 1d.25 Yundum Airport .... 3·00 3·50

1983.
517* 1d.10 Douglas DC-9-80 Super Eighty being loaded with mail at Yundum Airport 1·50 65

1983. Bicentenary of Manned Flight.
522* 60b. Montgolfier balloon (first manned flight, 1783) 35 40
523* 85b. Douglas DC-10 of Lufthansa 45 50
524* 90b. Junkers W.33 seaplane D-1167 Atlantis 45 50
526* 4d. Airship LZ-127 *Graf Zeppelin* .... 2·25 3·00

1984. 50th Anniv of Gambia-South America Trans-Atlantic Flight.
559 60b. Airship LZ-127 *Graf Zeppelin* .... 1·10 1·00
560 85b. Dornier Do-J II 10-t Wal flying boat of Lufthansa on catapult ship *Westfalen* .... 1·60 1·75
561 90b. Dornier Do-18 flying boat D-ABYM *Aeolus* of Lufthansa .... 1·75 2·50
562 1d.25 Dornier Do-J II 10-t Wal flying boat D-2069 of Lufthansa .... 1·75 2·75
559/562 *Set of 4* .... 5·50 7·25

1987.
706* 2b. Airship 10 20
708* 5b. Helicopter and aircraft carrier 20 20

1988.
786* 1d. Concorde of British Airways .... 2·50 1·00
787* 1d.25 Lindbergh's Ryan NYP Special *Spirit of St. Louis* .... 1·25 1·00
788* 2d. North American X-15 .... 1·60 1·40
789* 3d. Bell XS-1 .... 1·75 1·50

1988.
807* 25b. Airship LZ-127 *Graf Zeppelin* (wrongly inscribed "LZ-7") 90 35

1988.
841* 20d. Wilbur and Orville Wright and *Voyager* .... 5·50 6·00

1989.
MS959 Two sheets. (a) 15d. Hughes 369 Viking helicopter (inscribed "VICKING"); (b) 15d. Douglas DC-9 One Eleven Nightingale C.9 with Red Cross markings *Set of 2 sheets* .... 8·00 8·50

1990.
997* 12d. Sikorsky S-61B SH-3 Sea King helicopter .... 3·75 4·50

1990. RAF Aircraft of World War II.
999 10b. Bristol Type 142 Blenheim Mk I 90 50
1000 20b. Fairey Battle .... 1·25 50
1001 50b. Bristol Type 142 Blenheim Mk IV .... 1·50 50
1002 60b. Vickers-Armstrong Wellington Mk 1c 1·60 50
1003 75b. Armstrong Whitworth Whitley Mk V 1·60 50
1004 1d. Handley Page Hampden Mk I .... 1·60 50
1005 1d.25 Hawker Hurricane Mk I (foreground) and Supermarine Spitfire Mk IA .... 1·60 50
1006 2d. Avro Manchester .... 2·00 90
1007 3d. Short Stirling Mk I .... 2·00 1·90
1008 5d. Handley Page Halifax Mk I .... 2·50 2·50
1009 10d. Avro Type 683 Lancaster Mk III .... 3·50 4·25
1010 12d. de Havilland DH.98 Mosquito Mk IV. 3·50 4·25
999/1010 *Set of 12* .... 21·00 15·00
MS1011 Two sheets. (a) 15d. Supermarine Spitfire Mk IA; (b) 15d. Avro Type 683 Lancaster Mk III *Set of 2 sheets* .... 8·50 9·00

1990.
1037* 12d. Boeing 707 of Air Gambia .... 6·50 6·50

1992.
1342* 2d. Mitsubishi A6M Zero-Sen .... 1·75 1·25
1344* 2d. Aichi D3A "Val" bombers over Ford
Naval Air Station and Douglas SBD
Dauntless dive bombers on fire at
Pearl Harbor .... 1·75 1·25
1349* 2d. North American B-25B Mitchell .... 1·75 1·25
1350* 2d. Douglas SBD Dauntless dive bomber
(shown dropping a torpedo) .... 1·75 1·25

1993.
1410* 2d. Douglas DC-4 on Berlin Airlift 70 70
1411* 2d. Airship LZ-129 *Hindenburg* (wrongly
inscribed "LZ-127") 70 70
1422* 18d. Airship LZ-1, 1900 .... 3·75 4·25

1993. Aviation Anniversaries.
1526 2d. Hugo Eckener and airship LZ-127
Graf Zeppelin (inscribed "Zeppelin
Luftschiffe 3") 55 50
1527 2d. Guyot's balloon, 1785 .... 1·25 1·25
1528 5d. Hugo Eckener and airship LZ-3 .... 1·25 1·25
1529 5d. Sopwith Snipe .... 1·60 2·25
1530 5d. Hugo Eckener and airship LZ-127
Graf Zeppelin .... 1·90 2·25
1531 10d. Hot-air balloon *Comte d'Artois*, 17 ..... 2·75 3·50
1532 15d. Royal Aircraft Factory S.E.5 .... 9·00 10·50
1526/1532 *Set of 7* .... 9·00 10·50
MS1533 Three sheets. (a) 20d. Hugo Eckener and
airship LZ-127 *Graf Zeppelin* (inscribed "Zeppelin
Luftschiffe 3"); (b) 20d. Jean-Pierre Blanchard's
balloon with oars, 1784 (dated "1785"); (c) 20d.
Avro 504K *Set of 3 sheets* .... 17·00 17·00

1996. 65th Anniv of Britain's Victory in Schneider Trophy.
2358 4d. Spitfire prototype K5054 .... 80 80
2359 4d. First production Spitfire K9787 .... 80 80
2360 4d. Spitfire Mk1A 80 80
2361 4d. Spitfire LF Mk IXE with D-Day
markings 80 80
2362 4d. Spitfire Mk XII (first with Griffon
engine) 80 80
2363 4d. Spitfire Mk XIVC with jungle
markings 80 80
2364 4d. Spitfire Mk XIX of Royal Swedish Air
Force 80 80
2365 4d. Spitfire Mk XIX 80 80
2366 4d. Spitfire F Mk 22/24 (final variant) 80 80
2367 4d. Spitfire Mk XIX of Royal Swedish Air
Force 80 80
2368 4d. Spitfire Mk VB of United States Army
Air French Corps. 80 80
2369 4d. Spitfire Mk VC of Finnish Air Force 80 80
2370 4d. Spitfire Mk VB of Soviet Air Force 80 80
2371 4d. Spitfire Mk XIE of Netherlands East
Indies Air Force 80 80
2372 4d. Spitfire Mk XIE of Israeli Air Force 80 80
2373 4d. Spitfire Mk VIII of Royal Australian Air
Force 80 80
2374 4d. Spitfire Mk VB of Turkish Air Force 80 80
2375 4d. Spitfire Mk XII of Royal Danish Air
Force 80 80
2358/2375 *Set of 18* .... 13·00 13·00
MS2376 Two sheets. (a) 25d. Supermarine S.6B
seaplane taking off; (b) 25d. Supermarine S.6B
seaplane in flight *Set of 2 sheets* .... 10·00 10·00

1997.
2411* 3d. Model of Banjul International Airport 75 60

1997.
2704* 5d. Hughes H-4 Hercules *Spruce Goose* .. 1·00 1·00

1998. History of Aviation.
2857 5d. Wright *Flyer I*, 1903 .... 85 85
2858 5d. Curtiss A-1 Seaplane, 1910 .... 85 85
2859 5d. Farman Voisin biplane, 1907 .... 85 85
2860 5d. Bristol monoplane, 1911 .... 85 85
2861 5d. Antoinette IV, 1908 .... 85 85
2862 5d. Sopwith 'Bat Boat' amphibian 1912 .. 85 85
2863 5d. Short Type 38, 1913 .... 85 85
2864 5d. Fokker FVIIb/3m, 1925 .... 85 85
2865 5d. Junkers F.13 1919 .... 85 85
2866 5d. Pitcairn 'Mailwing' 1927 .... 85 85
2867 5d. Douglas Cloudster, 1920 .... 85 85
2868 5d. Curtiss T-32 Condor, 1934 .... 85 85
2857/2868 *Set of 12* .... 9·00 9·00
MS2869 Two sheets. (a) 25d. Albatros, 1913; (b) 25d.
Boeing Model 247D *Set of 2 sheets* .... 7·00 8·00

1998. 80th Anniv Royal Air Force.
2941 5d. SEPECAT Jaguar GR1A .... 1·25 1·25
2942 5d. Panavia Tornado GR1A .... 1·25 1·25
2943 5d. SEPECAT Jaguar GR1A .... 1·25 1·25
2944 5d. BAe Hawk 200 .... 1·25 1·25
2945 5d. SEPECAT Jaguar GR1A .... 1·25 1·25
2946 5d. BAe Harrier GR7 .... 1·25 1·25
2947 5d. Panavia Tornado GR1 firing missle .... 1·25 1·25
2948 5d. Panavia Tornado GR1 at low level ...... 1·25 1·25
2949 7d. Panavia Tornado GR1 (facing left) ..... 1·25 1·25
2950 7d. BAe Hawk T1A .... 1·25 1·25
2951 7d. SEPECAT Jaguar GR1A .... 1·25 1·25
2952 7d. Panavia Tornado GR1 (facing right) .. 1·25 1·25
2941/2952 *Set of 12* .... 13·50 13·50

MS2953 Six sheets. (a) 20d. Eurofighter EF-2000
Typhoon; (b) 25d. Bristol F2B and bird of prey;
(c) 25d. Bristol F2B and falcon; (d) 25d. Bristol
F2B and golden eagle; (e) 25d. Avro Type 683
Lancaster and Eurofighter EF-2000 Typhoon; (f)
25d. English Electric Lightning and Eurofighter
EF-2000 Typhoon *Set of 6 sheets* .... 17·00 18·00

1999.
3048* 6d. Bell X-14A .... 1·00 1·10

2000.
3299* 3d. Leonardo da Vinci's first design for
flying machine, 1480 .... 30 30

2000.
3317* 3d. Zeppelin in hangar 45 45
3322* 3d. Wright Brothers and Flyer 45 45

2000. Centenary of First Zeppelin Flight.
3438 15d. LZ-10 *Schwaben*, 1911 .... 2·00 2·25
3439 15d. LZ-127 *Graf Zeppelin*, 1928 .... 2·00 2·25
3440 15d. LZ-129 *Hindenburg*, 1936 .... 2·00 2·25
3438/3440 *Set of 3* .... 5·50 6·00
MS3441 25d. LZ-130 *Graf Zeppelin II* 1938 .... 4·00 4·25

2000.
3708* 7d. Blended body wing BWB-1 aircraft .... 1·40 1·40
3709* 7d. Boeing B767-400 ERX .... 1·40 1·40
3710* 7d. Lockheed Concept Fighter .... 1·40 1·40
3711* 7d. Boeing 'X' bomber .... 1·40 1·40
3712* 7d. Aerospaceplane X-30 .... 1·40 1·40
3713* 7d. Hotol space plane separating from
Antonov AN-225 Mryia .... 1·40 1·40
MS3726* Four sheets. (b) 25d. Nautic Air 400 flying
boat concept (other miniature sheets do not
show aircraft) .... 18·00 19·00

2000. 60th Anniv of Battle of Britain.
3830 5d. Bristol Blenheim of 29 Squadron .... 1·40 1·40
3831 5d. Helmut Wick shooting down Hawker
Hurricane .... 1·40 1·40
3832 5d. Supermarine Spitfire of 65 Squadron
attacking Dornier Do217 .... 1·40 1·40
3833 5d. Bristol Beaufighter IIF of 604
Squadron .... 1·40 1·40
3834 5d. Boulton Paul P.82 Defiants of 264
Squadron .... 1·40 1·40

3835	5d. Supermarine Spitfire in dogfight with Junkers Ju-87 Stuka	1·40	1·40
3836	5d. Supermarine Spitfire over Tower Bridge	1·40	1·40
3837	5d. Gloster Gladiator of 615 Squadron	1·40	1·40
3838	5d. Hawker Hurricane attacking Messerschmitt Bf 109	1·40	1·40
3839	5d. Supermarine Spitfire attacking two Messerschmitt Bf 109s	1·40	1·40
3840	5d. Flt-Lt. Gilliam attacking Dornier Do 217s	1·40	1·40
3841	5d. Two Hawker Hurricanes of 610 Squadron	1·40	1·40
3842	5d. Hawker Hurricanes of 85 Squadron	1·40	1·40
3843	5d. G.A.Langley attacking Messerschmitt Bf 109	1·40	1·40
3844	5d. Bristol Blenheim IV of 23 Squadron	1·40	1·40
3845	5d. Supermarine Spitfires of 222 Squadron taking off	1·40	1·40
3830/3845 Set of 16		20·00	20·00

MS3846 Two sheets. (a) 25d. Adolf Galland (commander of Group III of JG26); (b) 25d. Group Captain Frank Carey Set of 2 sheets .... 12·00 12·00
No. 3834 is inscribed Bolton-Paul in error.

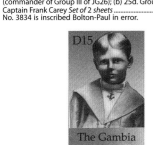

2002. Birth Centenary of Charles Lindbergh.

4423	15d. Lindbergh as boy	2·25	2·25
4424	15d. Lindbergh as teenager	2·25	2·25
4425	15d. Lindbergh in army uniform	2·25	2·25
4426	15d. Lindbergh as young man	2·25	2·25
4427	15d. Lindbergh as boy, with dog	2·25	2·25
4428	15d. Lindbergh wearing flying jacket	2·25	2·25
4429	15d. Lindbergh wearing suit and flying goggles	2·25	2·25
4430	15d. Anne Morrow Lindbergh	2·25	2·25
4423/4430 Set of 8		16·00	16·00

2003. Columbia Space Shuttle Commemoration.
MS4485 Four sheets. (a) 15d. Boeing 747-123 Space Shuttle Carrier, with shuttle on board; (d) 15d. Michael Anderson (astronaut) with Northrop T-38 Talon (other miniature sheet do not show aircraft) .... 32·00 38·00

2003. Centenary of Powered Flight.
MS4503 15d. Wright *Flyer I*, 1903 first powered flight; 15d. Ambroise's *Goupy 1*, 1908 first full-sized tri-plane (built by Voisin); 15d. Zeppelin LZ-7 *Deutschland* First commercial airship; 15d. Fokker F. VII-3m *Josephine Ford* Lt. Col. Richard E. Byrd flight over North Pole, 1926 (pilot, Floyd Bennett) .... 9·50 10·00
MS4504 15d. Granville Gee Bee, World Speed Record, 1932; 15d. Boeing 247D, 1933 First modern airliner; 15d. Douglas DC-3, 1935, world's most successful airliner; 15d. Lockheed Vega 5C High Speed Special, Amelia Earhart's solo Hawaii-California flight, 1935 .... 9·50 10·00
MS4505 15d. MacCready *Solar Challenger* 1980 Solar powered flight; 15d. Rutan Voyager, 1986 First non-stop unrefuelled flight around the world (other stamps in **MS**4505 do not show aircraft) .... 9·50 10·00
MS4506 Three sheets. (a) 40d. Vought V-173, 1942. Short take-off and landing research aircraft; (c) 40d. Ames AD-1 scissor-wing SST research aircraft, 1979 (other miniature sheet does not show aircraft) .... 15·00 16·00

2004. Last Flight of Concorde (2003).
MS4566 25d. Aerospatiale/BAe Concorde, French flag, and top of Eiffel Tower; 25d. Aeorspatiale/BAe Concorde, French flag and mid-section of Eiffel Tower; 25d. Aeorspatiale/BAe Concorde, French flag and lower-section of Eiffel Tower .... 10·00 11·00

MS4567 25d. Aerospatiale/BAe Concorde, and Australian flag; 25d. Aerospatiale/BAe Concorde, and Australian flag; 25d. Aerospatiale/BAe Concorde, and clouds .... 10·00 11·00
MS4568 25d. Aerospatiale/BAe Concorde, and Statue of Liberty, New York; 25d. Aerospatiale/BAe Concorde, US flag and New York Harbour sightseeing boat; 25d. Aerospatiale/BAe Concorde, and US flag .... 10·00 11·00
MS4569 60d. x 4 Concorde and BAe Hawk TIAs of Red Arrows display team .... 30·00 30·00
No. **MS**4566 depicts Concorde 214 F-BTSD.
No. **MS**4567/8 depicts Concorde 216 G-BOAF.
Stamps and margins of No. **MS**4566 form a composite background design showing the Eiffel Tower, Paris.

2004.
MS4665* Two sheets. (a) 25d. Heavy bombers over Normandy; 25d. North American B-25 Mitchell; 25d. Airspeed Horsa gliders; 25d. Paratroopers, Normandy; 25d. Paratroopers, map of Pegasus Bridge; 25d. Paratroopers, and map of Sainte Mere Eglise (other miniature sheet does not show aircraft) .... 2·75 2·75
MS4666* Two sheets. (b) 60d. Avro Type 683 Lancasters under construction (other miniature sheet does not show aircraft) .... 4·25 4·50

2004. Centenary (2003) of Powered Flight.

4679*	12d. Leonardo da Vinci and drawing	1·50	1·50
4680*	12d. Count Ferdinand von Zeppelin and modern airship	1·50	1·50
4681*	12d. William E. Boeing and Boeing P-12	1·50	1·50
4682*	12d. Capt. John 'Cat's Eyes' Cunningham* and Bristol Beaufighter Mk1F	1·50	1·50
4683*	12d. Capt. Edwin C. Musick and Martin Model 130 China Clipper	1·50	1·50
4684*	12d. Capt. Jock Lowe (longest serving Concorde pilot) and Concorde	1·50	1·50
4685*	12d. William Lear, inventor of first autopilot for jet aircraft and Learjet 24	1·50	1·50
4686*	12d. Jenny Murray, first woman to fly a helicopter around the world and Bell 206A JetRanger	1·50	1·50

No. 4682 is inscribed 'Cat Eyes'.

2004.
4728* 20d. USA 24c. stamp of 1918, showing in error Curtiss JN-4 *Jenny* inverted 15 20

2005.
4874* 25d. Boeing B-29 Superfortress over the Missouri (painting) .... 3·00 3·00
4875* 25d. Boeing B-29 Superfortress *Enola Gay* dropping atomic bomb, Hiroshima .... 3·00 3·00
4876* 25d. Grumman F6F Hellcats and Japanese aircraft over Pacific .... 3·00 3·00
4877* 25d. Grumman F6F Hellcats in battle .... 3·00 3·00

2006. 50th Death Anniv of Ludwig Durr (Zeppelin engineer).

4939	40d. Zeppelin NT-2006	3·00	3·00
4940	40d. US Navy Zeppelin ZRS-3, USS Los Angeles	3·00	3·00
4941	40d. US Navy Zeppelin ZRS-5, USS Macon	3·00	3·00
4939/4941 Set of 3		11·00	11·00

2006. Concorde.
4972 15d. Andre Turcat (first test pilot) .... 2·50 2·50
4973 15d. Take-off at Toulouse, 1969 .... 2·50 2·50

4974	15d. Arrival at Filton, 2003	2·50	2·50
4975	15d. G-BOAF in flight, 2003	2·50	2·50
4972/4975 Set of 4		9·00	9·00

2007. Centenary of First Helicopter Flight.

5042	15d. Bell Model 204 UH-1B/C Iroquois	2·00	2·00
5043	15d. Sikorsky S-65/RN53D Sea Stallion	2·00	2·00
5044	15d. Bell Model 204 UH-1 Iroquois (different)	2·00	2·00
5045	15d. Eurocopter Deutschland/Kawasaki BK117	2·00	2·00
5046	15d. Bensen B-8M Gyro Copter	2·00	2·00
5047	15d. Sikorsky (Augusta) AS-61 (SH-3H Sea King)	2·00	2·00
5042/5047 Set of 6		11·00	11·00

MS5048 65d. Bell AH-1 Huey Cobra .... 9·00 9·00

GEORGIA

North-west Asia

100 tetri = 1 lari

2000. 23rd Death Anniv of Alexander Kartveli (designer).

358	10t. Republic P-47 Thunderbolt	45	40
359	20t. Republic F-84 Thunderjet	70	65
360	80t. Republic F-105D Thunderchief	2·50	2·30
358/360 Set of 3		3·25	3·00

MS361 100t. Kartveli, F-105 and F-84 .... 4·00 3·75

2002.
397 50t. Sukhoi Su25 Scorpio (NATO reference Frogfoot) .... 1·20 95
398 80t. Mikoyan MiG 21U .... 2·75 2·50

2007.
504* 50t. Mil Mi-24 Hind .... 1·70 1·50

GERMANY

Central Europe, divided after the Second World War into Federal Republic (West Germany), West Berlin and Democratic Republic (East Germany); reunited 1990.

1919. 100 pfennig = 1 mark

1923. 100 rentenpfennig = 1 rentenmark

1928. 100 pfennig = 1 reichsmark

1919.
112* 40pf. L.V.G. Schneider biplane .... 15 3·50

1928.

443	1m. Airship LZ-127 *Graf Zeppelin*	28·00	40·00
444	2m. Airship LZ-127 *Graf Zeppelin*	48·00	55·00
445	4m. Airship LZ-127 *Graf Zeppelin*	31·00	40·00
443/445 Set of 3		95·00	£120

1930. First South American Flight. As Nos. 444/5, but additionally inscribed "I. SUDAMERIKA FAHRT".

456	2m. Airship I 7-127 *Graf Zeppelin*	£275	£350
457a	4m. Airship LZ-127 *Graf Zeppelin*	£275	£350

1931. Polar Flight of *Graf Zeppelin*. Nos. 443/5 overprinted **POLAR-FAHRT 1931.**

469	1m. Airship LZ-127 *Graf Zeppelin*	£130	£120
470	2m. Airship LZ-127 *Graf Zeppelin*	£190	£225
471	4m. Airship LZ-127 *Graf Zeppelin*	£475	£800
469/471	*Set of 3*	£700	£1000

1933. Chicago World Exhibition Flight. Nos. 443/5 overprinted **Chicagofahrt Weltausstellung 1933.**

510	1m. Airship LZ-127 *Graf Zeppelin*	£600	£400
511	2m. Airship LZ-127 *Graf Zeppelin*	60·00	£200
512	4m. Airship LZ 127 *Graf Zeppelin*	60 00	£200
510/512	*Set of 3*	£650	£700

1934.

535*	2m. Otto Lilienthal and Lilienthal biplane glider	19·00	20·00
536*	3m. Count Ferdinand von Zeppelin and airship LZ-127 *Graf Zeppelin*	35·00	45·00

1936. 10th Anniv of Lufthansa Airways.

600	40pf. Heinkel He 70 Blitz	6·25	3·50

1936.

603	50pf. Airship LZ-129 *Hindenburg*	21·00	85
604	75pf. Airship LZ-129 *Hindenburg*	23·00	1·20

1938. Birth Centenary of Count Zeppelin.

657	25pf. Count Ferdinand von Zeppelin and airship LZ-5	2·75	1·40
658	50pf. Airship gondola and airship LZ-127 *Graf Zeppelin*	4·00	1·40

1939.

699*	20pf. +10pf. Gliders under construction	1·10	2·20

1941. As No. 699, but with changed face value.

765*	20pf. +30pf. Gliders under construction	85	4·25

1943.

827*	25pf. +15pf. Junkers Ju 87B "Stuka" dive bombers	50	1·40
828*	30pf. +30pf. Aircraft dropping paratroops	75	2·10

1944. 25th Anniv of Air Mail Services.

854	6pf. +4pf. Focke Wulf Fw 200 Condor over Tempelhof Airport	15	1·30
855	12pf. +8pf. Dornier Do-26 flying boat (shown with floats)	15	1·30
856	42pf. +108pf. Junkers Ju 90B of Lufthansa	40	2·50
854/856	*Set of 3*	65	4·50

1944.

870*	20pf. +10pf. Arado Ar 196A	45	2·10

1944. As No. 699, but colour and face value changed.

881*	24pf. +36pf. Gliders under construction	25	1·50

MILITARY FIELDPOST STAMP

1942. No value indicated. Perforated or rouletted.

M804	– Junkers Ju 52/3m	35	50

Allied Occupation - French Zone
BADEN

1949.

FB55*	20pf. Douglas DC-4	5·75	13·00

RHINELAND PALATINATE

1949. As No. FB55 of Baden.

FR50*	20pf. Douglas DC-4	10·00	23·00

WURTTEMBERG

1949. As No. FB55 of Baden.

FW50*	20pf. Douglas DC-4	7·00	16·00

Federal Republic
100 pfennig = 1 deutschmark

1965. 10th Anniv of Lufthansa's Renewed Air Service.

1394*	60pf. Boeing 727-100	35	35

1969. 50th Anniv of German Airmail Services.

1482	20pf. Junkers Ju 52/3m D-2201 *Boelke* of Lufthansa	45	25
1483	30pf. Boeing 707 of Lufthansa	75	25

1975.

1742*	30pf. MBB-Bolkow Bo 105C helicopter	25	15
1754a*	230pf. Airliners at Frankfurt Airport	3·25	1·10
1754b*	250pf. Airliners at Frankfurt Airport	4·00	1·70

1976. 50th Anniv of Lufthansa.

1771	50pf. Junkers F-13 D-183 *Herta* of Deutsche Luft Hansa, 1926	1·10	35

1978. Aviation History (1st series).

1856	30pf. +15pf. Wilhelmine Reichart's balloon, 1820	65	55
1857	40pf. +20pf. Airship LZ-1, 1900	80	70
1858	50pf. +25pf. Bleriot XI, 1909	1·10	95
1859	70pf. +35pf. Hans Grade's monoplane, 1909	1·40	1·30
1856/1859	*Set of 4*	3·50	3·25

1979. Aviation History (2nd series).

1886	40pf. +20pf. Dornier Do-J Wal flying boat, 1922	65	60
1887	50pf. +25pf. Heinkel He 70 Blitz, 1932	90	90
1888	60pf. +30pf. Junkers W.33 D-1167 *Bremen*, 1928	1·10	1·10
1889	90pf. +45pf. Focke Achgelis Fa 61 helicopter, 1936	1·60	1·40
1886/1889	*Set of 4*	3·75	3·50

1980. Aviation History (3rd series).

1918	40pf. +20pf. Phoenix FS 24 glider, 1957	45	45
1919	50pf. +25pf. Lockheed L.1049G Super Constellation D-ALID of Lufthansa (wrongly dated "1950")	75	70
1920	60pf. +30pf. Airbus Industrie A300B2 F-OCAZ of Air France, 1972	1·10	95
1921	90pf. +45pf. Boeing 747-100 of Lufthansa, 1969	1·70	1·40
1918/1921	*Set of 4*	3·50	3·25

1981.

1959*	90pf. +45pf. Gliders	1·60	1·40

1987.

2201*	10pf. Boeing 747 and other airliners at Frankfurt Airport	55	20

1988.

2241*	60pf. Airbus Industrie A320	1·40	55

1991. Historic Mail Aircraft.

2357	30pf. Junkers F-13, 1930	45	45
2358	50pf. Hans Grade's monoplane, 1909	70	35
2359	100pf. Fokker F.III, 1922	1·80	45
2360	165pf. Airship LZ-127 *Graf Zeppelin*	3·00	2·75
2357/2360	*Set of 4*	5·25	3·50

1991. Centenary of First Heavier than Air Flight by Otto Lilienthal.

MS2408	100pf.+50pf. Otto Lilienthal and Lilienthal biplane glider	3·75	3·50

1992. 75th Death Anniv of Ferdinand von Zeppelin.
2443 165pf. Count Ferdinand von Zeppelin and
airship LZ-127 *Graf Zeppelin* .... 2·75 1·40

1992.
2486 100pf. Mail balloon............................ 1·80 70

1997.
MS2811 440pf.+220pf. Biplane .... 6·50 7·00

2000. Centenary of Inaugural Flight of Zeppelin LZ-1.
2977 110f. Zeppelin LZ-1............................ 1·30 95

2002.
3104 56c. Biplane (skywriting)....................... 1·00 90

2003. 75th Anniv of East-West North Atlantic Flight.
3215 144c. +56c. Junkers W-33 Bremen .... 5·00 4·25

2003.
3219 55c. Eurocopter EC135......................... 1·40 1·20

2004.
3258 55c. Paper airplanes........................... 1·80 1·40

2004.
3278 55c. Kite 2004................................. 1·80 1·40

2004.
3298 55c. Dornier Do X flying boat................... 2·00 1·50

2005. 50th Anniv of Resumption of German Air Traffic.
3347 155c. Lockheed L-1049 Super Constellation 5·00 3·75

2007.
MS3471 170c.+70c. Zeppelin LZ-127 *Graf Zeppelin*.. 7·50 7·00

2008. Glider World Championships, Lusse.
3522* 45c. +20c. Glider .... 2·00 1·70

2008.
3542 45c. +20c. Dornier Do-J Wal................... 2·00 1·70
3543 55c. +25c. Airbus A380....................... 2·50 2·00
3544 55c. +25c. Junkers Ju52/3m.................. 2·50 2·00
3545 145c. +55c. MBB BO 105...................... 6·25 5·00
3546 55c. +25c. As 3543, self-adhesive............. 2·50 2·00
3542/3546 Set of 5.............................. 16·00 13·00

West Berlin

100 pfennig = 1 deutschmark

1949.
B41* 15pf. Douglas C-54 of the U.S.A.F. over
Tempelhof Airport.......................... 20·00 1·00
B50* 1Dm. Douglas C-54 of the U.S.A.F. over
Tempelhof Airport.......................... 34·00 1·50

1959. 10th Anniv of Berlin Airlift.
B183 25pf. Aircraft on Berlin Airlift................ 55 50

1962. 50th Anniv of German Airmail Transport.
B225 60pf. Euler Gelberhund biplane, 1912, and
Boeing 707 .... 60 55

1974. Opening of Tegel Airport, Berlin.
B462 50pf. Airliners at Tegel Airport .... 1·20 75

1975. As Nos. 1742 and 1754a/b of Federal Republic.
B481* 30pf. MBB-Bolkow Bo 105C helicopter...... 40 20
B490a* 230pf. Airliners at Frankfurt Airport .... 2·75 2·30
B490b* 250pf. Airliners at Frankfurt Airport .... 4·00 3·50

1978. Aviation History (1st series).
B547 30pf. +15pf. Montgolfier balloon (first
manned free flight, 1783).................. 45 50
B548 40pf. +20pf. Lilienthal glider, 1891.............. 70 70
B549 50pf. +25pf. Wright Type A..................... 90 90
B550 70pf. +35pf. Etrich/Rumpler Taube, 1910 .. 1·50 1·50
B547/550 Set of 4.............................. 3·25 3·25

1979. Aviation History (2nd series).
B567 40pf. +20pf. Vampyr glider, 1921.............. 55 60
B568 50pf. +25pf. Junkers Ju 52/3m D-2202
Richthofen, 1932........................ 90 90
B569 60pf. +30pf. Messerschmitt Bf 108 D-1010,
1934.................................... 1·20 1·20
B570 90pf. +45pf. Douglas DC-3 NC-14988 of
American Airlines, 1935 .... 1·80 1·80
B567/570 Set of 4.............................. 4·00 4·00

1980. Aviation History (3rd series).
B589 40pf. +20pf. Vickers Viscount 810 of
Lufthansa (wrongly dated "1950")..... 85 80
B590 50pf. +25pf. Fokker F.27 Friendship *Condor*
of Lufthansa (wrongly dated "1955") 90 90
B591 60pf. +30pf. Sud Aviation SE 210 Caravelle
F-BKSZ of Air France, 1955 .... 1·20 1·10
B592 90pf. +45pf. Sikorsky S-55 helicopter OO-
SHB of Sabena, 1949 .... 1·70 1·60
B589/592 Set of 4.............................. 4·25 4·00

1987. As No. 2201 of Federal Republic.
B778* 10pf. Boeing 747 and other airliners at
Frankfurt Airport......................... 2·10 2·20

Democratic Republic

100 pfennig = 1 mark

1956. Establishment of East German Lufthansa Airline.
E250* 10pf. Ilyushin Il-14P DDR-ABA of Deutsche
Lufthansa................................ 90 25
E251* 15pf. Ilyushin Il-14P DDR-ABF of Deutsche
Lufthansa................................ 60 25
E252* 20pf. Ilyushin Il-14P DDR-ABA of Deutsche
Lufthansa................................ 60 25

1957.
E350 5pf. Stylised aircraft...................... 2·75 20
E351 20pf. Stylised aircraft...................... 25 20
E352 35pf. Stylised aircraft...................... 25 20
E353 50pf. Stylised aircraft...................... 45 20
E354 1Dm. Stylised aircraft...................... 1·30 20
E355 3Dm. Stylised aircraft...................... 2·20 45
E356 5Dm. Stylised aircraft...................... 5·25 80
E350/356 Set of 7.............................. 8·75 2·10

1958.
E397* 20pf. Baade-Bonin 152 .... 45 20

1959.
E462* 60pf. Ilyushin Il-14M 20 20

1961.
E546* 25pf. Ilyushin Il-12 .... 55 35

1962.
E615* 5pf. Pilot and Mikoyan Gurevich MiG-17 jet fighters 20 15

1962.
E654* 25pf. Nose of Ilyushin Il-14M at Leipzig Airport .... 1·10 95

1962.
E655 5pf. Ilyushin Il-18 .... 45 25

1963.
E698* 10pf. Ilyushin Il-18 .... 90 15

1968. Aerobatic World Championships, Magdeburg.
E1112 10pf. Zlin Z-226 Trener 6 DM-WKM 20 15
E1113 25pf. Zlin Z-226 Trener 6 DM-WKM and Zlin Z-226 Trener 6 DM-WKN.............. 75 60

1969. Interflug (airline) Aircraft.
E1245 20pf. Antonov An-24B of Interflug 20 15
E1246 25pf. Ilyushin Il-18 of Interflug .... 1·60 1·20
E1247 30pf. Tupolev Tu-134 of Interflug 20 20
E1248 50pf. Mil Mi-8 helicopter DM-SPA of Interflug 25 20
E1245/1248 *Set of 4* .... 2·00 1·60

1971.
E1423* 10pf. +5pf. Tupolev Tu-134 .... 20 15

1972. East German Aircraft.
E1467 5pf. Kamov Ka-26 helicopter.............. 20 20
E1468 10pf. Letov Z-37 Cmelak crop sprayer DM-SMC 20 20
E1469 35pf. Ilyushin Il-62M of Interflug.............. 25 20
E1470 1m. Stylised Ilyushin Il-62M .... 1·70 1·70
E1467/1470 *Set of 4* .... 2·10 2·10

1972.
E1492* 10pf. Light airplane.............. 20 20

1972.
E1509* 35pf. Jet airliner.............. 25 30

1974.
E1702* 25pf. Early airliner and Tupolev Tu-134...... 20 15

1976.
E1832* 20pf. Mikoyan Gurevich MiG-21 jet fighters 35 30

1977.
E1971* 20pf. Hans Grade's monoplane, 1909.......... 20 15

1978.
E2072* 35pf. Lilienthal monoplane glider.............. 1·40 1·20

1980.
E2237* 25pf. Ilyushin Il-62M at Schonefeld Airport 45 45
E2238* 35pf. PZL-106A Kruk crop-spraying airplane 70 70
E2239* 70pf. Antonov An-2 aerial photography biplane .... 1·40 1·40
MSE2240* 1m.+10pf. Ilyushin Il-62M .... 2·50 2·50

1982.
E2459 5pf. Stylised aircraft.............. 20 20
E2460 15pf. Stylised aircraft.............. 20 40
E2461 20pf. Stylised aircraft.............. 35 20
E2462 25pf. Stylised aircraft.............. 45 30
E2463 30pf. Stylised aircraft.............. 25 20
E2464 40pf. Stylised aircraft.............. 35 20
F2465 1m. Stylised aircraft.............. 1·30 55
E2466 3m. Stylised aircraft.............. 3·25 1·90
E2467 5m. Stylised aircraft.............. 4·50 1·70
E2459/2467 *Set of 9* .... 10·00 5·00

1983.
E2489* 20pf. Ilyushin Il-62, ship, letter, parcel........ 20 15

1984.
E2605* 20pf. Mil Mi-8 helicopter.............. 25 30

1985.
E2679* 50pf. Mil Mi-8 helicopter.............. 75 65

1987.
E2823 10pf. Gliders.............. 40 25

1990. Historic Flying Machines.
E3007 20pf. Designs for flying machines by Leonardo da Vinci 30 20
E3008 35pf. +5pf. Melchior Bauer's man-powered airplane design, 1764.............. 70 70
E3009 50pf. Albrecht Berblinger's man-powered flying machine, 1811.............. 80 80
E3010 90pf. Otto Lilienthal's design for a monoplane glider.............. 1·50 1·50
E3007/3010 *Set of 4* .... 3·00 3·00

GHANA

West Africa

1958. 12 pence = 1 shilling
20 shillings = 1 pound
1965. 100 pesewas = 1 cedi
1967. 100 new pesewas = 1 new cedi
1972. 100 pesewas = 1 cedi

1958.

194*	1s.3d. Bristol 175 Britannia 309 of Ghana Airways	75	20
195*	2s. Boeing 377 Stratocruiser of Ghana Airways	1·00	55
196*	2s.6d. Vickers VC-10 of Ghana Airways	80	95

1962.

275*	1s.3d. Douglas DC-8	65	15
276*	2s.6d. Douglas DC-8	80	2·50

1970. Inauguration of Kotoka Airport.

569	4n.p. Vickers VC-10 over Kotoka Airport	15	10
570	12½n.p. Control tower and tail of Vickers VC-10	25	15
571	20n.p. Kotoka Airport	40	30
572	40n.p. Kotoka Airport	75	80
569/572 Set of 4		1·40	1·25

1971.

599*	50n.p. Boeing 707	1·10	1·10

1978. 75th Anniv of Powered Flight.

840	8p. Wright *Flyer III*	20	10
841	30p. Handley Page H.P.42	30	30
842	60p. de Havilland DH.106 Comet 1	40	60
843	1c. Concorde	2·75	1·10
840/843 Set of 4		3·25	1·90
MS844 15p. Wright *Flyer III*; 40p. Handley Page H.P.42; 65p. de Havilland DH.106 Comet 1; 80p. Concorde		2·00	1·40

1978. Nos. 840/4 overprinted **CAPEX 78 JUNE 9-18 1978.**

845	8p. Wright *Flyer III*	15	15
846	30p. Handley Page H.P.42	25	25
847	60p. de Havilland DH.106 Comet 1	50	50
848	1c. Concorde	1·10	80
845/848 Set of 4		1·75	1·50
MS849 15p. Wright *Flyer III*; 40p. Handley Page H.P.42; 65p. de Havilland DH.106 Comet 1; 80p. Concorde		1·25	1·60

1980.

921*	20p. Boeing 737	10	10

1986.

1182*	25c. Douglas DC-10 of Ghana Airways	60	45
1183*	100c. Stewardess and outline of Douglas DC-10	2·25	3·00

1991.

1540*	20c. Airliner	55	20

1993.

1786*	20c. Airship LZ-3	85	30
1792*	800c. Airship LZ-10 Schwaben	3·75	5·00
MS1793 Four sheets. (a) 900c. Count Ferdinand von Zeppelin and airship LZ-1 (other sheets do not show aircraft) Set of 4 sheets		17·00	17·00

1993.

1827	50c. Airship LZ-127 *Graf Zeppelin*	50	30
1828	150c. Airship LZ-7 *Deutschland*	85	55
1829	400c. Avro Vulcan jet bomber	1·75	1·75
1830	400c. Ford 4-AT Trimotor of the U.S. Mail	1·75	1·75
1831	600c. Nieuport 27 biplane	2·25	2·25
1832	600c. Airship LZ-127 *Graf Zeppelin*	2·25	2·25
1833	800c. Airship LZ-10 *Schwaben*	3·75	4·00
1827/1833 Set of 7		11·50	11·50
MS1834 Three sheets. (a) 1000c. Airship LZ-127 *Graf Zeppelin*; (b) 1000c. Royal Aircraft Factory S.E.5A; (c) 1000c. Airplane Set of 3 sheets		15·00	15·00

1995. 50th Anniv of International Civil Aviation Organisation.

(a) Inscribed "50th Anniversary of Ghana Civil Aviation Authority"

2085	100c. Control tower and emblem	1·50	
2086	400c. Communications equipment	2·75	
2087	1000c. Douglas DC-10 taking off	4·00	

(b) Inscribed "50th Anniversary of the International Civil Aviation Organisation (ICAO)"

2088	100c. Control tower and emblem	40	20
2089	400c. Communications equipment	90	90
2090	1000c. Douglas DC-10 taking off	2·00	2·50
2085/2090 Set of 6		3·00	3·25

1998. History of Aviation.

2660	800c. Breguet Br.14 B2, France	70	70
2661	800c. Curtiss Model 67 BF2C-1 Goshawk USA	70	70
2662	800c. Supermarine Spitfire Mk IX, Great Britain	70	70
2663	800c. Fiat G.50 Freccia, Italy	70	70
2664	800c. Douglas B-18A Bolo USA	70	70
2665	800c. Boeing FB-5, USA	70	70
2666	800c. Bristol F2B Fighter ('*Brisfit*')*, Great Britain	70	70
2667	800c. Hawker Fury 1, Great Britain	70	70
2668	800c. Fiat CR-42 Falco, Italy	70	70
2669	800c. Messerschmitt Bf 109 E-7 Germany	70	70
2670	800c. Lockheed PV-2 Harpoon, USA	70	70
2671	800c. Airspeed AS.10 Oxford Mk.1 Great Britain	70	70
2672	800c. Junkers Ju 87D-1 Stuka, Germany	70	70
2673	800c. Yakovlev Yak-9D 'Frank' USSR	70	70
2674	800c. North American P-51D Mustang, USA	70	70
2675	800c. Douglas A-20G Havoc, USA	70	70
2676	800c. Supermarine Attacker F1 Great Britain	70	70
2677	800c. Mikoyan Gurevich MiG 15, USSR	70	70
2660/2677 Set of 18		11·00	11·00
MS2678 Two sheets. (a) 3000c. Supermarine Spitfires Mk I & Mk XIV; (b) 3000c. Mitsubishi AGM8 Reisen, Japan Set of 2 sheets		7·50	8·00

No. 2675 is wrongly inscribed "A-206".

1998.

2765*	1000c. Orville and Wilbur Wright	60	60
2766*	1000c. Wright *Flyer I*	60	60

1999. 80th Anniv of Royal Air Force.

2798	2000c. Lockheed C-130 Hercules	1·50	1·50
2799	2000c. Boeing HC Mk 2 Chinook	1·50	1·50
2800	2000c. Lockheed C-130 Hercules	1·50	1·50
2801	2000c. Panavia Tornado F. Mk3	1·50	1·50
2798/2801 Set of 4		5·50	5·50
MS2802 Two sheets. (a) 5500c. de Havilland Canada DHC-1 Chipmunk and Eurofighter EF-2000 Typhoon; (b) 5500c. Bristol F2B Set of 2 sheets		7·50	7·50

2000. Centenary of First Zeppelin Flight.

3060	1600c. LZ-129 *Hindenburg*, 1936	1·50	1·60
3061	1600c. LZ-9 *Ersatz Deutschland*, 1911	1·50	1·60
3062	1600c. LZ-4, 1908	1·50	1·60
3060/3062 Set of 3		4·00	4·25
MS3063 5000c. LZ-11 *Viktoria Luise*, 1912		4·25	4·75

2002. 75th Anniv of First Solo Trans-Atlantic Flight.

MS3324 (a) 8500c. Lindbergh and Ryan NYP Special *Spirit of St Louis*; (b) 8500c. Charles and Anne Lindbergh in Ryan NYP Special *Spirit of St Louis*		7·50	8·00
MS3325 15000c. Charles Lindbergh		4·50	5·00

2003. Centenary of Powered Flight.

MS3377 7000c. Ryan NYP Special *Spirit of St. Louis* (first non-stop solo transatlantic flight, 1927); 7000c. Lockheed Vega *Winnie Mae* (first solo round the world flight, 1933); 7000c. Heinkel He-178 (first turbojet aircraft, 1939); 7000c. Bell X-1 (first manned supersonic flight, 1947)		8·00	9·00

2006.

3535*	8000c. Hot air balloon	1·50	1·60
3536*	8000c. Montgolfier balloon (1783)	1·50	1·60
3537*	8000c. Modern hot air balloon	1·50	1·60
MS3538* 20000c. Zeppelin LZ-129 *Hindenburg* (1937)		4·00	4·25

2006. Nos. 2085/90 surch.

3595	4500c. on 100c. Control tower		
3596	4500c. on 400c. Communications equipment		
3597	4500c. on 1000c. Douglas DC-10 taking off.		
3598	6000c. on 100c. Control tower.		
3599	6000c. on 400c. Communications equipment		
3600	6000c. on 1000c. Douglas DC-10 taking off.		

2007. Antrak Air.

3683	40Gp. McDonnell Douglas MD-80	1·25	1·00
3684	70Gp. Aircraft in flight	2·25	2·25

GIBRALTAR

South-west Europe

1949. 12 pence = 1 shilling

20 shillings = 1 pound

1971. 100 pence = 1 pound

1949. As Nos. 114/15 of Antigua.
136*	2d. Airplane...	1·00	1·25
137*	3d. Jet-powered Vickers Viking..................	2·00	1·50

1953.
152*	5d. English Electric Canberra at Gibraltar Airport..	1·25	1·00

1960.
167*	7d. Hawker Siddeley Comet 4 over airport..	2·00	1·75

1967.
210*	2s. Fairey Swordfish over aircraft carrier H.M.S. *Ark Royal*	3·50	2·50

1978. 60th Anniv of Royal Air Force.
407	3p. Short S.25 Sunderland flying boat	15	10
408	9p. Caudron G-3	35	40
409	12p. Avro Shackleton M.R.2.....................	40	55
410	16p. Hawker Hunter F.6............................	45	1·00
411	18p. Hawker Siddeley H.S.801 Nimrod M.R.1...	50	1·10
407/411 *Set of 5*		1·70	2·75

1981. 50th Anniv of Gibraltar Airmail Service.
456*	55p. Jet airliner......................................	60	80

1982. Aircraft.
460	1p. Douglas DC-3 of Gibair.....................	25	2·00
461	2p. Vickers Viking 1B of Hunting Clan ...	30	2·00
462	3p. Airspeed A.S.57 Ambassador G-ALZN of B.E.A.	30	1·75
463	4p. Vickers Viscount 800 of Gibair..........	40	20
464	5p. Boeing 727-100 of Dan-Air................	90	60
465	10p. Vickers 953 Vanguard of B.E.A.	1·75	50
466	14p. Short S.45A Solent 2 flying boat of Aquila Airways..................................	1·75	3·50
467	15p. Fokker F.27 Friendship.....................	2·75	3·50
468	17p. Boeing 737 of Air Europe.................	1·00	75
469	20p. B.A.C. One Eleven 500 G-AWYV of British Caledonian................................	1·00	65
470	25p. Lockheed Constellation of B.O.A.C. ..	4·00	5·00
471	50p. Hawker Siddeley Comet 4B of B.E.A. ..	4·00	2·25
472	£1 Saro A.21 Windhover flying boat G-ABJP *General Godley* of Gibraltar Airways	5·50	2·25
473	£2 Hawker Siddeley Trident 2E of B.E.A. ..	6·50	5·00

88

474	£5 de Havilland DH.89A Dragon Rapide of Gibraltar Airways (shown with registration D-AGEE)	8·00	14·00
460/474 *Set of 15*		35·00	40·00

1982.
479*	14p. Hawker Hurricane Mk I and Supermarine Spitfires	25	70

1988.
589*	22p. Boeing 737	1·50	2·25

1993.
710*	24p. Panavia Tornado F Mk 3 and Handley Page 0/400 of the R.A.F	1·75	75

1995.
MS744 £1.05 Fairey Swordfish............................		3·25	4·00

1998. 80th Anniv of Royal Air Force.
829	24p. Saunders Roe (Saro) London..............	70	55
830	26p. Fairey Fox.....................................	75	60
831	38p. Handley Page Halifax GR.VI..............	95	1·25
832	50p. Hawker Siddeley Buccaneer S.2B......	1·25	2·50
829/832 *Set of 4*		3·25	4·50
MS833 42p. Sopwith Strutter; 26p. Bristol M.IB; 38p. Supermarine Spitfire XII; 50p. Avro Type 685 York		3·50	4·50

1999. RAF Fighter Aircraft.
883*	30p. Eurofighter EF-2000 Typhoon	1·10	1·25
884*	30p. Panavia Tornado F. Mk3	1·10	1·25
885*	30p. BAe Harrier II GR7..........................	1·10	1·25

2000. RAF Second World War Aircraft.
943*	30p. Supermarine Spitfire Mk IIA *Gibraltar*	1·75	1·75
944*	30p. Hawker Hurricane Mk IIC	1·75	1·75
945*	30p. Avro Type 683 Lancaster BI-III *City of Lincoln*...	1·75	1·75

2001. Modern Military Aircraft.
982*	40p. BAe Sea Harrier FA Mk.2..................	1·25	1·50
984*	40p. BAe Hawk T Mk.1............................	1·25	1·50
986*	40p. SEPECAT Jaguar GR1B.....................	1·25	1·50

2003. Centenary of Powered Flight.
1045*	30p. Wright Bros. *Flyer I*, 1903	90	65
1046*	40p. Charles Lindbergh and Ryan NYP Special *Spirit of St Louis* (first trans-Atlantic solo flight, 1927)...................	1·25	1·25
1047*	40p. Boeing 314 *Yankee Clipper* flying boat. (first trans-Atlantic scheduled air service, 1939)	1·25	1·25

1048*	42p. Saunders Roe (Saro) A21 Windhover (first scheduled air service between Gibraltar and Tangier, 1931).............	1·25	1·25
1049*	44p. Aerospatiale/BAe Concorde (first supersonic airliner, 1976)...................	1·40	1·40
1050*	66p. Space subject.................................	2·00	2·75
1045/1050 *Set of 6*...		7·25	7·75

2004.
1090*	47p. Handley Page Halifax	1·40	1·40

2006. 75th Anniv of Gibraltar Airmail Service.
1176	8p. Saunders Roe (Saro) A21 Windhover, 1931	50	30
1177	40p. Vickers Vanguard, 1959	1·75	90
1178	49p. Vickers Viscount	2·50	1·40
1179	£1.60 Boeing 737	5·50	6·00
1176/1179 *Set of 4*..			

2008. 90th Anniv of Royal Air Force.
1261	40p. Short 184 and Saro London...............	1·50	1·40
1262	40p. Supermarine Spitfire IV and Hawker Hurricane IIc..	1·50	1·40
1263	42p. Bristol Beaufighter II and Avro Type 683 Lancaster TS III	1·60	1·40
1264	42p. Hawker Hunter Mk 6 and Avro Type 696 Shackleton	1·60	1·40
1265	49p. Avro Type 698 Vulcan and de Havilland DH. 98 Mosquito	1·80	1·60
1266	49p. Panavia Tornado GR4 and SEPECAT Jaguar GR..	1·80	1·60
1261/1266 *Set of 6*...		8·75	8·00
MS1267 £2 Felixstowe F.3		6·50	7·00

GILBERT AND ELLICE ISLANDS

Pacific Ocean

1949. 12 pence = 1 shilling

20 shillings = 1 pound

1966. 100 cents = 1 dollar

1949. As Nos. 114/15 of Antigua.
59*	1d. Airplane...	40	1·25
60*	2d. Jet-powered Vickers Viking.................	2·00	3·00

1964. First Air Service.
82*	3d. de Havilland DH.114 Heron 2.............	70	30
84*	3s.7d. de Havilland DH.114 Heron 2.............	1·40	1·50

1974.
234*	25c. B.A.C. One Eleven DQ-FBO of Air Pacific..	25	30

GOLD COAST

West Africa
12 pence = 1 shilling
20 shillings = 1 pound

1949. As Nos. 114/15 of Antigua.
149*	2d. Airplane	25	20
150*	2½d. Jet-powered Vickers Viking	1·50	4·25

GREAT BRITAIN

Western Europe
1963. 12 pence = 1 shilling
20 shillings = 1 pound
1971. 100 pence = 1 pound

1963.
639*	2½d. Westland Widgeon III helicopter	25	25

1965. 25th Anniv of Battle of Britain.
671*	4d. Flight of Supermarine Spitfires	25	25
672*	4d. Pilot in cockpit of Hawker Hurricane Mk I	25	25
673*	4d. Wingtips of Supermarine Spitfire and Messerschmitt Bf 109	25	25
674*	4d. Supermarine Spitfires attacking Heinkel He 111H bomber	25	25
675*	4d. Supermarine Spitfire attacking Junkers Ju 87B "Stuka"	25	25
676*	4d. Hawker Hurricanes Mk I over wreck of Dornier Do-17Z	25	25

1967.
716*	1s.6d. Armstrong Whitworth A.W.650 Argosy of B.E.A.	25	40

1967.
754*	1s.6d. Engines of Vickers VC-10 and Gloster Whittle E28/39	20	25

1968.
769*	1s. Sopwith Camel biplane and silhouettes of English Electric Lightning jet fighters	15	15

1969. First Flight of Concorde.
784	4d. Concorde	25	25
785	9d. Plan and side views of Concorde	55	75
786	1s.6d. Nose and tail of Concorde	75	1·00
784/786 Set of 3		1·40	1·80

1969.
791*	5d. John Alcock, Arthur Whitten Brown and their Vickers FB-27 Vimy, 1919	10	15

795*	1s.9d Ross and Keith Smith's Vickers FB-27 Vimy G-EAOU, 1919	20	40

1974.
955*	5½p. Farman H.F.III biplane	25	30
957*	10p. Short S.21 flying boat G-ADHK *Maia*	50	40

1986. History of Royal Air Force.
1336	17p. Lord Dowding and Hawker Hurricane Mk I	50	10
1337	22p. Lord Tedder and Hawker Typhoon IB	75	95
1338	29p. Lord Trenchard and Airco (de Havilland) DH9A	1·25	1·25
1339	31p. Sir Arthur Harris and Avro Type 683 Lancaster	1·75	1·60
1340	34p. Lord Portal and de Havilland DH.98 Mosquito	1·75	1·90
1336/1340 Set of 5		5·50	5·25

1988.
1395*	34p. Handley Page H.P.45 G-AAXD *Horatius* of Imperial Airways	1·60	1·50

1991.
1549*	37p. Gloster Whittle E28/39	1·35	1·75

1994.
1808*	(1st) Biggles and Royal Aircraft Factory B.E.2C	60	50

1994.
1824*	25p. Douglas Boston of No. 88 Squadron, R.A.F. being loaded with smoke canisters	50	40

1997. British Aircraft Designers.
1984	20p. Reginald Mitchell/Supermarine Spitfire Mk IIA	75	40
1985	26p. Roy Chadwick/Avro Type 683 Lancaster Mk I	1·10	1·25
1986	37p. Ronald Bishop/de Havilland DH. 98 Mosquito B Mk XVI	1·40	1·25
1987	43p. George Carter/Gloster Meteor T. Mk7	1·50	1·60

1988	63p. Sir Sidney Camm/Hawker Hunter FGA MK 9	2·00	2·00
1984/1988 Set of 5		6·00	5·75

1999.
2073*	20p. Stylised airliner (Comet?) hugging globe	75	70

2002.
2262*	1st class Aircraft skywriting 'Hello'	1·00	1·00

2002. 50th Anniv of Passenger Jet Aviation.
2284*	2nd class Airbus Industries Airbus A340-600 (2002)	75	55
2285*	1st class Aerospatiale/BAe Concorde (1976)	1·00	80
2286*	(E) BAC Trident (1964)	1·25	1·25
2287*	45p. Vickers VC-10 (1964)	1·50	1·50
2288*	65p. de Havilland DH.106 Comet (1952)	2·00	2·25
No. 2285 also comes self-adhesive.			

2003.
2360*	2nd class Amy Johnson and de Havilland DH. 60G Gipsy Moth *Jason*	50	50

2003.
2397*	1st class Toy airplane (Meccano)	75	50

2004.
2428*	1st class Airplane (stylised)	50	50

2006.
2622*	1st class Queen at Heathrow Airport	45	50

2007.
2829*	69p. Westland Sea King	1·50	1·50

2008. Air Displays.

2855	1st class BAe Hawk T1s of Red Arrows	85	85
2856	48p. Parachutists	1·10	1·10
2857	50p. Red Arrows formation	1·10	1·10
2858	56p. Avro Type 698 Vulcan and Avro Type 707	1·30	1·30
2859	72p. Avro Type 504	1·60	1·60
2860	81p. Air race at Hendon	1·80	1·80
2855/2860 *Set of 6*		7·75	7·75

GREECE

South-east Europe

100 lepta = 1 drachma

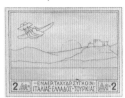

1926.

406	2d. Savoia Marchetti S-55C flying boat...	2·00	1·10
407	3d. Savoia Marchetti S-55C flying boat...	12·50	8·25
408	5d. Savoia Marchetti S-55C flying boat...	2·50	1·10
409	10d. Savoia Marchetti S-55C flying boat...	13·70	8·75
406/409 *Set of 4*		28·00	17·00

1933.

458	30d. Airship LZ-127 *Graf Zeppelin*	19·00	9·75
459	100d. Airship LZ-127 *Graf Zeppelin*	85·00	41·00
460	120d. Airship LZ-127 *Graf Zeppelin*	80·00	65·00
458/460 *Set of 3*		£170	£100

1933. Aeroespresso Company.

463*	3d. Marina Fiat MF.5 flying boat of Aero Espresso	1·10	85
465*	10d. Stylised Marina Fiat MF.5 flying boat	1·80	2·20
466*	20d. Marina Fiat MF.5 flying boat of Aero Espresso	12·00	7·75
467*	50d. Marina Fiat MF.5 flying boat of Aero Espresso	80·00	60·00

1933.

468	50l. Junkers G.24	55	45
469	1d. Junkers G.24	1·40	60
470	2d. Junkers G.24	1·60	1·10
471	5d. Junkers G.24	6·75	4·25
472	10d. Junkers G.24	19·00	11·50
473	25d. Junkers G.24	35·00	19·00
474	50d. Junkers G.24	50·00	45·00
468/474 *Set of 7*		£100	70·00

1938. No. D451 overprinted with Junkers G.24 airplane. Perforated or rouletted.

521	50l. Numeral design	20	25

1940.

544*	2d. Three monoplanes	80	75
545*	4d. Heston Phoenix	3·25	4·25
546*	6d. Heston Phoenix SX-AAH	6·00	5·00
547*	8d. Heston Phoenix	9·25	9·25
548*	16d. Heston Phoenix SX-AAH	22·00	18·00
549*	32d. Heston Phoenix	41·00	42·00
550*	45d. Heston Phoenix	41·00	42·00
551*	55d. Single-engine monoplane (shown with registration SX-ACA)	50·00	47·00
552*	65d. Three biplanes	47·00	46·00
553*	100d. Two biplanes	60·00	46·00

1941. Nos. D453, D455/6, D458 and D480 overprinted with Junkers G.24 airplane or surcharged also. Nos. 556/7 exist perforated or rouletted.

556	1d. on 2d. Numeral design	25	25
557	5d. Numeral design	1·60	25
558	10d. Numeral design	10	35
559	25d. Numeral design	70	1·60
560	50d. Numeral design	95	2·00
556/560 *Set of 5*		3·25	4·00

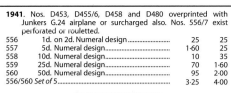

1946.

651*	1000d. Pilot and Supermarine Spitfire Mk IIB	3·50	35

1966. Inauguration of Olympic Airways Trans-Atlantic Flights.

1018	6d. Boeing 707 of Olympic Airways	35	30

1968. Royal Hellenic Air Force.

1094	2d.50 P.Z.L. P. 24 ramming Savola Marchettl S.M.79-11 Sparviero	70	50
1095	3d.50 Breguet 19, 1928.	20	25
1096	8d. Farman H.F.III biplane and Lockheed F-104G Super Starfighter	55	50
1094/1096 *Set of 3*		1·30	1·10

1978.

1428*	13d. Wright *Flyer I*	20	30

1980.

1537*	8d. Dassault Mirage III	10	20
1538*	12d. Piper PA-18 Super Cub and hangar...	15	20

1981.

1553*	3d. Potez 25 biplane, glider and model glider	10	20

1982.

1582*	30d. Airbus Industrie A300 of Olympic Airways	20	30

1999.

2107*	500d. Control Tower, Eleftherios Venizelos Airport, Athens and Boeing 747 taking off	2·20	2·40

1999.

2108*	20d. Agusta-Bell 201A	10	15
2110*	40d. Lockheed Martin F-16 Fighting Falcons	20	25
2111*	50d. Canadair CL-215	20	20
2114*	170d. Dassault Mirage 2000	85	85
2115*	250d. Helicopters	1·30	1·30

2004.

2274*	€2.85 Hot air balloon 2006	4·00	2·00

2006.

2425*	15c. Toy airplane	30	20

GREEK OCCUPATION OF ALBANIA

South-east Europe

100 lepta = 1 drachma

ΕΛΛΗΝΙΚΗ
ΔΙΟΙΚΗCΙC

1940. Nos. 544/53 of Greece overprinted with two lines of Greek characters.

36*	2d. Three monoplanes	55	1·00
37*	4d. Heston Phoenix	2·75	4·25
38*	6d. Heston Phoenix SX-AAH	3·75	5·25
39*	8d. Heston Phoenix	5·50	8·25
40*	16d. Heston Phoenix SX-AAH	11·00	16·00
41*	32d. Heston Phoenix	12·00	19·00
42*	45d. Heston Phoenix SX-AAH	12·00	19·00
43*	55d. Single-engine monoplane (shown with registration SX-ACA)	12·00	19·00
44*	65d. Three biplanes	12·00	19·00
45*	100d. Two biplanes	22·00	16·00
36/45 *Set of 10*		85·00	£110

GREENLAND

North Atlantic

100 ore = 1 krone

1971.

79*	80ore. Consolidated PBY-5A Catalina amphibian	40	40
84*	2k. Sikorsky S-61N helicopter DY-HAF	70	50

1988.
194	3k. +50ore. de Havilland Canada DHC-7 Dash Seven	2·30	2·20

2004. 50th Anniv of First Scheduled Flight, Denmark to Greenland.
445	8k.75 Airplane over map	2·60	2·50

2005.
480*	23k. Naval helicopter carrier	10·75	10·50

GRENADA

West Indies

100 cents = 1 dollar

1949. As Nos. 114/15 of Antigua.
168*	5c. Airplane	15	10
169*	6c. Jet-powered Vickers Viking	1·50	2·50

1961.
210*	25c. Douglas DC-3	55	25

1970.
410*	25c. Boeing 707	1·00	30

1970.
426*	60c. Ambulance being loaded onto Lockheed C-130 Hercules	90	1·50

1971.
455*	1c. Sikorsky S-61B SH-3 Sea King helicopter and aircraft carrier U.S.S. Iwo Jima	10	50

1974.
628*	½c. Concorde	30	10
629*	1c. Westland Wessex HU Mk 5 helicopter	30	10
630*	2c. Airship LZ-127 Graf Zeppelin, Vickers FB-27 Vimy (top right), Boeing 747-100 (centre) and de Havilland D.H.4	30	10

1975.
661*	35c. B.A.C. One Eleven at Pearls Airport	30	10

1976. Airplanes.
818	½c. Piper PA-23 Apache 235 of L.I.A.T. and B.A.C. One Eleven	10	10
819	1c. Beech 50 Twin Bonanza VP-LIF of L.I.A.T. and B.A.C. One Eleven	10	10
820	2c. de Havilland Canada DHC-6 Twin Otter 100 of L.I.A.T. and B.A.C. One Eleven	10	10
821	40c. Britten-Norman BN-2 Islander VP-LAS and B.A.C. One Eleven	60	10
822	50c. de Havilland DH.114 Heron 2 of L.I.A.T. and B.A.C. One Eleven	65	10
823	$2 Hawker Siddeley H.S.748 VQ-LIP of L.I.A.T. and B.A.C. One Eleven	2·00	50
818/823	Set of 6	3·25	1·30
MS824	$3 B.A.C. One Eleven 500	1·50	80

1978. 75th Anniv of First Zeppelin Flight and 50th Anniv of Lindbergh's Trans-Atlantic Flight.
907	½c. Count Ferdinand von Zeppelin and airship LZ-1	10	10
908	1c. Charles Lindbergh and Ryan NYP Special Spirit of St. Louis	10	10
909	2c. Airship LZ-7 Deutschland	10	10
910	22c. Lindbergh's Ryan NYP Special Spirit of St. Louis	30	10
911	75c. Charles Lindbergh and Ryan NYP Special Spirit of St. Louis	60	10
912	$1 Airship LZ-127 Graf Zeppelin	65	15
913	$3 Airship LZ-127 Graf Zeppelin	1·40	25
907/913	Set of 7	3·00	80
MS914	35c. Charles Lindbergh in Ryan NYP Special Spirit of St. Louis; $2 Count Ferdinand von Zeppelin and airship LZ-5	1·00	60

1978. 75th Anniv of Powered Flight.
962	5c. Wright Flyer III	10	10
963	15c. Wright Flyer I	10	10
964	18c. Wright Type A	10	10
965	22c. Wright Flyer I	15	10
966	50c. Orville Wright and Wright Type A	20	20
967	75c. Wright Type A	25	25
968	$3 Wilbur Wright and Wright Glider No. IV	80	70
962/968	Set of 7	1·50	1·40
MS969	$2 Wright Glider No. III	1·00	75

1979.
996*	18c. Balloon from the film Around the World in Eighty Days	35	20
999*	$3 Flying machine from Master of the World by Jules Verne	1·40	2·00

1981.
1166*	90c. Boeing 707 (on stamp No. 410)	70	50
MS1168	$5 Concorde (on stamp No. 628)	3·25	3·75

1983.
1243*	70c. Airport runway under construction	35	35

1983. Bicentenary of Manned Flight.
1262	30c. Airship N.1 Norge	60	30
1263	60c. Gloster VI seaplane	1·00	1·00
1264	$1.10 Curtiss NC-4 flying boat	3·50	4·50
1265	$4 Dornier Do-18 flying boat D-ABYM Aeolus of Lufthansa	1·60	1·75
1262/1265	Set of 4	6·00	6·75
MS1266	$5 Hot-air balloon	1·50	1·50

1985. Opening of Point Saline International Airport.
1393	70c. Hawker Siddeley H.S.748 of L.I.A.T.	2·50	1·00
1394	$1 Lockheed L-1011 TriStar 500 of Pan Am	3·25	1·50
1395	$4 Lockheed L-1011 TriStar 500 of Pan Am	6·50	8·00
1393/1395	Set of 3	11·00	9·50
MS1396	$5 Hawker Siddeley H.S.748 of L.I.A.T. at Point Saline Airport	5·50	3·75

1985. 40th Anniv of ICAO.
1397	10c. Douglas DC-8-61 of Air Canada	40	20
1398	50c. Lockheed L.1649A Starliner of Air Canada (inscribed "Super Constellation")	1·00	75
1399	60c. Vickers 952 Cargoliner of Air Canada at airport (inscribed "Vanguard")	1·25	85
1400	$4 de Havilland Canada DHC-6 Twin Otter 200/300 of L.I.A.T.	4·50	6·00
1397/1400	Set of 4	6·50	7·00
MS1401	$5 Hawker Siddeley H.S.748 of L.I.A.T.	3·00	3·00

1986.
1514*	$4 Westland WG-13 Lynx helicopter	3·50	3·50

1987.
1625*	10c. Paul Cornu's helicopter, 1907	1·25	65
1627*	30c. Airship LZ-1, 1900	1·40	80
1631*	90c. Blanchard and Jeffries' balloon, 1785	1·75	1·40

1987.
MS1712*	$5 Voyager and Wright Glider No. IV (inscribed "Flyer I")	3·00	4·00

1988. No. 1631 overprinted **OLYMPHILEX '88** and emblem.
1751*	90c. Blanchard and Jeffries' balloon, 1785	1·25	90

1988. Airships.

1810	10c. Airship LZ-127 *Graf Zeppelin*.............	50	20
1811	15c. Airship LZ 1, 1901..........................	60	25
1812	25c. Balloon *Washington*, 1862................	70	30
1813	45c. Airship LZ-129 *Hindenburg*..............	80	40
1814	50c. Goodyear Aerospace airship.............	80	40
1815	60c. Airship LZ-129 *Hindenburg*..............	90	50
1816	90c. Heinkel biplane docking with airship LZ-129 Hindenburg, 1936..................	1·40	80
1817	$2 Airship LZ-129 *Hindenburg*................	2·00	2·00
1818	$3 Airship LZ-129 *Hindenburg*................	2·50	2·50
1819	$4 Airship LZ-129 *Hindenburg*................	2·75	2·75
1810/1819 *Set of 10*.......................................		11·50	9·00

MS1820 Two sheets. (a) $5 Airship LZ-127 *Graf Zeppelin* (and spires of the Kremlin, Moscow); (b) $5 Airship LZ-129 *Hindenburg* (red and black flags on tail fins) *Set of 2 sheets* .... 4·75 5·50

1990.

2077*	$1 Hugo Eckener, Count Ferdinand von Zeppelin and airship LZ-127 *Graf Zeppelin*..............................	2·00	1·25

MS2081 Two sheets. (b) $6 Concorde (other sheet does not show aircraft) *Set of 2 sheets* .... 8·50 10·00

1990.

2109*	25c. Messerschmitt Bf 109....................	40	30
2116*	$2 North American B-25 Mitchell...........	2·00	1·75
2118*	$4 Focke Wulf Fw 190A........................	3·00	3·25

1990. 50th Anniv of United States Airborne Services.

2129	75c. Lockheed C-130 Hercules transport aircraft dropping paratroops	1·60	1·25

1992.

2467*	25c. Airship LZ-1...............................	1·00	30
2468*	50c. ENDOSAT robot airplane.................	1·25	55
2476*	$5 Count Ferdinand von Zeppelin and airship LZ-127 *Graf Zeppelin*............	4·50	4·75

MS2478* Five sheets (a) $6 Count Ferdinand von Zeppelin and airship LZ-127 *Graf Zeppelin* (other sheets do not show aircraft) *Set of 5 sheets* .... 25·00 26·00

1993. Aviation Anniversaries.

2636	35c. *Graf Zeppelin* over Vienna................	35	20
2637	45c. Blanchard's balloon	20	25
2638	50c. Westland Lysander........................	50	35
2639	75c. *Graf Zeppelin* over Pyramids............	75	55
2640	$2 Blanchard waving hat from balloon.	90	95
2641	$3 Hawker Typhoon.............................	2·00	2·50
2642	$5 *Graf Zeppelin* over Rio de Janeiro	3·25	3·75
2636/2642 *Set of 7*		7·00	7·75

MS2643 Three sheets. (a) $6 *Graf Zeppelin*; (b) $6 Blanchard's Balloon; (c) $6 Hawker Hurricane *Set of 3 sheets* .... 10·50 11·00

Nos. 2636, 2639, 2642 and **MS**2643a commemorate the 125th birth anniv Hugo Eckener (airship commander).
Nos. 2637, 2640 and **MS**2643b commemorate the bicentenary of first airmail flight.
Nos. 2638, 2641 and **MS**2643c commemorate the 75th anniv of the Royal Air Force.

1994.

2709*	$2 Northrop T-38 Talons in memorial flypast	1·25	1·40

1995. Fighter Aircraft.

2883	$2 Lavochkin LA7	1·75	1·50
2884	$2 Hawker Hurricane...........................	1·75	1·50
2885	$2 North American P-51D Mustang	1·75	1·50
2886	$2 Messerschmitt Bf 109......................	1·75	1·50
2887	$2 Bristol Type 152 Beaufighter	1·75	1·50
2888	$2 Messerschmitt Mc 262	1·75	1·50
2889	$2 Republic P-47 Thunderbolt	1·75	1·50
2890	$2 Hawker Tempest	1·75	1·50
2883/2890 *Set of 8*.......................................		12·50	11·00

MS2891 $6 Republic P-47 Thunderbolt (nose)........... 3·50 4·00

1995.

2907*	$2 Grumman F6F Hellcat.......................	1·75	1·50
2908*	$2 US divebomber (Midway)..................	1·75	1·50
2909*	$2 US aircraft (battle of Bismark Sea)	1·75	1·50
2911*	$2 US aircraft taking off from Henderson Field	1·75	1·50

MS2913* $6 Boeing B-29 Superfortress.................. 3·50 4·00

1995.

3049*	$1 Helicopter..................................	95	85

1996. Airships.

3203	30c. Zeppelin L-31 (Germany).................	50	50
3204	30c. Zeppelin L-35 (Germany).................	50	50
3205	50c. Zeppelin L-30 (Germany).................	65	50
3206	75c. Zeppelin L2-10 (Germany)...............	90	55
3207	$1.50 Zeppelin L-21 (Germany)...............	1·40	1·60
3208	$1.50 Zodiac Type 13 Spiess (France)......	1·40	1·60
3209	$1.50 N1 *Norge* (Roald Amundsen) (Norway)	1·40	1·60
3210	$1.50 Zeppelin LZ-127 *Graf Zeppelin* (Germany)	1·40	1·60
3211	$1.50 Zeppelin LZ-129 *Hindenburg* (Germany)	1·40	1·60
3212	$1.50 Zeppelin NT (Germany).................	1·40	1·60
3213	$3 Zeppelin L-3 (Germany)...................	2·25	2·50
3214	$3 Beardmore No 24 (Great Britain)........	2·25	2·50
3203/3214 *Set of 12*.....................................		14·00	15·00

MS3215 Two sheets. (a) $6 Zeppelin ZT (Germany); (b) $6 Zeppelin L-13 (Germany) *Set of 2 sheets* ...... 9·00 9·00

1998. History of the Supermarine Spitfire.

3600	$1.50 Supermarine Spitfire Mk I.............	1·10	1·10
3601	$1.50 Supermarine Spitfire Mk VIII.........	1·10	1·10
3602	$1.50 Supermarine Spitfire Mk III...........	1·10	1·10
3603	$1.50 Supermarine Spitfire Mk XVI.........	1·10	1·10
3604	$1.50 Supermarine Spitfire Mk V............	1·10	1·10
3605	$1.50 Supermarine Spitfire Mk XIX.........	1·10	1·10
3606	$1.50 Supermarine Spitfire Mk IX...........	1·10	1·10
3607	$1.50 Supermarine Spitfire Mk XII..........	1·10	1·10
3608	$1.50 Supermarine Spitfire Mk XII..........	1·10	1·10
3609	$1.50 Supermarine Spitfire Mk XI...........	1·10	1·10
3610	$1.50 Supermarine Spitfire Mk VIII.........	1·10	1·10
3611	$1.50 Supermarine Spitfire Mk VB..........	1·10	1·10
3600/3611 *Set of 12*.....................................		12·00	12·00

MS3612 Two sheets. (a) $6 Supermarine Spitfire Mk IA; (b) $6 Supermarine Spitfire Mk IX (different) *Set of 2 sheets* .... 8·50 9·50

1998. 80th Anniv of Royal Air Force.

3646	$2 Supermarine Spitfire Mk IIa	1·50	1·50
3647	$2 Supermarine Spitfire Mk XIb from above	1·50	1·50
3648	$2 Supermarine Spitfire Mk XIb from side	1·50	1·50
3649	$2 Hawker Hurricane Mk II c of Battle of Britain Memorial Flight................	1·50	1·50
3650	$2 Eurofighter EF-2000 Typhoon above clouds	1·50	1·50
3651	$2 BAe Nimrod MR 2P..........................	1·50	1·50
3652	$2 Eurofighter EF-2000 Typhoon at low level	1·50	1·50
3653	$2 Douglas C-47 Dakota	1·50	1·50
3646/3653 *Set of 8*		11·00	11·00

MS3654 Four sheets. (a) $6 Bristol F2B (and head of falcon); (b) $6 Bristol F2B (and head of goshawk); (c) $6 Hunting (Percival) P.84 Jet Provost and Eurofighter EF-2000 Typhoon; (d) $6 Vickers VC-10 and Eurofighter EF-2000 Typhoon *Set of 4 sheets* ... 16·00 17·00

2000. Centenary of First Zeppelin Flight.

4023	$3 LZ-130 *Graf Zeppelin II* 1938..............	2·00	2·25
4024	$3 LZ-2, 1906..................................	2·00	2·25
4025	$3 LZ-127 *Graf Zeppelin* 1928..............	2·00	2·25
4023/4025 *Set of 3*.......................................		5·50	6·00

MS4026 $6 LZ-129 *Hindenburg* 1936........................ 5·00 5·50

2000. 60th Anniv of Battle of Britain.

4296	$1.50 Messerschmitt Bf109E under attack.	1·40	1·40
4297	$1.50 Supermarine Spitfire	1·40	1·40
4298	$1.50 Fiesler Fi 103 V1 Flying Bomb.............	1·40	1·40
4299	$1.50 U-Boat under attack	1·40	1·40
4302	$1.50 Messerschmitt Bf 109E	1·40	1·40
4303	$1.50 German pilot parachuting	1·40	1·40
4304	$1.50 Hawker Hurricane Mk I	1·40	1·40
4305	$1.50 British airfield under attack............	1·40	1·40
4306	$1.50 Heinkel He IIIH on fire	1·40	1·40
4307	$1.50 RAF emblem on Supermarine Spitfire Mk XI.........................	1·40	1·40
4296/4307 *Set of 10*.....................................		15·00	15·00

MS4308 Two sheets. (a) $6 Supermarine Spitfire Mk IX; (b) $6 Hawker Hurricane Mk 1s on tarmac* *Set of 2 sheets* .... 13·00 14·00
No. 4304 is inscribed 'Hanker Hurricane HK1' and No. **MS**4308b 'HK1' both in error.

2003.

MS4828 $2 Toy airplane (other stamps in the miniature sheet do not show aircraft)...................... 5·50 6·00

2003. Centenary of Powered Flight.

MS4858 $2 Louis Bleriot and *Bleriot XI* (first powered flight across English Channel); $2 Johnnie Johnson and Supermarine Spitfire (World War II ace pilot with 38 victories); $2 Wright Brothers and Wright *Flyer I* (first controlled powered flight); $2 Jacqueline Cochran and North American F-86E Sabre (first woman to break sound barrier).................... 6·50 7·00

MS4859 $2 Alcock and Brown and Vickers FB27 *Vimy* (first non-stop transatlantic flight); $2 Amelia Earhart and Lockheed Vega 5B (first woman to fly the Atlantic); $2 Captain Charles 'Chuck' Yeager and Bell X-1 *Glamorous Glennis* (first manned supersonic flight); $2 Charles Lindbergh and Ryan NYP Special *Spirit of St Louis* (first non-stop solo transatlantic flight) *Set of 2 sheets* .... 6·50 7·00

2003.

MS4875 $1 SEPECAT Jaguar; $1 BAe Harrier GR7; $1 Surveillance aircraft (other stamps in the miniature sheet do not show aircraft)....................... 6·50 7·00

MS4876 $1 Aerospatiale SA 341 Gazelle helicopter; $1 SEPECAT Jaguar; $1 BAe Harrier GR7; $1 Boeing H-47 Chinook; $1 Panavia Tornado F. Mk3 (other stamps in the miniature sheet do not show aircraft) .... 6·50 7·00

2004. Last Flight (2003) of Concorde.
MS4921	$3 Concorde, French flag, Concorde at take-off; $3 Concorde, French flag, and spectators; $3 Concorde, French flag, and control tower (Concorde first flight, Toulouse, 1969)	8·50	8·50
MS4922	$3 Concorde, Union Jack, Singapore flag and roof of building; $3 Concorde, Union Jack, Singapore flag and skyscraper; $3 Concorde, Union Jack, Singapore flag and street (London to Singapore flights 1977)	8·50	8·50
MS4923	$3 Concorde and dome of US Capitol; $3 Concorde and Capitol building and statue; $3 Concorde, Capitol and plinth of statue (last flight, Paris to Washington, 2003)	8·50	8·50

2004.
4956*	$1 Air Chief Marshall Sir Arthur Tedder .	1·25	75
MS4959*	$2 British paratrooper at Merville Battery; $2 British paratroops and captured Merville Battery (other stamps on miniature sheet do not show aircraft)	7·50	8·00
MS4960	$2 Air strikes over Utah Beach (other stamps on miniature sheet do not show aircraft).	7·50	8·00

2005.
5051*	$2 Troops at Magawe airstrip	1·60	1·60
5053*	$2 Paratroops	1·60	1·60

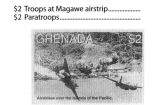

2005.
5063*	$2 Martin B-26 over Pacific Islands	1·75	1·75

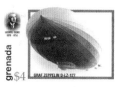

2006. 50th Death Anniv of Ludwig Durr (Zeppelin engineer).
5203	$4 Graf Zeppelin LZ-127	2·75	3·00
5204	$4 Zeppelin LT	2·75	3·00
5205	$4 Zeppelin L26	2·75	3·00
5203/5205 Set of 3		7·50	8·00

2007. Concorde.
5259*	$2 Andre Turcat (French test pilot)	1·50	1·50
5260*	$2 Brian Trubshaw (British test pilot)	1·50	1·50

2007. Centenary of First Helicopter Flight.
5332	$2 Sikorsky S-65/RH53D Sea Stallion	1·50	1·50
5333	$2 Bensen B-8M GyroCopter	1·50	1·50
5334	$2 Eurocopter Deutschland/Kawasaki BK117	1·50	1·50
5335	$2 Sikorsky (Agusta) AS-61	1·50	1·50
5332/5335 Set of 4		5·50	5·50
MS5336	$6 Boeing (Hughes/McDonnell Douglas) AH-64 Apache	7·25	7·25

GRENADINES OF GRENADA

West Indies

100 cents = 1 dollar

1974. As Nos. 628/30 of Grenada.
25*	8c. Westland Wessex HU Mk 5 helicopter	10	10
27*	35c. Airship LZ-127 Graf Zeppelin, Vickers FB-27 Vimy (top right), Boeing 747-100 (centre) and de Havilland D.H.4	15	10
28*	$1 Concorde	70	40

1975. As No. 661 of Grenada.
123*	35c. B.A.C. One Eleven at Pearls Airport	50	15

1976. Aircraft.
184	½c. Piper PA-23 Apache	10	10
185	1c. Beech 50 Twin Bonanza VP-LIF of L.I.A.T.	10	10
186	2c. de Havilland Canada DHC-6 Twin Otter 100 VP-LIR of L.I.A.T.	10	10
187	40c. Britten-Norman BN-2 Islander VP-LAE	30	10
188	50c. de Havilland DH.114 Heron 2 VP-LIA	40	10
189	$2 Hawker Siddeley H.S.748 VQ-LIP	1·25	25
184/189 Set of 6		2·00	70
MS190	$3 B.A.C. One Eleven 500 AI-PYL	1·00	1·00

1978. 75th Anniv of First Zeppelin Flight and 50th Anniv of Lindbergh's Trans-Atlantic Flight.
265	5c. Airship LZ-127 Graf Zeppelin (on Germany stamp No. 445)	20	10
266	15c. Concorde (on France stamp No. 1893)	60	10
267	25c. Airship LZ-127 Graf Zeppelin (on Liechtenstein stamp No. 117)	20	10
268	35c. Lindbergh's Ryan NYP Special Spirit of St. Louis (on Panama stamp No. 223)	20	10
269	50c. Airship LZ-127 Graf Zeppelin (on Russia stamp No. 579)	25	10
270	$3 Lindbergh's Ryan NYP Special Spirit of St. Louis (on Spain stamp No. 650)	75	30
265/270 Set of 6		2·00	70
MS271	75c. Lindbergh's Ryan NYP Special Spirit of St. Louis (on United States of America stamp No. A646); $2 Airship LZ-129 Hindenburg (on Germany stamp No. 603)	1·10	90

1978. 75th Anniv of Powered Flight.
286*	5c. Wright Flyer I	10	10
289*	25c. Wright Flyer III, 1905	10	10
290*	35c. Wright Glider No. 1	15	10
291*	75c. Wright Flyer I	25	25
292*	$3 Wright Type A	75	75
MS293	$2 Wright Glider No. III, Wright Glider No. IV, Wright Flyer I and Wright Type B	75	1·00

1979.
329*	75c. Westland Sea King	65	35
330*	$3 Balloon from Five Weeks in a Balloon by Jules Verne and airplane	1·25	1·00

1979.
335*	$3 Concorde	90	70

1980. No. 123 overprinted PEOPLE'S REVOLUTION 13 MARCH 1979.
369*	35c. B.A.C. One Eleven at Pearls Airport	20	10

1980. No. 335 overprinted LONDON 1980.
395*	$3 Concorde	2·75	2·00

1981. Famous Women Aviators.
453	30c. Amy Johnson and de Havilland DH.60G Gipsy Moth G-AAAH Jason, 1930	45	15
454	70c. Baroness De la Roche and Voisin "Boxkite", 1910	70	30
455	$1.10 Ruth Nichols and Lockheed Vega 5B Akita, 1931	80	40
456	$3 Amelia Earhart and Lockheed Vega 5B NR-7952, 1932	1·75	1·10
453/456 Set of 4		3·25	1·80

1981.
468*	10c. Boeing 747 SCA of NASA carrying Space Shuttle	30	10
471*	$3 Northrop T-38A Talon jet trainer of NASA escorting Space Shuttle	15	10

1982.
481*	$4 Airco (de Havilland) D.H.9 biplane and Concorde	2·25	1·25

1983.
549*	$1.10 Westland Whirlwind helicopter	45	45

1983. Bicentenary of Manned Flight.
563	40c. Short S.45A Solent 2 flying boat G-AKNU of Aquila Airways	85	20
564	70c. Curtiss R3C-2 seaplane, 1925	1·00	35
565	90c. Hawker Nimrod biplane, 1931	1·25	40
566	$4 Montgolfier balloon (first manned free flight, 1783)	3·25	2·75
563/566 Set of 4		5·75	3·25
MS567	$5 Airship LZ-11 Viktoria Luise	1·75	2·00

1984. No. 549 overprinted OPENING OF POINT SALINE INT'L AIRPORT.
637*	$1.10 Westland Whirlwind helicopter	95	75

1985. 40th Anniv of ICAO.
660	5c. Lockheed L.18 Lodestar	40	20
661	70c. Hawker Siddeley H.S.748	1·75	55
662	$1.10 Boeing 727-200	2·25	90
663	$4 Boeing 707	3·50	2·50
660/663 Set of 4		7·00	3·75
MS664	$5 Britten-Norman BN-2 Islander	3·50	3·00

1986.
764*	$4 Westland WG-13 Lynx helicopter	4·00	3·50

1987.
877*	60c. Rolls Royce "Flying Bedstead", 1954..	1·50	85

100TH ANNIVERSARY-STATUE OF LIBERTY
GRENADA
GRENADINES $1.10

1987.

901*	$1.10 Airships	90	1·00

GRENADA
GRENADINES
10¢

1988. Airships.

965	10c. Airship LZ-129 *Hindenburg*	70	20
966	20c. Airship LZ-129 *Hindenburg*	85	30
967	30c. U.S. Navy "K" Class airships, 1944	95	35
968	40c. Airship LZ-129 *Hindenburg*	1·00	45
969	60c. Airship LZ-127 *Graf Zeppelin* and airship LZ-129 *Hindenburg*	1·25	60
970	70c. Airship LZ-129 *Hindenburg*, U.S. Navy airship ZR-3 *Los Angeles* in hangar and Douglas DC-3 of American Airlines	1·25	70
971	$1 Airship LZ-130 *Graf Zeppelin* II, 1939	1·25	85
972	$2 Airship LZ-8 *Ersatz Deutschland*, 1912	1·60	1·60
973	$3 Airship LZ-127 *Graf Zeppelin*	2·50	2·25
974	$4 Airship LZ-129 *Hindenburg*	2·50	2·25
965/974 *Set of* 10		12·50	8·50
MS975 Two sheets. (a) $5 Airship LZ-127 *Graf Zeppelin* (nose at top right); (b) $5 Airship LZ-127 *Graf Zeppelin* (nose at left) *Set of 2 sheets*		8·00	10·00

GRENADA/GRENADINES 20¢
ROMMEL BEGINS RETREAT FROM EL ALAMEIN

1990.

1244*	20c. Hawker Hurricane Mk IIC	40	40
1251*	$6 Boeing B-29 Superfortress *Enola Gay*	3·50	3·50

60¢
Grenada / Grenadines

1991.

1369*	60c. Douglas World Cruiser seaplane, 1924	2·00	80

25c grenada·grenadines
75th Anniversary of the death of Count Ferdinand von Zeppelin

1992.

1566*	25c. Airship LZ-11 *Viktoria Luise*	75	30
1573*	$4 Douglas DC-3 transport aircraft on Berlin Airlift	3·25	3·50
1575*	$5 Airship LZ-129 *Hindenburg* on fire at Lakehurst, New Jersey, 1937	3·25	3·50
1576*	$6 Admiral Richard Byrd's Ford 4-AT-B Trimotor NX-4542 *Floyd Bennett* over the Antarctic, 1929 (inscribed "First air crossing of North Pole, 1926")	3·25	3·50
MS1577 Five sheets. (a) $6 Airship LZ-4 (other sheets do not show aircraft) *Set of 5 sheets*		18·00	20·00

Grenada
Grenadines
15c Avro Lancaster Bomber
75th Anniversary of the RAF

1993. Aviation Anniversaries.

1726	15c. Avro Type 683 Lancaster	30	25
1727	35c. Blanchard's Balloon crossing River Delaware	15	25
1728	50c. Zeppelin *Graf Zeppelin* over Rio de Janeiro	50	35
1729	75c. Hugo Eckener (Zeppelin commander)	65	50
1730	$3 President Washington handing passport to Blanchard	1·40	1·75
1731	$5 Short S.25 Sunderland flying boat	2·50	3·00
1732	$5 Eckener in *Graf Zeppelin*	2·50	3·00
1726/1732 *Set of* 7		7·25	8·25
MS1733 Three sheets. (a) $5 Supermarine Spitfire; (b) $6 Blanchard's balloon; (c) $6 Eckener with President Hoover *Set of 3 sheets*		11·50	12·50

Nos. 1726, 1731 and **MS**1733a commemorate the 75th Anniv of the Royal Air Force.

Nos. 1727, 1730 and **MS**1733b commemorate the bicentenary of first airmail flight.

Nos. 1728, 1729, 1732 and **MS**1733c commemorate the 125th birth anniv of Hugo Eckener.

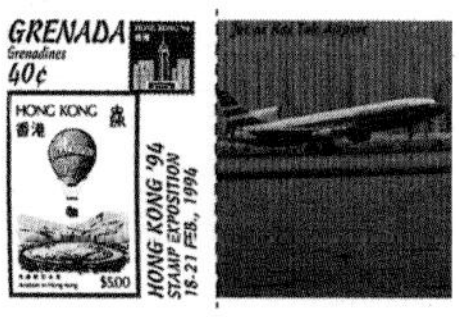
GRENADA
Grenadines
40¢
HONG KONG
HONG KONG '94
STAMP EXPOSITION
18-21 FEB., 1994

1994.

1748	40c. Hong Kong 1984 $5.00 stamp showing de Havilland DH.86 Dragon Express and Lockheed L-1011 TriStar at Kai Tak Airport	80	85
1749	40c. Grenada Grenadines 1988 20c. airship stamp showing Zeppelin *Hindenburg* over New York, 1937	80	85

$2 GRENADA•GRENADINES
AVRO LANCASTER AND THE "TALLBOY" BOMB

1995. Bombers.

1961*	$2 Avro Type 683 Lancaster	1·50	1·50
1962*	$2 Junkers Ju 88	1·50	1·50
1963*	$2 North American B-25 Mitchell	1·50	1·50
1964*	$2 Boeing B-17 Flying Fortress	1·50	1·50
1965*	$2 Petlyakov Pe-2	1·50	1·50
1966*	$2 Martin B-26 Marauder	1·50	1·50
1967*	$2 Heinkel He 111H	1·50	1·50
1968*	$2 Consolidated B-24 Liberator	1·50	1·50
1961/1968 *Set of* 8		11·00	11·00

1995.

1985*	$2 Mitsubishi G4M1 'Betty'	1·40	1·50
1986*	$2 Japanese submarine with seaplane	1·40	1·50
1987*	$2 Mitsubishi GM31 *Nell*	1·40	1·50
MS1991* $6 Aichi D3A1 *Val*		3·50	3·75

CONCEPT STRIKE FIGHTER
GRENADA
GRENADINES
70¢

1998. Aircraft Designs of the Future.

2544	70c. Concept strike fighter	50	40
2545	90c. Concept space shuttle	45	60
2546	$1 Velocity 173 RG Elite	75	75
2547	$1 Davis DA-9	75	75
2548	$1 Aerospatiale/BAe Concorde	75	75
2549	$1 Rutan Voyager	75	75
2550	$1 Factimobile	75	75
2551	$1 RAF 2000	75	75
2552	$1 Boomerang	75	75
2553	$1 N1M Flying Wing	75	75
2554	$2 Concept air and space jet	1·40	1·40
2555	$3 V jet II	1·75	1·75
2544/2555 *Set of* 12		9·00	9·25
MS2556 Two sheets. (a) $6 Concept Aeropod; (b) $6 Granville Bros. Gee Bee *Set of 2 sheets*		8·00	8·50

GRENADA
GRENADINES
The Royal Air Force 80th Anniversary
$2

1998. 80th Anniv of Royal Air Force.

2637	$2 Panavia Tornado GR1	1·60	1·60
2638	$2 BAe Hawk T1A	1·60	1·60
2639	$2 SEPECAT Jaguar GR1	1·60	1·60
2640	$2 BAe Harrier GR7	1·60	1·60
2641	$2 Boeing HC2 Chinook	1·60	1·60
2642	$2 BAe Harrier GR5 (silhouette)	1·60	1·60
2643	$2 Panavia Tornado F3 ADV	1·60	1·60
2644	$2 Boeing HC2 Chinook	1·60	1·60
2637/2644 *Set of* 8		11·50	11·50
MS2645 Four sheets. (a) $6 Bristol F2B and head of golden eagle; (b) $6 Bristol F2B and montagu's harrier in flight; (c) $6 Hawker Hunter and Eurofighter EF-2000 Typhoon; (d) $6 Panavia Tornado and Eurofighter EF-2000 Typhoon *Set of 4 sheets*		15·00	16·00

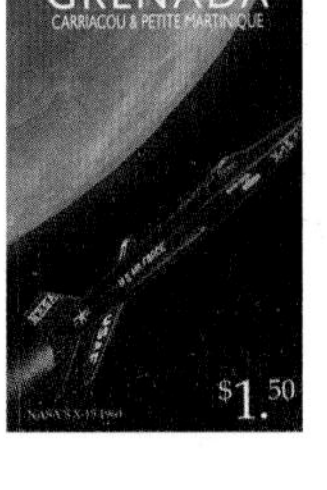
GRENADA
CARRIACOU & PETITE MARTINIQUE
$1.50

1999.

2807*	$1.50 North American X-15	1·00	1·00

GRENADA/CARRIACOU
& PETITE MARTINIQUE 20¢

2000.

2923*	20c. Sikorsky helicopter	35	35
2929*	20c. Aerospatiale/BAe Concorde	35	35

$3
GRENADA/CARRIACOU
& PETITE MARTINIQUE

2000. Centenary of First Zeppelin Flight.

3030	$3 Zeppelin LZ-3, 1906	2·00	2·00
3031	$3 Zeppelin LZ-56, 1915	2·00	2·00
3032	$3 Zeppelin LZ-88, 1917	2·00	2·00
3030/3032 *Set of* 3		5·50	5·50
MS3033 $6 Zeppelin LZ-1, 1900		4·25	4·50

PILOTS SCRAMBLE TO THEIR PLANES
GRENADA/CARRIACOU
& PETITE MARTINIQUE
$1

2000. 60th Anniv of Battle of Britain.

3202*	$1 RAF pilots 'scramble' to Supermarine Spitfires	1·00	90
3203*	$1 Barrage balloons	1·00	90
3204*	$1 Supermarine Spitfire B	1·00	90
MS3218* $6 Hawker Hurricane		9·00	9·00

$1.50
GRENADA CARRIACOU
& PETITE MARTINIQUE

2001.

3497*	$1.50 Hot air balloon	90	90

GRENADA CARRIACOU
PETITE MARTINIQUE
75¢
LT. GENERAL JAMES H. DOOLITTLE

2001.

3503*	75c. Gen. Doolittle and aircraft carrier	55	55
3505*	75c. Gen. Maxwell Taylor and Boeing B-17 Flying Fortress	55	55
3507*	75c. Gen. Curtis Le May and bombers	55	55
3508*	75c. Gen. Hoyt Vandenberg and fighter aircraft	55	55
3509*	75c. Explosion of A-bomb (poss. aircraft)	55	55
3517*	75c. Admiral Leahy and aircraft carrier (poss. aircraft)	55	55
3518*	75c. General Hap Arnold and Boeing B-29 Super fortress	55	55

GRENADA Carriacou
and Petite Martinique
$2

2003. 75th Anniv of First Solo Trans-Atlantic Flight.

MS3619 $2 Charles Lindbergh; $2 Lindbergh and Ryan NYP Special *Spirit of St Louis;* $2 Lindbergh and Ryan NYP Special *Spirit of St Louis;* $2 Charles Lindbergh		5·00	5·00
MS3620 $2 Lindbergh (looking forward); $2 Lindbergh (looking left); $2 Lindbergh on arrival in Paris; $2 Lindbergh and Ryan NYP Special *Spirit of St Louis Set of 2 sheets*		5·00	5·00

2003. Centenary of Powered Flight.
MS3625 $2 Wright Flyer; $2 Curtiss NC-4; $2
Douglas DWC (Douglas World Cruiser); $2 Fokker
Eindecker .... 3·25 3·25
MS3626 $2 Hansa Brandenberg D.1; $2 Royal
Aircraft Factory BE 2C; $2 Handley Page 0/400; $2
Avro 504 .... 3·25 3·25
MS3627 $2 Hawker Hart; $2 Martin B-10; $2
Armstrong Whitworth Siskin IIIA; $2 Loening OL-8 3·25 3·25
MS3628 Three sheets. (a) $6 Wright Glider No III; (b)
$6 Wright *Flyer II;* (c) $6 Gloster Gamecock .... 7·00 7·00

2004.
3681* $4 Denis Edwards, 6th Airborne Division .... 2·50 2·75
MS3684* $6 Gunner in British bomber .... 7·50 8·00

2005.
3786* $2 Lockheed P-38J Lightning.................... 1·40 1·40
3787* $2 North American P-51D Mustang .... 1·40 1·40
3788* $2 McDonnell Douglas F-4 Phantom II.. 1·40 1·40
3789* $2 Douglas C-47 Skytrain .... 1·40 1·40

2007. 50th Anniv of Ludwig Durr (Zeppelin engineer).
3848* $3 Zeppelin LZ-127 *Graf Zeppelin*............ 1·40 1·40
3849* $3 Dining room of Zeppelin LS-129
Hindenburg................................. 1·40 1·40
3850* $3 Marine airship L53........................... 1·40 1·40

2007. Centenary of First Helicopter Flight.
3912 $1.50 Eurocopter Deutschland Kawasaki
BK117.. 1·10 95
3913 $1.50 Bell Model 204 UH-1 Iroquois .... 1·10 95
3914 $1.50 Sikorsky S-65/RH-53D Sea Stallion .... 1·10 95
3915 $1.50 Bell Model 204 UH-1B/C Iroquois
(different)..................................... 1·10 95
3916 $1.50 Bensen B-8M GyroCopter .... 1·10 95
3917 $1.50 Bolkow (Eurocopter/MBB) BO 105 ... 1·10 95
3912/3917 *Set of 6* .... 6·00 5·25
MS3918 $6 Boeing (Hughes/McDonnell Douglas)
AH-64 Apache .... 4·25 4·25

GRENADINES OF ST. VINCENT

West Indies

100 cents = 1 dollar

1983. Bicentenary of Manned Flight.
250* 45c. Montgolfier balloon (first manned
free flight, 1783) 15 15
251* 60c. Ayres Turbo Thrush Commander....... 15 15
252* $1.50 Lebaudy-Juillot airship No. 1 *La
Jaune,* 1902.............................. 40 45

1988. Mustique Airlines.
559 15c. Britten-Norman BN-2 Islander of
Mustique Airways......................... 10 15
560 65c. Beech 58 Baron of Mustique Airways 15 35
561 75c. Britten-Norman BN-2 Islander of
Mustique Airways......................... 15 35
562 $5 Beech 58 Baron of Mustique Airways 1·00 2·25
559/562 *Set of 4*.. 1·30 2·75

1990.
659* 20c. Mitsubishi A6M Zero-Sen and
aircraft carrier.............................. 50 40
660* 45c. North American B-25 Mitchell
bombers....................................... 80 70
666* $6 Douglas SBD-3 Dauntless dive
bombers....................................... 4·25 4·25
MS667* $6 Avro Type 683 Lancaster Mk III of No. 617
Squadron, R.A.F .... 5·00 6·00

1991.
774* $1.50 Otto Lilienthal and glider .... 2·00 1·75

1991.
784* $1 Japanese fighters............................ 2·00 1·60
786* $1 Nakajima B5N2 "Kate" bombers .... 2·00 1·60
787* $1 Nakajima B5N2 "Kate" bombers
attacking "Battleship Row".............. 2·00 1·60
788* $1 Consolidated PBY-5A Catalina,
Douglas SBD Dauntless and other
aircraft on fire, Ford Island................ 2·00 1·60

1992.
893* 75c. Airship LZ-3................................... 2·50 1·75
901* $3 Douglas DC-6 transport aircraft on
Berlin Airlift.................................. 2·75 3·50
902* $4 Airship LZ-37 destroyed by
bombs and Flight Sub Lieutenant
Warneford's Morane Saulnier Type L 3·25 4·00
MS906* Seven sheets. (b) $6 Count von Zeppelin
(facing left); (c) $6 Count von Zeppelin (facing
right) (other miniature sheets do not show
aircraft) *Price for 7 sheets* .... 35·00 38·00

GUADELOUPE

West Indies

100 centimes = 1 franc

1945. As Nos. 207/13 of Cameroun.
202 50f. Fairey FC-1 airliner................................ 90 3·75
203 100f. Fairey FC-1 airliner.............................. 85 1·90

1947.
228* 50f. Latecoere 631 flying boat.................... 7·00 13·50
229* 100f. Short Hythe flying boat...................... 7·25 14·50
230* 200f. Sud Ouest SO.30P Bretagne .... 11·50 21·00

GUATEMALA

Central America

100 centavos = 1 quetzal

1930.
254 6c. Fokker F.10A Super Trimotor 95 60

1931. No. 254 overprinted **EXTERIOR – 1931.**
260 6c. Fokker F.10A Super Trimotor .... 2·10 2·00

1935. Inscr "INTERIOR".
305* 50c. La Aurora Airport (purple)................. 27·00 21·00
305a* 50c. La Aurora Airport (blue) .... 6·00 4·25

1935. As Nos. 305/a, but inscr "EXTERIOR".
317* 1q. La Aurora Airport (blue) .... 38·00 38·00
318* 1q. La Aurora Airport (green) .... 11·00 10·50

1937.
340* 15c. La Aurora Airport................................. 3·50 5·00

1937. Designs inscribed "INTERIOR" overprinted with Douglas DC-2
airplane.
345* 2c. Quezaltenango... 35 35
346* 3c. Lake Atitlan... 1·40 1·80
347* 4c. Progressive colony on Lake Atitlan ... 35 35
348* 6c. Carmen Hill... 60 35
349* 10c. Relief map... 3·00 3·25
350* 15c. National University.................................. 2·20 1·40
351* 30c. Plaza Espana... 5·50 4·25
352* 50c. Aurora Police Station............................. 7·25 6·50
353* 75c. Aurora Amphitheatre............................. 14·50 15·00
354* 1q. La Aurora Airport................................. 16·00 16·00
345/354 *Set of 10*... 46·00 45·00

1937. Designs inscribed "EXTERIOR" overprinted with Douglas
DC-2 airplane.
355* 1c. Seventh Avenue................................... 35 35
356* 2c. Liberators' Monument 35 35
357* 3c. National Printing Offices...................... 70 70
358* 5c. National Museum.................................. 6·00 4·25
359* 10c. Centre Park.. 1·80 1·40
360* 15c. Escuintla Park....................................... 70 35
361* 20c. Mobile Police.. 4·25 2·50
362* 25c. Slaughter-house, Escuintla.................. 3·50 3·50
363* 30c. Campo de Marte Stadium.................... 1·80 1·80
364* 50c. Plaza Barrios... 14·00 14·00
365* 1q. Polytechnic... 14·50 14·50
366* 1q.50 La Aurora Airport............................... 18·00 18·00
355/366 *Set of 12*... 60·00 55·00

1939. Overprinted with flying quetzal.
378* 3c. La Aurora Airport................................. 35 35

1972. 50th Anniv of Guatemala Air Force.
924 5c. Boeing P-26A "Peashooter" (lower
left) and North American P-51
Mustang 70 25
925 10c. Bleriot XI.. 1·30 30

1976.
MS1026 Three sheets. (b) 1q. Bell Model 205 UH-1H Iroquois helicopter (other sheets do not show aircraft) *Price for 3 sheets* .... 21·00 19·00

1981.
1194* 7c. Charles Lindbergh and Ryan NYP Special *Spirit of St. Louis* 70 40

1987. 40th Anniv of ICAO.
1275 8c. Boeing 727 .... 30 20
1276 10c. Boeing 727 .... 35 20

GUERNSEY

Western Europe

1970. 12 pence = 1 shilling

20 shillings = 1 pound

1971. 100 pence = 1 pound

1970.
33* 4d. Hawker Hurricanes Mk II 20 20

1973. 50th Anniv of Air Service.
84 2½p. Supermarine Sea Eagle amphibian G-EBGS of British Marine Air Navigation.. 10 10
85 3p. Westland Wessex trimotor G-ADEW . 10 10
86 5p. de Havilland DH.89 Dragon Rapide G-AGSH *James Keir Hardie* of B.E.A 25 25
87 7½p. Douglas DC-3 G-AHCW 30 30
88 9p. Vickers Viscount 800 G-AOHM *Anne Marie* 40 40
84/88 *Set of 5* .... 1·00 1·00

1981.
241* 12p. Britten-Norman BN-2A Mk III "short nose" Trislander of Aurigny Air Services 25 20

1982.
262* 29p. Beechcraft Skipper 77..................... 65 1·10

1988.
421* 16p. Vickers Viscount 800....................... 35 35

1988.
429* 16p. Westland Wessex HU Mk 5 helicopter... 35 25
431* 32p. Westland Wessex HU Mk 5 helicopter... 1·00 90

1989. 50th Anniv of Guernsey Airport and RAF 201 Squadron's affiliation with Guernsey.
456 12p. de Havilland DH.86 Dragon Express of Guernsey Airways........................... 35 30
457 12p. Supermarine Southampton II flying boat 35 30
458 18p. de Havilland DH.89 Dragon Rapide G-AGSH of B.E.A 50 50
459 18p. Short S.25 Sunderland Mk V flying boat 50 50
460 35p. British Aerospace BAe 146 of Air UK. 1·00 90
461 35p. Avro Shackleton M.R.3.................... 1·00 1·00
456/461 *Set of 6*... 3·25 3·25

1994.
MS638 £2 Supermarine Spitfire Mk V fighters............ 4·00 4·25

1994.
646* 24p. Handley Page HPR. 7 Herald................ 55 50
647* 35p. Britten-Norman BN-2A Mk III Trislander...................................... 75 75

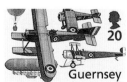

1998. 80th Anniv of Royal Air Force.
774 20p. Fairey IIIC, balloon, Sopwith Camel, Avro 504... 50 50
775 25p. Fairey Swordfish, de Havilland DH.82 Tiger Moth, Supermarine Walrus, Gloster Gladiator.............................. 60 60

---

776 30p. Hawker Hurricane, Supermarine Spitfire, Vickers Type 271 Wellington, Short S.25 Sunderland, Westland Lysander, Bristol Type 142 Blenheim 70 70
777 37p. de Havilland DH.98 Mosquito, Avro Type 683 Lancaster, British Taylorcraft Auster Mk III, Airspeed Horsa glider 90 85
778 43p. English Electric Canberra, Hawker Sea Fury, Bristol Sycamore, Hawker Hunter, Handley Page HP.80 Victor, English Electric (BAe) Lightning......... 1·00 1·25
779 63p. Panavia Tornado GRI, BAe Hawk, BAe Sea Harrier, Westland Lynx, Hawker Siddeley (BAe) Nimrod .... 1·40 1·50
774/779 *Set of 6* .... 4·50 5·00

2000. 60th Anniv of Battle of Britain.
857 21p. Bristol Type 142 Blenheim.............. 50 50
858 26p. Hawker Hurricane......................... 60 55
859 36p. Boulton Paul P.82 Defiant II.......... 95 85
860 40p. Gloster Gladiator.......................... 1·00 95
861 45p. Bristol Type 156 Beaufighter IF...... 1·10 1·25
862 65p. Supermarine Spitfire IIC............... 1·50 1·50
857/862 *Set of 6* .... 5·00 5·00

2003. Dambusters Raid.
979* 22p. Avro Type 683 Lancaster................ 45 50
980* 27p. Flight of Lancasters crossing English Channel.. 55 60
981* 36p. Lancasters in enemy searchlights...... 70 75
982* 40p. Dropping bouncing bombs............... 80 85

2007.
1144* 45p. BAe Sea Harriers............................ 1·10 1·10
1146* 50p. Westland Sea King .... 1·20 1·20

Alderney

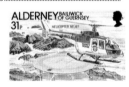

1985. 50th Anniv of Alderney Airport.
A18 9p. Westland Wessex HU Mk 5 helicopter XV 732 of the Queen's Flight .... 1·40 70
A19 13p. Britten-Norman BN-2A Mk III "long nose" Trislander of Aurigny Air Services .... 1·75 1·00
A20 29p. de Havilland DH.114 Heron 1B G-AOXL (shown with Morton Air Services markings).............................. 3·00 2·75
A21 31p. de Havilland DH.89A Dragon Rapide G-AHLL *Sir Henry Lawrence* of B.E.A.... 3·50 3·50
A22 34p. Saro A.21 Windhover flying boat G-ABJP *City of Portsmouth* of Jersey Airways.. 3·50 3·50
A18/22 *Set of 5*... 12·00 10·50

1991.
A49* 31p. MBB-Bolkow Bo 105D helicopter G-BATC of Trinity House .... 2·00 2·25

1995. Birth Centenary of Tommy Rose (aviator).
A78 35p. Royal Aircraft Factory SE5A........... 95 95

A79	35p.	Miles M.19 Master II and other Miles Aircraft	95	95
A80	35p.	Miles M.57 Aerovan and Miles M.33 Monitor	95	95
A81	41p.	Miles M.3B Falcon Six winning King's Cup Air Race, 1935	1·10	1·10
A82	41p.	Miles M.2 Hawk Speed Six winning Manx Air Derby, 1947	1·10	1·10
A83	41p.	Miles M.3B Falcon Six breaking UK-Cape record, 1936	1·10	1·10
A78/83	*Set of 6*		5·50	5·50

2002.

A199*	36p.	Doctor loading patient onto aircraft	70	75
A200*	40p.	Pilot and Britten-Norman BN-2A Mk III Trislander	80	85

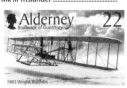

2003. Centenary of Powered Flight.

A204	22p.	Wright Brothers *Flyer I*, 1903	45	50
A205	27p.	Alcock and Brown's Vickers FB-27 Vimy, 1919	55	60
A206	36p.	Douglas DC-3, 1936	70	75
A207	40p.	de Havilland DH.106 Comet 4, 1946.	80	85
A208	45p.	Aerospatiale/BAe Concorde, 1969	90	95
A209	65p.	Airbus Industries Airbus A380	1·25	1·40
A204/209	*Set of 6*		4·25	4·50

2004.

A244*	36p.	Airport service fire truck	1·20	1·20
A246*	45p.	Airport training ground	1·50	1·50

GUINEA

West Africa

1959. 100 centimes = 1 franc

1973. 100 caury = 1 syli

1986. 100 centimes = 1 franc

1959.

219	100f.	Lockheed L.1049 Super Constellation	2·40	1·30
220	200f.	Lockheed L.1049 Super Constellation	5·75	1·90
221	500f.	Lockheed L.1049 Super Constellation	8·25	4·00
219/221	*Set of 3*		15·00	6·50

1960. Nos. 219/21 overprinted **Jeux Olympiques Rome 1960** and Olympic rings.

250*	100f.	Lockheed L.1049 Super Constellation	10·50	7·75
251*	200f.	Lockheed L.1049 Super Constellation	18·00	11·00
252*	500f.	Lockheed L.1049 Super Constellation	47·00	37·00

1963. Nos. 219/20 overprinted **PREMIER SERVICE DIRECT CONAKRY-NEW YORK PAN AMERICAN 30 JUILLET 1963.**

409	100f.	Lockheed L.1049 Super Constellation	2·75	1·10
410	200f.	Lockheed L.1049 Super Constellation	4·75	2·20

1965.

470*	100f.	Stewardess and Convair 990A Coronado	1·90	75

1965.

507*	40f.	Ilyushin Il-18 of Air Guinea at Gbessia Airport	75	45

1966. No. 470 overprinted with pyramid, sphinx and **JEUX PANARABES CAIRE 1965.**

532*	100f.	Stewardess and Convair 990A Coronado	1·80	75

1974.

861*	10s.	Boeing 707	1·50	70
MS862*		Two sheets. (a) 10s. Balloon (other sheet does not show aircraft) *Set of 2 sheets*	17·00	17·00

1979.

1002*	10s.	Airplane from *The Amazing Adventure of Barsac* by Jules Verne	2·00	80
1003*	20s.	Balloon from *Five Weeks in a Balloon* by Jules Verne (air)	3·00	55

1979. Aviation History.

1005	3s.	William Samuel Henson's *Aerial Steam Carriage*, 1842	45	10
1006	5s.	Wright Type A (inscribed "*Flyer I*")	75	25
1007	65.50	Caudron C-460 F-ANAR, 1934	95	25
1008	7s.	Lindbergh's Ryan NYP Special *Spirit of St. Louis*, 1927	1·30	25
1009	8s.50	Bristol Type 156 Beaufighter, 1940	1·70	40
1010	10s.	Bleriot XI, 1909	2·10	40
1011	20s.	Boeing 727-100 of United Airlines, 1963	3·75	80
1012	20s.	Concorde	3·75	80
1005/1012	*Set of 8*		13·00	3·00

1982.

1049*	7s.	Boeing 747 (lower left) and Douglas DC-10	1·50	55

1983. Bicentenary of Manned Flight.

1082	5s.	Marquis d'Arlandes, Jean-Francois Pilatre de Rozier and Montgolfier balloon (first manned free flight, 1783)	75	25
1083	7s.	Jean-Francois Pilatre de Rozier and Montgolfier balloon *Marie Antoinette*, 1784	1·00	40
1084	10s.	Henri Dupuy de Lome and his airship, 1872	1·50	55
1085	15s.	Major A. Parseval and his *Airship No. 1*, 1906	2·30	90

1086	20s.	Count Ferdinand von Zeppelin and airship LZ-120 *Bodensee* (air)	2·75	90
1087	25s.	Ben Abruzzo, Max Anderson, Larry Newman and balloon *Double Eagle II*	3·50	1·30
1082/1087	*Set of 6*		10·00	4·00
MS1088	30s.	Nadar and his balloon *Le Geant*, 1863, and Alberto Santos-Dumont and his airship *Ballon No. 6*, 1901	4·50	1·60

1984.

1125*	15s.	Louis Bleriot and Bleriot XI	2·30	65
1127*	25s.	Auguste Piccard and his stratosphere balloon *F.N.R.S.*, 1931 (air)	3·25	1·20

1984.

1137*	7s.	Airship LZ-127 *Graf Zeppelin*	1·10	40
1140*	20s.	Latecoere 28-3 seaplane F-AJNQ *Comte de la Vaulx* (air)	2·75	1·20
1141*	25s.	Savoia Marchetti S-73	3·25	1·60

1986.

MS1267*	600f.	Marcel Dassault, Dassault Mirage III and Dassault Rafale A	7·50	2·75

1990.

1410*	400f.	Concorde of Air France	4·25	85

1991.

1436*	100f.	Fairey Swordfish	1·20	25
1437*	150f.	Aichi D3A "Val" bomber	1·50	45
1438*	200f.	Mitsubishi A6M Zero-Sen in flames..	1·80	55
1439*	250f.	Hawker Hurricane Mk II	2·50	80
1441*	450f.	Grumman TBF Avenger (air)	4·50	1·20
MS1442*	750f.	Boeing B-17G Flying Fortress	7·00	1·40

1991. No. 1410 surcharged.

1450*	100f.	on 400f. Concorde of Air France	95	45

1992.

1499*	350f.	Meeting of *Graf Zeppelin* and Santos-Dumont's flying boat and Count von Zeppelin	3·75	60

1995. Aircraft.

1641	100f. Beagle Pup-150 (Great Britain)	45	20
1642	150f. Gardan GY-80 Horizon (France)	75	25
1643	250f. Piper J-3 Cub (USA)	1·30	45
1644	500f. Piper PA-28 Cherokee Arrow (USA)	2·50	90
1645	500f. Pilatus PC-6 Porter (Switzerland)	2·50	90
1646	500f. Valmet L-90TP Redigo (Finland)	2·50	90
1641/1646	Set of 6	9·00	3·25
MS1647	1000f. Dornier Do-27 (Germany)	5·00	2·30

APPENDIX

The following stamps have either been issued in excess of postal needs or have not been made available to the public in reasonable quantities at face value. Miniature sheets, imperforate stamps, etc are excluded from this section.

1983.
Bicentenary of Manned Flight. 100s.

GUINEA-BISSAU

West Africa

100 centavos = 1 peso

1977.

519*	5p. A.E.G. J-II biplane	35	15

1978. Airships.

540	3p.50 Santos-Dumont's airship *Ballon No. 6*, 1901	25	15
541	5p. Beardmore airship R-34 crossing the Atlantic, 1919	35	15
542	10p. Airship N.1 *Norge* over the North Pole	55	20
543	20p. Airship LZ-127 *Graf Zeppelin*	1·40	50
544	25p. Airship LZ-129 *Hindenburg* (air)	1·75	70
545	30p. Airship LZ-127 *Graf Zeppelin* and Concorde	2·25	75
540/545	Set of 6	6·00	2·20

1978. History of Aviation.

575*	3p.50 Wilbur and Orville Wright and Wright *Flyer I*	20	10
576*	10p. Alberto Santos-Dumont and his biplane *14 bis*	45	20
577*	15p. Louis Bleriot and Bleriot XI	75	35
578*	20p. Charles Lindbergh and Ryan NYP Special *Spirit of St. Louis* (air)	90	40
MS581*	50p. Concorde	3·00	3·00

1980. History of Aviation. Air Aces of World War I.

631	3p.50 Ernst Udet and Fokker D.VII	25	15
632	5p. Charles Nungesser and Nieuport 17	35	25

633	6p. Baron Manfred von Richthofen and Fokker Dr-1	55	25
634	30p. Francesco Baracca and SPAD XIII	1·75	70
635	35p. Willy Coppens de Houthulst and Hanriot HD-1 (air)	2·10	75
636	40p. Charles Guynemer and SPAD VII	2·50	90
631/636	Set of 6	6·75	2·50
MS637	50p. Commandant De Rose and Nieuport 17	2·25	2·25

1983. Bicentenary of Manned Flight.

727	50c. Montgolfier balloon (tethered flight, 1783)	10	10
728	2p.50 Charles' hydrogen balloon, 1783	15	10
729	3p.50 Charles Green's balloon *Royal Vauxhall*, 1836	20	10
730	5p. Gaston Tissandier's balloon *Zenith*, 1875	30	10
731	10p. Salomon Andrée's balloon *Ornen*, 1897	60	20
732	20p. Stratosphere balloon *Explorer II*	1·25	40
733	30p. Hot-air balloons	2·00	60
727/733	Set of 7	4·25	1·40
MS734	50p. Gas balloon	3·00	3·00

1984. 40th Anniv of ICAO.

832	8p. Sud Aviation SE 210 Caravelle	25	10
833	22p. Douglas DC-6B	80	30
834	80p. Ilyushin Il-76	2·25	90
832/834	Set of 3	3·00	1·20

1985.

930*	20p. Piper PA-30 Twin Commanche	40	15
932*	40p. Helicopter	75	35

1985.

970*	25p. Hang-glider	35	15
973*	80p. Free-falling from airplane	1·50	60

GUYANA

South America

100 cents = 1 dollar

1990.

2726*	$17.80 Mail balloon, Paris, 1870	65	70
2732*	$20 Airship LZ-127 *Graf Zeppelin*	65	70
2733*	$20 Dornier Do-J II 10-t Wal flying boat of Lufthansa	65	70
2734*	$20 Short S.8 Calcutta flying boat	65	70
2735*	$20 Junkers Ju 52/3m	65	70
2736*	$20 Douglas 0-2-M biplane of the U.S. Mail	65	70
2737*	$20 Airco (de Havilland) DH.4 biplane of the U.S. Mail	65	70
2738*	$20 Alcock and Brown's Vickers FB-27 Vimy, 1919	65	70

2741*	$20 Westland Dragonfly helicopter G-AKCU	65	70
2743*	$20 Boeing 314 flying boat *Yankee Clipper*	65	70
2744*	$20 Boeing 747-200 of Pan Am	65	70
2745*	$20 Concorde of Air France	65	70

1991. 50th Anniv of Japanese Attack on Pearl Harbour.

3199*	$50 Mitsubishi A6M Zero-Sen	85	85
3200*	$50 USS Arizona under attack	85	85
3201*	$50 Aichi D3A1 "VAL"	85	85
3203*	$50 Curtiss P-40 Warhawks taking off	85	85
3205*	$50 Boeing B-17 Flying Fortress crash landing at Bellows Field	85	85

1992.

MS3280*	Four sheets. (d) $225 Poster for film 'Zeppelin' (other miniature sheets do not show aircraft) *Price for 4 sheets*	15·00	17·00

1992.

3464*	$12.80 Count von Zeppelin and Zeppelin over Lake Constance	50	35
3467*	$100 Aero medical airlift	2·00	2·00
3474*	$225 Von Zeppelin and Zeppelin preparing for take off	3·50	3·50
MS3475*	Four sheets. (a) $225 Count Ferdinand von Zeppelin (other miniature sheets do not show aircraft) *Price for 4 sheets*	15·00	16·00

1993.

3606*	$100 Douglas DC-3 cargo plane	1·25	1·25
3608*	$100 Aerospatiale/BAe Concorde	1·25	1·25
3609*	$100 Count Ferdinand von Zeppelin and *Graf Zeppelin*	1·25	1·25

1993.

3632*	$12.80 Grumman TBM Avenger attacking *Yamoto* (Japanese battleship)	80	50
3635*	$100 Boeing B-29 Superfortresses raiding Japan	2·25	1·75

1993.

3641*	$50 Bristol Type 156 Beaufighter of RAAF, Battle of Bismark Sea, (2-4 Mar 1943)	80	80
3642*	$50 Lockheed P-38 Lightning of USAAF attacking Admiral Yamamotos' Mitsubishi GM41 *Betty* Bougainville, (7 April 1943)	80	80
3643*	$50 Consolidated B-24 Liberator bombers, Tarawa, (17-19 September, 1943)	80	80
3644*	$50 North American B-25 Mitchell bomber, Rabaul, (12 October 1943)	80	80
3645*	$50 US Navy aircraft attacking Makin (19 November, 1943)	80	80
3646*	$50 USAAF bombers, first daylight raid over Germany (27 January 1943)	80	80
3647*	$50 RAF de Havilland DH.98 Mosquito on first daylight raid over Berlin (30 January, 1943)	80	80
3648*	$50 Allied aircraft over Hamburg (24-30 July 1943)	80	80
3649*	$50 Consolidated B-24 Liberators bombing Ploesti oil refineries, Rumania, (1 August 1943)	80	80

3650*	$50 German night fighter attacking Allied bombers over Berlin, (18 November, 1943)		80	80
3657*	$50 Grumman FM-2 Wildcats sinking U-118 (FM-2 is the designation of the Grumman F4F-8 built by General Motors)		80	80

1994.

3925*	$60 X-30 National Aerospace Plane (project)		90	90
3926*	$60 Messerschmitt Me 163B Komet		90	90

1994. 50th Anniv of D-Day. Aircraft.

3938	$6 Supermarine Spitfire Mk XI		40	15
3939	$35 North American B-25 Mitchell		85	50
3940	$190 Republic P-47 Thunderbolts		3·00	3·50
3938/3940 Set of 3			3·75	3·75
MS3941 $325 Avro Type 683 Lancaster of 419 Squadron			4·75	5·00

1994.

3942*	$60 Airspeed AS-51, D-Day		90	80
3943*	$60 Horsaglider, D-Day		90	80
3945*	$60 US fighters attacking train		90	80
3953*	$60 RAF attacking Amiens prison		90	80
3957*	$60 Fiesler Fi 103 V1 Flying bomb		90	80

1995.

4435*	$60 Allied plane dropping supplies		85	90

1995.

4441*	$60 Northrop P-61 Black Widow		85	90
4443*	$60 Martin B-26 Marauder		85	90

1997.

5166*	$60 Byrd (flight over N. Pole) and Rockwell Commander		75	75

1998. Aircraft.

5299	$80 Wright *Flyer I*, 1903		75	75
5300	$80 Bleriot XI, 1911		75	75
5301	$80 Curtiss JN-4 Jenny, 1919		75	75
5302	$80 Zeppelin LZ-10 *Schwaben* 1911		75	75
5303	$80 Handley Page HP.18 (Type W-8b) Inscribed W-8B, 1923		75	75
5304	$80 de Havilland DH.66 Hercules, 1926		75	75
5305	$80 LTV (Vought) A7K Corsair II		75	75
5306	$80 Grumman A6E Intruder		75	75
5307	$80 Lockheed U-2		75	75
5308	$80 Sikorsky UH-60A Black Hawk		75	75
5309	$80 Lockheed Martin F-16 Fighting Falcon		75	75
5310	$80 McDonnell Douglas F-4 Phantom II		75	75
5299/5310 Set of 12			9·00	9·00
MS5311 Two sheets. (a) $300 Republic Fairchild A-10 Thunderbolt II (Warthog); (b) $300 Aerospatiate HH65A Dolphin Set of 2 sheets			5·00	5·50

1998. 80th Anniv of Royal Air Force.

5393	$100 Avro Type 683 Lancaster B2		90	90
5394	$100 Consolidated PBY 5 Catalina			
5395	$100 BAe Hawk T1As (Red Arrows)		90	90
5396	$100 Avro Type 683 Lancaster and de Havilland DH.98 Mosquito		90	90
5397	$100 BAe Hawk T1A		90	90
5398	$100 Lockheed C-130 Hercules		90	90
5399	$100 Panavia Tornado GR1		90	90
5400	$100 BAe Hawk 200 in desert camouflage		90	90
5401	$150 BAe Nimrod R1P		1·25	1·25
5402	$150 Panavia Tornado F Mk3 ADV		1·25	1·25
5403	$150 Boeing CH 47 Chinook		1·25	1·25
5404	$150 Panavia Tornado GR1A in front of hangar		1·25	1·25
5393/5404 Set of 12			11·00	11·00
MS5405 Six sheets. (a) $200 Bristol F2B (with eagle); (b) $200 Supermarine Spitfire and Eurofighter EF-2000 Typhoon; (c) $300 de Havilland DH.82 Tiger Moth and Eurofighter EF-2000 Typhoon; (d) $300 Eurofighter EF-2000 Typhoon; (e) $300 Bristol F2B (with harriers); (f) $300 Bristol F2B (with golden eagle) Set of 6 sheets			12·00	13·00

1999. First Non-stop Round-the-World Balloon Flight.

5645	$150 *Breitling Orbiter 3*		1·25	1·40
5646	$150 Flight logo		1·25	1·40
5647	$150 Bertrand Piccard (balloonist)		1·25	1·40
5648	$150 Brian Jones (balloonist)		1·25	1·40
5645/5648 Set of 4			4·50	5·00
MS5649 $300 *Breitling Orbiter 3*			2·75	3·00

1999.

5740*	$35 Harriet Quimby (first American woman pilot, 1911)		35	35

2000. Centenary of First Zeppelin Flight.

5878	$200 Count Ferdinand von Zeppelin and Zeppelin LZ-1, 1900		1·60	1·75
5879	$200 Count Ferdinand von Zeppelin and Zeppelin LZ-2, 1906		1·60	1·75
5880	$200 Count Ferdinand von Zeppelin and Zeppelin LZ-9, 1911		1·60	1·75
5878/5880 Set of 3			4·25	4·75
MS5881 $400 Zeppelin LZ-127, 1928			3·25	3·50

2001.

6130*	$60 Charles Lindbergh (first solo transatlantic flight, 1927)		55	60
6134*	$60 Amelia Earhart (first solo flight from Hawaii to California, January 1935)		55	60

2003. Centenary of Powered Flight.

6384	$100 Avro Triplane (probably No 4)		60	65
6385	$100 First British powered flight		95	1·00
MS6386 Two sheets. (a) $150 Wright *Flyer*; $150 SPAD 13 (more correctly, S.XIII); $150 Sopwith F.1 Camel; $150 Albatros DII (only one S); (b) $150 Scout Experimental 5A; $150 Airco (de Havilland) D.H.4; $150 Wright Brothers plane			4·75	4·75
MS6387 Two sheets. (a) $400 Fokker D.VIIs; (b) $400 Wright Brothers plane over water Set of 4 sheets			4·75	4·75

2004.

MS6471* $150 Paratroopers drop from Douglas C-47 Skytrains (other stamps in the miniature sheet do not show aircraft)			4·50	4·75

2005.

6510*	$200 Supermarine Spitfire (RAF)		1·60	1·75

2006. Hot Air Balloons and Airships.

6567	$200 De Beer's Zeppelin NT		1·60	1·60
6568	$200 Lockheed Martin LTA 2004		1·60	1·60
6569	$200 Stratellite concept airship		1·60	1·60
6567/6569 Set of 3			4·25	4·25
MS6570 $400 Skybus airship, Switzerland			3·00	3·25

2007. Concorde.

6648	$100 Concorde prototype 002 rollout, Filton, September 1968		80	55
6649	$100 Prototype 002 seen from above, Filton, September 1968		80	55
6650	$100 Concorde and BAe Hawk T1s of Red Arrows, 1985		80	55
6651	$100 Silhouettes of Concorde, Red Arrows and *Queen Elizabeth II* (liner)		80	55
6648/6651 Set of 4			3·00	2·00

HAITI

West Indies

100 centimes = 1 gourde

1929.
306	25c. Fokker F.10A Super Trimotor	45	35
307	50c. Fokker F.10A Super Trimotor	60	35
308	75c. Fokker F.10A Super Trimotor	1·50	1·10
309	1g. Fokker F.10A Super Trimotor	1·60	1·40
306/309 *Set of 4*		3·75	3·00

1933. No. 301 surcharged **COLUMBIA VOL-DIRECT N.-Y.—P.-AU-P. BOYD-LYON 60 CTS.** and airplane.
311a	60c. on 20c. Map	60·00	65·00

1933.
325	50c. Fokker F.10A Super Trimotor (orange)	4·75	75
326	50c. Fokker F.10A Super Trimotor (olive)	4·75	75
327	50c. Fokker F.10A Super Trimotor (red)	3·00	1·70
328	50c. Fokker F.10A Super Trimotor (black)	1·80	75
329	60c. Fokker F.10A Super Trimotor	95	45
330	1g. Fokker F.10A Super Trimotor	1·50	45
325/330 *Set of 6*		15·00	4·25

1944. No. 329 surcharged **0.10.**
372*	0.10 on 60c. Fokker F.10A Super Trimotor	45	35

1955.
515	10c. Sikorsky S-55 helicopter (blue)	25	15
516	10c. Sikorsky S-55 helicopter (green)	25	15
517	10c. Sikorsky S-55 helicopter (orange)	25	15
518	10c. Sikorsky S-55 helicopter (black)	25	15
519	20c. Sikorsky S-55 helicopter (red)	30	15
520	20c. Sikorsky S-55 helicopter (green)	30	15
515/520 *Set of 6*		1·40	80

1955.
521	10c. Sikorsky S-55 helicopter	25	15
522	20c. Sikorsky S-55 helicopter	30	15
523	10c. Sikorsky S-55 helicopter (air) (inscribed "AVION")	25	15
524	20c. Sikorsky S-55 helicopter	30	15
521/524 *Set of 4*		1·00	55

1955.
541*	50c. Douglas DC-4	65	20
543*	75c. Douglas DC-4	90	45

1960. Aviation Week.
735	20c. Sud Aviation SE 210 Caravelle of Air France	15	10
736	50c. Boeing 707 and Wright *Flyer I* (brown and green)	40	20
737	50c. Boeing 707 and Wright *Flyer I* (blue and green)	40	20
738	50c. Boeing 707 and Wright *Flyer I* (black and green)	40	20
739	1g. Sud Aviation SE 210 Caravelle of Air France	90	20

740	1g.50 Airplane overprint (on stamp No. 311a) and Boeing 707	95	35
735/740 *Set of 6*		3·00	1·10

1961. Nos. 735 and 739/40 surcharged **18e CONFERENCE INTERNATIONALE DU SCOUTISME MONDIAL. LISBONNE SEPTEMBRE 1961+0,25** and Scout emblem.
776	20c. +25c. Sud Aviation SE 210 Caravelle of Air France	30	25
777	1g. +25c. Sud Aviation SE 210 Caravelle of Air France	40	30
778	1g.50 +25c. Airplane overprint (on stamp No. 311a) and Boeing 707	50	45
776/778 *Set of 3*		1·10	90

1964. Port-au-Prince International Airport.
901	10c. Port-au-Prince International Airport	20	10
902	25c. Port-au-Prince International Airport	25	15
903	50c. Port-au-Prince International Airport	35	20
904	1g. Port-au-Prince International Airport	45	35
905	50c. Port-au-Prince International Airport (air) (inscribed "POSTE AERIENNE")	35	20
906	1g.50 Port-au-Prince International Airport	60	35
907	2g.50 Port-au-Prince International Airport	1·20	55
901/907 *Set of 7*		3·00	1·70

1965. Nos. 901/7 overprinted **1965.**
908	10c. Port-au-Prince International Airport	15	10
909	25c. Port-au-Prince International Airport	25	20
910	50c. Port-au-Prince International Airport	35	20
911	1g. Port-au-Prince International Airport	45	35
912	50c. Port-au-Prince International Airport (air)	35	20
913	1g.50 Port-au-Prince International Airport	60	35
914	2g.50 Port-au-Prince International Airport	95	65
908/914 *Set of 7*		2·75	1·80

1968. Inauguration of Duvalier Airport.
1084	5c. Boeing 727-100 over Duvalier Airport	15	15
1085	10c. Boeing 727-100 over Duvalier Airport	15	10
1086	25c. Boeing 727-100 over Duvalier Airport	25	15
1087	50c. Boeing 727-100 over entrance to Duvalier Airport (air)	35	20
1088	1g.50 Boeing 727-100 over entrance to Duvalier Airport	60	45
1089	2g.50 Boeing 727-100 over entrance to Duvalier Airport	80	75
1084/1089 *Set of 6*		2·10	1·60

1968. Boesman's Balloon Flight.
1104	70c. Dr. Jan Boseman and balloon PH-BOX	60	45
1105	1g.75 Dr. Jan Boseman and balloon PH-BOX	1·20	90

1968. Galiffet's Balloon Flight.
1106	70c. Airplane (in airmail cachet dated 2 May 1925)	45	55
1107	70c. Airplane (in airmail cachet dated 2 September 1925)	45	55
1108	70c. Airplane (in airmail cachet dated 28 March 1927)	45	55
1109	70c. Airplane (in airmail cachet dated 12 July 1927)	45	55
1110	70c. Airplane (in airmail cachet dated 13 September 1927)	45	55

1111	70c. Airplane (in airmail cachet dated 6 February 1928)	45	55
1106/1111 *Set of 6*		2·50	3·00

A background design on each stamp shows part of Galiffet's balloon of 1784.

1968.
1116*	20c. Farman M.F.7 floatplane	20	15
1119*	50c. Farman M.F.7 floatplane (air)	35	20

1971. 40th Anniv (1969) of Airmail Service.
1237	20c. Fokker F.10A Super Trimotor (on stamp No. 307) and balloon	20	15
1238	50c. Fokker F.10A Super Trimotor (on stamp No. 307) and balloon	35	20
1239	1g. Fokker F.10A Super Trimotor (on stamp No. 307) and Concorde	80	40
1240	1g.50 Fokker F.10A Super Trimotor (on stamp No. 307) and Concorde	1·20	50
1237/1240 *Set of 4*		2·30	1·10
MS1241	50g. Fokker F.10A Super Trimotor (on stamp No. 307)	5·75	3·75

1972. Nos. 1237/40 overprinted **INTERPEX 72** and emblem.
1244	20c. Fokker F.10A Super Trimotor (on stamp No. 307) and balloon	20	20
1245	50c. Fokker F.10A Super Trimotor (on stamp No. 307) and balloon	30	30
1246	1g. Fokker F.10A Super Trimotor (on stamp No. 307) and Concorde	50	40
1247	1g.50 Fokker F.10A Super Trimotor (on stamp No. 307) and Concorde	60	50
1244/1247 *Set of 4*		1·40	1·30

1972. Nos. 1237/40 overprinted **HAIPEX 5eme. CONGRES** and emblem.
1253	20c. Fokker F.10A Super Trimotor (on stamp No. 307) and balloon	15	10
1254	50c. Fokker F.10A Super Trimotor (on stamp No. 307) and balloon	30	20
1255	1g. Fokker F.10A Super Trimotor (on stamp No. 307) and Concorde	40	30
1256	1g.50 Fokker F.10A Super Trimotor (on stamp No. 307) and Concorde	60	40
1253/1256 *Set of 4*		1·30	90

1972. Nos. 1238/40 overprinted **BELGICA 72** and emblem.
1257	50c. Fokker F.10A Super Trimotor (on stamp No. 307) and balloon	30	20
1258	1g. Fokker F.10A Super Trimotor (on stamp No. 307) and Concorde	40	30
1259	1g.50 Fokker F.10A Super Trimotor (on stamp No. 307) and Concorde	60	40
1257/1259 *Set of 3*		1·20	80

OFFICIAL STAMPS

1960. Nos. 736/40 overprinted **OFFICIEL.**
O742	50c. Boeing 707 and Wright Flyer I (brown and green)		55
O743	50c. Boeing 707 and Wright Flyer I (blue and green)		55
O744	50c. Boeing 707 and Wright Flyer I (black and green)		55
O745	1g. Sud Aviation SE 210 Caravelle of Air France		75
O746	1g.50 Airplane overprint (on stamp No. 311a) and Boeing 707		1·20
O742/746 *Set of 5*			3·25

Nos. O742/6 were only issued precancelled.

HATAY

Asia Minor

100 centimes = 1 piastre

1938. Nos. 322/9 of Syria overprinted **SANDJAK D'ALEXANDRETTE.**
13	½p. Savoia Marchetti S-73	4·00	2·00
14	1p. Potez 62 F-ANDO	4·00	2·00
15	2p. Savoia Marchetti S-73	8·00	4·00
16	3p. Potez 62 F-ANDO	8·00	4·00
17	5p. Savoia Marchetti S-73	24·00	10·00
18	10p. Potez 62 F-ANDO	24·00	10·00
19	15p. Savoia Marchetti S-73	32·00	12·00
20	25p. Potez 62 F-ANDO	47·00	16·00
13/20 *Set of 8*		£140	55·00

HONDURAS

Central America

1930. 100 centavos = 1 peso

1933. 100 centavos = 1 lempira

1930.
314	5c. Ryan B-5 Brougham	60	35
315	10c. Ryan B-5 Brougham	1·10	70
316	15c. Ryan B-5 Brougham	1·50	95
317	20c. Ryan B-5 Brougham	1·70	85
318	1p. Ryan B-5 Brougham	6·25	5·50
314/318 Set of 5		10·00	7·50

1931. Nos. 314/18 overprinted **T.S.de C.**
337*	5c. Ryan B-5 Brougham	3·75	3·50
338*	10c. Ryan B-5 Brougham	5·50	5·50
339*	15c. Ryan B-5 Brougham	9·25	9·00
339a*	20c. Ryan B-5 Brougham	9·25	9·00
339b*	1p. Ryan B-5 Brougham	19·00	18·00

1935.
369	8c. Ryan B-5 Brougham	25	25
370	10c. Ryan B-5 Brougham	35	25
371	15c. Ryan B-5 Brougham	75	25
372	20c. Airplane	1·20	60
373	40c. Airplane	1·40	35
374	50c. Airplane	12·50	4·75
375	1l. Airplane	4·50	3·50
369/375 Set of 7		19·00	9·00

1956.
563*	30c. Toncontin Airport	50	35

1966.
694*	20c. Curtiss C-46 Commando	35	35

1967. No. E570 surcharged **L. 0.10.**
716*	10c. on 20c. Lockheed Constellation	60	25

1972.
799*	8c. Chance Vought F4U-5 Corsair fighters	35	10

1983. 50th Anniv of Honduras Air Force.
1003	3c. Curtiss T-32 Condor II	10	10
1004	15c. North American T-6 Texan	25	10
1005	25c. Chance Vought F4U-5 Corsair	50	35
1006	65c. Douglas C-47 Skytrain	1·00	60
1007	1l. Cessna A-37B Dragonfly	1·50	95
1008	2l. Dassault Super Mystere SMB-11	3·00	2·40
1003/1008 Set of 6		5·75	4·00
MS1009 1l.55 Bell Model 205 UH-1H Iroquois helicopter		3·00	3·00

1987.
1060*	60c. Lockheed L-1011 Tristar	70	25

1999.
1478*	5l.40 Lockheed C-130 Hercules	1·10	1·00
1484*	5l.40 Sikorsky S.76 on beach	1·10	1·00

2000.
1596*	10l. Thomas Canfield Pounds (founder of Central American Airline)	2·50	1·30

EXPRESS LETTER STAMPS

1956. Overprinted **ENTREGA INMEDIATA.**
E570	20c. Lockheed Constellation	1·40	60

1972. As No. 1005, but inscribed "ENTREGA INMEDIATA".
E811	20c. Chance Vought F4U-5 Corsair	60	60

1975. No. E811 surcharged **L. 0.60.**
E848	60c. on 20c. Chance Vought F4U-5 Corsair	1·90	1·20

OFFICIAL STAMPS
1956. As No. 563, in new colours, overprinted **OFICIAL.**
O582*	30c. Toncontin Airport	35	25

HONG KONG

South-east coast of China

100 cents = 1 dollar

1941.
168*	$1 Short S.23 Empire "C" Class flying boat G-ADVB	6·00	2·00

1949. As Nos. 114/15 of Antigua.
173*	10c. Airplane	4·50	1·00
174*	20c. Jet-powered Vickers Viking	17·00	4·50

1984. Aviation in Hong Kong.
450	40c. de Havilland DH.86 Dragon Express G-ACWD *Dorado* of Imperial Airways	1·00	15
451	$1 Sikorsky S-42B flying boat NC-16734 *Hong Kong Clipper* of Pan Am	1·75	1·75
452	$1.30 Boeing 747 of Cathay Pacific at Kai Tak Airport	2·25	1·75
453	$5 Baldwin Brothers' balloon, 1891	7·00	12·00
450/453 Set of 4		11·00	14·00

1986.
517*	50c. Boeing 747	80	30

1998. Inauguration of Hong Kong International Airport, Chek Lap Kok.
924	$1.30 Observation Lounge	30	20
925	$1.60 Couple boarding train	35	20
926	$2.50 Train and suspension bridge	50	40
927	$2.60 Concourse and mail vans at Airmail Centre	55	40
928	$3 Aircraft in bays	70	40
929	$5 Airplane taking off	1·10	40
924/929 Set of 6		3·25	2·10
MS930 $5 Airplane taking off		1·10	1·00

HONG KONG, CHINA 中國香港

1998.
MS931 $5 de Havilland DH.86 Dragon Express *Dorado* (Hong Kong-Penang Service, 1936)		1·40	1·10

1998.
940	$1.30 Dragonfly kite	30	20
941	$2.50 Dragon kite	50	30
942	$3.10 Butterfly kite	50	50
943	$5 Goldfish kite	1·00	60
940/943 Set of 4		2·10	1·40

1999.
988*	$50 Hong Kong International Airport	9·75	4·25

2002.
1108*	$5 Aircraft in flight over Hong Kong Airport	65	55

2004.
1254*	$5 Kawasaki OH-1 helicopters	70	35

2006.
1386*	$2.50 Aerospatiale AS 332 Super Puma	65	30

HUNGARY

Central Europe
1933. 100 filler = 1 pengo
1946. 100 filler = 1 forint

1933.
554*	10fi. Lockheed Model 8A Sirius NR115W *Justice for Hungary*	1·25	45
555*	16fi. Lockheed Model 8A Sirius NR115W *Justice for Hungary*	1·25	45
558*	48fi. "Spirit of Flight" on wing of Lockheed Model 8A Sirius	13·00	2·50
559*	72fi. "Spirit of Flight" on wing of Lockheed Model 8A Sirius	22·00	2·75

1936.
580	10fi. Fokker F.VIIb/3m	30	25
581	20fi. Fokker F.VIIb/3m	30	25
582	36fi. Fokker F.VIIb/3m	45	25
583	40fi. Fokker F.VIIb/3m	45	25
584	52fi. Fokker F.VIIb/3m	60	75
585	60fi. Fokker F.VIIb/3m	16·00	2·00
586	80fi. Fokker F.VIIb/3m	2·10	55
587	1p. Fokker F.VIIb/3m	2·10	45
588	2p. Fokker F.VIIb/3m	5·00	1·60
589	5p. Fokker F.VIIb/3m	18·00	18·00
580/589 *Set of 10*		41·00	22·00

1940. Admiral Horthy Aviation Fund.
659*	10fi. +10fi. Glider	60	50
660*	20fi. +20fi. Aircraft	90	1·10

1941. Admiral Horthy Aviation Fund.
681*	10fi. +10fi. Model glider	65	55
682*	20fi. +20fi. Glider	65	55

1941.
710*	20fi. +30fi. Fighter	30	40

1942. Horthy Aviation Fund.
714*	12fi. +12fi. Aircraft	85	60
715*	20fi. +20fi. Airplane	85	60

1942. Mourning for Stephen Horthy and Horthy Aviation Fund.
721	20fi. Aircraft	25	20
722	30fi. +20fi. Aircraft	35	25

1943. Horthy Aviation Fund.
765	8fi. +8fi. Model glider	70	40
766	12fi. +12fi. Gliders	70	40
767	20fi. +20fi. Aircraft	1·25	65
768	30fi. +30fi. Cant Z.1007 bis Alcione bomber and gliders	70	65
765/768 *Set of 4*		3·00	1·90

1948.
1031*	6fi. David Schwartz and his aluminium airship, Count Ferdinand von Zeppelin and airship LZ-127 *Graf Zeppelin*	25	40
1032*	8fi. Airship LZ-127 *Graf Zeppelin*	25	30
1033*	10fi. Louis Bleriot, Bleriot XI and Douglas DC-4	45	50

1949.
1071	2fo. Lisunov Li-2	80	65

1949.
1078	50fi. Airliner	3·75	3·75

1950.
1092*	3fo. Lisunov Li-2	2·40	40

1950.
1100*	2fo. Douglas DC-4	6·75	6·50

1950.
1118*	1fo.70 Model gliders	1·25	75

1950.
1132	20fi. Lisunov Li-2	10	10
1133	30fi. Lisunov Li-2	10	10
1134	70fi. Lisunov Li-2	20	10
1135	1fo. Lisunov Li-2	20	10
1136	1fo.60 Lisunov Li-2	70	10
1137	2fo. Lisunov Li-2	45	10
1138	3fo. Lisunov Li-2	2·10	30
1139	5fo. Lisunov Li-2 (blue)	1·10	45
1140	10fo. Lisunov Li-2 at Budaors Airport	3·50	75
1140a	20fo. Lisunov Li-2 at Budaors Airport	14·50	4·00
1132/1140a *Set of 10*		21·00	5·50

1950.
1153*	3fo. Glider	2·25	1·10

1951.
1177*	40fi. Model airplane	45	20

1951.
1196*	2fo. Lisunov Li-2	1·60	65

1953.
1321*	3fo. Ilyushin Il-12	2·10	55
1322*	5fo. Ilyushin Il-12	3·00	2·00

1954.
1366	40fi. Boy building model glider	20	10
1367	50fi. Boy launching model glider	30	10
1368	60fi. Gliders	20	20
1369	80fi. Pilot and Libis KB-6T Matajur	30	20
1370	1fo. Airplane and parachutists	30	20
1371	1fo.20 Letov C-4 biplane	45	30
1372	1fo.50 Lisunov Li-2 HA-LIA of Malev	1·25	45
1373	2fo. Mikoyan Gurevich MiG-15 jet fighter	1·60	65
1366/1373 *Set of 8*		4·25	2·00

1955. As No. 1139, but on silver paper.
1437	5fo. Lisunov Li-2 (blue on silver)	13·50	13·50

1957.
1489*	1fo. (+4fo.) Tupolev Tu-104A	75	75

1958.
1535* 1fo. Tupolev Tu-104A................................ 45 30

1958.
1538 3fo. Ilyushin Il-14P.............................. 90 30
1539 5fo. Ilyushin Il-14P.............................. 1·10 45

1958.
1542 20fi. Ilyushin Il-14P............................ 10 10
1543 30fi. Ilyushin Il-14P............................ 10 10
1544 70fi. Ilyushin Il-14P............................ 10 10
1545 1fo. Tupolev Tu-104A......................... 20 10
1546 1fo.60 Ilyushin Il-14P........................ 35 10
1547 2fo. Ilyushin Il-14P............................ 60 10
1548 3fo. Ilyushin Il-14P............................ 60 20
1549 5fo. Ilyushin Il-14P............................ 1·00 25
1550 10fo. Ilyushin Il-14P.......................... 60 60
1551 20fo. Ilyushin Il-14P.......................... 5·50 85
1542/1551 *Set of 10* .... 8·25 2·20

1959.
1555* 40fi. Helicopter................................ 1·50 25

1959.
1571* 3fo. Aladar Zselyi's monoplane, 1910....... 1·90 1·40

1962. Development of Flight.
1820* 40fi. Glider HA-7015 and Lilienthal monoplane glider.................... 10 10
1821* 60fi. Zlin Z-226 Trener 6 HA-TRN and Rakos' monoplane, 1912................. 25 10
1822* 80fi. Airship LZ-127 *Graf Zeppelin* and Montgolfier balloon (first manned free flight, 1783).......................... 30 10
1823* 1fo. Ilyushin Il-18B HA-NOA of Malev and Wright Flyer I.......................... 35 10
1824* 1fo.40 Nord 3202 sports airplane and Peter Nesterov's Nieuport biplane making "loop the loop" manoeuvre, 1913...... 35 25
1825* 2fo. Mil Mi-6 helicopter and Asboth's helicopter.............................. 55 20
1826* 3fo. Myasichev Mya-4 and N.E. Shukovsky's wind tunnel.............. 60 30

1963.
1894* 2fo.60 Ilyushin Il-18........................... 65 65

1963.
1908* 1fo.20 Airliner being loaded with mail......... 2·40 75

1965.
2056* 20fi. Mil Mi-4 helicopter..................... 10 10

1966.
2182 1fo. Josef Toth's monoplane, 1912 (?)...... 40 15
2183 2fo. Ilyushin Il-18............................ 70 35

MS2220 10fo. Ilyushin Il-18 at Ferihegy Airport...... 4·50 6·00

1966.
2226 20fi. Ilyushin Il-18 of Malev.............. 10 10
2227 50fi. Ilyushin Il-18 of Malev.............. 10 10
2228 1fo. Ilyushin Il-18 of Malev.............. 15 10
2229 1fo.10 Ilyushin Il-18 of Malev.......... 20 10
2230 1fo.20 Ilyushin Il-18 of Malev.......... 20 10
2231 1fo.50 Ilyushin Il-18 of Malev.......... 30 10
2232 2fo. Ilyushin Il-18 of Malev.............. 35 10
2233 2fo.50 Ilyushin Il-18 of Malev.......... 40 10
2234 3fo. Ilyushin Il-18 of Malev.............. 55 15
2235 4fo. Ilyushin Il-18 of Malev.............. 1·60 1·25
2236 5fo. Ilyushin Il-18 of Malev.............. 70 20
2237 10fo. Ilyushin Il-18 of Malev............ 1·90 40
2238 20fo. Ilyushin Il-18 of Malev............ 3·00 60
2226/2238 *Set of 13* .... 8·50 3·00

1967. Airmail Stamp Exhibition, Budapest.
2264* 2fo. +1fo. David Schwartz's aluminium airship, 1897............................ 85 85
2265* 2fo. +1fo. Erno Horvath's monoplane, 1911................................. 85 85
2266* 2fo. +1fo. PKZ-2 helicopter, 1918.......... 85 85
2269* 2fo. +1fo. Mil Mi-1 helicopter.............. 85 85
2270* 2fo. +1fo. Tupolev Tu-154................... 85 85

1967.
2273 1fo. Airplane................................. 30 10

1968. 50th Anniv of Budapest-Vienna Airmail Service.
2369 2fo.60 Ilyushin Il-18 of Malev.............. 60 15

1970.
MS2533* 2fo.50 Sikorsky S-61B Sea King helicopter (sheet contains three other 2fo.50 designs).......... 2·50 2·75

1971.
MS2608* 2fo.+1fo. Ilyushin Il-14P (on stamp No. 1547) (sheet contains three other 2fo.+ 1fo. designs).......................... 3·00 3·25

1973.
2799 3fo. Mikoyan-Gurevich MiG-21.................. 45 25

1973.
MS2808* 10fo. Ilyushin Il-62M...................... 3·25 3·00

1974.
2881* 1fo.20 Mail balloon.......................... 20 10
2884* 6fo. Tupolev Tu-154........................ 1·40 35
MS2885* 2fo.50 Tupolev Tu-154 (sheet contains three other 2fo.50 designs)............ 3·00 3·75

1974.
2911* 3fo. Mil Mi-4 Helicopters and jet fighter.. 55 15

1974. International Airmail Exhibition, Budapest.
2913 2fo. +1fo. Hansa Brandenburg C-1 biplane, 1918......................... 1·00 1·00
2914 2fo. +1fo. Airship LZ-127 *Graf Zeppelin* .... 1·00 1·00
2915 2fo. +1fo. Balloon........................... 1·00 1·00
2916 2fo. +1fo. Mil Mi-1 helicopter HA-HE........ 1·00 1·00
2913/2916 *Set of 4*............................... 3·50 3·50

1977.
3113	3fo. Airship LZ-127 *Graf Zeppelin* (on stamp No. 2914)	1·10	1·25

1977.
3134	60fi. Tupolev Tu-154 of Malev	15	10
3135	1fo.20 Douglas DC-8-62 of Swissair	20	10
3136	2fo. Ilyushin Il-62M of C.S.A.	30	10
3137	2fo.40 Airbus Industrie A30084 of Lufthansa	35	10
3138	4fo. Boeing 747 of Pan Am	45	10
3139	5fo. Tupolev Tu-144 of Aeroflot	65	10
3140	10fo. Concorde of Air France	1·90	30
3141	20fo. Ilyushin Il-86 of Aeroflot	2·75	75
3134/3141	*Set of 8*	6·00	1·50

1977. Famous Aviators and their Airplanes.
3142	40fi. Montgolfier balloon (first manned free flight, 1783)	10	10
3143	60fi. David Schwartz and his aluminium airship, 1897	20	10
3144	1fo. Alberto Santos-Dumont and his airship *Ballon No. 5*, 1901	30	10
3145	2fo. K.E. Tsiolkovsky and Lebaudy-Juillot airship *Lebedj*	45	10
3146	3fo. Roald Amundsen and airship N.1 *Norge*	70	20
3147	4fo. Hugo Eckener and Airship LZ-127 *Graf Zeppelin*	1·00	30
3148	5fo. Count Ferdinand von Zeppelin and airship LZ-127 *Graf Zeppelin*	1·50	50
3142/3148	*Set of 7*	3·75	1·30
MS3149	20fo. Airship LZ-127 *Graf Zeppelin*	4·00	4·00

1978.
3177	40fi. Louis Bleriot and Bleriot XI, 1909	15	10
3178	60fi. John Alcock, Arthur Whitten Brown and their Vickers FB-27 Vimy, 1919 (shown with a nose skid)	20	10
3179	1fo. Albert C. Read and Curtiss NC-4 flying boat	25	10
3180	2fo. HermanN Kohl, Gunther Hunefeld, James Fitzmaurice and Junkers W.33 *Bremen*	55	10
3181	3fo. Amy Johnson, Jim Mollison and de Havilland DH.60G Gipsy Moth G-AAAH *Jason*,1930	75	15
3182	4fo. Gyorgy Endresz, Sandor Wilczec (inscribed "Sandor Magyar") and Lockheed Model 8A Sirius NR115W *Justice for Hungary* (incorrect in detail)	95	20
3183	5fo. Wolfgang von Gronau and Dornier Do-J II 8-t Wal flying boat D-2053 *Gronland Wal*	1·00	70
3177/3183	*Set of 7*	3·50	1·30
MS3184	20fo. Wilbur and Orville Wright and Wright Flyer I	3·75	4·00

1981. *Graf Zeppelin* Flights.
3366	1fo. Airship LZ-127 *Graf Zeppelin*	15	10
3367	2fo. Airship LZ-127 *Graf Zeppelin*	45	10
3368	3fo. Airship LZ-127 *Graf Zeppelin*	45	10
3369	4fo. Airship LZ-127 *Graf Zeppelin*	60	10
3370	5fo. Airship LZ-127 *Graf Zeppelin*	70	25
3371	6fo. Airship LZ-127 *Graf Zeppelin*	75	25
3372	7fo. Airship LZ-127 *Graf Zeppelin*	85	80
3366/3372	*Set of 7*	3·50	1·50

1981.
MS3384	5fo. Airship LZ-127 *Graf Zeppelin* (sheet contains three other 5fo designs)	4·50	4·00

1983. Bicentenary of Manned Flight.
3483	1fo. Jet airliner and Menner's balloon, 1811	15	10
3484	1fo. Jet airliner and captive observation balloon, 1896	15	10
3485	2fo. Jet airliner, balloon and car pursuit race,1904	40	15
3486	2fo. Jet airliner and hot-air balloon *Pannonia* HA-001, 1977	40	15
3487	4fo. Jet airliner and hot-air balloon *Malev* HA-901, 1981	70	35
3488	4fo. Jet airliner and hot-air balloon HA-804 of the Hungarian National Defence Union, 1982	70	35
3489	5fo. Jet airliner and non-rigid airship HA-B-501, 1981	95	50
3483/3489	*Set of 7*	3·00	1·50
MS3490	20fo. Jet airliner and hot-air balloons	3·00	3·00

1984. World Aerobatics Championship, Bekescsaba.
3566*	2fo. Airplane 4020	35	10

1985.
3631*	5fo. Hang-glider	80	40

1987.
3788*	6fo. Admiral Richard E. Byrd and Ford 4-AT-B Trimotor NX-4542 *Floyd Bennett*	1·10	45
MS3789*	20fo. Helicopter	6·00	5·75

1988. 150th Birth Anniv of Ferdinand von Zeppelin (airship pioneer).
3821	2fo. Count Ferdinand von Zeppelin and airship LZ-2, 1905	40	15
3822	4fo. Count Ferdinand von Zeppelin and airship LZ-4, 1908	70	25
3823	4fo. Count Ferdinand von Zeppelin and airship LZ-10 *Schwaben*, 1911	70	25
3824	8fo. Count Ferdinand von Zeppelin and airship LZ-127 *Graf Zeppelin*	1·25	45
3821/3824	*Set of 4*	2·75	1·00

1988. Hungarian Biplanes.
3863	1fo. Lloyd C.II biplane	10	10
3864	2fo. Hansa Brandenburg C-I biplane	25	10
3865	4fo. Ufag C.I biplane	40	15
3866	10fo. Gerle 13 scout HA-AAI	95	55
3867	12fo. WM 13 trainer HA-AKT	1·25	55
3853/3867	*Set of 5*	2·75	1·30

1989. Old Timer Rally and 60th Anniv of Gliding in Hungary.
3911	3fo. Messenger glider	45	15
3912	5fo. Pal glider	75	30

1991. Centenary of First Heavier-than-Air Flight by Otto Lilienthal.
4040	7fo. Otto Lilienthal and monoplane gliders	40	30
4041	12fo. Wright Flyer I and Lilienthal monoplane glider	70	55
4042	20fo. Santos-Dumont's biplane *14 bis* and Lilienthal monoplane glider	1·10	85
4043	30fo. Aladar Zselyi's monoplane, 1910 and Lilienthal monoplane glider	1·60	1·40
4040/4043	*Set of 4*	3·50	2·75

1994. 50th Anniv of ICAO.
4174	56fo. Douglas DC-3	35	30

2000. 50th Anniv of Ferihegy International Airport.
4510	136fo. Airport building and Lisunov Li-2	1·50	1·25

2000.
4529	120fo. Boeing 767-200	1·50	1·10

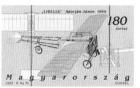

2002.
4609	180fo. Adorjan Janos's, *Libelle*, 1910	80	40
4610	190fo. Lloyds C.II biplane, 1915	85	40

2003.
4669   140fo. Gerle 13, 1933.................................   75   35
4670   160fo. L-2 Roma, 1925................................   85   40

2005.
4884   85fo. MD520 helicopter..............................   45   20

2006.
4920   120fo. Boeing 767-200ER (1993) ....
4921   140fo. Lockheed Sirius 8A (1931) ....

2006.
4966*   120fo. Boy with model airplanes...................   1·10   55

2007.
4988*   (62fo.) Air balloons...................................   85   45
4990*   (62fo.) Air balloon and student   85   45
4991*   (62fo.) Air balloon and students   85   45
4992*   (62fo.) Air balloon and students   85   45

POSTAGE DUE STAMPS

1973.
D2851*   1fo.20 Ilyushin Il-18...............................   20   10

1987.
D3815*   20fo. Biplane...   1·50   20

ICELAND

North Atlantic

100 aurar = 1 krona

1928. Nos. 122 and 92 overprinted with airplane.
156	10a. King Christian X (red)		1·20	8·75
157	50a. Kings Christian IX and Frederik VIII		75·00	85·00

1930.
174	15a. Airplane		23·00	38·00
175	20a. Airplane		23·00	38·00
176	35a. Airplane		45·00	75·00
177	50a. Airplane		45·00	75·00
178	1k. Airplane		45·00	75·00
174/178 Set of 5			£160	£275

1934.
208	10a. Avro 504K		1·90	1·90
209	20a. Avro 504K		4·00	4·25
210a	25a. Monoplane		17·00	13·00
211	50a. Monoplane		4·50	6·25
212	1k. Monoplane		28·00	26·00
213	2k. Monoplane		11·50	11·00
208/213 Set of 6			60·00	55·00

1947.
271	15a. Grumman G-21 Goose amphibian		65	75
272	30a. Consolidated PBY-5 Catalina flying boat		65	1·00
273	75a. Douglas DC-3		65	75
274	1k. Grumman G-21 Goose amphibian		65	75
275	1k.80 Douglas DC-3		12·50	11·00
276	2k. Consolidated PBY-5 Catalina flying boat		1·30	1·60
277	2k.50 Consolidated PBY-5 Catalina flying boat		24·00	1·00
278	3k. Douglas DC-4		1·30	1·90
279	3k.30 Douglas DC-4		6·75	5·50
271/279 Set of 9			44·00	22·00

1951.
312*	3k. Saab 90 Scandia		3·25	3·00

1959. 40th Anniv of Iceland Civil Aviation.
366	3k.50 Vickers Viscount 700 of Icelandair and Avro 504K biplane		65	60
367	4k.05 Douglas DC-4 and Avro 504K biplane		65	80

1969. 50th Anniv of Icelandic Aviation.
463	9k.50 Boeing 727		50	55
464	12k. Canadair CL-44-D4 of Loftleidir (inscribed "Rolls-Royce 400")		50	55

1973.
508*	80k. Beech Model 18		1·10	85

1978. 50th Anniv of Domestic Flights.
563	60k. Dr. Alexander Johanneson, Junkers W.34 *Island 1* and Junkers F-13 *Island 2*		30	30
564	100k. Fokker F.27 Friendship TF-FIK of Flugfelag Islands		60	40

1987. Opening of Leif Eriksson Terminal, Keflavik Airport.
693	100k. Tail of Boeing 727 at Keflavik Airport		4·25	1·70

1993. 65th Anniv of First Icelandic Postal Flight.
811	30k. Junkers F-13 seaplane D-483 *Sulan* of Flugfelag Islands		1·90	75
812	30k. Waco YKS-7 seaplane TF-ORH		1·90	75
813	30k. Grumman G-21 Goose amphibian TF-RVK		1·90	75
814	30k. Consolidated PBY-5 Catalina flying boat TF-TSP of Flugfelag Islands		1·90	75
811/814 Set of 4			7·00	2·75

1994. 50th Anniv of ICAO.
833	100k. Airliner		3·25	2·20

1995. 40th Anniv of Iceland-Luxembourg Air Link.
850	35k. Boeing 757		1·00	85

1997.
879	35k. de Havilland DH.89A Dragon Rapide		1·10	80
880	35k. Stinson S.R.8B Reliant		1·10	80
881	35k. Douglas DC-3 Dakota		1·10	80
882	35k. de Havilland Canada DHC-6 Twin Otter		1·10	80
879/882 Set of 4			4·00	3·00

2001.
982	20k. Eurocopter (Aerospatiale) AS 332 Super Puma and Fokker F27 aircraft		90	85

2001.
990	55k. Olsen-Jonasson Ognin		1·20	1·40
991	80k. Klemm KL-25E		1·80	1·70

IFNI

North-west Africa

100 centimos = 1 peseta

1943.
27	5c. Airplane		20	20
28	25c. Airplane		20	20
29	50c. Airplane		25	25
30	1p. Airplane		25	25
31	1p.40 Airplane		25	25
32	2p. Airplane		1·10	1·10
33	5p. Airplane		1·50	1·50
34	6p. Airplane		21·00	21·00
27/34 Set of 8			22·00	22·00

1947. Design as Nos. 1010/17 of Spain overprinted **IFNI**.
36	5c. Juan de la Cierva and Cierva C.30A autogyro		2·50	60
37	10c. Juan de la Cierva and Cierva C.30A autogyro		2·50	60

1953.
87	60c. Douglas DC-4		15	15
88	1p.20 Douglas DC-4		20	15
89	1p.60 Douglas DC-4		25	15
90	2p. Douglas DC-4		1·70	20
91	4p. Douglas DC-4		95	20
92	10p. Douglas DC-4		5·25	1·20
87/92 Set of 6			7·75	1·80

1966.
216	1p. Douglas DC-8		20	20
217	1p.50 Douglas DC-8		20	20
218	2p.50 Airco (de Havilland) D.H.9C biplanes		1·10	1·10
216/218 Set of 3			1·40	1·40

INDIA

Southern Asia

1929. 12 pies = 1 anna

16 annas = 1 rupee

1957. 100 naye paise = 1 rupee

1964. 100 paisa = 1 rupee

1929.
220	2a. de Havilland DH.66 Hercules		2·25	75
221	3a. de Havilland DH.66 Hercules		1·75	2·25
222	4a. de Havilland DH.66 Hercules		3·75	1·25
223	6a. de Havilland DH.66 Hercules		2·25	1·00
224	8a. de Havilland DH.66 Hercules		4·00	1·00
225	12a. de Havilland DH.66 Hercules		15·00	6·00
220/225 Set of 6			26·00	11·00

1937.
258* 12a. Armstrong Whitworth A.W.27 Ensign 1...... 18·00 1·10

1940. As No. 258, but with king's head larger.
277* 14a. Armstrong Whitworth A.W.27 Ensign 1...... 18·00 2·00

1947.
303* 12a. Douglas DC-4...... 2·00 2·75

1948. Inauguration of India-UK Flights.
304 12a. Lockheed Constellation of Air India . 1·50 3·00

1954.
349* 2a. Lockheed Constellation 30 10
350* 4a. Douglas DC-4...... 4·00 1·50
351* 14a. Lockheed Constellation ...... 1·50 40

1955.
363* 10a. Lockheed Constellation 35 10
364* 12a. de Havilland DH.82A Tiger Moth under construction ...... 3·25 10
365* 14a. Douglas DC-3...... 5·00 60
367* 1r.2a. Lockheed Constellation ...... 2·25 4·50
368* 1r.8a. Douglas DC-3...... 9·00 5·00

1958. Silver Jubilee of Indian Air Force.
397 15np. Westland Wapiti biplane and Hawker Hunter...... 1·00 25
398 90np. Westland Wapiti biplane and Hawker Hunter...... 1·25 2·00

1961. 50th Anniv of First Official Airmail Flight, Allahabad–Naini.
434 5np. Humber Sommer biplane (in postmark) ...... 1·10 30
435 15np. Boeing 707 VT-DJK of Air India and Humber Sommer biplane...... 1·10 30
436 1r. Henri Pecquet in Humber Sommer biplane ...... 3·75 2·75
434/436 Set of 3 ...... 5·25 3·00

1963.
468 15np. Mil Mi-4 helicopter...... 1·25 10
469 1r. Nord 2501 Noratlas...... 1·50 65

1965.
511* 20p. Hindustan Aircraft Industries Ajeet jet fighter...... 6·00 10

1966.
527 15p. Hindustan Aircraft Industries Ajeet jet fighters...... 1·75 60

1968.
561 15p. Jet airliner...... 60 15

1969. 20th Anniv of "All-up" Airmail Scheme.
587 20p. Rafi Ahmed Kidwai and Lockheed Constellation...... 1·50 30

1973.
674* 1r.45 Hindustan Aircraft Industries Ajeet jet fighters (?) ...... 1·40 1·60

1973. 25th Anniv of India's International Services.
686 1r.45 Boeing 747 of Air India...... 4·00 4·00

1976. Inauguration of Indian Airlines Airbus Service.
834 2r. Airbus Industrie A300B4 of Air India 2·50 2·25

1978. 75th Anniv of Powered Flight.
905 1r. Wilbur and Orville Wright and Wright Flyer I...... 1·00 30

1979. Mail-carrying Aircraft.
942 30p. de Havilland DH.80A Puss Moth VT-ADN...... 50 25
943 50p. Hindustan Aircraft Industries Chetak helicopter...... 70 45
944 1r. Boeing 737 of Indian Airlines...... 85 75
945 2r. Boeing 747 of Air India...... 1·10 95
942/945 Set of 4...... 2·75 2·20

1979. Flying and Gliding.
952 30p. Hindustan Aircraft Industries HAL-26 Pushpak VT-DPU and Rohini-1 glider 1·40 1·00

1982. 50th Anniv of Indian Air Force.
1053 1r. Westland Wapiti biplane and Mikoyan Gurevich MiG-25 jet fighter 5·50 1·75

1982. 50th Anniv of Civil Aviation in India.
1054 3r.25 J. Tata and de Havilland DH.80A Puss Moth VT-ADN...... 5·00 2·00

1983.
1072 1r. Hindustan Aircraft Industries Chetak helicopter...... 4·75 2·50

1983. Bicentenary of Manned Flight.
1104 1r. Hot-air balloon Udan Khatola ...... 1·25 20
1105 2r. Montgolfier balloon (first manned free flight, 1783)...... 1·75 1·50

1984.
1114* 1r. Hawker Siddeley Sea Harrier...... 2·00 2·25

1986.
1184 2r. Aircraft and helicopters on aircraft carrier Vikrant...... 7·50 6·50

1986. 75th Anniv of First Official Airmail Flight, Allahabad-Naini.
1185 50p. Humber Sommer biplane, Boeing 747 (lower left), Douglas DC-3 and de Havilland DH.80A Puss Moth (lower right)...... 2·25 2·00
1186 3r. Airbus Industrie A300 of Indian Airlines and Humber Sommer biplane...... 4·75 7·00

1992.
1499* 2r. Hang-glider 25 20

1992.
1512   1r. Fokker F.27A Troopship .... 1·25   40

1992. 60th Anniv of Indian Air Force.
1516   1r. Mikoyan Gurevich MiG-29 (top) and
          Ilyushin Il-76 .... 1·25   1·50
1517   10r. Mikoyan Gurevich MiG-27 and
          Westland Wapiti biplane .... 2·25   2·50

1992.
1521   1r. Helicopter .... 2·00   60

1993.
1533   1r. Antonov An-32 transport aircraft
          dropping paratroops .... 1·25   30

1993. 60th Anniv of No. 1 Squadron, Indian Air Force.
1534   1r. Westland Wapiti .... 1·25   30

1994.
1607   2r. Stylised airliners and other images...   30   30

1997.
1762   2r. Mikoyan MiG-29 *Fulcrum*   40   30

1998. 50th Anniv of First Air India International Flight.
1794*   6r. Lockheed   L-1029   Super
          Constellation   75   85

1998. Indian Women in Aviation.
1813   8r. de Havilland DH.82 Tiger Moth and
          helicopter .... 1·40   1·40

1998. Birth Centenary of Lt. Indra Lal Roy (World War I pilot).
1824   3r. Airco (de Havilland) D.H.4   75   55

1999.
1835   10r. Dassault Mirage 2000   40   40

1999.
1838   3r. SEPECAT Jaguar .... 1·40   75

1999.
1848   3r. HAL HT-2   50   50

1999.
1850   3r. Boeing 737   50   50

2000.
1902*   3r. HAL Ajeet   35   40

2003. Centenary of Powered Flight.
2112   5r. HAL HT-2 trainer, 1951   50   50
2113   5r. HAL HF-24 Marut, ground attack
          aircraft, 1961   50   50
2114   5r. HAL LCA, Light Combat Aircraft,
          2001   50   50
2115   15r. HAL Dhruv, advanced light
          helicopter .... 1·50   1·75
2112/2115 *Set of* 4 .... 2·75   3·00

2005.
2294   5r. Stylised airliner.....................................   50   50

2005. 55th Anniv of 16 Squadron, Air Force.
2303   5r. SEPECAT Jaguar, Consolidated B-24
          Liberator, English Electric Canberra..   50   50

2006.
2309*   5r. BAe Sea Harrier.....................................   50   50
2310*   5r. Westland Sea King helicopter   50   50
2311*   5r. HAL/Dornier 228...................................   50   50

2006.
2368*   5r. HAL Chetak   50   50

2007. 75th Anniv of Indian Air Force.
2428   5r. HAL   Dhruv   advanced   light
          helicopter   50   50
2429   5r. Beriev (Ilyushin) A-50 'Mainstay'........   50   50
2430   5r. Westland Wapiti   50   50
2431   15r. Ilyushin Il-78 'Midas' tanker and two
          Sukhoi Su-30 Mk1..................................... 1·25   1·40
2428/2431 *Set of* 4 .... 2·50   2·75

2007.
2433   5r. Parachutist   50   50

INDO-CHINA

South-east Asia

100 cents = 1 piastre

1933.
197   1c. Farman F.190   10   1·60
198   2c. Farman F.190   10   1·20
199   5c. Farman F.190 .... 1·40   1·50
200   10c. Farman F.190 .... 1·00   45
201   11c. Farman F.190 .... 2·75   3·25
202   15c. Farman F.190 .... 3·50   1·80
203   16c. Farman F.190 .... 1·20   3·75

204	20c. Farman F.190		3·75	1·20
205	30c. Farman F.190		1·20	10
206	36c. Farman F.190		3·75	10
207	37c. Farman F.190		1·40	20
208	39c. Farman F.190		80	3·75
209	60c. Farman F.190		2·00	1·40
210	66c. Farman F.190		2·50	1·40
211	67c. Farman F.190		1·30	3·50
212	69c. Farman F.190		50	5·00
213	1p. Farman F.190		90	10
214	2p. Farman F.190		1·00	10
215	5p. Farman F.190		3·75	50
216	10p. Farman F.190		6·25	2·00
217	20p. Farman F.190		20·00	8·50
218	30p. Farman F.190		23·00	10·00
197/218 Set of 22			75·00	46·00

1949. As No. 254 of Cameroun.

340	3p. Lockheed Constellation		2·50	3·25

INDONESIA

South-east Asia

100 sen = 1 rupiah

1958. National Aviation Day.

758	10s. Convair CV 340		15	10
759	15s. Hiller 12C "Skeeter" helicopter		15	15
760	35s. Nurtiano Nu-2 Sikumbang		35	25
761	50s. Convair CV 340		65	40
762	75s. de Havilland DH.100 Vampire		1·10	55
758/762 Set of 5			2·20	1·30

1964.

1000*	2r. Lockheed L.188 Electra of Garuda		15	15
1003*	5r. Douglas DC-3		15	15
1007*	25r. Convair 990A Coronado		35	15

1965. No. 1007 overprinted '65 Sen.

1076*	25s. on 25r. Convair 990A Coronado		25	10

1967. Aviation Day.

1156	2r.50 Pilot and Mikoyan Gurevich MiG-21.		35	25
1157	4r. Convair 990A Coronado at airport		35	20
1158	5r. Lockheed C-130 Hercules		55	25
1156/1158 Set of 3			1·10	60

1969. 50th Anniv of First England-Australia Flight by Ross and Keith Smith.

1253	75r. Ross and Keith Smith's Vickers Vimy G-EAOU, 1919		55	50
1254	100r. Ross and Keith Smith's Vickers Vimy G-EAOU, 1919		55	55

1975.

1397*	120r. Fokker F.28 Fellowship		90	35

1979. 30th Anniv of Garuda Indonesian Airways.

1531	40r. Douglas DC-3 RI-ODI of Garuda		80	35
1532	75r. Douglas DC-9-30 of Garuda		1·00	35
1533	100r. Douglas DC-10 of Garuda		1·80	1·00
1531/1533 Set of 3			3·25	1·50

1980.

1568*	150r. Hang-glider		1·30	75

1980.

1591	12r.50 Casa-Nurtiano CN-235		35	10

1982.

1666	250r. Sud Aviation SE 3160 Alouette III helicopter		1·50	35

1983. Indonesian Aircraft.

1715	275r. Casa-Nurtiano CN-235 PK-NZG		1·20	55

1984.

1735*	75r. Casa-Nurtiano CN-235 under construction		25	15

1984. 40th Anniv of ICAO.

1771	275r. Boeing 747-200 of Garuda		1·20	75

1985.

1777*	75r. Boeing 747 (tail) of Garuda		35	15

1988.

1904	350r. Jet airliner		1·10	50

1989. 40th Anniv of Garuda Airline.

1919	350r. Boeing 747		2·00	55

1991. World Parachuting Championships.

2021	500r. Parachutists		1·00	15

1992.

2044*	300r. Airtech CN235		55	15

1994. 50th Anniv of ICAO.

2167	700r. Douglas DC-3		80	25

1995. Inaugural Flight of IPTN N.250.

2182	700r. IPTN 250		65	65

1996.

2246*	300r. Nusantara N-2130 over Soekarno - Hatta Airport		25	25

1997.

2301*	300r. Aircraft		25	25

1997.

2340*	700r. IPTN CN-235, CN-250 and Nusantara N-2130 airliners		55	55

1997. Blue Falcon Aerobatic Team (Air Force).

2346*	300r. Lockheed Martin F-16 Fighting Falcon		25	25

1999. 50th Anniv of Garuda Indonesia (state airline).
2486	500r. Airline emblem	10	10
2487	700r. Jet engine	15	15
2488	2000r. Pilot, stewardess and Boeing 747	40	40
2486/2488 Set of 3		60	60

2000.
2667*	4000r. Boeing 747	1·50	1·50

2001.
2733*	1000r. Helicopter	20	20

2002. Kite Flying.
2803	1000r. Bird-shaped kite	15	15
2804	1000r. Lion kite	15	15
2805	1000r. Rhomboid kite	15	15
2806	1000r. Winged kite	15	15
2807	1000r. Box and glider kites	15	15
2803/2807 Set of 5		70	70

2003.
2911*	2000r. Nurtanio Pringgoadisuryo (aviation enigineer)	20	20

IRAN

Western Asia

1927. 20 chahis = 1 kran

10 krans = 1 toman

1932. 100 dinars = 1 rial

1927. Nos. 337/52 overprinted with biplane and **POSTE AERIENNE** in French and Persian.
642	1c. Persian lion symbol	1·60	80
643	2c. Persian lion symbol	1·60	80
644	3c. Persian lion symbol	1·60	80
645	6c. Persian lion symbol	1·60	80
646	9c. Persian lion symbol	3·25	80
647	10c. Persian lion symbol	5·00	80
648	13c. Persian lion symbol	6·50	2·10
649	26c. Persian lion symbol	6·50	2·10
650	1k. Persian lion symbol	6·50	2·10
651	2k. Persian lion symbol	6·50	2·10
652	3k. Persian lion symbol	21·00	8·25
653	4k. Persian lion symbol	33·00	12·50
654	5k. Persian lion symbol	33·00	8·25
655	10k. Persian lion symbol	£450	£160
656	20k. Persian lion symbol	£300	£160
657	30k. Persian lion symbol	£300	£160
642/657 Set of 16		£1000	£475

1928. Fiscal stamps surcharged with Junkers F-13, **Poste aerien** in French and Persian, and value.
657a	3k. Persian lion symbol	£100	33·00
657b	5k. Persian lion symbol	25·00	8·25
657c	1t. Persian lion symbol	25·00	8·25
657d	2t. Persian lion symbol	25·00	8·25
657e	3t. Persian lion symbol	29·00	12·50
657a/657e Set of 5		£180	65·00

1929. Fiscal stamps surcharged with Junkers F-13, **Poste aerienne** in French and Persian, and value.
658	1c. Persian lion symbol	80	50
659	2c. Persian lion symbol	80	25
660	3c. Persian lion symbol	80	25
661	5c. Persian lion symbol	80	25
662	10c. Persian lion symbol	80	25
663	1k. Persian lion symbol	1·50	80
664	2k. Persian lion symbol	4·00	1·60
665	3k. Persian lion symbol	80·00	21·00
666	5k. Persian lion symbol	16·00	4·00
667	10k. Persian lion symbol	21·00	8·25

668	20k. Persian lion symbol	25·00	8·25
669	30k. Persian lion symbol	33·00	12·50
658/669 Set of 12		£160	50·00

1935.
732*	30d. de Havilland DH.82 Tiger Moth biplanes at Teheran Airport	1·60	40

1952.
988	50d. Lockheed L.1049 Super Constellation	75	25
989	1r. Lockheed L.1049 Super Constellation	90	25
990	2r. Lockheed L.1049 Super Constellation	75	25
991	3r. Lockheed L.1049 Super Constellation	1·10	25
992	5r. Lockheed L.1049 Super Constellation	1·10	25
993	10r. Lockheed L.1049 Super Constellation	1·90	30
994	20r. Lockheed L.1049 Super Constellation	3·00	45
995	30r. Lockheed L.1049 Super Constellation	4·50	75
996	50r. Lockheed L.1049 Super Constellation	11·50	1·50
997	100r. Lockheed L.1049 Super Constellation	70·00	3·75
998	200r. Lockheed L.1049 Super Constellation	55·00	7·50
988/998 Set of 11		£130	14·00

1953.
1003*	3r. Lockheed L.1049 Super Constellation	11·50	5·75
1004*	5r. Lockheed L.1049 Super Constellation	23·00	11·50
1005*	10r. Lockheed L.1049 Super Constellation	30·00	30·00
1006*	20r. Lockheed L.1049 Super Constellation	60·00	60·00

1963.
1315	6r. Formation of aircraft	1·90	55

1965. Inauguration of Jet Services by Iranian National Airlines.
1391	14r. Boeing 727-100 of Iranian National Airlines	2·30	40

1966.
1458	14r. Boeing 707	90	25

1968.
1563*	10r. Douglas DC-8	45	25

1969. No. 1281 surcharged with Boeing 707, new value and Persian text.
1600	4r. on 14r. +6r. Refugees	2·00	60
1601	10r. on 14r. +6r. Refugees	2·00	60
1602	14r. on 14r. +6r. Refugees	2·00	60
1600/1602 Set of 3		5·50	1·60

1974.
1866	4r. Douglas DC-9-80 Super Eighty	40	25
1867	10r. Douglas DC-9-80 Super Eighty	1·50	25
1868	12r. Douglas DC-9-80 Super Eighty	1·50	40
1869	14r. Douglas DC-9-80 Super Eighty	1·70	40
1870	20r. Douglas DC-9-80 Super Eighty	2·30	55
1871	50r. Douglas DC-9-80 Super Eighty	5·75	1·40
1866/1871 Set of 6		12·00	3·00

1974. 50th Anniv of Imperial Iranian Air Force.
1872	10r. Airco (de Havilland) D.H.9A, 1924	1·50	40
1873	10r. McDonnell Douglas F-4D Phantom II	1·50	40

1975. Iran Air's First Teheran-New York Flight.
1950	10r. Boeing 747SP of Iran Air	60	40

1976.
1974*	6r. Bell Model 205 UH-1H Iroquois helicopter	1·10	45

1983.
2210	5r. Jet fighter	55	25

1986.
2331	40r. Sikorsky S-70 Black Hawk helicopters	1·20	75

1986.
2355*	10r. Helicopter	40	25

1987. 25th Anniv of Iranair.
2373	30r. Nose and tail of Airbus Industrie A300 of Iran Air	40	25

1988. Destruction of Iranair Passenger Airplane.

2483	45r. Boeing 737 of Iran Air being struck by surface-to-air missile	1·10	55

1989.

2508*	20r. Boeing 747.300/400	60	40

1989.

2520*	30r. Airplane	90	40

1992. Establishment of Postal Air Service.

2670	60r. Embraer EMB-110 Bandeirante	1·10	55

1992.

2718	100r. Airplane	1·50	60

1997.

2931*	1000r. Imam Khomeini International Airport, Teheran	60	30

1997.

2937	200r. Fokker 100	1·20	75

1999.

2983	250r. McDonnell Douglas F-4 Phantom II, Bell 212	1·10	1·00

2001.

3053*	250r. Augusta-Bell 206A Jet Rangers	1·10	1·00

2001.

3061*	500r. Sikorsky S-61 helicopter	2·10	2·00

2003. Air Force Day.

3096	300r. Grumman F-14A Tomcat	70	60
3097	400r. Northrop F-5E Tiger II	90	85
3098	500r. Grumman F-14A Tomcat	1·10	1·10
3099	600r. McDonnell Douglas F-4 Phantom II	1·40	1·30
3100	700r. Mikoyan MiG-29	1·60	1·60
3096/3100 Set of 6		5·25	5·00

2003.

3133*	600r. Antonov An-124 Ruslan	85	75

2004.

3165	650r. Northrop F-5E Tiger II (bottom), Grumman F-14A Tomcat (middle) and McDonnell Douglas F-4 Phantom II (top)	60	55

2005.

3186	850r. Antonov-140	75	75
3187	850r. Iran-140	75	75

IRAQ

Western Asia

1000 fils = 1 dinar

1949.

330	3f. Vickers Viking 1BYI-ABP *Al Mahfoutha* of Iraqi Airways	25	25
331	4f. Vickers Viking 1BYI-ABP *Al Mahfoutha* of Iraqi Airways	25	25
332	5f. Vickers Viking 1BYI-ABP *Al Mahfoutha* of Iraqi Airways	25	25
333	10f. Vickers Viking 1BYI-ABP *Al Mahfoutha* of Iraqi Airways	3·25	1·30
334	20f. Vickers Viking 1BYI-ABP *Al Mahfoutha* of Iraqi Airways	1·40	60
335	35f. Vickers Viking 1BYI-ABP *Al Mahfoutha* of Iraqi Airways	1·40	60
336	50f. Vickers Viking 1BYI-ABP *Al Mahfoutha* of Iraqi Airways	2·20	1·00
337	100f. Vickers Viking 1BYI-ABP *Al Mahfoutha* of Iraqi Airways	5·75	2·10
330/337 Set of 8		13·00	5·75

1958.

413*	20f. de Havilland DH.112 Venom FB.50 jet fighters	1·10	1·10

1964.

646	10f. Lockheed F-80C Shooting Star	50	25
647	30f. Lockheed F-80C Shooting Star	90	60

1965. Inauguration of Hawker Siddeley Trident 1E Aircraft by Iraqi Airways.

704	5f. Hawker Siddeley Trident 1E of Iraqi Airways	35	35
705	10f. Hawker Siddeley Trident 1E of Iraqi Airways	35	35
706	40f. Hawker Siddeley Trident 1E of Iraqi Airways	3·75	75
704/706 Set of 3		4·00	1·30

1969. Inauguration of Baghdad International Airport.

848*	20f. Baghdad International Airport	1·30	40

1969. 50th Anniv of First England-Australia Flight by Ross and Keith Smith.

861	15f. Ross and Keith Smith's Vickers Vimy G-EAOU, 1919	2·20	1·10
862	35f. Ross and Keith Smith's Vickers Vimy G-EAOU, 1919	3·50	2·75

1981.

1468	30f. Mikoyan Gurevich MiG-25	50	25
1469	35f. Mikoyan Gurevich MiG-25	1·00	40
1470	75f. Mikoyan Gurevich MiG-25	1·70	85
1468/1470 Set of 3		3·00	1·30

1981. 50th Anniv of Air Force.

1475*	5f. Mil Mi-24 helicopters	15	15
1476*	10f. Antonov An-2 biplane trainer	35	15
1478*	120f. de Havilland D.H.89 Dragon Rapide biplane and Mikoyan Gurevich MiG-21 jet fighters (air)	3·50	2·10

1985. 54th Anniv of Air Force.

1649	10f. Dassault Mirage F1	25	10
1650	60f. Jet fighters	1·20	65
1651	70f. Jet fighters	1·30	65
1652	160f. Dassault Mirage F1	3·25	1·70
1649/1652 *Set of 4*		5·50	2·75
MS1653 200f. Jet fighters		4·25	4·25

1986. 55th Anniv of Air Force.

1716	30f. Dassault Mirage F1	65	25
1717	50f. Jet fighters	1·30	35
1718	100f. Dassault Mirage F1	2·50	1·40
1719	150f. Jet fighters	3·75	1·80
1716/1719 *Set of 4*		7·25	3·50

1986.

1729	30f. Mil Mi-8 helicopter	85	25
1730	40f. Jet fighters	1·10	40
1731	100f. Mil Mi-8 helicopter	2·20	1·20
1732	150f. Jet fighters	3·75	1·70
1729/1732 *Set of 4*		7·00	3·25
MS1733 250f. Mil Mi-8 helicopter		4·25	4·25

1987.

1763*	40f. Helicopters and jet fighters	35	35
1765*	100f. Helicopters and jet fighters	90	90

1989.

MS1886 250f. Boeing 737		3·50	3·50

1989.

1893	50f. Boeing 707	1·00	50
1894	100f. Boeing 707	2·10	65
1895	150f. Boeing 707	3·25	1·00
1893/1895 *Set of 3*		5·75	1·90

2002.

2135*	25d. Dassault Mirage F1	40	40

2002.

2145	25d. Aircraft gunsights	25	25
2146	50d. Aircraft gunsights	40	40

2002.

2155*	100d. Boeing 737	1·00	1·00

IRELAND

Western Europe

1961. 12 pence = 1 shilling

20 shillings = 1 pound

1971. 100 pence = 1 pound

2002. 100 cents = 1 euro

1961. Silver Jubilee of Aer Lingus.

184	6d. de Havilland DH.84 Dragon Mk 2 EI-ABI *Iolar* and Boeing 720 EI-ALA of Aer Lingus	1·75	3·50
185	1s.3d. de Havilland DH.84 Dragon Mk 2 EI-ABI *Iolar* and Boeing 720 EI-ALA of Aer Lingus	2·25	5·00

1978. 50th Anniv of First East-West Trans-Atlantic Flight.

419	10p. Junkers W.33 D-1167 *Bremen*	20	15
420	17p. Junkers W.33 D-1167 *Bremen*	35	1·10

1985.

608*	44p. Richard Crosbie's balloon, 1785	1·00	1·75

1986. 50th Anniv of Aer Lingus.

637	28p. Boeing 747-200 of Aer Lingus	1·40	75
638	46p. de Havilland DH.84 Dragon Mk 2 EI-ABI *Iolar* of Aer Lingus	1·90	3·00

1986.

644*	24p. Bell 206B JetRanger III helicopter	1·50	75

1988.

694*	28p. Airbus Industrie A320	3·00	55

1988.

697*	46p. Short-Mayo composite (Short S.20 seaplane G-ADHJ *Mercury* and Short S.21 flying boat G-ADHK *Maia*)	1·25	1·75

1988.

703*	28p. Helicopter	70	1·10

1994.

894*	28p. Biplane skywriting	90	75

1994.

926*	52p. Vickers FB-27 Vimy of Alcock and Brown	1·50	1·60

1997.

1116*	32p. Aer Lingus Boeing 737	1·00	1·50

1998. Pioneers of Irish Aviation.

1155	28p. Lady Mary Heath and Avro Type 581 Avian II	60	55
1156	32p. Col. James Fitzmaurice and Junkers W.33 *Bremen*	65	60
1157	44p. Captain J.P. Saul and Fokker F.VIIa/3m *Southern Cross*	1·25	1·25
1158	52p. Captain Charles Blair and Sikorsky VS-44A	1·50	1·50
1155/1158 *Set of 4*		3·50	3·50

1999. Commercial Aviation.
1266	30p. Douglas DC-3	65	50
1267	32p. Pilatus-Britten BN-2 Norman Islander	75	55
1268	40p. Boeing 707	80	1·40
1269	45p. Lockheed Constellation	90	1·50
1266/1269	Set of 4	2·75	3·50

2000. Military Aviation.
	(a) Designs 37×26 mm		
1364	30p. Hawker Hurricane Mk IIC	80	80
1365	30p. Bristol F2B Mk II	80	80
1366	45p. de Havilland DH.115 Vampire T	1·10	1·25
1367	45p. Eurocopter (Aerospatiale) SE 316 Alouette III	1·10	1·25
	(b) Designs 33×22 mm. Self-adhesive		
1368	30p. Hawker Hurricane Mk IIC	70	70
1369	30p. Bristol F2B Mk II	70	70
1370	45p. de Havilland DH.115 Vampire T 55	70	70
1371	45p. Eurocopter (Aerospatiale) SE 3160 Alouette III	70	70
1364/1371	Set of 8	6·00	6·25

2001.
1387*	30p. Charles Lindbergh and Ryan NYP Special *Spirit of St Louis*	2·00	2·00

2003. Centenary of Powered Flight.
1598	41c. Harry Ferguson flying first Irish monoplane, 1909	80	60
1599	50c. Alcock and Brown's Vickers FB-27 Vimy over Galway after first trans-Atlantic flight, 1919	1·10	80
1600	57c. Wright *Flyer I*, 1903	1·25	1·50
1601	57c. Lillian Bland's biplane, 1910	1·25	1·50
1598/1601	Set of 4	4·00	4·00
MS1602	€5 Wright *Flyer I*, 1903	8·50	10·00

ISLE OF MAN

North-west Europe

100 pence = 1 pound

1978. 60th Anniv of Royal Air Force.
107	6p. Short Type 184 seaplane	15	10
108	7p. Bristol Scout C	15	15
109	11p. Boulton Paul P.82 Defiant	25	25
110	13p. SEPECAT Jaguar	25	25
107/110	Set of 4	70	65

1981.
208*	20p. Supermarine Spitfire	35	35

1984. 50th Anniv of First Official Airmail to the Isle of Man and 40th Anniv of ICAO.
267	11p. de Havilland DH.84 Dragon Mk 2 G-ACXI of Railway Air Service	35	30
268	13p. de Havilland DH.86A Dragon Express G-ADJV *Ronaldsway* of Blackpool and West Coast Air Services	40	30
269	26p. Douglas DC-3 G-AGZB of B.E.A. over Ronaldsway Airport	70	65
270	28p. Vickers Viscount 800 of B.E.A.	70	65
271	31p. Britten-Norman BN-2 Islander G-AXXH of Telair over Ronaldsway Airport	70	65
267/271	Set of 5	2·50	2·30

1990. 50th Anniv of Battle of Britain.
449*	15p. Bristol Type 142 Blenheim Mk I (top), Hawker Hurricane Mk I, barrage balloons and Dornier Do-17 in flames	35	20
450*	15p. Supermarine Spitfire (top), Westland Lysander Mk I and Vickers Supermarine Walrus flying boat	35	20
451*	24p. Supermarine Spitfire (in air) and Hawker Hurricanes Mk I being rearmed	80	25
452*	24p. Supermarine Spitfires (in air) and Hawker Hurricanes Mk I	80	25
453*	29p. Barrage balloons	1·00	50

1990.
458*	37p. Hawker Hurricanes Mk I	1·25	1·25

1991.
477*	26p. British Aerospace ATP of Manx Airline over Ronaldsway Airport	1·00	30

1992.
502	23p. Armstrong Whitworth Whitley Mk V (left) and two Douglas DC-3 Dakotas	70	25
503	23p. Four Douglas DC-3 Dakotas (top), General Aircraft G.A.L.49 Hamilcar glider and two Airspeed A.S.51 Horsa gliders	70	25
504	28p. General Aircraft G.A.L.49 Hamilcar gliders (left) and two Douglas DC-3 Dakotas	80	30
505	28p. Douglas DC-3 Dakota	80	30
506	39p. Bristol Britannia C.1 (left), Blackburn Beverley C1 and Westland Belvedere H.C.1 helicopter	1·25	40
507	39p. Westland Wessex helicopter (left), Hawker Siddeley Harrier and Westland Commando helicopter	1·25	40
502/507	Set of 6	5·00	1·70

1994.
593*	24p. British Aerospace Hawk T.1 jet trainers of the Red Arrows display team	65	60

1994.
610*	30p. US paratroops and aircraft	1·00	30
611*	30p. British paratroops and aircraft	1·00	30

1995.
641*	10p. Supermarine Spitfire	30	15
642*	10p. Hawker Typhoon	30	15
643*	20p. Avro Type 683 Lancaster	55	25
644*	20p. Grumman TBM Avenger	55	25

1997. Manx Aircraft.
747	21p. Sopwith Tabloid	45	25
748	21p. Grumman Tiger (1996 Schneider Trophy)	45	25
749	25p. BAe ATP (15th Anniversary, Manx Airlines)	55	25
750	25p. BAe 146-200 (15th Anniversary, Manx Airlines)	55	25
751	31p. Boeing 757-200 (largest aircraft to land on Isle of Man)	70	35
752	31p. Farman biplane (first Manx flight, 1911)	70	35
753	36p. Supermarine Spitfire	80	40
754	36p. Hawker Hurricane	80	40
747/754	Set of 8	4·50	2·30

No. 752 is inscribed EARMAN in error.

2003. Centenary of Powered Flight.
1067	23p. de Havilland DH.83 Fox Moth and Saunders Roe (Saro) Cloud	45	50
1068	27p. de Havilland DH.61 Giant Moth and DH.80 Puss Moth	55	60
1069	37p. Avro Type 652 Anson and Boeing B-17 Flying Fortress	75	80
1070	40p. Eurofighter EF-2000 Typhoon and Avro Type 698 Vulcan	80	85
1071	67p. Handley Page Herald and Bristol Wayfarer	1·40	1·50
1072	82p. Aerospatiale/BAe Concorde and Airbus Industries Airbus A380	1·75	1·90
1067/1072	Set of 6	5·25	5·50

2003. 60th Anniv of Attack on German Dams by No. 617 (Dambusters) Squadron.
MS1073	£2 Avro Type 683 Lancaster attacking Mohne Dam	4·00	4·25

2004.
1137*	68p. Consolidated B-24 Liberators and North American P-51 Mustangs	2·20	70
1138*	68p. Airspeed AS 51 Horsa gliders	2·20	70
MS1139*	50p. Troops and aircraft (other stamps in miniature sheet do not show aircraft)	6·50	6·50

H.P. 0/400 and Bristol F2B Fighter

2008. 90th Anniv of Royal Air Force.

1406	31p. Handley Page 0/400 and Bristol F2B	75	75
1407	31p. Avro 504N and Westland Wapiti........	75	75
1408	31p. Hawker Hurricane and Short S25 Sunderland	75	75
1409	90p. Gloster Meteor and Westland Whirlwind	2·10	2·10
1410	90p. Hawker Hunter and English Electric Canberra	2·10	2·10
1411	90p. Hawker Siddeley (BAe) Harrier and Lockheed C-130 Hercules..................	2·10	2·10
1406/1411	*Set of 6*	7·50	7·50

ISRAEL

Western Asia

1952. 1000 prutot = 1 Israeli pound

1960. 100 agorot = 1 Israeli pound

1980. 100 agorot = 1 shekel

1952.

64b	100p. Douglas DC-6....................	85	60
64c	120p. Douglas DC-6....................	1·20	85

1953.

76	10p. Lockheed L.1049 Super Constellation	35	20
77	70p. Douglas DC-6	35	25
78	100p. Lockheed L.1049 Super Constellation	35	20
79	150p. Lockheed L.1049 Super Constellation	35	20
80	350p. Douglas DC-6	50	50
81	500p. Douglas DC-6	1·10	85
81a	750p. Boeing 377 Stratocruiser	15	15
82	1000p. Douglas DC-4	4·25	3·25
82a	3000p. Douglas DC-3	40	40
76/82a	*Set of 9*	7·00	5·50

1955.

105*	10p. Immigrants disembarking from Douglas DC-3....................	10	10

1959. 10th Anniv of Civil Aviation in Israel.

165	500p. Bristol 175 Britannia 313 of El Al	35	25

1962.

223	I£3 Bristol 175 Britannia	14·50	11·00

1962.

229	12a. Sud Aviation SO 4050 Vatour IIA jet fighter......................	65	65
230	30a. Sud Aviation SO 4050 Vatour IIA jet fighters......................	1·20	1·00

1962.

237	55a. Boeing 707 of El Al..................	1·10	1·00

1966.

330*	80a. Silhouettes of Dassault Mirage IIICJ jet fighters....................	25	25

1966.

351*	I£1 Boeing 707....................	50	40

1967. Military Aircraft.

358	15a. Taylorcraft Auster AOP.5..........	15	15
359	30a. Dassault Mystere IVA..........	35	35
360	80a. Dassault Mirage IIICJ..........	50	50
358/360	*Set of 3*	90	90

1968.

377	10a. Boeing 720B of El Al..........	15	15
378	30a. Boeing 720B of El Al..........	15	15
379	40a. Boeing 720B of El Al..........	15	15
380	50a. Boeing 720B of El Al..........	35	35
381	55a. Boeing 720B of El Al..........	35	35
382	60a. Boeing 720B of El Al..........	40	35
383	80a. Boeing 720B of El Al..........	40	35
384	I£1 Boeing 720B of El Al..........	60	50
385	I£1.50 Boeing 720B of El Al..........	60	50
386	I£3 Boeing 720B of El Al..........	1·00	90
377/386	*Set of 10*	3·75	3·25

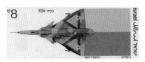

1970. Israeli Aircraft Industry.

450	I£1 Israeli Aircraft Industry IAI-201 Arava......................	50	40

1983.

913*	8s. Israeli Aircraft Industry Kfir-C2..........	25	20

1985. Aviation in the Holy Land.

950	50s. Vedrines' Bleriot XI, 1913..........	30	30
951	150s. Short S.17 Kent flying boat G-ABFA *Scipio* of Imperial Airways	65	65
952	250s. de Havilland DH.82A Tiger Moth G-ACYN of Palestine Flying Club, 1934..........	1·00	1·00
953	300s. Short S.16 Scion II VQ-PAA of Palestine Airways..........	1·20	1·20
950/953	*Set of 4*	2·75	2·75

1986. 50th Anniv of Ben Gurion Airport.

1005	90a. Ben Gurion Airport viewed through windows of airliner	1·60	1·60

1987.

MS1022	120s. Douglas DC-6 (on stamp No. 64c)	8·00	8·00

1994. Ayalon Valley Hot Air Balloon Race.

1243	85a. Inflating balloon	65	55
1244	85a. Balloons in air	65	55
1245	85a. Balloon hovering over target (cross on ground)	65	55
1243/1245	*Set of 3*	1·80	1·50

1995.

1294	1s.80 Flying model plane	1·00	80

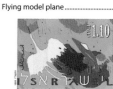

1996.

1346*	1s.10 Bird and Lockheed Martin F-16 Fighting Falcon..................	85	75

1997.

1378*	1s.15 Noordyun Norseman	65	55

1997.

1382	2s.10 Children leaving airliner (stylised).....	1·20	90

1998. Aircraft. War of Independence.

1407	2s.20 de Havilland DH.89 Dragon Rapide..	90	70
1408	2s.20 Supermarine Spitfire	90	70
1409	2s.20 Boeing B-17 Flying Fortress	90	70
1407/1409	*Set of 3*	2·40	1·90

2001.
MS1558* 1s.20 Hot Air balloon (painting) (other stamps in the miniature sheet do not show aircraft) .... 4·50 4·50

2003. Centenary of Powered Flight.
1640	2s.30 Glider, 1902 (Wright's ?)	80	50
1641	3s.30 Engine and Wright Brothers	1·10	70
1642	5s.90 Wright Brothers flying Wright *Flyer*	1·90	1·30
1640/1642 *Set of 3*		3·50	2·20

2003. 50th Anniv of Israeli Aircraft Industries.
1653　3s.30 Paper airplane and circuit board .... 1·10 80

2004. Ben Gurion Airport.
1719　2s.70 Boeing 747 over Ben Gurion Airport 75 45

ITALIAN COLONIES

General Issues
Africa
100 centesimi = 1 lira

1932. Nos. 326 and 330 of Italy overprinted **COLONIE ITALIANE.**
30*	50c. Leonardo da Vinci's drawing of a "Flying Man"	70	3·00
34*	7l.70 +2l. Leonardo da Vinci's drawing of a "Flying Man"	1·40	10·50

1933.
48*	3l. Savoia Marchetti S-55X flying boat...	7·75	10·50
49*	5l. Savoia Marchetti S-55X flying boat...	7·75	10·50
51*	10l. +2l.50 Savoia Marchetti S-55X flying boat	11·50	28·00
52*	50l. Savoia Marchetti S-55X flying boat...	11·50	28·00

1933.
63*	50c. Macchi Castoldi MC-72 seaplane.......	5·25	6·00
64*	75c. Savoia Marchetti S-71	5·25	6·00
65*	1l. Macchi Castoldi MC-72 seaplane.......	5·25	6·00
66*	3l. Savoia Marchetti S-71	5·25	15·00
67*	10l. Macchi Castoldi MC-72 seaplane.......	5·25	16·00
68*	12l. Savoia Marchetti S-71	5·25	20·00

1934.
75　25l. Marina Fiat MF.5 flying boat .... 23·00 80·00

1934.
81*	50c. Marina Fiat MF.5 flying boat	8·75	22·00
82*	75c. Marina Fiat MF.5 flying boat	8·75	22·00
83*	5l. Marina Fiat MF.5 flying boat	32·00	44·00
84*	10l. Marina Fiat MF.5 flying boat	32·00	44·00
85*	15l. Marina Fiat MF.5 flying boat	32·00	44·00
86*	25l. Marina Fiat MF.5 flying boat	32·00	90·00
87*	50l. Marina Fiat MF.5 flying boat	32·00	90·00

EXPRESS LETTER STAMPS
1932. As Nos. E348/9 of Italy.
E16	2l.25 +1l. Savoia Marchetti S-55A flying boat	4·75	13·50
E17	4l.50 +1l.50 Savoia Marchetti S-55A flying boat	4·75	17·00

ITALIAN EAST AFRICA

East Africa
100 centesimi = 1 lira

1938.
21*	25c. Savoia Marchetti S-73	1·80	2·30
22*	50c. Savoia Marchetti S-74	39·00	10
23*	60c. Savoia Marchetti S-73	1·10	6·25
24*	75c. Savoia Marchetti S-73	1·80	1·60
25*	1l. Savoia Marchetti S-74	10	10
26*	1l.50 Savoia Marchetti S-74	70	35
27*	2l. Savoia Marchetti S-73	70	90
28*	3l. Savoia Marchetti S-73	1·10	3·50
29*	5l. Savoia Marchetti S-74	2·40	2·40
30*	10l. Savoia Marchetti S-74	6·00	5·25
31*	25l. Savoia Marchetti S-73	12·00	12·50

1940.
51*	50c. Savoia Marchetti S-66 flying boat......	65	2·75
52*	1l. Savoia Marchetti S.M.83	65	2·75
53*	2l. +75c. Savoia Marchetti S-66 flying boat	80	2·25
54*	5l. +2l. Savoia Marchetti S.M.83	80	2·25

1941.
62*	1l. Savoia Marchetti S.M.83 (value in centre)	26·00	
63*	1l. Savoia Marchetti S.M.83 (value at lower left)	1·80	

EXPRESS LETTER STAMPS

1938.
E32	2l. Savoia Marchetti S-73	90	2·75
E33	2l.50 Savoia Marchetti S-73	90	4·50

ITALIAN OCCUPATION OF CEPHALONIA AND ITHACA

Mediterranean
100 lepta = 1 drachma

1941. No. 521 of Greece (rouletted) further overprinted **ITALIA Occupazione Militare Italiana isole Cefalonia e Itaca** across a pair of stamps.
18*　50lep. Numeral design with Junkers G.24 overprint .... 60·00 75·00
Prices for this stamp are for unsevered pairs.

ITALIAN OCCUPATION OF CORFU AND PAXOS

Mediterranean
100 lepta = 1 drachma

1941. No. 521 of Greece (perforated or rouletted) further overprinted **CORFU.**
22*　50lep. Numeral design with Junkers G.24 overprint .... 4·50 2·40

ITALY

Southern Europe
1930. 100 centesimi = 1 lira
2002. 100 cents = 1 euro

1930. Trans-Atlantic Mass Formation Flight.
303　7l.70 Savoia Marchetti S-55A flying boats. £300 £850

1932.
326*	50c. Leonardo da Vinci's drawing of a "Flying Man"	1·40	1·50
330*	7l.70 +2l. Leonardo da Vinci's drawing of a "Flying Man"	8·00	27·00

1932.
366*　50c. Savoia Marchetti S-55A flying boat... 3·50 2·00

1933. Graf Zeppelin.
372	3l. Airship LZ-127 *Graf Zeppelin*	6·50	14·00
373	5l. Airship LZ-127 *Graf Zeppelin*	9·75	14·00
374	10l. Airship LZ-127 *Graf Zeppelin*	9·75	35·00
375	12l. Airship LZ-127 *Graf Zeppelin*	13·50	55·00
376	15l. Airship LZ-127 *Graf Zeppelin*	13·50	65·00
377	20l. Airship LZ-127 *Graf Zeppelin*	18·00	70·00
372/377 *Set of 6*		65·00	£225

1933. Balbo Trans-Atlantic Mass Formation Flight by Savoia Marchetti S-55X Flying Boats.
379*　5l.25 +44l.75 Savoia Marchetti S-55X flying boats .... 85·00 £1300

1934. As No. 275, surcharged **1934 XII PRIMO VOLO DIRETTO ROMA = BUENOS-AYRES TRIMOTORE "LOMBARDI-MAZZOTTI"**, emblem, Savoia Marchetti S-71 airplane and value.
391	2l. on 2l. Arrows	3·25	32·00
392	3l. on 2l. Arrows	3·25	38·00
393	5l. on 2l. Arrows	3·25	50·00
394	10l. on 2l. Arrows	3·25	60·00
391/394 *Set of 4*		12·00	£160

1934.
402*　25c. Marina Fiat MF.5 flying boat 55 80

403*	50c. Marina Fiat MF.5 flying boat		55	50
404*	75c. Marina Fiat MF.5 flying boat		55	1·90
405*	1l. +50c. Marina Fiat MF.5 flying boat		55	5·25
406*	2l. +1l.50 Marina Fiat MF.5 flying boat		55	7·50
407*	3l. +2l. Marina Fiat MF.5 flying boat		55	7·50

1934.

418*	50c. Marina Fiat MF.5 flying boat		6·00	5·25
419*	75c. Savoia Marchetti S-55X flying boat		6·25	6·25
420*	5l. +2l.50 Marina Fiat MF.5 flying boat		26·00	65·00
421*	10l. +5l. Marina Fiat MF.5 flying boat		31·00	75·00

1934.

435*	25c. Italian "P" Type airship		1·30	1·40
436*	50c. Marina Fiat MF.5 flying boat		1·30	1·60
437*	75c. Marina Fiat MF.5 flying boat		1·30	2·30
438*	80c. Italian "P" Type airship		2·40	2·75
439*	1l. +50c. Caproni Ca 101		4·25	9·00
440*	2l. +1l. Pomilio PC type biplane		5·50	15·00
441*	3l. +2l. Marina Fiat MF.5 flying boat		8·75	15·00

1936.

485*	25c. Savoia Marchetti S-55A flying boat		1·80	1·40
486*	50c. Caproni Ca 101		2·50	1·40
488*	1l.+1l. Caproni Ca 101		9·00	30·00

1945.

670*	1l. Caproni Campini N-1		20	20
672*	3l.20 Caproni Campini N-1		20	20
674*	10l. Caproni Campini N-1		20	10
677*	50l. Caproni Campini N-1 (green)		18·00	9·25
678*	50l. Caproni Campini N-1 (violet)		15	10

1947. No. 672 surcharged **LIRE 6-.**

687	6l. on 3l.20 Caproni Campini N-1		20	15

1947.

690*	20l. Heinkel He 70 Blitz		85	55
693*	50l. Heinkel He 70 Blitz		2·50	1·40

1948.

911	100l. Douglas DC-2		3·00	10
912	300l. Douglas DC-2		40	30
913	500l. Douglas DC-2		90	55
914	1000l. Douglas DC-2		1·60	1·30
911/914	Set of 4		5·25	2·00

For the 100l. in a smaller size see No. 1297.

1949.

725	50l. Douglas DC-4		50·00	4·25

1951.

783*	20l. Helicopter		7·50	1·00

1952. First Civil Aeronautics Law Conference, Rome.

823	60l. Savoia Marchetti S.M.95C		12·00	11·50

1952.

827*	60l. Airplane		5·00	1·80

1956. As No. 677, but colour changed, surcharged **1956 Visita del Presidente della Repubblica negli U.S.A. e nel Canada L. 120.**

930	120l. on 50l. Caproni Campini N-1 (mauve)		65	1·60

1961.

1053	170l. Douglas DC-8		2·30	4·25
1054	185l. Douglas DC-8		2·30	5·25
1055	205l. Douglas DC-8		8·50	13·00
1053/1055	Set of 3		12·00	20·00

1965. Night Airmail Service.

1145	40l. Douglas DC-6B		10	10
1146	90l. Sud Aviation SE 210 Caravelle		10	30

1967. 50th Anniv of First Airmail Stamp.

1192	40l. Pomilio PE type biplane		10	10

1968.

1235*	50l. Italian "M" Type airship and Caquot observation balloons and aircraft		10	10

1971. As No. 911 but smaller, 20×26 mm.

1297	100l. Douglas DC-2		15	25

1973. 50th Anniv of Military Aviation.

1349	20l. Fiat G-91 PAN aerobatic jet aircraft of Frecce Tricolori		10	10
1350	25l. Savoia Marchetti S-55X flying boats.		10	10
1351	50l. Fiat G-91Y jet fighters		10	10
1352	90l. Fiat CR-32 biplanes		10	30
1353	180l. Caproni Campini N-1		10	30
1354	150l. Lockheed F-104S Starfighter (air)		10	30
1349/1354	Set of 6		55	1·10

1973.

1382	25l. Sud Aviation SE 210 Super Caravelle 12 of Alitalia		10	30

1981. Italian Aircraft (1st series).

1715	200l. Agusta A.109 helicopter		15	15
1716	200l. Partenavia P.68B Victor I-PART		15	15
1717	200l. Aeritalia G.222		15	15
1718	200l. Aermacchi MB 339		15	15
1715/1718	Set of 4		55	55

1982. Italian Aircraft (2nd series).

1748	300l. Panavia MRCA Tornado		45	65
1749	300l. Savoia SIAI 260 Turbo I-FAIR		45	65
1750	300l. Piaggio P-166 DL-3 Turbo I-PIAE		45	65
1751	300l. Nardi NH 500 helicopter		45	65
1748/1751	Set of 4		1·60	2·30

1983. Italian Aircraft (3rd series).

1792	400l. Savoia SIAI 211 I-SIJE		1·40	65
1793	400l. Agusta A.129 Mangusta helicopter ..		40	65
1794	400l. Caproni C22J glider I-CAVJ		40	65
1795	400l. Aeritalia/Aermacchi AM-X		40	65
1792/1795	Set of 4		1·40	2·30

1984.

1833*	450l. Hughes 500 helicopter		1·20	65

1986. 40th Anniv of Alitalia (national airline).

1941	550l. Aircraft tail plane		55	15
1942	650l. Airplane and landing lights		70	15

1986.

1951	550l. Lockheed C-130 Hercules		50	15
1952	650l. Airplane		60	15

ITALY

1995.
2304* 750l. Martin B-26 Marauders parachuting supplies 55 65

1996.
2361* 750l. Carina Negrone (pilot) and biplane .. 60 50

1997.
MS2412* 750l. Bologna 1910 cancellation aerogramme from Balboa flight and postcard with 1917 25c. airmail stamp (Aerophilately) (other stamps on the miniature sheet do not show aircraft) .... 5·25 4·00

1998. 75th Anniv of Italian Air Force.
2520* 800l. Eurofighter EF-2000 Typhoon 65 50

1999. 50th Anniv of Grand Turin Air Crash.
2557* 800l. Players and airplane 65 50

2001.
2684 800l. Bell UH-1 Iroquois helicopter 55 50

2003. Centenary of First Powered Flight.
2836 52c. Mario Calderara (first Italian pilot)..... 2·10 1·00
2837 52c. Mario Cobianchi (pilot) and biplane... 2·10 1·00
2838 52c. Gianni Caproni (aircraft designer) ..... 2·10 1·00
2839 52c. Alessandro Marchetti (aircraft designer).................... 2·10 1·00
2836/2839 Set of 4 .... 7·50 3·50

2005. Centenary of First Italian Dirigible.
2947 €3 Almerico da Schio and dirigible......... 4·00 2·00

2005. Frecce Tricolori (Italian Air Force Aerobatic Display Team).
2953 45c. Team of Aermacchi MB-339 PAN 60 30
2954 60c. Team of Aermacchi MB-339 PAN (different)...................... 85 45

2007. 10th Death Anniv of M. Poggiali (pilot and poet).
3098 60c. Panavia Tornado 10S/ECR.................... 2·25 1·10

EXPRESS LETTER STAMPS

1932.
E348 2l.25 +1l. Savoia Marchetti S-55A flying boat .... 6·00 15·00
E349 4l.50 +1l.50 Savoia Marchetti S-55A flying boat .... 6·25 15·00

1933.
E370 2l. Savoia Marchetti S-55A flying boat... 10 80
E371 2l.25 Savoia Marchetti S-55A flying boat... 3·25 55·00

1934.
E442 2l.+ 1l.25 Caproni Ca 101.................... 5·25 14·00
E443 4l.50 +2l. Caproni Ca 101.................... 7·25 14·00

MILITARY POST STAMPS
1943. No. E370 overprinted **P.M.**
M601* 2l. Savoia Marchetti S-55A flying boat............. 1·40 17·00

Italian Social Republic
EXPRESS LETTER STAMPS
1944. No. E370 overprinted **G.N.R.**
E43* 2l. Savoia Marchetti S-55A flying boat... £700 £1100

IVORY COAST

West Africa

100 centimes = 1 franc

1940. As Nos. 117/21 of Dahomey.
173 1f.90 Twin-engine airliner .... 55 2·50
174 2f.90 Twin-engine airliner .... 1·10 3·25
175 4f.50 Twin-engine airliner 75 80
176 4f.90 Twin-engine airliner .... 75 2·75
177 6f.90 Twin-engine airliner .... 85 1·40
173/177 Set of 5 .... 3·50 9·50

1942. As No. 143k of Dahomey.
179 50f. Twin-engine airliner .... 2·00 3·25

1962. As No. 307 of Cameroun.
213 50f. Boeing 707 airliners of Air Afrique .... 1·60 90

1966. As No. 438 of Cameroun.
279 30f. Douglas DC-8F Jet Trader of Air Afrique.................... 85 50

1967.
286 30f. Sikorsky S-43 amphibian F-AOUM .... 2·75 1·30

1969. 10th Anniv of Aerial Navigation Security Agency for Africa and Madagascar (ASECNA). As No. 552 of Cameroun.
329 30f. Airliner over airport 80 45

1970.
340 30f. Douglas DC-8.................... 2·75 1·30

1977.
490 60f. Douglas DC-8 of Air Afrique .... 1·00 50

1977. History of Flying.
497 60f. Wilbur and Orville Wright and Wright Type A.................... 90 35
498 75f. Louis Bleriot and Bleriot XI.................... 1·00 25
499 100f. Captain Ross M. Smith and Vickers Vimy G-EAOU, 1919 .... 1·30 25
500 200f. Charles Lindbergh and Ryan NYP Special *Spirit of St. Louis* .... 2·75 65
501 300f. Concorde .... 4·50 1·40
497/501 Set of 5 .... 9·50 2·50
MS502 500f. Charles Lindbergh and Ryan NYP Special *Spirit of St. Louis* .... 6·50 2·40

1977. History of the Airship.
503 60f. Airship *Ville de Paris*.................... 80 25
504 65f. Launch of airship LZ-1 .... 80 25
505 150f. Airship LZ-10 *Schwaben* .... 1·90 50
506 200f. Airship LZ-120 *Bodensee* .... 2·75 70
507 300f. Airship LZ-127 *Graf Zeppelin* .... 4·00 1·30
503/507 Set of 5 .... 9·25 2·75
MS508 500f. Airship LZ-127 *Graf Zeppelin* (air) .... 7·00 2·40

1979. Concorde.
MS599* 500f. Concorde .... 7·25 2·40

1979. 20th Anniv of ASECNA (African Air Safety Organization).
621 60f. Concorde.................... 80 30

1981.
671 30f. Cessna Citation III 35 10
672 60f. Cessna Citation III 90 35

1983. Bicentenary of Manned Flight.
760	100f. Montgolfier balloon (first manned free flight, 1783)......................................	1·00	35
761	125f. Charles' hydrogen balloon, 1783	1·40	45
762	150f. Balloon *Armand Barbes* and another balloon, Paris, 1870................................	1·70	55
763	350f. Balloon *Double Eagle II*........................	4·25	1·20
764	500f. Advertising airship................................	6·25	1·80
760/764 *Set of 5*..............		13·00	4·00

1985.
837*	200f. Jet airliner...	2·30	1·60

1987.
951	155f. Airliner...	1·50	1·00
952	195f. Airliner...	1·80	1·20

1987.
954	155f. McDonnell Douglas DC-10	1·50	85

1994.
1096*	150f. Fokker 100..	80	25
1099*	200f. Fokker 100..	1·10	45
MS1102*	500f. Airplane and other images..................	9·00	9·00

2002.
1279	180f. +20f. Biplane	90	35
1280	400f. +20f. Biplane	1·90	75

JAMAICA

West Indies

1949. 12 pence = 1 shilling

20 shillings = 1 pound

1969. 100 cents = 1 dollar

1949. As Nos. 114/15 of Antigua.

145*	1½d. Airplane	20	15
146*	2d. Jet-powered Vickers Viking	1·25	4·25

1960.

178*	2d. Bristol 175 Britannia 312 of B.O.A.C ..	45	10

1964.

227*	1s. 6d Airliner at Palisadoes International Airport	4·00	15

1966. No. 227 overprinted **ROYAL VISIT MARCH 1966.**

251*	1s. 6d Airliner at Palisadoes International Airport	2·00	2·00

1969. No. 227 surcharged **C-DAY 8th September 1969 15c.**

287*	15c. on 1s.6d. Airliner at Palisadoes International Airport	50	90

1970. As No. 227, but inscribed in decimal currency.

314*	15c. Airliner at Palisadoes International Airport	2·75	3·00

1972.

352*	10c. Stewardess and tail of Vickers VC-10 of Air Jamaica	20	10

1972. No. 352 overprinted **TENTH ANNIVERSARY INDEPENDENCE 1962–1972.**

360*	10c. Stewardess and tail of Vickers VC-10 of Air Jamaica	30	10

1979. No. 352 overprinted **TENTH ANNIVERSARY AIR JAMAICA 1st APRIL 1979.**

478	10c. Stewardess and tail of Vickers VC-10 of Air Jamaica	50	50

1984. Seaplanes and Flying Boats.

596	25c. de Havilland DH.60G Gipsy Moth seaplane of Caribbean Airways	1·50	20
597	55c. Consolidated Commodore flying boat of Pan Am	2·00	85
598	$1.50 Sikorsky S-38A flying boat NC-9976 of Pan Am	3·25	4·00
599	$3 Sikorsky S-40 flying boat *American Clipper* of Pan Am	4·00	6·00
596/599 *Set of 4*		9·50	10·00

1986.

652*	55c. Boeing 737 of Air Jamaica	2·75	40

1993.

830*	$1.10 Air cadet and Britten-Norman BN-2 Islander	60	40

1994. 25th Anniv of Air Jamaica.

847	50c. Douglas DC-9 of Air Jamaica	35	25
848	$1.10 Douglas DC-8 of Air Jamaica	35	25
849	$5 Boeing 727 of Air Jamaica	75	75
850	$50 Airbus Industrie A300 of Air Jamaica	3·50	6·00
847/850 *Set of 4*		4·50	6·50

1995.

890*	$1.10 Antonov An-32	55	25
892*	$5 Fairchild C-119 Flying Boxcar	80	1·40

1999.

945*	$25 Lockheed Constellation, 1950	2·50	2·50
946*	$30 Airbus Industries Airbus A-310, 1999	2·50	2·75

1999. 30th Anniv of Air Jamaica (national airline).

947	$10 Airbus Industries Airbus A-310	80	40
948	$25 Airbus Industries Airbus A-320	1·50	1·75
949	$30 Airbus Industries Airbus A-340	1·75	2·00
947/949 *Set of 3*		3·75	3·75

JAPAN

Eastern Asia

100 sen = 1 yen

1919. Nos. 232 and 298 overprinted with airplane.

196	1½s. Numeral design	£375	£150
197	3s. Numeral design	£650	£450

1929.

257	8½s. Nakajima-built Fokker F.VIIb/3m	60·00	50·00
258	9½s. Nakajima-built Fokker F.VIIb/3m	17·00	11·00
259	16½s. Nakajima-built Fokker F.VIIb/3m	20·00	20·00
260	18s. Nakajima-built Fokker F.VIIb/3m	19·00	8·25
261	33s. Nakajima-built Fokker F.VIIb/3m	55·00	11·00
257/261 *Set of 5*		£150	90·00

1937.

323*	12s. Mitsubishi B5N1	1·00	1·00

1937. Aerodrome Fund.

336	2s. +2s. Nakajima-built Douglas DC-2	2·75	1·80
337	3s. +2s. Nakajima-built Douglas DC-2	2·75	2·10
338	4s. +2s. Nakajima-built Douglas DC-2	3·50	1·90
336/338 *Set of 3*		8·00	5·25

1942.

397*	6s. Aircraft	65	65

1945. No gum. Imperf.

416*	5s. Kawasaki Ki-61 Hien	40	30

1951.

625	15y. Douglas DC-4	5·75	4·50
626	20y. Douglas DC-4	38·00	2·75
627	25y. Douglas DC-4	37·00	50
628	30y. Douglas DC-4	29·00	45
629	40y. Douglas DC-4	9·75	50
630	55y. Douglas DC-4	£250	46·00
631	75y. Douglas DC-4	£180	25·00
632	80y. Douglas DC-4	37·00	5·75
633	85y. Douglas DC-4	60·00	21·00
634	125y. Douglas DC-4	20·00	5·75
635	160y. Douglas DC-4	46·00	6·25
625/635 *Set of 11*		£650	£110

1952. As Nos. 625/35, but without "00" after value.

671	15y. Douglas DC-4	2·10	95
672	20y. Douglas DC-4	60·00	1·30
673	25y. Douglas DC-4	1·20	10
674	30y. Douglas DC-4	4·50	10
675	40y. Douglas DC-4	5·50	25
676	55y. Douglas DC-4	90·00	6·75
677	75y. Douglas DC-4	£160	16·00
678	80y. Douglas DC-4	£120	4·50
679	85y. Douglas DC-4	5·00	2·75
680	125y. Douglas DC-4	10·00	3·75
681	160y. Douglas DC-4	43·00	4·50
671/681 *Set of 11*		£450	37·00

1953.

707	70y. Douglas DC-4	4·00	15
708	80y. Douglas DC-4	5·75	15
709	115y. Douglas DC-4	2·75	20
710	145y. Douglas DC-4	18·00	2·10
707/710 *Set of 4*		27·00	2·30

1960. 50th Anniv of Japanese Aviation.

832	10y. Douglas DC-8 and Farman H.F. III biplane	80	30

1967. Inauguration of Round-the-World Air Service.

1087	15y. Douglas DC-8 of Japan Air Lines	40	10

1978. Opening of Narita Airport, Tokyo.

1495	50y. Airliners at Tokyo International Airport	80	10

1979.
1535　　50y. Boeing 747 .... 1·00　10

1989. Ninth Hot Air Balloon World Championship.
2027　　62y. Hot-air balloons .... 1·00　25

1994. Opening of Kansai International Airport, Osaka.
2314　　80y. Airport and Boeing 747 bearing
　　　　　airport code on tailplane .... 1·40　60
2315　　80y. Airport and Boeing 747 bearing
　　　　　airport code on tailplane .... 1·40　60
2316　　80y. Boeing 747 approaching airport .... 1·40　60
2314/2316 *Set of 3* .... 3·75　1·60

1995.
2363　　110y. Fokker F.VII/3m on stamp and
　　　　　biplane .... 1·90　80
2364　　110y. Stamp and loading freight onto
　　　　　Fokker F.VIII/3m .... 1·90　80

1995.
2379　　50y. Radio-controlled model aircraft .... 85　35
2380　　80y. Radio-controlled model helicopter .. 1·40　55

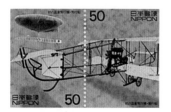

1999.
2627*　　50y. Biplane Kaishiki No. 1 (first Japanese-
　　　　　built aircraft) (foreground) .... 1·30　95
2628*　　50y. Airship Yamadashki No. 1 .... 1·30　95

2000.
2717*　　50y. Mitsubishi L3Y2 'Tina' and .... 1·30　95
2718*　　50y. Mitsubishi Ki-15 (Army Type 97)
　　　　　Kamikaze airplanes .... 1·30　95

2000.
2787*　　80y. Girl and dog in balloon .... 2·10　1·50

2002. 50th Anniv of Japanese Civil Aviation.
3057　　80y. Boeing 777 in flight and Douglas
　　　　　DC-7 on ground .... 1·30　1·30

2005. Opening of Chuba International Airport.
3304a　　80y. Boeing 747 .... 1·60　1·30

2007.
3517*　　80y. Pilatus PC-6 Turbo Porter .... 1·50　1·20
3527*　　80y. Pilatus PC-6 Turbo Porter .... 1·60　1·30

JAPANESE OCCUPATION OF CHINA

Eastern Asia

100 cents = 1 dollar (yuan)

IV. Nanking and Shanghai

20

付巳爱空航之函信内図

1941. Nos. 559 and 561/3 of China surcharged with value and line
of Chinese characters.
1　　10s. on 50c. Junkers F-13 .... 1·90　2·40
2　　18s. on 90c. Junkers F-13 .... 2·40　3·75
3　　20s. on $1 Junkers F-13 .... 7·00　7·00
5　　25s. on 90c. Junkers F-13 .... 2·40　3·75
6　　35s. on $2 Junkers F-13 .... 2·75　2·75
7　　60s. on 35s. on $2 Junkers F-13 .... 2·75　3·75
1/7 *Set of 6* .... 20·00　23·00

250

1945. Nos. 422, 556, 560 and 562 of China surcharged with value,
bomb and Chinese characters.
128　　$150 on 15c. Junkers F-13 .... 35　20
129　　$250 on 25c. Junkers F-13 .... 85　20
130　　$600 on 60c. Junkers F-13 .... 35　20
131　　$1000 on $1 Junkers F-13 .... 4·25　3·00
128/131 *Set of 4* .... 5·25　3·25

JAPANESE OCCUPATION OF NETHERLANDS INDIES

South-east Asia

100 cents = 1 gulden

III. Japanese Naval Control Area

1942. No. 360 of Netherlands Indies overprinted with anchor and
three Japanese characters.
106*　　30c. Nose of Pander S.4 Postjager .... £275　£400

JAPANESE OCCUPATION OF THE PHILIPPINES

South-east Asia

100 centavos = 1 peso

1943. Nos. 566 and 569 of Philippines surcharged with Japanese
characters, **1-23-43** and value.
J13　　2c. on 8c. Boeing 314 flying boat .... 1·20　1·60
J14　　5c. on 1p. Boeing 314 flying boat .... 1·70　1·90

1944. Nos. 567/8 of Philippines surcharged **REPUBLIKA NG
PILIPINAS 5-7-44** and value.
J43　　5c. on 20c. Boeing 314 flying boat .... 2·10　2·75
J44　　12c. on 60c. Boeing 314 flying boat .... 3·00　3·75

OFFICIAL STAMPS
1944. No. 569 of Philippines overprinted **REPUBLIKA NG
PILIPINAS (K. P.).**
JO47　　1p. Boeing 314 flying boat .... 8·25　9·50

JERSEY

North-west Europe

1969. 12 pence = 1 shilling

20 shillings = 1 pound

1970. 100 pence = 1 pound

1969.
26*　　2s.6d B.A.C. One Eleven (left) and Vickers
　　　　Viscount 700 at Jersey Airport .... 1·25　1·00

1970. As No. 26, but inscribed in decimal currency.
54*　　10p. B.A.C. One Eleven and Vickers
　　　　Viscount 700 at Jersey Airport .... 40　40

1973. Jersey Aviation History.

89	3p.	Balloon *L'Armee de la Loire*, Paris, 1870	10	10
90	5p.	Astra seaplane, 1912	10	10
91	7½p.	Supermarine Sea Eagle amphibian G-EBFK of British Marine Air Navigation	35	35
92	9p.	de Havilland D.H.86 Dragon Express G-ACYF *Giffard Bay* of Jersey Airways	45	45
89/92		Set of 4	90	90

1974.

110*	20p.	B.A.C. One Eleven 200 of British Airways	35	40

1975. 50th Anniv of Royal Air Force Association, Jersey Branch.

133	4p.	Armstrong Whitworth Siskin IIIA	10	10
134	5p.	Supermarine Southampton I flying boat	15	10
135	10p.	Supermarine Spitfire Mk 1	40	25
136	25p.	Folland Fo.141 Gnat T1 trainer of the Red Arrows display team	70	50
133/136		Set of 4	1·20	85

1976.

145*	11p.	B.A.C. One Eleven of British Airways and tail of B.A.C. One Eleven of British Caledonian at Jersey Airport	25	25

1979. 25th Anniv of International Air Rally.

208	6p.	Percival Mew Gull G-AEXF *Golden City*	10	10
209	8p.	de Havilland Canada DHC-1 Chipmunk trainer OO-PHS of the Royal Antwerp Aviation Club	25	15
210	10½p.	Druine D.31 Turbulent	25	20
211	11p.	de Havilland DH.82A Tiger Moth	30	25
212	13p.	North American AT-6 Harvard F-BRGB	40	35
208/212		Set of 5	1·20	95

1980.

243*	17½p.	Goodyear Aerospace airship *Europa*	40	40

1984. 40th Anniv of ICAO.

340	9p.	Bristol Type 170 Freighter Mk 32 G-ANWM of B.U.A.	20	15
341	12p.	Airspeed A.S.57 Ambassador 2 G-ALZO of Dan-Air	35	35
342	26p.	de Havilland DH.114 Heron 1B G-AMYU of Jersey Airways	75	75
343	31p.	de Havilland DH.89A Dragon Rapide G-AGPH of Jersey and Guernsey Airways	1·00	1·00
340/343		Set of 4	2·10	2·00

1985.

364*	34p.	Air Training Corps cadet and glider	90	90

1986.

385*	31p.	B.A.C. One Eleven 500	1·00	1·10

1987. 50th Anniv of Jersey Airport.

409	10p.	de Havilland DH.86 Dragon Express G-ACZP *Belcroute Bay* of Jersey Airways at Jersey Airport	25	25
410	14p.	Boeing 757 of British Airways and Douglas DC-9-15 of British Midland	40	45
411	22p.	Britten-Norman BN-2A Mk III "long nose" Trislander (foreground) and Britten-Norman BN-2 Islander, both of Aurigny Air Services	55	50
412	29p.	Shorts 330 G-OJUK of Jersey European and Vickers Viscount 800 of British Air Ferries	90	90
413	31p.	B.A.C. One Eleven 500 of British Caledonian and Handley Page H.P.R.7 Dart Herald G-ASKK of Air UK	95	95
409/413		Set of 5	2·75	2·75

1988.

443*	16p.	de Havilland Canada DHC-7 Dash Seven and control tower at Jersey Airport	40	45

1989.

477*	17p.	British Aerospace Hawk T.1 jet trainers of the Red Arrows display team over Jersey Airport, and Boeing 737 of British Airways and Fokker F.27 Friendship 200 of Air UK on the ground	50	55

1990. 50th Anniv of Battle of Britain.

530	14p.	British Aerospace Hawk T.1 of the Red Arrows display team	40	45
531	18p.	Supermarine Spitfire	55	60
532	24p.	Hawker Hurricane Mk I	85	85
533	34p.	Vickers-Armstrong Wellington	1·50	1·60
534	37p.	Avro Type 683 Lancaster	1·60	1·60
530/534		Set of 5	4·50	4·50

1993. 75th Anniv of Royal Air Force and 50th Anniv of Royal Air Force Association and 40th Anniv of First Air Display on Jersey.

618	17p.	Douglas DC-3 Dakota	45	30
619	23p.	Wight seaplane	60	65
620	28p.	Avro Shackleton A.E.W.2	70	70
621	33p.	Gloster Meteor Mk III and de Havilland DH.100 Vampire FB.5	80	85
622	39p.	Hawker Siddeley Harrier GR.1A	1·00	1·10
623	57p.	Panavia Tornado F Mk 3	1·50	1·60
618/623		Set of 6	4·50	4·75

1994.

659*	18p.	Airspeed AS 51 Horsa gliders and Douglas C-47 tow planes	55	50
663*	30p.	Supermarine Spitfires	80	75

1994.

676*	35p.	Vickers Type 953 Vanguard of BEA	85	85
677*	41p.	Shorts 360 of Aurigny Air Services	1·10	1·00

1997. 60th Anniv of Jersey Airport.

807	20p.	de Havilland DH.95 Flamingo	45	40
808	24p.	Handley Page HPR.5 Marathon	55	40
809	31p.	de Havilland DH.114 Heron	65	65
810	37p.	Boeing 737-236	95	95
811	43p.	Britten-Norman BN-2A Mk III Trislander	1·10	1·10
812	63p.	BAe 146-200	1·75	1·75
807/812		Set of 6	5·00	4·75

1999.

888*	43p.	de Havilland DH.86 Dragon Express	95	1·10

2000. 60th Anniv of Battle of Britain.

962	22p.	Supermarine Spitfire Mk Ia	50	55
963	26p.	Hawker Hurricane Mk I	60	65
964	36p.	Bristol Blenheim Mk IV	80	85
965	40p.	Vickers Wellington Mk Ic	90	95
966	45p.	Boulton Paul P.82 Defiant Mk I	1·00	1·10
967	65p.	Short S.25 Sunderland Mk I	1·50	1·60
962/967		Set of 6	4·75	5·25

2003. Centenary of Powered Flight.

1074	23p.	Sanchez-Besa Hydroplane	50	55
1075	29p.	Supermarine S6B	65	70
1076	38p.	de Havilland DH.84 Dragon	80	85
1077	40p.	de Havilland DH.89a Rapide	85	90
1078	47p.	Vickers 701 Viscount	1·00	1·10
1079	68p.	BAC One Eleven	1·50	1·60
1074/1079		Set of 6	4·75	5·25
MS1080	£2	Jacob Ellehammer's biplane, 1906	4·25	4·50

2005.

1185*	32p.	Britten-Norman BN-2 Islander	65	70
1186*	33p.	Eurocopter AS355 Ecurevil II	65	70
1189*	70p.	Westland Sea King	1·40	1·50

2007. 60th Anniv of Jersey International Air Display.
1326	34p. Dornier Do-24 ATT	1·00	1·00
1327	37p. Avro Type 698 Vulcan B2	1·10	1·10
1328	42p. Junkers Ju52/3m	1·30	1·30
1329	51p. Sukhoi Su-27 'Flanker'	1·50	1·50
1330	57p. Boeing B-52 Stratofortress	1·70	1·70
1331	74p. Concorde	2·20	2·20
1326/1331 *Set of 6*		8·00	8·00
MS1332 £2.50 BAe Hawk T1s of the Red Arrows		7·25	7·25

JIND

Indian sub-continent

12 pies = 1 anna

16 annas = 1 rupee

1937. No. 258 of India overprinted **JIND STATE**.
120*	12a. Armstrong Whitworth A.W.27 Ensign I	2·75	30·00

JOHORE

South-east Asia

100 cents = 1 dollar

1949. As Nos. 114/15 of Antigua.
148*	10c. Airplane	30	40
149*	15c. Jet-powered Vickers Viking	2·00	1·25

JORDAN

Middle East

1949. 1000 milliemes = 1 pound

1950. 1000 fils = 1 dinar

1949.
285*	1m. Lockheed L.049 Constellation	25	25
286*	4m. Lockheed L.049 Constellation	45	45
287*	10m. Lockheed L.049 Constellation	60	60
288*	20m. Lockheed L.049 Constellation	1·00	1·00

1950.
295	5f. Lockheed Constellation	70	50
296	10f. Lockheed Constellation	70	50
297	15f. Lockheed Constellation	70	50
298	20f. Lockheed Constellation	95	80
299	50f. Lockheed Constellation	1·60	80
300	100f. Lockheed Constellation	2·75	1·90
301	150f. Lockheed Constellation	4·00	2·75
295/301 *Set of 7*		10·00	7·00

1954.
470*	5f. Vickers Viscount 700	25	15
433*	10f. Vickers Viscount 700	50	50
434*	25f. Vickers Viscount 700	70	50
435*	35f. Vickers Viscount 700	85	50
436*	40f. Vickers Viscount 700	1·00	50
437*	50f. Vickers Viscount 700	1·40	70
438*	100f. Vickers Viscount 700	1·60	1·20
439*	150f. Vickers Viscount 700	2·75	1·60

1965.
683*	10f. North American X-15 being launched from Boeing B-52H Stratofortress	35	35
685*	20f. North American X-15 being launched from Boeing B-52H Stratofortress	70	50

1973. Royal Jordanian Aero Club.
990*	5f. Farman H.F.III biplane	60	25
991*	10f. Farman H.F.III biplane	60	25
992*	15f. Piper PA-28 Cherokee 140 (air)	60	25
993*	20f. Beech B55 Baron	70	25

1975. 10th Anniv of ALIA (Royal Jordanian Airlines).
1121*	30f. Boeing 707 of Alia	35	15

1977.
1211*	10f. Airliner	15	10

1982.
1324*	40f. Dassault Mirage F1C	95	35

1983. Opening of Queen Alia International Airport.
1370	10f. Queen Alia International Airport	25	10
1371	25f. Queen Alia International Airport	70	15
1372	40f. Queen Alia International Airport	1·10	35
1373	50f. Queen Alia International Airport	1·40	70
1374	100f. Queen Alia International Airport	2·50	1·70
1370/1374 *Set of 5*		5·25	2·75

1988. 25th Anniv of Royal Jordanian Airline.
1574*	80f. Boeing 737	1·20	70

1993.
1682*	5f. Northrop F-5E	15	15

1994. 50th Anniv of ICAO.
1746	80f. Douglas DC-3 and Boeing 737	45	45
1747	125f. Douglas DC-3 and Boeing 737	60	60
1748	160f. Douglas DC-3 and Boeing 737	85	85
1746/1748 *Set of 3*		1·70	1·70

JORDANIAN OCCUPATION OF PALESTINE

Middle East

1000 milliemes = 1 pound

1949. Nos. 285/8 of Jordan overprinted **PALESTINE** in English and Arabic.
P30*	1m. Lockheed Constellation	45	45
P31*	4m. Lockheed Constellation	45	45
P32*	10m. Lockheed Constellation	70	70
P33*	20m. Lockheed Constellation	70	70

KAMPUCHEA

South-east Asia

100 cents = 1 riel

1983. Bicentenary of Manned Flight.
446	20c. Montgolfier balloon (first manned free flight, 1783)	20	10
447	30c. Balloon	25	10
448	50c. Charles' hydrogen balloon, 1783	35	10
449	1r. Blanchard and Jeffries' balloon, 1785	65	20
450	1r.50 Salomon Andree's balloon flight over the Arctic	90	25
451	2r. Piccard's stratosphere balloon F.N.R.S., 1931	1·30	35
452	3r. Hot-air balloons	1·80	70
446/452 Set of 7		5·00	1·60
MS453 6r. Hot-air balloon		5·75	1·10

1984.
504	5r. Ilyushin Il-62M	4·00	20
505	10r. Ilyushin Il-62M	7·50	35
506	15r. Ilyushin Il-62M	11·00	45
507	25r. Ilyushin Il-62M	18·00	80
504/507 Set of 4		36·00	1·60

1986. As Nos. 504/7, but inscribed "R.P. DU KAMPUCHEA" and other inscriptions altered.
695	5r. Ilyushin Il-62M	3·50	20
696	10r. Ilyushin Il-62M	7·25	35
697	15r. Ilyushin Il-62M	9·00	45
698	25r. Ilyushin Il-62M	16·00	80
695/698 Set of 4		32·00	1·60

1986. Aircraft.
771	20c. Concorde (inscribed "CONCORD")	20	10
772	50c. Douglas DC-10	25	10
773	80c. Boeing 747SP	35	10
774	1r. Ilyushin Il-62M	65	20
775	1r.50 Ilyushin Il-86	90	25
776	2r. Antonov An-124 (wrongly inscribed "AN-124")	1·30	35
777	3r. Airbus Industrie A300	1·80	70
771/777 Set of 7		5·00	1·60

1987. Experimental Aircraft Designs.
831	20c. Horatio F. Phillips' "multiplane" model, 1893	20	10
832	50c. John Stringfellow's steam-powered model airplane, 1848	25	10
833	80c. Thomas Moy's model airplane *Aerial Steamer*, 1875	35	10
834	1r. Leonardo da Vinci's "ornithopter" design, 1490	65	20
835	1r.50 Sir George Cayley's "convertiplane", 1843	1·10	20
836	2r. Sir Hiram Maxim's "Flying Test Rig"	1·30	20
837	3r. William Samuel Henson's *Aerial Steam Carriage*, 1842	2·00	25
831/837 Set of 7		5·25	1·00
MS838 6r Leonardo da Vinci's drawing of a "Flying Man"		4·25	90

KATANGA

Central Africa

100 centimes = 1 franc

1961.
73	3f.50 Farman H.F.III biplane	3·00	3·25
74	6f.50 Boeing 707 90K-EZA of Air Katanga	65	65
75	8f. Farman H.F.III biplane	3·00	3·25
76	10f. Boeing 707 90K-EZA of Air Katanga	65	65
73/76 Set of 4		6·50	7·00

KATHIRI STATE OF SEIYUN

see Aden Protectorate States

KAZAKHSTAN

Central Asia

2001. 100 tyin (ty) = 1 tenge (t)

2001.
MS307 100t. Ilyushin Il-62		5·00	4·75

2002.
384	20t. Illushin Il-86 over Almaty Airport	65	55
385	40t. Tupolev Tu-144	1·30	1·10

KEDAH

South-east Asia

100 cents = 1 dollar

1949. As Nos. 114/15 of Antigua.
72*	10c. Airplane	25	1·25
73*	15c. Jet-powered Vickers Viking	2·00	1·50

KELANTAN

South-east Asia

100 cents = 1 dollar

1949. As Nos. 114/15 of Antigua.
57*	10c. Airplane	25	30
58*	15c. Jet-powered Vickers Viking	2·25	1·75

1987. Helicopters.
846	20c. Kamov Ka-15 helicopter	20	10
847	50c. Kamov Ka-18 helicopter	25	10
848	80c. Westland WG-13 Lynx helicopter	35	10
849	1r. Sud Aviation SA 341 Gazelle helicopter	65	20
850	1r.50 Sud Aviation SA 330E Puma helicopter	90	20
851	2r. Boeing-Vertol CH-47 Chinook helicopter	1·30	20
852	3r. Boeing UTTAS helicopter	1·80	25
846/852 Set of 7		5·00	1·00
MS853 6r. Fairey Rotodyne helicopter		4·25	1·10

KENYA

East Africa

100 cents = 1 shilling

1980. Flying Doctor Service.
173*	1s. Piper PA-30B Twin Commanche of the Flying Doctor service	20	10
174*	3s. Piper PA-30B Twin Commanche of the Flying Doctor service	65	1·00
175*	5s. Piper PA-30B Twin Commanche of the Flying Doctor service	90	1·60

1981.
204*	5s. Three Boeing 707s and other airliners at Jomo Kenyatta International Airport	70	65

1983.
282*	3s.50 Boeing 707	2·00	3·00

1984. 40th Anniv of ICAO.
309*	2s.50 Kenya School of Aviation	85	70
310*	3s.50 Boeing 737 of Kenya Airways and other airliners at Moi International Airport	1·40	1·50

1986.
387*	5s. Piper PA-30B Twin Commanche landing at game park airstrip	5·50	3·00

1988.
458*	3s. de Havilland Australia DHA.3 Drover 3 (top) and Piper PA-30B Twin Commanche of the Flying Doctor Service	3·00	1·25

1988.
489*	7s. Airbus Industrie A310-300 *Harambee Star* of Kenya Airways	5·50	3·00

KENYA, UGANDA AND TANGANYIKA

East Africa
100 cents = 1 shilling

1935.
117* 65c. Armstrong Whitworth A.W.15 Atalanta...... 4·25 2·00

1949. As Nos. 114/15 of Antigua.
159* 20c. Airplane...... 15 10
160* 30c. Jet-powered Vickers Viking...... 1·75 2·25

1967.
235 30c. de Havilland DH.89 Dragon Rapide.. 30 10
236 50c. Vickers Super VC-10 of East African Airways...... 40 10
237 1s.30 Hawker Siddeley Comet 4B of East African Airways...... 85 30
238 2s.50 Fokker F.27 Friendship of East African Airways...... 1·25 3·00
235/238 Set of 4...... 2·50 3·25

1971.
305* 2s.50 Vickers Super VC-10 at Kilimanjaro International Airport...... 1·00 3·25

1973.
345* 1s.50 Nairobi Airport...... 50 20

1974.
358* 2s.50 Vickers Super VC-10...... 1·00 2·00

1947.
362* 2s.50 Vickers Super VC-10 of East African Airways being loaded with mail ...... 55 1·50

1975.
375* 50c. Boeing 727 at Entebbe International Airport...... 30 10

1975.
387* 50c. Fokker F.27 Friendship at Nairobi Airport...... 1·00 40
388* 1s. Douglas DC-9 at Kilimanjaro Airport 1·10 40
389* 2s. Vickers Super VC-10 at Entebbe Airport...... 3·50 3·25

KHMER REPUBLIC

South-east Asia
100 cents = 1 riel

1974.
390* 250r. Concorde...... 14·00 7·50

KIRIBATI

Pacific Ocean
100 cents = 1 dollar

1980.
113* 25c. Britten-Norman BN-2 Islander of Air Tungaru at Bonriki Airport...... 15 10

1980.
138* 25c. Britten-Norman BN-2 Islander at Bonriki Airport...... 15 10

1982. Inauguration of Tungaru Airline.
179 12c. Riley Turbo Skyliner T3-ATA of Air Tungaru (inscribed "de Havilland DH.114 Heron")...... 15 10
180 30c. Britten-Norman BN-2A Mk III "short nose" Trislander DD-FCC...... 20 20
181 35c. Casa C-212 Aviocar of Air Tungaru.... 20 25
182 50c. Boeing 727-200 of Air Tungaru........ 30 35
179/182 Set of 4...... 75 80

1993.
406* 23c. Consolidated B-24 Liberator...... 75 75
410* 23c. Vought Sikorsky OS2U Kingfisher seaplane...... 75 75
413* 23c. Grumman F6F Hellcat in lagoon...... 75 75
415* 23c. Grumman F6F Hellcat landing on Betio Island...... 75 75
418* 75c. Grumman F4F Wildcat fighters...... 1·25 1·25

1995. American Aircraft.
489 23c. Grumman TBF Avenger...... 60 45
490 40c. Curtiss SOC.3-1 Seagull...... 80 70
491 50c. Consolidated B-24 Liberator...... 90 90
492 60c. Grumman G-21 Goose...... 1·10 1·10
493 75c. Martin B-26 Marauder...... 1·40 1·50
494 $1 Northrop P-61 Black Widow...... 1·60 1·75
489/494 Set of 6...... 5·75 5·75

1997. Nos. 489/94 overprinted **PACIFIC 97 World Philatelic Exhibition, San Francisco, California 29 May-8 June.**
528 23c. Grumman TBF Avenger...... 40 35
529 40c. Curtiss SOC.3-1 Seagull...... 60 55
530 50c. Consolidated B-24 Liberator...... 70 70
531 60c. Grumman G-21 Goose...... 80 90
532 75c. Martin B-26 Marauder...... 90 1·10
533 $1 Northrop P-61 Black Widow...... 1·10 1·40
528/533 Set of 6...... 4·00 4·50

1998.
569* 25c. Airplane...... 30 30

1999.
583* $1 Lockheed Model 10 Electra and Amelia Earhart...... 2·00 2·00

2003. Centenary of Powered Flight.
677 25c. Sopwith Camel...... 50 35
678 50c. Northrop Alpha...... 70 50
679 60c. de Havilland DH.106 Comet...... 80 65
680 75c. Boeing 727...... 90 75
681 $1 English Electric Canberra...... 1·40 1·10
682 $2.50 Lockheed Martin F-22 Raptor...... 3·00 3·50
677/682 Set of 6...... 6·50 6·25
MS683 40c. Mitsubishi A6M-5 Zero-Sen; 60c. Grumman F6F Hellcat...... 1·60 1·75

2005.
731* 75c. Mitsubishi A6M Zero-Sen...... 1·25 1·25
736* 75c. Grumman F6F-3 Hellcats...... 1·25 1·25

2006. 30th Anniv of Concorde's Inaugural Flight.
770* $1.50 Aerospatiale/BAe Concorde...... 3·00 3·00
771* $1.50 Aerospatiale/BAe Concorde...... 3·00 3·00

2008. 90th Anniv of the Royal Air Force.
822 25c. Avro Type 696 Shackleton...... 40 25
823 50c. Hawker Siddeley (BAe) Harrier...... 80 50
824 75c. Eurofighter EF-2000 Typhoon...... 1·00 60
825 $2.50 Dambusters Raid (may show Avro Lancaster)...... 2·25 2·50
822/825 Set of 4...... 4·00 3·50

KOREA

Eastern Asia
South Korea

1947. 100 cheun = 1 won

1953. 100 weun = 1 hwan

1962. 100 chon = 1 won

1947. Inauguration of Air Mail Service.
94	50w. Douglas DC-4	13·50	3·75
126	150w. Douglas DC-4 (blue)	3·75	1·50
127	150w. Douglas DC-4 (green)	22·00	13·00

1950. Opening of Internal Air Mail Service.
133	60w. Douglas DC-2	37·00	7·50

1952.
196	1200w. Douglas DC-3	2·50	75
197	1800w. Douglas DC-3	2·50	75
198	4200w. Douglas DC-3	6·50	1·00
196/198 Set of 3		10·50	2·30

1953. As Nos. 196/8, but inscribed in new currency.
210	12h. Douglas DC-3	3·00	65
211	18h. Douglas DC-3	3·75	75
212	42h. Douglas DC-3	4·50	1·20
210/212 Set of 3		10·00	2·30

1954.
216	25h. Douglas DC-6	6·25	1·40
217	35h. Douglas DC-6	6·25	1·60
218	38h. Douglas DC-6	6·25	1·80
219	58h. Douglas DC-6	6·25	2·00
258	70h. Douglas DC-6	11·50	3·75
220	71h. Douglas DC-6	15·00	2·40
259	110h. Douglas DC-6	11·50	3·75
260	205h. Douglas DC-6	19·00	3·75

1960.
354	40h. Douglas DC-8	1·90	75

1961.
417	50h. Douglas DC-8	23·00	6·25
418	100h. Douglas DC-8	31·00	10·00
419	200h. Douglas DC-8	46·00	12·50
420	400h. Douglas DC-8	55·00	13·00
417/420 Set of 4		£140	38·00

1962. 10th Anniv of Korea's Entry into ICAO.
450	4w. Aircraft and emblem	2·30	75

1962. As Nos. 417/20, but inscribed in new currency.
454	5w. Douglas DC-8	95·00	17·00
512	10w. Douglas DC-8	15·00	4·75
513	20w. Douglas DC-8	55·00	7·75
563	39w. Douglas DC-8	11·50	2·30
514	40w. Douglas DC-8	29·00	6·25
564	64w. Douglas DC-8	10·00	2·75
565	78w. Douglas DC-8	27·00	4·75
566	112w. Douglas DC-8	13·00	2·75

1966.
634*	7w. Douglas DC-9	3·75	1·20

1968.
757*	7w. Pilot and Northrop F-5A Freedom Fighters	7·75	2·30

1969. 20th Anniv of Korean Air Force.
816	10w. Northrop F-5A Freedom Fighters	5·50	75
817	10w. McDonnell Douglas F4D Phantom II	7·00	75

1970.
861*	10w. Nieuport 28 biplane, 1922	2·75	95

1970.
876*	10w. Boeing 707	9·25	3·75

1973.
1085	110w. Boeing 747-200 of Korean Air Lines	10·00	3·75
1086	135w. Boeing 747-200 of Korean Air Lines	11·00	3·75
1087	145w. Boeing 747-200 of Korean Air Lines	14·00	4·75
1088	180w. Boeing 747-200 of Korean Air Lines	35·00	7·00
1085/1088 Set of 4		65·00	17·00

1974.
1116	10w. Boeing 747	1·00	25

1977.
1204	20w. McDonnell Douglas F-4 Phantom II	40	10

1977. 25th Anniv of Korean Membership of ICAO.
1310	20w. Boeing 747-200 of Korean Air Lines	60	15

1977.
1311	20w. Jet airliner	45	10

1978.
1334	20w. McDonnell Douglas F-4D Phantom II	40	10

1979. 10th Anniv of Korean Air Lines.
1396	20w. Boeing 747-200 of Korean Air Lines	40	10

1981. Third Model Aeronautic Competition.
1487	10w. Model glider	60	10
1488	20w. Elastic-powered model airplane	60	10
1489	40w. Line-controlled model airplane	60	20
1490	50w. Radio-controlled model airplane	75	30
1491	80w. Radio-controlled model helicopter	1·00	40
1487/1491 Set of 5		3·25	1·00

1981. National Aviation Day.
1499	40w. Airliner	50	10

1983.
1553	60w. Airliner	60	10

1983.
1575*	70w. Douglas DC-8-60 Super Sixty	1·00	25

1984.
1618	70w. Jet airliner	70	10

1984.
1641	70w. Jet airliner	50	10

1985.
1699	70w. Boeing 747 of Korean Air Lines	80	30
1700	370w. Boeing 747 of Korean Air Lines (air)	3·00	95

1989. 29th International Civil Airports Association World Congress, Seoul.
1886	80w. Boeing 747 at Seoul Airport	60	15

1993.
2078	110w. Ilyushin Il-86	60	25

1994.
2122*	330w. Boeing 747	2·10	40
2122a*	340w. Boeing 747 facing left	2·10	50
2122b*	380w. Boeing 747 facing left	2·30	55
2123*	390w. Boeing 747 (different)	3·00	50
2124*	400w. Boeing 747	2·10	40
2127*	560w. Boeing 747	3·50	65
2131*	1300w. Boeing 747	6·75	1·20
2132*	1340w. Boeing 747	5·75	1·80
2132a*	1380w. Boeing 747 facing left	6·25	2·00

1995.
2155*	440w. Toy airplane (cartoon)	1·60	65

2001. Inauguration of Incheon Airport.
2486	170w. Boeing 747 above Incheon Airport	70	40

2002. Transport.
2550	280w. Stylised airplane	1·50	50
2551	310w. Stylised airplane	1·60	55
2551a	420w. Stylised airplane	1·40	95
2552	1380w. Stylised airplane	4·50	2·50
2553	1410w. Stylised airplane	4·75	2·75
2554	1580w. Stylised airplane	5·00	4·00
2555	1610w. Stylised airplane	5·00	4·00
2550/2555 Set of 7		21·00	13·50

North Korea

100 cheun = 1 won

1954. Imperforate or perforated.
N78	10w. Mikoyan Gurevich MiG-15 jet fighters	£110	£110

1958. Imperforate or perforated.
N141	20w. Lisunov Li-2	7·00	1·20

1961.
N345*	5ch. Boy with model glider	1·70	15

1963.
N446*	5ch. Pilot and Mikoyan Gurevich MiG-15 jet fighters	50	10

1966. Industrial Uses of Aircraft.
N729	2ch. Yakovlev Yak-12M	50	10
N730	5ch. Yakovlev Yak-18U	7·25	80
N731	10ch. Lisunov Li-2	1·70	30
N732	40ch. Lisunov Li-2	1·70	30
N729/732 Set of 4		10·00	1·40

1966.
N749*	2ch. Antonov An-2	1·00	20

1967.
N783*	10ch. Kim Hwa Ryong and Lavochkin La-11	1·30	20

1970.
N973*	40ch. Jet fighters	1·50	25

1971.
N1008*	10ch. Tail of airplane	65	15
N1010*	10ch. Mikoyan Gurevich MiG-15 jet fighters	65	15

1972.
N1115*	10ch. Pilot and Mikoyan Gurevich MiG-21 jet fighters	50	15

1973.
N1132*	40ch. Pilot, helicopter and Mikoyan Gurevich MiG-21 jet fighters	1·00	65

1973.
N1200	2ch. Mil Mi-4 helicopter	75	15
N1201	5ch. Airplane	25	15
N1202	10ch. Ilyushin Il-18	35	15
N1203	40ch. Tupolev Tu-104A	85	20
N1204	90ch. Ilyushin Il-62M	1·40	40
N1200/N1204 Set of 5		3·25	95

1974.
N1225*	10ch. Lisunov Li-2	1·10	20

1974.
N1239*	60ch. Model airplane	1·70	35

1974.
N1275*	40ch. Antonov An-12	1·30	30

1974. Civil Aviation.
N1292	2ch. Antonov An-2 biplane of Korean National Airlines	85	15
N1293	5ch. Lisunov Li-2 of Korean National Airlines	85	15
N1294	10ch. Ilyushin Il-14P of Korean National Airlines	1·10	20
N1295	40ch. Antonov An-24 of Korean National Airlines	1·50	45
N1296	60ch. Ilyushin Il-18 of Korean National Airlines	2·75	70
N1292/N1296 Set of 5		6·25	1·50
MSN1297 90ch. Airliner		6·25	4·75

1975.
N1440*	5ch. Gliders	60	10
N1441*	5ch. Radio-controlled model airplane	60	10
N1442*	10ch. Biplane	75	20

1976.
N1516*	5ch. Ilyushin Il-62M	35	10

1976. World Model Plane Championships (1975).
N1568*	20ch. Model airplane	60	20
N1569*	40ch. Model glider	1·00	50

1977.
N1625*	30ch. Mil Mi-8 helicopter	1·50	40
N1626*	40ch. Ilyushin Il-18 of Korean National Airlines	1·70	45

1977.
N1668	10ch. Airliner	30	15

1978.
N1699*	15ch. Mil Mi-8 helicopter	1·20	25
N1700*	25ch. Tupolev Tu-154	1·10	25

1978.
N1718	2ch. Tupolev Tu-144	2·10	50
N1719	5ch. Airplane	35	15
N1720	10ch. Airplane	65	15
N1721	30ch. Airplane	1·30	40
N1722	50ch. Tupolev Tu-144 (air)	1·50	85
N1718/1722 *Set of 5*		5·25	1·80

1978. Airplanes.
N1769	2ch. Douglas DC-8-63 of Swissair (top) and Comte AC-4 Gentleman HB-KIL of Alpar Bern	75	15
N1770	10ch. Ilyushin Il-62M (top) and Avia BH-25 L-BABF, both of C.S.A	1·00	15
N1771	15ch. Douglas DC-8-63 of Alitalia (top) and Savoia Marchetti S-71	1·10	25
N1772	20ch. Tupolev Tu-144 of Aeroflot (top) and Kalinin K-5 CCCP-3-6	1·30	25
N1773	25ch. Tupolev Tu-154 of Korean National Airlines and Antonov An-2 biplane	1·30	25
N1774	30ch. Ilyushin Il-18 of Korean National Airlines (top) and airplane	1·30	25
N1775	40ch. Concorde (top) and Wibault 283 trimotor F-AMYD, both of Air France	3·00	75
N1769/N1775 *Set of 7*		8·75	1·80
MSN1776	50ch. Airbus Industrie A300B2 (top) and Focke Wulf A-17 Mowe, both of Lufthansa	2·75	60

1979. Airships.
N1833	10ch. Clement-Bayard airship *Fleurus*, 1912	1·30	30
N1834	20ch. Airship N.1 *Norge*	1·30	30
MSN1835	50ch. Airship LZ-127 *Graf Zeppelin*	2·20	60

1979.
N1909*	20ch. Boy with model biplane	1·70	40
N1913*	30th. Boy with model airplane	2·50	60
MSN1915	Four sheets. (a) 80ch. Concorde (other sheets do not show aircraft) *Price for 4 sheets*	29·00	6·75

1980.
N1953	30ch. Tupolev ANT-9 PS9 (on Russia stamp No. 645), monoplane (on German local stamp) and two biplanes (on Switzerland stamps Nos. 322a and 386)	3·75	1·00
N1954	50ch. Airplane (on France stamp No. 553)	5·50	1·40

1980.
N1958*	10ch. Polikarpov Po-2 biplane	1·30	50

N1959*	10ch. Mil Mi-4 helicopter	1·50	50
N1961*	10ch. Airliner	3·50	1·30

1980.
N1972*	40ch. Ilyushin Il-18 and Tupolev Tu-154	3·50	1·30

1980. Conquerors of Sky and Space.
N1974	10ch. Wilbur and Orville Wright, Wright *Flyer I* and Wright Type A	85	30
N1975	20ch. Louis Bleriot and Bleriot XI	1·30	50
N1976	30ch. Anthony Fokker, Fokker F.VIIa/3m (top), Fokker E.III Eindecker (right) and Fokker monoplane *Haarlem Spin*	1·70	65
N1977	40ch. Secondo Campini, Sir Frank Whittle, Caproni Campini N-1, Gloster Whittle E28/39 and other jet aircraft	2·50	85
N1974/N1977 *Set of 4*		5·75	2·10
MSN1978	70ch. Airship LZ-127 *Graf Zeppelin*	3·25	1·00

1980.
N2016	10ch. Airship LZ-127 *Graf Zeppelin* (on Germany stamp No. 469 and Russia stamp No. 584)	1·20	40
N2017	20ch. Airship LZ-127 *Graf Zeppelin* (on Germany stamp No. 470 and Russia stamp No. 585)	2·50	90
N2018	30ch. Airship LZ-127 *Graf Zeppelin* (on Germany stamp No. 471 and Russia stamp No. 586)	3·50	1·30
N2016/N2018 *Set of 3*		6·50	2·30
MSN2019	50ch. Airship LZ-127 *Graf Zeppelin* (on Russia stamp No. 587)	8·50	3·50

1980. 25th Anniv of First Post-War Flight of Lufthansa.
N2029	20ch. Convair CV 340 of Lufthansa	6·25	2·50

1981.
N2073*	10ch. Dornier Do-X flying boat	3·50	65
N2074*	20ch. Airship LZ-120 *Bodensee*	3·50	65

1981.
N2135   20ch. Boeing 747-200 of Lufthansa.............   3·25   50

1981.
N2136* 10ch. Concorde and airship LZ-127 *Graf Zeppelin*...   3·75   60
N2137* 20ch. Concorde, Breguet Br 763 Provence and Santos-Dumont's biplane *14 bis*   4·50   1·10

1982. Bicentenary of Manned Flight (1st issue).
N2243   10ch. Airship *Nulli Secundus II*, 1908 (inscribed "Baldwin's Airship").............   1·50   50
N2244   10ch. Pauley and Egg's dirigible balloon *The Dolphin*, 1818   2·75   85
N2245   20ch. Tissandier Brothers' airship, 1883.......   1·80   60
N2246   20ch. Guyton de Morveau's balloon with oars,1784   2·75   85
N2247   30ch. Parseval airship PL-VII, 1912................   2·50   65
N2248   30ch. Sir George Cayley's airship design, 1837.............   2·75   85
N2249   40ch. Comte de Lennox's balloon *Eagle*, 1834.............   2·75   65
N2250   40ch. Camille Vert's balloon *Poisson Volant*, 1859.............   2·75   65
N2251   80ch. Dupuy de Lome's airship, 1872.........   2·75   85
N2243/N2251 *Set of 9*   20·00   5·75
MSN2252 80ch. Masse's oar-powered balloon design, 1784.............   5·00   2·50

1982. Bicentenary of Manned Flight (2nd issue).
N2253   10ch. Balloon from engraving *Utopic Balloon Post* by B.A. Dunker, 1784....   1·30   50
N2254   10ch. Montgolfier balloon (tethered flight, 1783)..............   4·25   1·00
N2255   20ch. Montgolfier balloon *Le Martial*, 1783   2·50   1·00
N2256   20ch. Montgolfier balloon (first manned free flight, 1783)..............   4·25   1·00
N2257   30ch. Pierre Testu-Brissy's balloon ascent on horseback, 1798   3·75   1·70
N2258   30ch. Charles' hydrogen balloon, 1783 ....   4·25   1·00
N2259   40ch. Gaston Tissandier's balloon *Zenith*, 1875.............   5·00   2·10
N2260   40ch. Blanchard and Jeffries' balloon, 1785   4·25   1·00
N2261   80ch. Henri Giffard's balloon *Le Grand Ballon Captif*, 1878   4·25   1·00
N2252/2261 *Set of 9*   30·00   9·25
MSN2262 80ch. Balloon..............   5·00   2·50

1983. Luposta International Airmail Exhibition, Cologne.
N2280   30ch. Airship *Gross Basenach II* (foreground) and airship LZ-127 *Graf Zeppelin*.......   4·25   1·30
N2281   40ch. Parseval airship PL-II ....   4·25   1·30

1983.
N2309   10ch. Tupolev Tu-154.........................   2·10   40

1983.
N2334   40ch. Tupolev Tu-144 (on stamp No. N1718) ....   4·25   1·70

1983.
N2351* 40ch. Tupolev Tu-154........................   6·25   1·40

1986.
N2619* 10ch. Concorde and Wibault 283 trimotor F-AMYD of Air France (on stamp No. N1775) ....   2·20   40

1987.
N2695* 20ch. Tupolev Tu-144......................   90   30
N2696* 20ch. Concorde......................   90   30
N2697* 30ch. Count Ferdinand von Zeppelin and airship LZ-4   1·30   40
N2698* 80ch. Count Ferdinand von Zeppelin and drawings of airships LZ-1, modified LZ-1, LZ-2, LZ-3, rebuilt LZ-3, LZ-7 *Deutschland*, LZ-8 *Ersatz Deutschland*, LZ-10 *Schwaben* and LZ-11 *Viktoria Luise*...............   3·75   1·50

1987. Birth Centenary of Roland Garros (aviator).
N2739* 20ch. Roland Garros and Bleriot XI ....   1·80   30

1988.
N2758* 40ch. Montgolfier balloon (first manned free flight, 1783) and modern hot-air balloons ....   1·10   40

1988. 150th Birth Anniv of Count Ferdinand von Zeppelin (airship pioneer).
N2801   10ch. Airship LZ-13 *Hansa*......................   35   10
N2802   20ch. Airship LZ-10 *Schwaben*   65   30
N2803   30ch. Airship LZ-11 *Viktoria Luise*   90   40
N2804   40ch. Airship LZ-3.........................   1·30   45
N2801/N2804 *Set of 4*   3·00   1·10

1989.
N2844* 30ch. Model glider..............................   75   30

1989.
N2898* 5ch. Douglas DC-9-80 Super Eighty..........   40   10

1990.
N2963* 30ch. Tupolev Tu-154.........................   1·40   45
N2964* 40ch. Concorde ....   1·40   45

1997.
N3670* 10ch. Airplanes (with badge and missile)...   25   10

1997. 20th Anniv of North Korea Membership of ICAO.
MSN3701* Three sheets. (a) 2×20ch. Tupolev Tu-134; (b) 2×30ch. Tupolev Tu-154; (c) 2×50ch. Ilyushin Il-62 *Set of 3 sheets*..............   5·75   4·00

1998.
N3734 10ch. Soldiers and balloons.......................... 25 10

2000.
N4070* 1w. Yakovlev Yak-9P................................ 2·10 1·60

2002. Centenary of First Zeppelin Airship Flight.
N4190 40ch. Zeppelin LZ1 .... 80 70
N4191 80ch. Zeppelin LZ .... 1·60 1·40
N4192 1w.20 Zeppelin NT .... 2·50 2·10
N4190/N4192 *Set of 3* .... 4·50 3·75
MSN4193 Two sheets. (a) 2w.40 Zeppelin NT
(different); (b) 2w.40 As Nos. N4190/**MS**N4193a
Set of 2 sheets .... 15·00 13·00

2002.
N4222 10ch. Airplane.............................. 35 30

2002.
N4230 10ch. Helicopter............................ 35 30

2002.
N4233* 3w. Tupolev Tu-104.......................... 35 30

2004. Aircraft.
N4441 3w. Airbus Industries Airbus A340-600 ... 30 25
N4442 97w. Aerospatiale/BAe Concorde........... 2·50 2·30
N4443 104w. *Graf Zeppelin II* .... 2·75 2·40
N4444 116w. Junkers .... 3·00 2·50
N4441/4444 *Set of 4* .... 7·75 6·75

2005.
N4528 3w. Helicopter................................ 30 25

KUWAIT

Arabian Peninsula

1933. 12 pies = 1 anna

16 annas = 1 rupee

1957. 100 naye paise = 1 rupee

1961. 1000 fils = 1 dinar

1933. Nos. 220/3 of India overprinted **KUWAIT**.
31 2a. de Havilland DH.66 Hercules.............. 16·00 27·00
32 3a. de Havilland DH.66 Hercules.............. 3·50 2·50
33 4a. de Havilland DH.66 Hercules.............. £120 £200
34 6a. de Havilland DH.66 Hercules.............. 5·00 4·50
31/34 *Set of 4* £130 £200

1939. No. 258 of India overprinted **KUWAIT**.
46* 12a. Armstrong Whitworth A.W.27 Ensign I 20·00 75·00

1942. No. 277 of India overprinted **KUWAIT**.
63* 14a. Armstrong Whitworth A.W.27 Ensign I 15·00 18·00

1961.
153* 25f. Vickers Viscount 700 of Kuwait
Airways...................................... 1·25 25
160* 100f. Vickers Viscount 700 of Kuwait
Airways...................................... 3·00 25

1963.
191 4f. Hunting Percival Jet Provost trainers 65 50
192 5f. Hunting Percival Jet Provost trainers 95 80
193 20f. Hunting Percival Jet Provost trainers 4·75 3·50
194 50f. Hunting Percival Jet Provost trainers 9·75 6·00
191/194 *Set of 4* .... 14·50 9·75

1964. 10th Anniv of Kuwait Airways.
255 20f. Hawker Siddeley Comet 4C (top) and
Douglas DC-3 of Kuwait Airways 55 25
256 25f. Hawker Siddeley Comet 4C (top) and
Douglas DC-3 of Kuwait Airways 70 25
257 30f. Hawker Siddeley Comet 4C (top) and
Douglas DC-3 of Kuwait Airways 80 40
258 45f. Hawker Siddeley Comet 4C (top) and
Douglas DC-3 of Kuwait Airways ...... 1·10 55
255/258 *Set of 4* .... 2·75 1·30

1969. Inauguration of Boeing 707 Aircraft by Kuwait Airways.
430 10f. Boeing 707 of Kuwait Airways 40 15
431 20f. Boeing 707 of Kuwait Airways 80 30
432 25f. Boeing 707 of Kuwait Airways .... 1·20 55
433 45f. Boeing 707 of Kuwait Airways .... 2·10 70
430/433 *Set of 4* .... 4·00 1·50

1973.
578 10f. Boeing 707 .... 50 10
579 20f. Boeing 707 .... 90 15
580 70f. Boeing 707 .... 2·75 1·10
578/580 *Set of 3* .... 3·75 1·20

1979. 25th Anniv of Kuwait Airways.
848 30f. Boeing 747 (foreground) and
Douglas DC-3 of Kuwait Airways 80 40
849 80f. Boeing 747 (foreground) and
Douglas DC-3 of Kuwait Airways ...... 2·00 1·20

1984. 30th Anniv of Kuwait Airways.
1033 30f. Douglas DC-3 of Kuwait Airways 90 65
1034 80f. Douglas DC-3 of Kuwait Airways ...... 2·40 1·30

1984.
1053 15f. Airplane.............................. 50 25
1054 30f. Airplane.............................. 95 50
1055 80f. Airplane.............................. 2·50 1·40
1053/1055 *Set of 3* .... 3·50 1·90

1990.
1225 50f. Weather balloon 90 50
1226 100f. Weather balloon .... 1·80 95
1227 150f. Weather balloon .... 2·50 1·50
1225/1227 *Set of 3* .... 4·75 2·75

1993. 40th Anniv of Kuwait Air Force.
1363 50f. Airforce emblem....................... 40 40
1364 150f. Airforce emblem....................... 1·40 1·40

1994. 50th Anniv of ICAO.
1400 100f. ICAO and Kuwait International
Airport emblems......................... 1·00 1·00
1401 150f. Emblems and control tower............ 1·50 1·50
1402 350f. Boeing 747 and '50 years'............. 3·50 3·50
1400/1402 *Set of 3* .... 5·50 5·50

1994. 40th Anniv of Kuwait Airways.
1403	50f. Airbus A310	50	50
1404	100f. Airbus A310	95	95
1405	150f. Airbus A310	1·50	1·50
1403/1405 *Set of 3*		2 75	2 75

2000. International Civil Aviation Day.
1636	50f. ICAO emblem and stylised airplane.	50	50
1637	150f. ICAO emblem and stylised airplane.	1·50	1·50
1638	250f. ICAO emblem and stylised airplane.	2·40	2·40
1636/1638 *Set of 3*		4·00	4·00

2000. Kuwait International Airport.
1639	50f. Emblem	50	50
1640	150f. Emblem	1·50	1·50
1641	250f. Emblem	2·40	2·40
1639/1641 *Set of 3*		4·00	4·00

2004. 50th Anniv of Kuwait Airways.
1808	25f. Boeing 727	30	30
1809	50f. Aircraft and maintenance crew	60	60
1810	75f. Airbus Industries Airbus A340 in flight	90	90
1811	100f. Airbus Industries Airbus A340 on runway	1·20	1·20
1812	125f. Boeing B747 and support trucks	1·50	1·50
1813	150f. Passengers embarking	1·90	1·90
1808/1813 *Set of 6*		5·75	5·75

KYRGYZSTAN

Central Asia

2001. 100 tyin = 1 som

2001.
222	10s. Military airplane (stylised)	1·00	90

2003.
273*	1s. Airliner	25	20

2005.
341	3s.60 Paper airplane	40	30

LAOS

South-east Asia
100 cents = 1 kip

1962.
124*   50c. Douglas DC-3 50   50

1965.
155*   25k. Sud Est SE 2010 Armagnac at Wattay
       Airport 35   20

1967.
202*   60k. +15k. Douglas DC-4 at flooded
       airport .... 1·30   1·30

1968.
231*   15k. Douglas C-47 35   20

1978.
459*   300k. Aircraft being shot down .... 1·80   1·10

1983. Bicentenary of Manned Flight.
646   50c. Charles' hydrogen balloon, 1783 15   15
647   1k. Blanchard and Jeffries' balloon,
       1785 20   15
648   2k. Vincenzo Lunardi's balloon (flight
       from London to Ware, 1784) 35   15
649   3k. Hot-air balloon 75   20
650   4k. Massed balloon ascent, 1890 90   35
651   10k. Piccard's stratosphere balloon
       F.N.R.S., 1931 .... 2·50   75
646/651 Set of 6 .... 4·25   1·60
MS652 10k. Balloon Double Eagle II .... 2·50   95

1984.
796*   2k. Fokker F.27 Friendship of Air Laos 65   20

1985.
844*   50c. Fiat biplane 15   15
845*   1k. Cant Z.501 Gabbiano flying boat 20   15
846*   2k. Marina Fiat MF.5 flying boat 45   15
847*   3k. Macchi Castoldi MC-100 flying boat . 65   20
848*   4k. Anzani biplane 90   30
849*   5k. Ambrosini biplane 95   30
850*   6k. Piaggio P-148 .... 1·30   45
MS851* 10k. Marina Fiat MF.4 flying boat .... 2·50   1·00

1986.
906   20k. Boeing 747-100 .... 3·75   30
907   50k. Ilyushin Il-86 .... 8·75   80

1990.
1188* 40k. Mail balloons, Paris, 1870 90   20
MS1192* 95k. Douglas DC-8 .... 2·20   1·10

1990.
1220* 80k. Airliner over control tower .... 2·20   90

1996. Morane-Saulnier Type A1.
1512   25k. Morane monoplane 15   15
1513   60k. Sopwith Camel 15   15
1514   150k. Airco (de Havilland) DH.4 30   15
1515   250k. Albatros D.III 50   30
1516   800k. Caudron G3 .... 1·80   90
1512/1516 Set of 5 .... 2·50   1·50

2000.
1665* 2000k. Airport and airplane 75   75

2000.
1717   4000k. Airport .... 1·30   1·30

LATAKIA

Middle East
100 centimes = 1 piastre

1931. Nos. 261/70 of Syria overprinted **LATTAQUIE** in French and Arabic.
86   0p.50 Potez 29-4 biplane F-AIVD (yellow) ... 1·60   2·50
87   0p.50 Potez 29-4 biplane F-AIVD (brown) .. 2·50   3·75
88   1p. Potez 29-4 biplane F-AIVD .... 2·25   2·50
89   2p. Potez 29-4 biplane F-AIVD .... 4·25   4·50
90   3p. Potez 29-4 biplane F-AIVD .... 3·50   4·75
91   5p. Potez 29-4 biplane F-AIVD .... 7·25   11·00
92   10p. Potez 29-4 biplane F-AIVD ...... 9·50   9·00
93   15p. Potez 29-4 biplane F-AIVD ...... 10·50   14·50
94   25p. Potez 29-4 biplane F-AIVD ...... 26·00   38·00
95   50p. Potez 29-4 biplane F-AIVD ...... 32·00   42·00
96   100p. Potez 29-4 biplane F-AIVD ..... 34·00   34·00
86/96 Set of 11 .... £120   £150

LATVIA

Eastern Europe
1921. 100 kapeikas = 1 rublis
1923. 100 santimu = 1 lats

1921. Imperforate or perforated.
84A   10r. Bleriot XI .... 5·00   5·00
85A   20r. Bleriot XI .... 5·00   5·00

1928. As Nos. 84/5, but inscribed in "SANTIMU" or "SANTIMI".
155   10s. Bleriot XI .... 7·50   1·70
156   15s. Bleriot XI .... 3·50   1·70
157   25s. Bleriot XI .... 6·25   1·90
155/157 Set of 3 .... 16·00   4·75

1930. Imperforate or perforated.
181A 10-20s. Klemm Kl-20 .... 11·00   16·00
182A 15-30s. Klemm Kl-20 .... 11·00   16·00

1930. Nos. 155/7 surcharged **LATVIJAS AIZSARGI** and value.
206A 50 on 10s. Bleriot XI .... 14·50   17·00
207A 1 lats on 15s. Bleriot XI .... 14·50   17·00
208A 1 lats 50 on 25s. Bleriot XI ...... 14·50   17·00
206A/208A Set of 3 .... 39·00   46·00

1932. Pioneers of Aviation. Imperforate or perforated.
228A* 15-75s. Charles' hydrogen balloon, 1783 .... 21·00   22·00
229A* 20-100s. Wright Type A .... 21·00   22·00
230A* 25-125s. Bleriot XI .... 21·00   22·00

1933. As Nos. 155/7, but imperforate, overprinted **LATVIJA-AFRIKA 1933** or surcharged also.
235   10s. Bleriot XI .... 65·00   90·00
236   15s. Bleriot XI .... 65·00   90·00
237   25s. Bleriot XI .... 65·00   90·00
238   50s. on 15s. Bleriot XI £300   £550
239   100s. on 25s. Bleriot XI £300   £550
235/239 Set of 5 .... £700   £1200

1933. Wounded Latvian Airmen Fund. Imperforate or perforated.
240A 3-53s. Monoplane .... 38·00   44·00
241A 7-57s. Biplane .... 38·00   44·00
242A 35-135s. Airplane .... 38·00   44·00
240A/242A Set of 3 .... £100   £120

1933. Wounded Latvian Airmen Fund. Imperforate or perforated.

243A	8-68s. Glanville Brothers' Gee Bee Super Sportster R-1	50·00	80·00
244A	12-112s. Supermarine S6B seaplane, 1931	50·00	80·00
245A	30-130s. Airship LZ-127 *Graf Zeppelin*	60·00	80·00
246A	40-190s. Dornier Do-X flying boat	50·00	80·00
243A/246A *Set of 4*		£190	£325

2007.

692	22s. Hot air balloon	1·30	1·30

LEBANON

Middle East

100 centiemes = 1 piastre

1926. Nos. 65 and 67/9 overprinted with Bleriot XI airplane.

75	2p. Zahle	4·25	9·75
76	3p. Deir el-Kamar	3·00	10·00
77	5p. Sidon	4·25	10·50
78	10p. Tripoli	3·00	10·00
75/78 *Set of 4*		13·00	36·00

1926. Nos. 75/8 further surcharged **Secours aux Refugies Afft.** and premium in French and Arabic.

91	2p. +1p. Zahle (Bleriot XI overprint)	4·25	14·50
92	3p. +2p. Deir el-Kamar (Bleriot XI overprint)	4·00	13·00
93	5p. +3p. Sidon (Bleriot XI overprint)	3·50	13·00
94	10p. +5p. Tripoli (Bleriot XI overprint)	4·00	19·00
91/94 *Set of 4*		14·00	55·00

1927. Nos. 75/8 further overprinted **Republique Libanaise.**

118	2p. Zahle (Bleriot XI overprint)	5·25	10·00
119	3p. Deir el-Kamar (Bleriot XI overprint)	3·25	8·50
120	5p. Sidon (Bleriot XI overprint)	5·00	8·50
121	10p. Tripoli (Bleriot XI overprint)	3·75	9·75
118/121 *Set of 4*		16·00	33·00

1928. Nos. 60, 62, 65, 67/70, 135 and 146/7 overprinted with Bleriot XI airplane and **Republique Libanaise** in French and Arabic, or with airplane only (50c. on 75c.).

151	50c. Tripoli	80	4·50
152	50c. on 75c. Beit ed-Din (with Arabic overprint)	1·30	2·30
153	1p. Baalbek	2·30	3·25
141	2p. Zahle	3·75	6·75
154	2p. on 1p.25 Mouktana (with Arabic overprint)	2·30	2·75
142	3p. Deir el-Kamar	2·50	4·25
143	5p. Sidon	4·25	5·25
144	10p. Tripoli	4·25	3·00
155	15p. on 25p. Beirut (with Arabic overprint)	£160	£190
156	25p. Beirut	£110	£120

1930.

181	50c. Potez 29-4 biplane	1·50	1·70
182	1p. Potez 29-4 biplane	60	85
183	2p. Potez 29-4 biplane	95	1·30
184	3p. Potez 29-4 biplane	2·00	1·70
185	5p. Potez 29-4 biplane	1·60	1·50
186	10p. Potez 29-4 biplane	2·30	1·40
187	15p. Potez 29-4 biplane	1·90	1·20
188	25p. Potez 29-4 biplane	2·50	2·00
189	50p. Potez 29-4 biplane	6·25	6·00
190	100p. Potez 29-4 biplane	7·75	9·00
181/190 *Set of 10*		25·00	23·00

1936.

191	50c. Front view of two aircraft	3·00	2·50
192	1p. Outlines of two aircraft	3·75	3·75
193	2p. Front view of two aircraft	2·00	2·75
194	3p. Outlines of two aircraft	2·75	2·75
195	5p. Front view of two aircraft	5·00	4·50
196	10p. Outlines of two aircraft	5·25	6·00
197	15p. Outlines of two aircraft	34·00	32·00
198	25p. Front view of two aircraft	£110	£120
191/198 *Set of 8*		£150	£160

1937.

226*	50c. Two aircraft	10	30
227*	1p. Two aircraft	1·70	1·60
228*	2p. Two aircraft	2·00	1·60
229*	3p. Two aircraft	4·50	3·75
230*	5p. Two aircraft	2·30	1·10

1938.

238	2p. Airplane	2·75	4·75
239	3p. Airplane	3·75	4·50
240	5p. Airplane	4·00	7·75
241	10p. Airplane	10·00	17·00
238/241 *Set of 4*		18·00	31·00

1938.

242	10p. Maurice Nogues and Liore et Olivier LeO H.24-3 flying boat of Air Union..	5·25	9·75

1942.

256*	10p. Airplane	3·50	3·50
257*	50p. Airplane	4·25	4·25

1944.

269*	25p. Airplane	3·50	2·20
270*	50p. Airplane	3·50	2·20
271*	100p. Airplane	3·50	3·00
272*	200p. Airplane	4·25	3·00
273*	300p. Airplane	14·50	14·50
274*	500p. Airplane	39·00	27·00

1944. Nos. 269/74 overprinted with a line of Arabic characters.

284*	25p. Airplane	4·25	4·25
285*	50p. Airplane	8·50	8·50
286*	100p. Airplane	9·25	9·25
287*	200p. Airplane	17·00	17·00
288*	300p. Airplane	22·00	22·00
289*	500p. Airplane	42·00	42·00

1947.

334	25p. Airplane	1·00	40
335	50p. Airplane	1·40	85
336	75p. Airplane	3·00	1·30
337	150p. Airplane Set of 4	5·00	2·50
334/337 *Set of 4*		9·25	4·50

1949.

392*	25p. Sikorsky S-51 helicopter	6·00	3·00
393*	50p. Sikorsky S-51 helicopter	9·25	4·75

1950.

422	10p. Airliner	60	10
423	15p. Airliner	95	10
424	20p. Airliner	3·00	40
425	25p. Airliner	5·00	1·00
426	50p. Airliner	8·50	2·50
422/426 *Set of 5*		16·00	3·75

1951.

438*	10p. Douglas DC-3	95	15
439*	15p. Douglas DC-3	2·10	15
440*	20p. Douglas DC-3	2·10	25
441*	25p. Douglas DC-3	2·20	25
442*	35p. Douglas DC-3	6·00	3·00
443*	50p. Douglas DC-3	11·00	2·20

1952.

454*	5p. Lockheed Constellation over Beirut Airport	35	10
455*	10p. Lockheed Constellation over Beirut Airport	50	15
456*	15p. Lockheed Constellation over Beirut Airport	95	15
457*	20p. Lockheed Constellation over Beirut Airport	1·50	35
458*	25p. Lockheed Constellation over Beirut Airport	1·50	40
459*	35p. Lockheed Constellation over Beirut Airport	2·50	50
460*	50p. Lockheed Constellation	8·50	60
461*	100p. Lockheed Constellation	60·00	15·00
462*	200p. Lockheed Constellation	34·00	4·75
463*	300p. Lockheed Constellation	47·00	10·00

1953.

473*	5p. Douglas DC-4	35	10
474*	10p. Douglas DC-4	70	10
475*	15p. Douglas DC-4	95	10
476*	20p. Douglas DC-4	1·50	10
477*	25p. Douglas DC-4	3·75	15
478*	35p. Douglas DC-4	5·50	25
479*	50p. Douglas DC-4	7·75	50
480*	100p. Douglas DC-4	14·50	5·00

1954.

491*	5p. Douglas DC-6	40	10
492*	10p. Douglas DC-6	85	10
493*	15p. Douglas DC-6	95	10
494*	20p. Douglas DC-6	1·40	10
495*	25p. Douglas DC-6	1·50	25
496*	35p. Douglas DC-6	2·10	25
497*	50p. Douglas DC-6	6·75	40
498*	100p. Douglas DC-6	11·00	70
499*	200p. Douglas DC-6	22·00	2·20
500*	300p. Douglas DC-6	38·00	4·75

1954. Opening of International Airport, Beirut.

501	10p. Douglas DC-6B at Khalde Airport	60	15
502	25p. Douglas DC-6B at Khalde Airport	1·50	40
503	35p. Douglas DC-6B at Khalde Airport	2·10	75
504	65p. Douglas DC-6B at Khalde Airport	5·00	3·00
501/504 *Set of 4*		8·25	3·75

1957. Design as Nos. 497/500.

564*	10p. Douglas DC-6	35	10
565*	15p. Douglas DC-6	40	10
566*	20p. Douglas DC-6	50	15
567*	25p. Douglas DC-6	85	15

1959.
609*	5p. Douglas DC-6B at Khalde Airport......	70	10
610*	10p. Douglas DC-6B at Khalde Airport......	70	10
611*	15p. Douglas DC-6B at Khalde Airport......	95	10
612*	20p. Douglas DC-6B at Khalde Airport......	1·30	15
613*	25p. Douglas DC-68 at Khalde Airport......	1·70	25

1969.
1059*	7p.50 Paraskiing..	20	10

1969.
1066*	30p. Sud Aviation SE 3160 Alouette III helicopter..	60	35

1971.
1106*	25p. Dassault Mirage IIICJ jet fighters........	60	25

1974.
1179*	50p. Airliner..	1·00	60

1974.
1212*	20p. Sikorsky S-55 helicopter........................	70	15

2005.
1427*	L £100 Rafic Hariri International Airport........	10	10

LEEWARD ISLANDS

West Indies

12 pence = 1 shilling

20 shillings = 1 pound

1949. As Nos. 114/15 of Antigua.
119*	2½d. Airplane...	15	2·25
120*	3d. Jet-powered Vickers Viking.................	2·00	2·25

LESOTHO

Southern Africa

1966. 100 cents = 1 rand

1979. 100 (li)sente = 1 maloti

1966. No. 90 of Basutoland overprinted **LESOTHO.**
117B*	12½c. de Havilland DH.106 Comet 1........	30	20

1969.
169*	12½c. Douglas DC-3 over Leabua Jonathan Airport......................................	35	10

1976.
299*	25c. Cessna 182 Skylane..................................	1·40	2·50

1976.
317*	25c. Britten-Norman BN-2 Islander...........	50	35

1978. 75th Anniv of First Powered Flight.
361	5c. Wright *Flyer III*...................................	15	30
362	25c. Wilbur and Orville Wright and Wright *Flyer III*...	40	60

1983. Bicentenary of Manned Flight.
545	7s. Montgolfier balloon (first manned free flight, 1783).......................................	15	10
546	30s. Wilbur and Orville Wright and Wright *Flyer I*..	30	40
547	60s. Bleriot XI	50	1·25
548	1m. Concorde..	2·25	2·50
545/548 *Set of 4*..		3·00	3·75
MS549 6s. Dornier Do-28D Skyservant 7P-LAF of Lesotho Airways (inscribed "Dornier 228") (sheet also contains Nos. 545/8)...........................		2·75	2·75

1985.
659*	50s. Fokker F.27 Friendship of Lesotho Airways at Maseru Airport....................	95	85

1987.
764*	4m. Charles Yeager and Bell X-1	2·75	4·50

1989.
862	12s. Pilatus PC-6 Turbo Porter of the Red Cross...	50	10
863	20s. Cessna 208 Caravan I of the Red Cross...	60	20
864	55s. de Havilland Canada DHC-6 Twin Otter 200/300 of the Red Cross..........	90	50
865	3m. Douglas DC-3 of the Red Cross...........	2·75	3·50
862/865 *Set of 4*...		4·25	3·75
MS866 4m. Douglas DC-3 of the Red Cross.................		6·50	3·75

1991.
1013*	2m. de Havilland DH.60G Gipsy Moth......	2·00	2·25

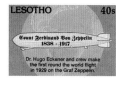

1993.
1129*	40s. Airship LZ-127 *Graf Zeppelin*................	1·40	40
1131*	4m. Lieutenant Robinson's Royal Aircraft Factory B.E.2C shooting down Schutte Lanz SL-11 airship	3·75	4·50

1994. 50th Anniv of ICAO.
1210	35s. de Havilland Canada DHC-6 Twin Otter..	50	15
1211	50s. Fokker F.27 Friendship, on runway....	65	20
1212	1m. Fokker F.27 Friendship, over Moshoeshoe International Airport ...	1·00	70
1213	1m.50 Cessna 207	1·40	1·75
1210/1213 *Set of 4*...		3·25	2·50

2000. Centenary of First Zeppelin Flight.
1711	8m. Count Ferdinand von Zeppelin and Zeppelin LZ-127 *Graf Zeppelin*, 1928	2·00	2·00
1712	8m. LZ-130 *Graf Zeppelin* 1938...................	2·00	2·00
1713	8m. LZ-10 *Schwaben*, 1911	2·00	2·00
1711/1713 *Set of 3*...		5·50	5·50
MS1714 15m. LZ-130 *Graf Zeppelin II*, 1938................		3·75	4·00

2002.
MS1889* 20m. Queen inspecting RAF Guard of Honour...		6·50	7·00

2004. Centenary of Powered Flight.
MS1916 6m. Bleriot's Canard at Bagatelle, 1906; 6m. Bleriot's double-winged Libellule, 1907; 6m. Bleriot's No. VIII in Toury-Artenay cross-country flight, 1908; 6m. Bleriot's XI-2 (inscribed X12 in error) test flight, 1909....................		5·00	5·50
MS1917 5m. Bleriot's No. XI *Set of 2 sheets*..............		4·00	4·25

133

LESOTHO M4

2005.
1963* 4m. Flight crew of Boeing B-29
Superfortress *Bockscar* .... 1·10 1·10

LIBERIA

West Africa

100 cents = 1 dollar

1936. First Air Mail Service of 28th February.
530	1c. Ford "Tin Goose"............................	25	10
531	2c. Ford "Tin Goose"............................	25	10
532	3c. Ford "Tin Goose"............................	40	10
533	4c. Ford "Tin Goose"............................	40	15
534	5c. Ford "Tin Goose"............................	45	15
535	6c. Ford "Tin Goose"............................	45	20
530/535 *Set of 6*............................		2·00	70

1938.
566*	2c. Three-engine flying boat................	15	10
570*	10c. Three-engine flying boat................	25	10
571*	20c. Sikorsky S-43 amphibian................	30	15
574*	$1 Sikorsky S-43 amphibian................	1·40	25

1941. Nos. 575/7 overprinted with airplane, portrait of Sir Rowland Hill and **AIR MAIL POSTAGE STAMP CENTENNIAL ROWLAND HILL 1840–1940**.
581*	3c. Immigrant ships................................	1·40	1·40
582*	5c. Immigrant ships................................	1·40	1·40
583*	10c. Immigrant ships................................	1·40	1·40

1941. Nos. 575/7 surcharged with cross, airplane and **RED CROSS TWO CENTS AIR MAIL**.
587*	+2c. on 3c. Immigrant ships....................	1·40	1·40
588*	+2c. on 5c. Immigrant ships....................	1·40	1·40
589*	+2c. on 10c. Immigrant ships....................	1·40	1·40

1941. Nos. 566, 570/1 and 574 overprinted **First Flight LIBERIA-U.S. 1941** or surcharged **50c** also.
595*	50c. on 2c. Three-engine flying boat........	£150	75·00
599*	50c. on 10c. Three-engine flying boat......	45·00	38·00
600*	50c. on 20c. Sikorsky S-43 amphibian......	£1500	£150
603*	$1 Sikorsky S-43 amphibian................	45·00	30·00

1942. Nos. 595, 599/600 and 603 overprinted with bars over "1941".
605*	50c. on 2c. Three-engine flying boat........	6·00	6·75
609*	50c. on 10c. Three-engine flying boat......	5·25	6·25
610*	50c. on 20c. Sikorsky S-43 amphibian......	5·25	6·25
613*	$1 Sikorsky S-43 amphibian................	6·25	7·50

1942.
614	10c. Boeing 314A flying boat....................	20	10
615	12c. Boeing 247..	30	10
616	24c. Boeing 247..	35	10
617	30c. Boeing 314A flying boat....................	35	10
618	35c. Boeing 314A flying boat....................	40	15
619	50c. Boeing 314A flying boat....................	50	15
620	70c. Boeing 314A flying boat....................	55	30
621	$1.40 Boeing 314A flying boat....................	75	50
614/621 *Set of 8*................................		3·00	1·40

1944. Nos. 530/2 and 566 surcharged with new values.
643*	10c. on 2c. Three-engine flying boat........	27·00	30·00
640*	30c. on 1c. Ford "Tin Goose"....................	80·00	50·00
641*	50c. on 3c. Ford "Tin Goose"....................	20·00	23·00
642*	70c. on 2c. Ford "Tin Goose"....................	50·00	50·00

1948. First Liberian International Airways Flight, Monrovia-Dakar.
674	25c. Douglas DC-3 EL-AAA of Liberian International Airways............................	1·50	1·00
675	50c. Douglas DC-3 EL-AAA of Liberian International Airways............................	2·40	1·50

1953.
729	12c. Douglas DC-3....................................	15	15
730	25c. Douglas DC-3....................................	75	30
731	35c. Douglas DC-3....................................	1·60	30
732	50c. Douglas DC-6....................................	65	25
733	70c. Douglas DC-3 at Roberts Field Airport..	1·25	40
734	$1 Douglas DC-3....................................	1·40	55
729/734 *Set of 6*................................		5·25	1·80

1954. As Nos. 729/34, but colours changed, inscribed "COMMEMORATING PRESIDENTIAL VISIT U.S.A. - 1954".
750	12c. Douglas DC-3....................................	20	20
751	25c. Douglas DC-3....................................	80	25
752	35c. Douglas DC-3....................................	4·00	1·50
753	50c. Douglas DC-6....................................	80	30
754	70c. Douglas DC-3 at Roberts Field Airport..	1·10	50
755	$1 Douglas DC-3....................................	1·60	3·25
750/755 *Set of 6*................................		7·75	5·50

1957. First Anniv of Inauguration of Liberia-USA Direct Air Service.
791	3c. Douglas DC-6B *John Alden* of Pan Am at Idlewild Airport, New York...	15	15
792	5c. Douglas DC-6B *John Alden* of Pan Am at Roberts Field Airport................	20	20
793	12c. Douglas DC-6B *John Alden* of Pan Am at Idlewild Airport, New York (air)..	30	25
794	15c. Douglas DC-6B *John Alden* of Pan Am at Roberts Field Airport................	30	25
795	25c. Douglas DC-6B *John Alden* of Pan Am at Idlewild Airport, New York.......	45	25
796	50c. Douglas DC-6B *John Alden* of Pan Am at Roberts Field Airport................	85	30
791/796 *Set of 6*................................		2·00	1·30

1971.
1061*	12c. Sikorsky S-61B SH-3 Sea King helicopter....................................	40	15

1974.
1188*	3c. Boeing 707 of Air Afrique....................	30	10
1190*	15c. Boeing 707 of Air Afrique....................	25	20

1974.
1220*	10c. Hawker Hurricane Mk I, Supermarine Spitfire and Junkers Ju 87B "Stuka"...	30	10

1976.
1282*	50c. Wright *Flyer I*, Airship LZ-127 *Graf Zeppelin* and Concorde....................	1·75	60

1978. Progress in Aviation.
1327	2c. Dornier Do-X flying boat....................	10	10
1328	3c. Boeing 747 SCA of NASA carrying Space Shuttle *Enterprise*....................	10	10
1329	5c. Edward Rickenbacker and Douglas DC-3..	10	10
1330	25c. Charles Lindbergh and Ryan NYP Special *Spirit of St. Louis*....................	45	20
1331	35c. Louis Bleriot and Bleriot XI..............	65	35
1332	50c. Wilbur and Orville Wright and *Flyer I*	90	55
1327/1332 *Set of 6*................................		2·10	1·30
MS1333 80c. Concorde of British Airways....................		1·40	1·40

1978. 75th Anniv of First Zeppelin Flight.
1334	2c. Santos-Dumont's airship *Ballon No. 9 La Badaleuse*, 1903	10	10
1335	3c. Thomas Baldwin's airship U.S. *Military No. 1*, 1908	10	10
1336	5c. Tissandier Brothers' airship, 1883.......	10	10
1337	25c. Parseval airship PL-VII, 1912...............	40	20
1338	40c. Airship *Nulli Secundus II*, 1908........	75	35
1339	50c. Beardmore airship R-34....................	85	55
1334/1339 *Set of 6*................................		2·10	1·30
MS1340 75c. Goodyear Aerospace airship (air)..........		1·40	1·40

1979.
1379*	3c. Boeing 707 of Air Afrique (on stamp No. 1190)....................................	10	10
1384*	50c. Concorde..	1·50	90
MS1385* $1 Curtiss JN-4 "Jenny"....................		3·00	3·00

1988.
1709*	35c. Britten-Norman BN-2 Islander of Air Liberia....................................	60	60

REGISTRATION STAMPS

1941. No. 576 surcharged with airplane and **AIR MAIL REGISTERED 10 CENTS 10**.
R593*	10c. on 5c. Immigrant ships....................	1·40	1·40

SPECIAL DELIVERY STAMP

1941. No. 576 surcharged with airplane, postman and **AIR MAIL SPECIAL DELIVERY 10 CENTS 10**.
S591*	10c. on 5c. Immigrant ships....................	1·40	1·40

LIBYA

North Africa 1936

100 centesimi = 1 lira

1952. 1000 milliemes = 1 pound

1972. 1000 dirhams = 1 dinar

1936. Nos. 96 and 99 of Cyrenalca overprinted **LIBIA**.
70	50c. Airplane	1·70	35
71	1l. Caproni Ca 101	3·50	17·00

1937. Nos. 116/22 of Tripolitania overprinted **LIBIA**.
72	50c. Marina Fiat MF.5 flying boat	10	10
73	60c. Marina Fiat MF.5 flying boat	60	
74	75c. Marina Fiat MF.5 flying boat	60	17·00
75	80c. Marina Fiat MF.5 flying boat	60	31·00
76	1l. Marina Fiat MF.5 flying boat	1·50	85
77	1l.20 Marina Fiat MF.5 flying boat	60	38·00
78	1l.50 Marina Fiat MF.5 flying boat	60	
79	5l. Marina Fiat MF.5 flying boat	60	
72/79 *Set of 7*		4·75	

1937.
82*	50c. Airplane	2·20	4·25
83*	1l. Airplane	2·20	4·25

1937. Nos. 82/3 overprinted **XI FIERA DI TRIPOLI**.
86*	50c. Airplane	10·50	24·00
87*	1l. Airplane	10·50	24·00

1938.
94*	50c. Caproni Ca 133	1·00	1·90
95*	1l. Caproni Ca 133	1·00	4·00

1939.
109*	25c. Fiat G18V	25	1·30
110*	50c. Fiat G18V	35	1·30
111*	1l. Fiat G18V	45	1·70

1940.
119*	50c. Savoia Marchetti S.M.75	50	85
120*	1l. Savoia Marchetti S-73	50	1·70
121*	2l. +75c. Savoia Marchetti S.M.75	85	5·25
122*	5l. +2l.50 Savoia Marchetti S-73	85	7·75

1965. Inauguration of Kingdom of Libya Airlines.
355	5m. Sud Aviation SE 210 Super Caravelle of Kingdom of Libya Airlines	10	10
356	10m. Sud Aviation SE 210 Super Caravelle of Kingdom of Libya Airlines	20	10
357	15m. Sud Aviation SE 210 Super Caravelle of Kingdom of Libya Airlines	70	10
355/357 *Set of 3*		90	25

1968.
409	55m. Fokker F.27 Friendship	95	30

1969. Face values in white.
444	5m. Jet fighters	25	10
445	10m. Jet fighters	35	20
446	15m. Jet fighters	55	25
447	25m. Jet fighters	85	40
448	45m. Jet fighters	1·00	60
449	60m. Jetfighters	2·10	1·00
444/449 *Set of 6*		4·50	2·30

1970. As Nos. 444/9, but face values in black.
457	5m. Jet fighters	25	10
458	10m. Jet fighters	35	20
459	15m. Jet fighters	55	25
460	25m. Jet fighters	85	40
461	45m. Jet fighters	1·00	60
462	60m. Jet fighters	2·10	1·00
457/462 *Set of 6*		4·50	2·30

1977.
758*	20d. Jet fighter	15	10
759*	25d. Concorde	30	15
762*	150d. Boeing 727	1·75	90
MS764* Two sheets. (a) 300d. Airship LZ-127 *Graf Zeppelin* (other sheet does not show aircraft) *Price for 2 sheets*		4·50	4·50

1978. Inauguration of Tripoli International Airport.
823	40d. Tripoli International Airport	30	10
824	115d. Tripoli International Airport	1·25	65

1978.
828*	30d. Dassault Mirage III	60	15

1978. 75th Anniv of First Powered Flight.
855	20d. Lilienthal biplane glider	10	10
856	25d. Lindbergh's Ryan NYP Special *Spirit of St. Louis*	10	10
857	30d. Admiral Richard Byrd's Ford 4-AT-B Trimotor NX-4542 *Floyd Bennett*	80	25
858	50d. Bleriot 5190 Santos-Dumont flying boat F-ANLE and airship LZ-127 *Graf Zeppelin*	95	35
859	115d. Wilbur and Orville Wright and Wright Type A	1·10	75
855/859 *Set of 5*		2·75	1·40
MS860 Two sheets (a) 100d. Concorde; (b) 100d. Boeing 727-200 *Set of 2 sheets*		2·10	2·10

1979.
MS922* Two sheets. (a) 50d. Jet fighters (other sheet does not show aircraft) *Price for 2 sheets*		1·10	1·10

1980.
1014*	25d. Boeing 727-200	60	15

1981.
1079*	5d. Sud Aviation SE 3160 Alouette III helicopter and Dassault Mirage F.1	15	10
1080*	5d. Jet fighter	15	10
MS1099* 50d. Helicopters and Dassault Mirage F.1		30	30

1982.
1173*	100d. Model airship	75	50

1982.
1225*	15d. Pilot and Tupolev Tu-22 Blinder and Mikoyan-Gurevich MiG-23	15	10
MS1231* 200d. Mikoyan Gurevich MiG-25 jet fighters		1·90	95

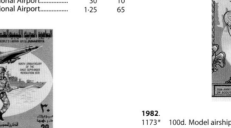

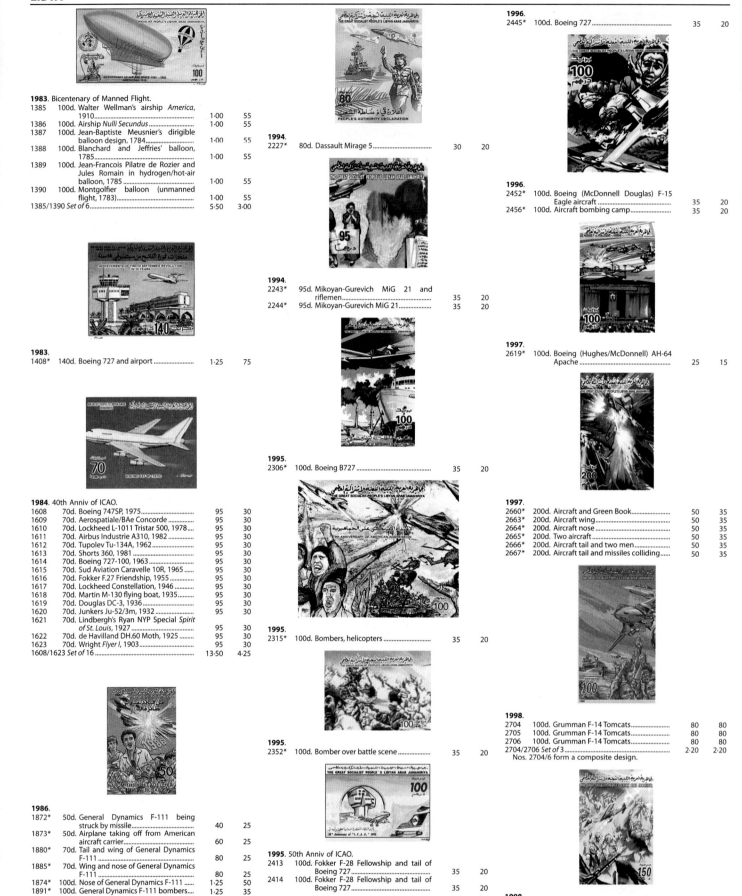

1983. Bicentenary of Manned Flight.

1385	100d. Walter Wellman's airship *America*, 1910..........	1·00	55
1386	100d. Airship *Nulli Secundus*	1·00	55
1387	100d. Jean-Baptiste Meusnier's dirigible balloon design, 1784	1·00	55
1388	100d. Blanchard and Jeffries' balloon, 1785..........	1·00	55
1389	100d. Jean-Francois Pilatre de Rozier and Jules Romain in hydrogen/hot-air balloon, 1785..........	1·00	55
1390	100d. Montgolfier balloon (unmanned flight, 1783)..........	1·00	55
1385/1390 *Set of 6*..........		5·50	3·00

1983.

1408*	140d. Boeing 727 and airport..........	1·25	75

1984. 40th Anniv of ICAO.

1608	70d. Boeing 747SP, 1975..........	95	30
1609	70d. Aerospatiale/BAe Concorde..........	95	30
1610	70d. Lockheed L-1011 Tristar 500, 1978..........	95	30
1611	70d. Airbus Industrie A310, 1982..........	95	30
1612	70d. Tupolev Tu-134A, 1962..........	95	30
1613	70d. Shorts 360, 1981..........	95	30
1614	70d. Boeing 727-100, 1963..........	95	30
1615	70d. Sud Aviation Caravelle 10R, 1965..........	95	30
1616	70d. Fokker F.27 Friendship, 1955..........	95	30
1617	70d. Lockheed Constellation, 1946..........	95	30
1618	70d. Martin M-130 flying boat, 1935..........	95	30
1619	70d. Douglas DC-3, 1936..........	95	30
1620	70d. Junkers Ju-52/3m, 1932..........	95	30
1621	70d. Lindbergh's Ryan NYP Special *Spirit of St. Louis*, 1927..........	95	30
1622	70d. de Havilland DH.60 Moth, 1925..........	95	30
1623	70d. Wright *Flyer I*, 1903..........	95	30
1608/1623 *Set of 16*..........		13·50	4·25

1986.

1872*	50d. General Dynamics F-111 being struck by missile..........	40	25
1873*	50d. Airplane taking off from American aircraft carrier..........	60	25
1880*	70d. Tail and wing of General Dynamics F-111..........	80	25
1885*	70d. Wing and nose of General Dynamics F-111..........	80	25
1874*	100d. Nose of General Dynamics F-111..........	1·25	50
1891*	100d. General Dynamics F-111 bombers.....	1·25	35

1992.

2096*	300d. Boeing 727..........	1·25	65

1994.

2227*	80d. Dassault Mirage 5..........	30	20

1994.

2243*	95d. Mikoyan-Gurevich MiG 21 and riflemen..........	35	20
2244*	95d. Mikoyan-Gurevich MiG 21..........	35	20

1995.

2306*	100d. Boeing B727..........	35	20

1995.

2315*	100d. Bombers, helicopters..........	35	20

1995.

2352*	100d. Bomber over battle scene..........	35	20

1995. 50th Anniv of ICAO.

2413	100d. Fokker F-28 Fellowship and tail of Boeing 727..........	35	20
2414	100d. Fokker F-28 Fellowship and tail of Boeing 727..........	35	20

1996.

2445*	100d. Boeing 727..........	35	20

1996.

2452*	100d. Boeing (McDonnell Douglas) F-15 Eagle aircraft..........	35	20
2456*	100d. Aircraft bombing camp..........	35	20

1997.

2619*	100d. Boeing (Hughes/McDonnell) AH-64 Apache..........	25	15

1997.

2660*	200d. Aircraft and Green Book..........	50	35
2663*	200d. Aircraft wing..........	50	35
2664*	200d. Aircraft nose..........	50	35
2665*	200d. Two aircraft..........	50	35
2666*	200d. Aircraft tail and two men..........	50	35
2667*	200d. Aircraft tail and missiles colliding......	50	35

1998.

2704	100d. Grumman F-14 Tomcats..........	80	80
2705	100d. Grumman F-14 Tomcats..........	80	80
2706	100d. Grumman F-14 Tomcats..........	80	80
2704/2706 *Set of 3*..........		2·20	2·20
Nos. 2704/6 form a composite design.			

1998.

2786*	150d. Aircraft attacking..........	1·10	70

2000.
2853* 100d. Boeing 727 .... 75 50

2001.
2898* 100d. Boeing (McDonnell Douglas) F-15 Eagle 75 50
2899* 100d. Boeing (McDonnell Douglas) F-15 Eagle 75 50
2900* 100d. Pilot 75 50
2901* 100d. Boeing (McDonnell Douglas) F-15 Eagle 75 50
2902* 100d. Parachute 75 50

2002.
2974* 100d. Boeing 727 and engine .... 1·20 80

2003.
MS3007 500d. Boeing 727 and service women (other stamps in the miniature sheets do not show aircraft) .... 14·00 14·00

LIECHTENSTEIN

Central Europe

100 rappen = 1 franc

1930.
110 15r. Biplane .... 4·25 6·00
111 20r. Biplane .... 11·50 12·00
112 25r. Biplane .... 5·75 19·00
113 35r. Biplane .... 9·00 13·00
114 45r. Monoplane .... 25·00 44·00
115 1f. Monoplane .... 40·00 30·00
110/115 Set of 6 .... 85·00 £110

1931.
116 1f. Airship LZ-127 Graf Zeppelin ...... 28·00 24·00
117 2f. Airship LZ-127 Graf Zeppelin ...... 80·00 £225

1935. No. 115 surcharged 60 Rp.
150 60r. on 1f. Monoplane .... 21·00 32·00

1936.
151 1f. Airship LZ-129 Hindenburg .... 26·00 55·00
152 2f. Airship LZ-127 Graf Zeppelin over Schaan Airport .... 24·00 55·00

1948. Pioneers of Flight.
259* 10r. Leonardo da Vinci and his drawing of a "helicopter" 65 20

260* 15r. Joseph Montgolfier and balloon (first manned free flight, 1783) .... 65 1·00
262* 25r. Wilhelm Kress and his flying machine .... 1·10 1·25
263* 40r. Etienne Robertson and balloon .... 1·30 1·60
264* 50r. William Samuel Henson and his Aerial Steam Carriage, 1842 .... 1·70 1·60
265* 1f. Otto Lilienthal and Lilienthal biplane glider .... 3·50 2·40
266* 2f. Salomon Andree and balloon .... 4·00 3·75
267* 5f. Wilbur Wright and Flyer I .... 5·25 4·75

1960.
395 30r. Bell 47J Ranger helicopter .... 1·80 1·90
396 40r. Boeing 707 .... 4·00 1·90
397 50r. Convair 990A Coronado .... 6·00 3·75
398 75r. Douglas DC-8 .... 2·00 2·00
395/398 Set of 4 .... 12·50 8·50

1979.
720 40r. Comte AC-8 St. Gallen 55 50
721 80r. Airship LZ-127 Graf Zeppelin 95 75

1983.
817* 40r. Montgolfier balloon (first manned free flight, 1783) 50 35

2004.
1322 1f.30 Hot air balloon (cartoon) .... 1·10 1·10

LITHUANIA

Eastern Europe

1921 100 skatiku = 1 auksinas

1922. 100 centu = 1 litas

1990. 100 kopeks = 1 rouble

1992. talons

1921.
106* 1a. Junkers F-13 .... 1·70 85
107* 2a. Three Junkers F-13 monoplanes .... 1·70 85
108* 5a. Junkers F-13 .... 1·70 1·60

1921.
109 20s. Junkers F-13 .... 2·50 2·10
110 40s. Junkers F-13 .... 2·50 2·10
111 60s. Junkers F-13 .... 2·50 2·10
112 80s. Junkers F-13 .... 2·50 2·10
113 1a. Junkers F-13 .... 2·50 2·10
114 2a. Junkers F-13 .... 2·50 2·10
115 5a. Junkers F-13 .... 2·50 2·10
109/115 Set of 7 .... 16·00 13·00

1922.
118 1a. Junkers F-13 .... 3·00 3·50
119 3a. Junkers F-13 .... 3·00 3·50
120 5a. Junkers F-13 .... 3·00 3·50
118/120 Set of 3 .... 8·00 9·50

1922.
121 2a. Junkers F-13 .... 1·70 1·70
122 4a. Junkers F-13 .... 1·70 1·70
123 10a. Junkers F-13 .... 1·70 1·70
121/123 Set of 3 .... 4·50 4·50

1922. Nos. 106/8, 120 and 121/3 surcharged with new values.
181* 20c. on 1a. Junkers F-13 .... 21·00 17·00
182* 20c. on 2a. Three Junkers F-13s .... 21·00 17·00
183* 25c. on 2a. Junkers F-13 .... 1·70 1·10
184* 30c. on 4a. Junkers F-13 .... 1·70 1·70
185* 50c. on 5a. Junkers F-13 (No. 108) .... 3·50 1·70
186* 50c. on 10a. Junkers F-13 .... 1·70 1·50
187* 1l. on 5a. Junkers F-13 (No. 120) .... 30·00 17·00

1924.
223 20c. Biplane .... 1·20 65
224 40c. Biplane .... 1·70 90
225 60c. Biplane .... 1·70 90
226 1l. Biplane .... 3·50 85
223/226 Set of 4 .... 7·25 3·00

1924. Nos. 223/6 surcharged KARO NASLAICIAMS and premium.
242* 20c. +20c. Biplane .... 21·00 21·00
243* 40c. +40c. Biplane .... 21·00 21·00
244* 60c. +60c. Biplane .... 21·00 21·00
245* 1l. +1l. Biplane .... 21·00 21·00

1930.
316* 20c. Bleriot XI .... 1·30 85
317* 40c. Bleriot XI .... 1·70 90
318* 60c. Bleriot XI .... 3·10 1·00
319* 1l. Bleriot XI .... 3·75 1·70

1932. Imperforate or perforated.
330* 15c. Airplane 85 60
331* 20c. Airplane .... 6·75 2·40

1934.
390* 40c. Bellanca monoplane Lituanica 10 10
392* 1l. Wreckage of Bellanca monoplane Lituanica 10 10
393* 3l. Bellanca monoplane Lituanica .... 85 1·80
394* 5l. Bellanca monoplane Lituanica .... 3·50 3·50

1936.
408 15c. Felix Vaitkus and airplane .... 1·70 50
409 30c. Felix Vaitkus and airplane .... 3·50 50
410 60c. Felix Vaitkus and airplane .... 4·25 1·50
408/410 Set of 3 .... 8·50 2·20

1993.
535*   80c. Steponas Darius, Stasys Girenas and
          Bellanca CH-300 *Lituanica*, 1933........   1·50   1·20

1998. Birth Centenary of Antanas Gustaitis (pilot and constructor).
673   2l. ANBO-41 (reconnaissance aircraft) ...   1·30   80
674   3l. ANBO-VIII (light bomber).....................   1·70   1·00

2003. 13th European Hot-Air Balloon Championships, Vilnius.
815   1l.30 Hot air balloons.............................   85   80

2003. Aviation Museum, Kaunas.
822   1l. Plastic glider BK-7   95   65
823   1l. Training glider BRO-12   95   65

1988.
1224*   20f. Boeing 747..................................   1·50   1·00

1995. 40th Anniv of Luxembourg-Iceland Air Link.
1401   16f. Boeing 757..................................   85   65

2001.
1566*   18f. MD Helicopters MD Explorer..............   1·70   1·30

LUXEMBOURG

Western Europe
1931. 100 centimes = 1 franc
1940. 100 pfennig = 1 reichsmark
1944. 100 centimes = 1 franc

1931.
296a   50c. Biplane.....................................   75   1·30
297   75c. Biplane.....................................   60   1·60
298   1f. Biplane.......................................   60   1·60
299   1¼f. Biplane.....................................   60   1·60
300   1¾f. Biplane.....................................   60   1·60
300a   3f. Biplane......................................   1·30   5·75
296a/300a *Set of 6* ....   4·00   12·00

1968.
828   50f. Fokker F.27 Friendship of Luxair........   3·75   25

1981.
1072   8f. Gliders......................................   65   40
1073   16f. Cessna 172F Skyhawk LX-AIZ and
          Cessna 182H Skylane at Findel
          Airport ....   1·00   80
1074   35f. Boeing 747-200F of Cargolux over
          Findel Airport..............................   1·90   90
1072/1074 *Set of 3*.......................................   3·25   1·90

MACAO

South-east coast of China

100 avos = 1 pataca

1938. As Nos. 401/9 of Angola.

382*	1a. Airplane	95	50
383*	2a. Airplane	1·50	80
384*	3a. Airplane	3·00	1·20
385*	5a. Airplane	4·25	2·25
386*	10a. Airplane	5·75	2·75
387*	20a. Airplane	11·50	5·25
388*	50a. Airplane	18·00	7·50
389*	70a. Airplane	27·00	9·50
390*	1p. Airplane	48·00	17·00
382/390 Set of 9		£110	42·00

1960.

481	50a. Boeing 707	3·00	50
482	76a. Boeing 707	6·00	1·60
483	3p. Boeing 707	17·00	2·40
484	5p. Boeing 707	22·00	2·40
485	10p. Boeing 707	35·00	2·75
481/485 Set of 5		75·00	8·75

1972. 50th Anniv of First Flight from Lisbon to Rio de Janeiro.

519	5p. Fairey IIID seaplane *Santa Cruz*	22·00	5·25

1989. Aircraft.

702	50a. Piaggio P-136L flying boat	55	30
703	70a. Martin M-130 flying boat of Pan Am	1·00	30
704	2p.80 Fairey IIID seaplane	1·40	75
705	4p. Hawker Osprey seaplane	3·00	1·20
702/705 Set of 4		5·25	2·30
MS706 7p.50 de Havilland DH.80A Puss Moth CR-GAA		28·00	12·00

1995. International Airport.

912	1p. Terminal building and Boeing 747 taking off	40	25
913	1p.50 Terminal building (different)	70	35
914	2p. Loading Boeing 747 and cargo building	1·10	50
915	3p. Control tower	1·50	75
912/915 Set of 4		3·25	1·70
MS916 8p. Boeing 747 taking off		13·00	5·75

1996. Paper Kites.

958	3p.50 Dragonfly kite	1·60	75
959	3p.50 Butterfly kite	1·60	75
960	3p.50 Owl kite	1·60	75
961	3p.50 Swallow kite	1·60	75
958/961 Set of 4		5·75	2·75
MS962 8p. Chinese dragon kite		11·50	5·50

1999. 75th Anniv of Sarmento de Beires and Brito Pais's Portugal-Macao Flight.

1093	3p. Breguet 16 Bn2 Patria	1·20	1·00
1094	3p. Airco (de Havilland) D.H.9	1·20	1·00

2004. 10th Anniv of Air Macao.

MS1441 8p. Airbus A310		1·60	1·60

MACEDONIA

Europe

1991. 100 paras = 1 dinar

1992. 100 deni (de.) = 1 denar (d.)

1992.

11	10d. Red Cross airplane	15	15

2003. Centenary of Powered Flight.

440	50d. Wright Brothers and *Flyer*	1·50	1·50

2005. 50th Anniv of Macedonia Aircraft.

498	36d. Glider	80	80

MADAGASCAR AND DEPENDENCIES

Indian Ocean off East Africa

100 centimes = 1 franc

1935.

153	50c. Bloch 120 F-AKDY of S.N.A.M	2·50	2·50
154	90c. Bloch 120 F-AKDY of S.N.A.M	1·00	4·75
155	1f.25 Bloch 120 F-AKDY of S.N.A.M	2·75	4·00
156	1f.50 Bloch 120 F-AKDY of S.N.A.M	2·30	2·75
157	1f.60 Bloch 120 F-AKDY of S.N.A.M	1·10	4·00
158	1f.75 Bloch 120 F-AKDY of S.N.A.M	14·00	5·50
159	2f. Bloch 120 F-AKDY of S.N.A.M	2·75	2·50
160	3f. Bloch 120 F-AKDY of S.N.A.M	1·10	2·30
161	3f.65 Bloch 120 F-AKDY of S.N.A.M	1·60	90
162	3f.90 Bloch 120 F-AKDY of S.N.A.M	80	3·00
163	4f. Bloch 120 F-AKDY of S.N.A.M	38·00	3·00
164	4f.50 Marcel Bloch F-AKDY of S.N.A.M	19·00	1·20
165	5f.50 Bloch 120 F-AKDY of S.N.A.M	1·00	3·75
166	6f. Bloch 120 F-AKDY of S.N.A.M	1·00	2·50
167	6f.90 Bloch 120 F-AKDY of S.N.A.M	85	2·75
168	8f. Bloch 120 F-AKDY of S.N.A.M	4·00	5·25
169	8f.50 Bloch 120 F-AKDY of S.N.A.M	4·25	4·00
170	9f. Bloch 120 F-AKDY of S.N.A.M	1·40	2·75
171	12f. Bloch 120 F-AKDY of S.N.A.M	60	2·50
172	12f.50 Bloch 120 F-AKDY of S.N.A	3·75	5·25
173	15f. Bloch 120 F-AKDY of S.N.A.M	70	2·30
174	16f. Bloch 120 F-AKDY of S.N.A.M	3·25	6·25
175	20f. Bloch 120 F-AKDY of S.N.A.M	5·50	5·75
176	50f. Bloch 120 F-AKDY of S.N.A.M	7·50	11·50
153/176 Set of 24		£110	80·00

1942. Nos. 155/6, 158, 161, 168/9, 171/2, 174 and 176 overprinted **FRANCE LIBRE** or surcharged also.

244*	1f. on 1f.25 Bloch 120 F-AKDY of S.N.A.M	10·50	15·00
245*	1f.50 Bloch 120 F-AKDY of S.N.A.M	13·00	14·50

246*	1f.75 Bloch 120 F-AKDY of S.N.A.M	£120	£110
247*	3f. on 3f.65 Marcel Bloch F-AKDY of S.N.A.M	2·50	45
248*	8f. Bloch 120 F-AKDY of S.N.A.M	4·75	5·50
249*	8f. on 8f.50 Bloch 120 F-AKDY of S.N.A.M	4·00	1·80
250*	12f. Bloch 120 F-AKDY of S.N.A.M	6·25	6·00
251*	12f.50 Bloch 120 F-AKDY of S.N.A.M	4·75	3·50
252*	16f. Bloch 120 F-AKDY of S.N.A.M	10·00	9·50
253*	50f. Bloch 120 F-AKDY of S.N.A.M	7·25	6·75

1943. As Nos. 207/13 of Cameroun.

268	1f. Fairey FC-1 airliner	20	1·50
269	1f.50 Fairey FC-1 airliner	15	1·20
270	5f. Fairey FC-1 airliner	15	30
271	10f. Fairey FC-1 airliner	60	1·20
272	25f. Fairey FC-1 airliner	60	3·50
273	50f. Fairey FC-1 airliner	45	55
274	100f. Fairey FC-1 airliner	65	30
268/274 Set of 7		2·50	7·75

1946.

317*	200f. Douglas DC-2	2·50	7·75

1949. As No. 254 of Cameroun.

320	25f. Lockheed Constellation	1·50	1·50

1954. As No. 264 of Cameroun.

330	15f. Bomber	3·25	80

1993.

1017*	500f. Wright Brothers and *Flyer*	60	25

1993. 75th (1992) Death Anniv of Ferdinand von Zeppelin.

1060*	500f. Loading goods onto Lockheed C-130 Hercules	35	25
1065*	3500f. Zeppelin LZ-4 (1908) and Count Ferdinand von Zeppelin	4·00	60

1994. Aircraft.

1141	10f. Boeing 737 (Lufthansa)	10	10
1142	10f. Concorde (Air France)	10	10
1143	10f. Boeing 767	10	10
1144	10f. Boeing 767	10	10
1145	60f. Boeing 747 (British Airways)	10	10
1146	60f. Dornier Do-X	10	10
1147	60f. Shinmeiwa (ShinMaywa since 1992)	10	10
1148	60f. Airbus A310	10	10
1149	640f. Airbus A310	45	15
1150	640f. Hydro 2000 flying boat (project)	45	15
1151	640f. Boeing 314 flying boat	45	15
1152	640f. Boeing 737	45	15
1153	5000f. Airbus A310	3·50	1·10
1154	5000f. McDonnell Douglas MD-10	3·50	1·10
1155	5000f. Douglas DC-9	3·50	1·10
1156	5000f. Boeing 737	3·50	1·10
1141/1156 Set of 16		15·00	5·25

1994.

1185*	3000f. Airplanes over battle scene	2·25	75

MALACCA

South-east Asia

100 cents = 1 dollar

1949. As Nos. 114/15 of Antigua.
18*   10c. Airplane.. 30   50
19*   15c. Jet-powered Vickers Viking................. 2·00   2·75

MALAGASY REPUBLIC

Indian Ocean off East Africa

100 centimes = 1 franc

1962.
44*   100f. Boeing 707.............................. 1·90   1·20

1963. Malagasy Commercial Aviation.
55   500f. Douglas DC-8 of Air Madagascar....... 9·75   4·25

1963.
69   45f. Silhouette of Douglas DC-8-60 Super
        Sixty...................................... 70   25
70   85f. Silhouette of Douglas DC-8-60 Super
        Sixty...................................... 1·20   60

1967. History of Malagasy Aviation.
131   5f. Jean Raoult's Bleriot XI, 1911.............. 70   35
132   45f. Bernard Bougault and flying boat,
        1926...................................... 1·40   65
133   500f. Jean Dagnaux and Breguet 19A2
        biplane, 1927 (air)....................... 10·50   5·00
131/133 Set of 3.................................... 11·50   5·50

1968.
141   500f. Airliner over Tananarive-Ivato
        International Airport..................... 8·75   4·25

1970.
188   200f. Boeing 737 of Air Madagascar............. 3·25   1·40

1976. 75th Anniv of Zeppelin.
346   40f. Count Ferdinand von Zeppelin and
        airship LZ-127 *Graf Zeppelin* 55   25
347   50f. Count Ferdinand von Zeppelin and
        airship LZ-127 *Graf Zeppelin* 80   25
348   75f. Count Ferdinand von Zeppelin and
        airship LZ-127 *Graf Zeppelin* .... 1·30   40
349   100f. Count Ferdinand von Zeppelin and
        airship LZ-127 *Graf Zeppelin* .... 1·60   50
350   200f. Count Ferdinand von Zeppelin and
        airship LZ-127 *Graf Zeppelin* (air) ...... 3·25   80
351   300f. Count Ferdinand von Zeppelin and
        airship LZ-127 *Graf Zeppelin* .... 4·75   1·10
346/351 *Set of 6*................................... 11·00   3·00
MS352 450f. Airship LZ-127 *Graf Zeppelin*.................. 5·50   2·20

1979. 20th Anniv of ASECNA (African Air Safety Organisation).
419   50f. Concorde.................................. 75   25

1980.
423   50f. Mikoyan Gurevich MiG-21................... 55   25

1983. Bicentenary of Manned Flight.
MS487 500f. Montgolfier balloon (first manned free
        flight, 1783)............................. 6·00   3·00

1985.
546*   50f. Republic P-47 Thunderbolts............... 1·10   45

1987.
635   60f. Piper PA-23 Aztec 55   25
636   60f. de Havilland Canada DHC-6 Twin
        Otter of Air Madagascar.................. 55   25
637   150f. Boeing 747-200 of Air Madagascar... 1·30   55
635/637 *Set of 3*.................................. 2·20   95

1990.
802*   250f. Hughes H-4 Hercules flying boat,
        Boeing 747 and "flying boat of the
        future"................................... 45   10
805*   2000f. Concorde.............................. 2·30   40

1990.
824   350f. Boeing 747.............................. 1·90   35

1991.
848*   1250f. Concorde of Air France................. 2·20   70

MALAWI

Central Africa

100 tambalas = 1 kwacha

1972. Malawi Aircraft.
408   3t. Vickers Viscount 700 of Air Malawi.... 40   10
409   8t. Hawker Siddeley H.S.748 of Air
        Malawi................................... 60   10
410   15t. Britten-Norman BN-2 Islander
        7Q-YKC of Air Malawi 85   30
411   30t. B.A.C. One Eleven 7Q-YKF of Air
        Malawi................................... 1·40   2·75
408/411 *Set of 4*.................................. 3·00   3·00

1977.
547*   4t. Vickers Super VC-10 over Chileka
        Airport.................................. 40   10

1983. Bicentenary of Manned Flight.
679   7t. Boeing 727, Douglas DC-9 and two
        Boeing 747 airliners at Kamuzu
        International Airport.................... 10   10
680   20t. Kamuzu International Airport........... 25   15
681   30t. B.A.C. One Eleven 7Q-YKF of Air
        Malawi at Kamuzu International
        Airport.................................. 40   45
682   1k. Short S.23 Empire "C" Class flying
        boat..................................... 1·10   2·50
679/682 *Set of 4*.................................. 1·70   2·75

1986.
754*   1k. B.A.C. One Eleven at Kamuzu International Airport .... 3·50   6·00

1988.
807*   50t. B.A.C. One Eleven 7Q-YKF of Air Malawi .... 2·50   75

2004. Centenary of Powered Flight.
MS1023 75k. Vickers FB.27 Vimy; 75k. Airco (de Havilland) D.H.9A; 75k. Messerschmitt Bf. 109; 75k. Mitsubishi A6M3 Zero-Sen .... 4·00   4·50
MS1024 180k. Fiat CR.2 *Price for 2 sheets* .... 3·00   3·25

MALAYSIA

South-east Asia
100 cents = 1 dollar

1965. Opening of International Airport, Kuala Lumpur.
18   15c. Concorde over Kuala Lumpur International Airport 40   10
19   30c. Concorde over Kuala Lumpur International Airport 60   20

1966.
39*   15c. Concorde .... 1·90   15

1973. Foundation of Malaysian Airline System.
110   15c. Boeing 737 of Malaysian Airline System 35   10
111   30c. Boeing 737 of Malaysian Airline System 65   60
112   50c. Boeing 737 of Malaysian Airline System 95   1·60
110/112 *Set of 3* .... 1·80   2·10

1983.
267*   15c. Northrop F-5E Tiger II .... 1·25   15

1987.
382* $1 Boeing 747 of Malaysian Airline System at Kuala Lumpur Airport and Boeing 747 in flight .... 1·00   30

1989. Inaugural Malaysia Airlines 747 Non-stop Flight to London.
427   20c. Boeing 747-400 of Malaysian Airline System (Big Ben at lower right) .... 2·25   2·25
428   20c. Boeing 747-400 of Malaysian Airline System (Palace of Westminster at lower right) .... 2·25   2·25
429    $1 Boeing 747-400 of Malaysian Airline System .... 4·50   5·50
427/429 *Set of 3* .... 8·00   9·00

1992.
475*   30c. Boeing 747 60   85

1993.
516*   30c. SME MD3-160M light airplane 50   20
517*   50c. Eagle X-TS light airplane 80   90

1995. 50th Anniv of IATO.
581   30c. Boeing 747 50   75
582   30c. Boeing 747 50   75
583   50c. Boeing 747 70   1·00
584   50c. Boeing 747 70   1·00
581/584 *Set of 4* .... 2·20   3·25

1997. 50th Anniv of Aviation in Malaysia.
641   30s. Boeing 747-400 over map 75   15
642   50s. Boeing 747 over Kuala Lumpur .... 1·10   60
643   1r. Tailfins of four airliners .... 1·50   2·25
641/643 *Set of 3* .... 3·00   2·75

1998. Opening of Kuala Lumpur International Airport.
685   30s. Boeing 747 at airport 70   20
686   50s. Airport terminals 85   60
687   1r. Airbus 300 in flight .... 1·75   2·25
685/687 *Set of 3* .... 3·00   2·75
MS688 2r. Globe and control tower .... 2·25   2·75

1999.
827*   50s. Boeing 747 .... 1·00   70

2000.
844*   30s. Man with kite 60   60
846*   30s. Airport 60   60
MS850* 1r. Douglas DC-8 .... 2·50   2·75

2002. Express Rail Link from Kuala Lumpur to Kuala Lumpur International Airport.
1062   30s. Station, Kuala Lumpur 75   25
1063   50s. Train and station .... 1·40   1·40
1064   50s. Train and International Airport .... 1·40   1·40
1062/1064 *Set of 3* .... 3·25   2·75
MS1065 Two sheets. (a)1r. KLIA express and high speed train; 1r. KLIA express and local train. (b) 2r. KLIA express *Price for 2 sheets* .... 5·50   6·00

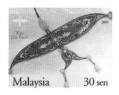

2005.
1246*   1r. Kuala Lumpur International Airport . ... 1·50   1·60

2005. Traditional Kites.
1300   30s. Wau Jala Budi 25   10
1301   50s. Wau Bulan 45   25
1302   1r. Wau Kucing 80   90
1300/1302 *Set of 3* .... 1·40   1·10
MS1303 2r. Wau Merak .... 1·25   1·40

2007. Air Transport in Malaysia.
1400   30s. Shorts SC.7 Skyvan 25   30
1401   50s. de Havilland Canada DHC-7-110 Dash 7 50   50
1402   50s. GAF N.22 Nomad 50   50
1400/1402 *Set of 3* .... 1·10   1·20
MS1403 1r. Airspeed AS.65 Consul; 1r. Douglas DC-3 75   85

MALDIVE ISLANDS

Indian Ocean
100 larees = 1 rupee

1967. Inauguration of Hulule Airport.
225   2l. Hawker Siddeley H.S.748 over Hulule Airport 20   50
226   5l. Hawker Siddeley H.S.748 over Hulule Airport 25   10
227   10l. Hawker Siddeley H.S.748 over Hulule Airport 30   10
228   15l. Hawker Siddeley H.S.748 over Hulule Airport 50   10
229   30l. Hawker Siddeley H.S.748 over Hulule Airport .... 1·00   10

230	50l. Hawker Siddeley H.S.748 over Hulule Airport	1·75	20
231	5r. Hawker Siddeley H.S.748 over Hulule Airport	5·50	5·50
232	10r. Hawker Siddeley H.S.748 over Hulule Airport	7·50	9·00
225/232 Set of 8		15·00	14·00

1968. Development of Civil Aviation.

272	2l. Montgolfier balloon (first manned free flight, 1783) and airship LZ-130 *Graf Zeppelin II* (wrongly dated "1928")	20	75
273	3l. Boeing 707-420 Intercontinental (wrongly dated "1958") and Douglas DC-3	20	75
274	5l. Lilienthal biplane glider (wrongly dated "1892") and Wright Type A	20	20
275	7l. Boeing 733 (project) and Concorde	1·75	1·00
276	10l. Montgolfier balloon and airship LZ-130 *Graf Zeppelin II*	45	20
277	50l. Lilienthal biplane glider and Wright Type A	1·50	30
278	1r. Boeing 707-420 Intercontinental and Douglas DC-3	2·25	50
279	2r. Boeing 733 (project) and Concorde	18·00	11·00
272/279 Set of 8		22·00	13·00

1974.

509*	3l. Airship LZ-127 *Graf Zeppelin* and Boeing 747	10	30

1974.

535*	1l. Avro Type 683 Lancaster	25	50
536*	2l. Fairey Swordfish torpedo bombers	25	50
538*	4l. Fairey Albacore torpedo bombers and aircraft carrier H.M.S. *Indomitable*	30	50
539*	5l. de Havilland DH.98 Mosquito bombers	30	30
542*	5r. Short S.25 Sunderland flying boat	13·00	14·00
MS543* 10r. Fairey Albacore torpedo bombers and aircraft carrier H.M.S. *Indomitable*		17·00	20·00

1975.

622*	3r. Convair, Hulule Airport	4·50	3·00

1977. 50th Anniv of Lindbergh's Trans-Atlantic Flight and 75th Anniv of First Navigable Airships.

713*	2l. Charles Lindbergh and Ryan NYP Special *Spirit of St. Louis*	20	20
714*	3l. Lindbergh's Miles Mohawk	20	20
715*	4l. Lebaudy-Juillot airship *Morning Post*, 1910 (inscribed "Lebaudy I built by H. Juillot 1902")	20	20
716*	5l. Count Ferdinand von Zeppelin and airship LZ-127 *Graf Zeppelin*	20	20
717*	1r. U.S. Navy airship ZR-3 *Los Angeles*	1·00	30
719*	10r. Vickers airship R-23, 1917	2·50	6·00
MS720* 5r. Lindbergh's Ryan NYP Special *Spirit of St. Louis*; 7r.50 German Navy airship L-31 (LZ-72)		13·00	18·00

1978. 75th Anniv of First Powered Flight.

730*	1l. Otto Lilienthal and Lilienthal biplane glider (wrongly dated "1890")	20	40
731*	2l. Octave Chanute and his glider, 1896	20	40
732*	3l. Wright Glider No. II, 1901 (wrongly dated "1900")	20	40
733*	4l. Sir Alliott Verdon Roe in his Triplane I, 1909	20	40
734*	5l. Wilbur Wright in Wright Type A	30	40
735*	10l. Avro Type D biplane, 1911	80	40
737*	95l. Clifton Hadley's triplane, 1910	6·00	2·25
738*	5r. Royal Aircraft Factory B.E.2A biplanes, Upavon, 1914	12·00	11·00
MS739* 10r. Wright Type A		14·00	16·00

1978.

789*	50l. Boeing 737 of Maldives International Airline	1·00	35

1981. Male International Airport.

936	5l. Boeing 737 of Maldives International Airline taking off from Male International Airport	20	20
937	20l. Boeing 737 of Maldives International Airline	40	20
938	1r.80 Douglas DC-9.30 being refuelled	75	40
939	4r. Plan of Male International Airport	1·00	2·00
936/939 Set of 4		2·10	3·00
MS940 5r. Boeing 727 airliners at Male International Airport		2·00	2·75

1983. Bicentenary of Manned Flight.

992	90l. Blohm und Voss HA 139A seaplane D-AMIE *Nordsee*	2·25	70
993	1r.45 Macchi Castoldi MC-72 seaplane	2·75	1·25
994	4r. Boeing F4B-3 biplane fighter	4·50	3·25
995	5r. Renard and Krebs' airship *La France*, 1884	4·50	3·50
992/995 Set of 4		12·50	8·00
MS996 10r. Nadar's balloon *Le Geant*, 1863		3·00	4·00

1983.

1010*	1r. Boeing 747	1·50	60

1984. 40th Anniv of ICAO.

1059	7l. Boeing 737 of Air Maldives	70	35
1060	4r. Lockheed L-1011 TriStar of Air Lanka	3·00	1·75
1061	6r. Douglas DC-10-30 of Alitalia	3·50	2·75
1062	8r. Lockheed L-1011 TriStar	3·75	3·50
1059/1062 Set of 4		10·00	7·50
MS1063 15r. Short S.7 Skyvan 8Q-CADDI		3·75	4·00

1988.

1281*	10r. Lockheed L-1011 TriStar	9·50	6·50

1989.

1355*	3r. Concorde	5·00	2·25

1990.

1409*	1r. Wreckage of Mitsubishi A6M Zero-Sen	55	40
1410*	2r.50 Barrage balloons, Normandy Landings, 1944	90	80

1991.

1482*	1r. Anthony Fokker in his monoplane *Haarlem Spin*	80	45
MS1489* Two sheets. (a) 20r Junkers Ju 88 (other sheet does not show aircraft) Set of 2 sheets		15·00	15·00

1991.

1575*	3r.50 Claire Chennault and Curtiss P-40B Tomahawk II fighters of the Flying Tigers	1·75	1·50
1578*	3r.50 James Doolittle and North American B-25B Mitchell bomber	1·75	1·50
1579*	3r.50 Raymond Spruance and Douglas SBD Dauntless dive bomber	1·75	1·50

1992.

1588	6r. Otto Lilienthal in Lilienthal glider No. 16	2·50	2·25

1992.

MS1711 Sixteen sheets. (a) 25r. Airship LZ-129 *Hindenburg* on fire at Lakehurst, New Jersey, 1937; (j) 25r. Mil Mi-26 helicopter; (p) 25r. Grumman TBF Avenger (other sheets do not show aircraft) Set of 16 sheets		55·00	55·00

1993.

1754*	1r. German Navy airship L-13 (LZ-45) on bombing raid over London	1·00	45
1765*	15r. Lockheed F-104G Starfighters	6·00	6·00
1766*	20r. Airship (inscribed "Graf Zeppelin")	6·00	6·00

1993. Aviation Anniversaires.

1913*	3r.50 Airship LZ-127 *Graf Zeppelin*	2·00	65
1915*	10r. Hugo Eckener and airship LZ-127 *Graf Zeppelin*	2·75	2·75

1916*	15r. Curtiss JN-4H "Jenny" being loaded with Philadelphia-Washington mail, 1918	3·75	4·25
1917*	20r. Airship U.S.S. *Macon*, 1933	3·75	4·25
MS1918*	Two sheets. (a) 25r. Santos-Dumont's airship *Ballon No. 5*, Paris, 1901 (b) 25r. Jean-Pierre Blanchard's balloon at Philadelphia, 1793 *Set of 2 sheets*	6·50	7·50

1994. 50th Anniv of ICAO.

2156	50l. Boeing 747	50	25
2157	1r. de Havilland DH.106 Comet 4	60	25
2158	2r. Male International Airport	85	55
2159	3r. Lockheed L.1049A Starliner	1·25	85
2160	8r. Airbus A-310	2·00	2·40
2161	10r. Dornier Do-228	2·00	2·50
2156/2161 *Set of 6*		6·50	6·00
MS2162 25r. Concorde		4·50	5·00

1995.

2255*	5r. Boeing B-17 Flying Fortress	85	85
2256*	5r. Ilushin Il-1	85	85
2258*	5r. Supermarine Spitfire and Fieseler Fi.103 (V-1 Flying Bomb)	85	85

1995.

2279*	6r.50 +50l. Grumman F6F-3 Hellcat	1·50	1·50
2280*	6r.50 +50l. Vought F4U-1 Corsair	1·50	1·50
2281*	6r.50 +50l. Douglas SBD Dauntless	1·50	1·50
MS2285* 6r.50+50l. Vought F4U-1 Corsair		4·00	4·50

1998. Aircraft in Longest Continuous Production.

2889	5r. Yakovlev Yak-18 (from 1947)	90	90
2890	5r. Beech Bonanza (from 1947)	90	90
2891	5r. Piper Cub (1937–82)	90	90
2892	5r. Tupolev Tu-95 (1954–90)	90	90
2893	5r. Lockheed C-130 Hercules (from 1954)	90	90
2894	5r. Piper PA-28 Cherokee (from 1961)	90	90
2895	5r. Mikoyan-Gurevich MiG-21 (from 1959)	90	90
2896	5r. Pilatus PC-6 Turbo-Porter (from 1960)	90	90
2897	5r. Antonov An-2 (from 1949)	90	90
2889/2897 *Set of 9*		7·25	7·25
MS2898 25r. Boeing KC-135E (from 1956)		3·75	4·00

1998.

2916	2r. Boeing 747 HS (NOT 737)	60	30
2917	5r. Canadair CL-215	1·00	1·00
2918	5r. Lockheed CP-140 Orion	1·00	1·00
2919	5r. Yakovlev Yak-54	1·00	1·00
2920	5r. Cessna 150	1·00	1·00
2921	5r. Canadair CL-215	1·00	1·00
2922	5r. Canadair CL 215 SAR	1·00	1·00
2923	5r. de Havilland Canada DHC-6 Twin Otter	1·00	1·00
2924	5r. Ag Commander A9 Quail	1·00	1·00
2925	5r. FSW version of Lockheed Martin F-16	1·00	1·00
2926	5r. V-Jet II	1·00	1·00
2927	5r. Pilatus PC-12 Porter	1·00	1·00
2928	5r. Cessna Citation Exel	1·00	1·00
2929	5r. Pitts S-7 Special	1·00	1·00
2930	5r. Cessna T-37	1·00	1·00
2931	5r. Gulfstream Peregrine Business Jet	1·00	1·00
2932	5r. Beech 58 Baron	1·00	1·00
2933	7r. Boeing 747-8	1·25	1·40
2934	8r. Boeing 747-400	1·40	1·50
2935	10r. Boeing 737	1·50	1·60
2916/2935 *Set of 20*		19·00	19·00
MS2936 Two sheets. (a) 25r. Beech Model 18; (b) 25r. Dassault Falcon 50 *Set of 2 sheets*		8·50	9·00

2000.

3170*	7r. Seaplane	1·25	1·25

2000. First Manned Hot Air Balloon Flight (1783).

3175*	3r. Montgolfier Brothers and balloon	75	75

2000.

3261*	7r. Male International Airport	1·10	1·25

2000. Centenary of First Zeppelin Flight.

3271	13r. LZ-127 *Graf Zeppelin*, 1928	1·75	1·90
3272	13r. LZ-130 *Graf Zeppelin II*, 1938	1·75	1·90
3273	13r. LZ-9 *Ersatz*, 1911	1·75	1·90
3271/3273 *Set of 3*		4·75	5·25
MS3274 25r. LZ-88 (L-40), 1917		3·75	4·00
No. 3272 inscribed LZ-127 in error.			

2001. 60th Anniv of Battle of Britain.

3481*	5r. Armourers with Heinkel He III	1·00	1·00
3482*	5r. Junkers Ju-87 Stukas	1·00	1·00
3484*	5r. Heinkel He III over Greenwich	1·00	1·00
3486*	5r. Supermarine Spitfire seen from German bomber	1·00	1·00
3487*	5r. Supermarine Spitfire on fire	1·00	1·00
3489*	5r. Hawker Hurricanes	1·00	1·00
3490*	5r. RAF planes taking off	1·00	1·00
3491*	5r. British fighters in formation	1·00	1·00
3492*	5r. German bomber crashing	1·00	1·00
3493*	5r. British fighters attacking	1·00	1·00
3494*	5r. German bomber in sea	1·00	1·00
3495*	5r. Remains of Heinkel He III in flames	1·00	1·00
MS3496* Two sheets. (a) 25r. Hawker Hurricane; (b) 25r. Messerschmitt Bf 109 *Set of 2 sheets*		7·50	8·00

2002. 75th Anniv of First Solo Trans-Atlantic Flight.

3785	12r. Charles Lindbergh and Ryan NYP Special *Spirit of St. Louis*	1·75	1·75
3786	12r. Lindbergh in flying helmet and Ryan NYP Special *Spirit of St. Louis*	1·75	1·75
3787	12r. Lindbergh holding propeller	1·75	1·75
3788	12r. Lindbergh in overalls and *Spirit of St. Louis*	1·75	1·75
3789	12r. Donald Hall (designer of *Spirit of St. Louis*)	1·75	1·75
3790	12r. Charles Lindbergh (pilot)	1·75	1·75
3791	12r. Lindbergh under wing of *Spirit of St. Louis*	1·75	1·75
3792	12r. Lindbergh, Mahoney and Hall at Ryan Airlines	1·75	1·75
3785/3792 *Set of 8*		12·50	12·50

2003. Centenary of Powered Flight.

MS3880 10r. Santos-Dumont monoplane No. 20 *Demoiselle*, on ground, 1909; 10r. Santos-Dumont monoplane No. 20 *Demoiselle*, taking off, 1909; 10r. Voisin-Farman No. 1 biplane, 1908; 10r. Glenn Curtiss *Gold Bug*, 1909		4·50	5·00
MS3881 10r. Santos-Dumont's *Airship No. 1*; 10r. Santos-Dumont's *Airship No. 4*; 10r. Santos-Dumont's *Ballon No. 14* and *14 bis* biplane; 10r. Santos-Dumont's *Airship No. 16*		4·50	5·00
MS3882 Two sheets. (a) 25r. Santos-Dumont's *Ballon No. 6* circling the Eiffel Tower, Paris, 1901. (b) 25r. Santos-Dumont's *14 bis* biplane, 1906 *Set of 2 sheets*		6·00	7·00

2004. Last Flight of Concorde (2003).

MS3926 1r. F-BVFD over Rio de Janeiro; 1r. F-BVFC over New York; 1r. F-BTSD over Honolulu; 1r. F-BTDS over Lisbon; 1r. F-BVFA over Washington; 1r. F-BVFD over Dakar; 1r. G-BOAC over Singapore; 1r. G-BOAA over Sydney; 1r. G-BOAD over Hong Kong; 1r. G-BOAD over Amsterdam; 1r. G-BOAE over Tokyo; 1r. G-BOAF over Madrid		1·10	1·20
MS3927 Three sheets. (a) 25r. G-BOAC against Union Jack; (b) 25r. G-BOAG over London; (c) 25r. G-BOAG against museum exhibits		6·75	7·00

2006. 50th Death Anniv of Ludwig Durr (Zeppelin engineer).

4051	15r. International Airship Exhibition, Frankfurt, Germany, 1909	1·75	1·90
4052	15r. Hot air balloons at International Airship Exhibition, Frankfurt, Germany, 1909	1·75	1·90
4053	15r. Zeppelin LZ-129 *Hindenburg*	1·75	1·90
4051/4053 *Set of 3*		4·75	5·25

MALI

West Africa

100 centimes = 1 franc

1963.

72	25f. Aero 145 ambulance airplane	45	25
73	55f. Douglas DC-3 TZ-ABF of Air Mali	1·20	55
74	100f. Ilyushin Il-18 of Air Mali	2·10	95
72/74 *Set of 3*		3·25	1·60

1964.

85*	20f. Airplane spraying locusts	1·50	55

1967.
| 141* | 50f. Francesco de Lana-Terzi's "Aerial Ship", 1670 | 95 | 45 |
| 143* | 200f. Leonardo da Vinci's drawing of a "bird-powered" flying machine | 3·50 | 1·60 |

1967. 30th Anniv of Amelia Earhart's Flight via Gao.
| 145 | 500f. Amelia Earhart | 11·00 | 4·75 |

1969.
182	50f. Montgolfier balloon (first manned free flight, 1783)	85	30
183	150f. Ferdinand Ferber's Glider No. 5, 1902	2·50	75
184	300f. Concorde	5·50	1·90
182/184 *Set of 3*		8·00	2·50

1969. Nos. 182/4 overprinted with Apollo lunar module and **L'HOMME SUR LA LUNE JUILLET 1969 APOLLO 11.**
202	50f. Montgolfier balloon	95	80
203	150f. Ferdinand Ferber's Glider No. 5, 1902	3·00	1·80
204	300f. Concorde	4·50	3·25
202/204 *Set of 3*		7·50	5·25

1969. 10th Anniv of Aerial Navigation Security Agency for Africa and Madagascar (ASECNA). As No. 552 of Cameroun.
| 215 | 100f. Airliner over airport | 1·00 | 50 |

1972.
| 323* | 250f. Montgolfier balloon (first manned free flight, 1783) | 4·00 | 1·60 |

1972. First Mali Airmail Flight by Balloon, Bamako-Timbuktu.
| 372 | 200f. Balloon and Breguet 14T biplane | 1·30 | 65 |
| 373 | 300f. Balloon and Concorde | 2·30 | 95 |

1973.
| 407* | 75f. Sikorsky S-61B Sea King helicopter | 50 | 30 |

1974.
| 440* | 90f. Breguet 14T biplane and Douglas DC-8 of Air Mali | 70 | 50 |

1974.
| 470 | 100f. Boeing 707 | 95 | 55 |
| 471 | 110f. Boeing 707 | 95 | 55 |

1975. 50th Death Anniv of Clement Ader (aviation pioneer).
| 519 | 100f. Clement Ader and his *Avion III* | 1·00 | 45 |

1976. First Commercial Flight by Concorde.
| 520 | 500f. Concorde of Air France | 4·75 | 2·00 |

1976.
| 554 | 200f. Vickers Viscount 800 | 1·70 | 80 |

1977. 50th Anniv of Lindbergh's Trans-Atlantic Flight.
| 577 | 420f. Charles Lindbergh and Ryan NYP Special *Spirit of St. Louis* | 2·50 | 1·10 |
| 578 | 430f. Lindbergh's Ryan NYP Special *Spirit of St. Louis* | 3·00 | 1·10 |

1977. History of the Zeppelin.
587	120f. Airship LZ-1	75	40
588	130f. Airship LZ-127 *Graf Zeppelin*	85	40
589	350f. Airship LZ-129 *Hindenburg* on fire at Lakehurst, New Jersey, 1937	2·30	85
590	500f. Count Ferdinand von Zeppelin and airship LZ-127 *Graf Zeppelin*	3·00	95
587/590 *Set of 4*		6·25	2·30

1977. First Commercial Flight by Concorde, Paris-New York. No. 520 overprinted **PARIS NEW-YORK 22.11.77.**
| 612 | 500f. Concorde of Air France | 12·00 | 7·25 |

1978. History of Aviation.
663	80f. Curtiss JN-4 "Jenny" (on United States of America stamp No. A548 with centre inverted) and Douglas DC-3	45	15
664	100f. Piccard's stratosphere balloon *F.N.R.S.*, 1931 (on Belgium stamp No. 622) and Stampe and Renard SV-4	55	25
665	120f. Concorde (on France stamp No. 1823) and Clement Ader's *Avion III*	75	25
666	130f. L.V.G. Schneider biplane (on Germany stamp No. 112) and Junkers Ju 52/3m	75	40
667	320f. Douglas DC-4 (on Japan stamp No. 671) and Mitsubishi A6M Zero-Sen	1·70	70
663/667 *Set of 5*		3·75	1·60

1979. Third Anniv of First Commercial Concorde Flight.
674	120f. Concorde and Clement Ader's monoplane *Eole*	75	40
675	130f. Concorde and Wright *Flyer I*	95	45
676	200f. Concorde and Lindbergh's Ryan NYP Special *Spirit of St. Louis*	1·50	70
674/676 *Set of 3*		3·00	1·40

1979.
| 699* | 130f. Airship LZ-127 *Graf Zeppelin* | 80 | 20 |
| 700* | 180f. Concorde | 95 | 40 |

1979. 20th Anniv of ASECNA (African Air Safety Organisation).
| 737 | 120f. Concorde | 85 | 35 |

1980.
| 739* | 250f. Douglas DC-10 | 1·60 | 60 |

1980.
| 786* | 100f. Concorde | 95 | 30 |

1980.
| 806 | 300f. Boeing 737 | 2·00 | 80 |

1980.
| 808* | 120f. Douglas DC-9 | 60 | 25 |

1981.
MS873* 700f. Boeing 747 SCA of NASA carrying
Space Shuttle .... 4·75 2·50

1981.
891   400f. Concorde (top) and Latecoere 28...... 2·50 90

1981. No. MS873 overprinted **JOE ENGLE RICHARD TRULY 2eme VOL SPATIALE**.
MS895 700f. Boeing 747 SCA of NASA carrying
Space Shuttle .... 5·50 3·25

1981.
896   700f. Cars being loaded onto Breguet Br
       763 Provence.. 3·50 1·30

1983. Bicentenary of Manned Flight.
952   500f. Balloon *Double Eagle II*......................... 3·75 1·00
953   700f. Montgolfier balloon (first manned
       free flight, 1783).. 4·00 1·50

1983.
968*   700f. Boeing 737................................. 6·50 1·80

1984. Microlight Aircraft.
998   270f. Microlight airplane......................... 1·60 55
999   350f. Lazor Gemini motorised hang-
       glider.. 1·90 80

1985. 25th Anniv of ASECNA (African Air Safety Organisation).
1080   700f. Sud Aviation SE 210 Caravelle (top)
       and Boeing 727-200 .... 6·75 3·50

1986. 50th Anniv of Disappearance of Jean Mermoz (aviator).
1109   150f. Jean Mermoz, Latecoere 300 flying
        boat F-AKGF *Croix du Sud* and
        technical drawings............................. 1·70 70
1110   600f. Jean Mermoz, CAMS 53 flying boat
        and front view of monoplane............ 6·00 2·50
1111   625f. Jean Mermoz and Latecoere 28-3
        seaplane F-AJNQ *Comte de la Vaulx*.. 6·25 3·00
1109/1111 *Set of 3* .... 12·50 5·50

1986. 10th Anniv of First Commercial Flight by Concorde. Nos. 674/6 surcharged **1986-10e Anniversaire du 1er Vol Commercial Supersonique** and new values.
1112   175f. on 120f. Concorde and Clement
        Ader's monoplane *Eole*...................... 1·70 90
1113   225f. on 130f. Concorde and Wright Flyer I 2·00 1·10
1114   300f. on 200f. Concorde and Lindbergh's
        Ryan NYP Special *Spirit of St. Louis*..... 3·25 1·60
1112/1114 *Set of 3* .... 6·25 3·25

1988. 15th Anniv of First North Atlantic Flight by Concorde.
1136   500f. Concorde of Air France.......................... 4·75 2·30

1992. No. 1080 surcharged **20f.**
1188*   20f. on 700f. Sud Aviation SE 210
        Caravelle and Boeing 727.................... 2·75 1·80

1994.
1274*   300f. Hawker Typhoons and troops............. 1·40 40
1275*   300f. Hawker Typhoons and tanks............. 1·40 40
1280*   400f. Hawker Typhoon and North
        American B-25 Mitchell........................ 1·80 45
1281*   400f. Supermarine Spitfire .... 1·80 45
1282*   400f. Supermarine Spitfire on fire .... 1·80 45
1283*   400f. Paratrooper.................................. 1·80 45
1285*   400f. Paratroopers................................ 1·80 45

MALTA

Mediterranean

1949. 12 pence = 1 shilling

20 shillings = 1 pound

1972. 10 mils = 1 cent

100 cents = 1 pound

1949. As Nos. 114/15 of Antigua.
251*   2½d. Airplane.. 30 10
252*   3d. Jet-powered Vickers Viking................. 3·00 1·00

1974.
517*   4c. Boeing 720B of Air Malta 15 10
519*   7c.5 Boeing 720B of Air Malta 20 10
521*   25c. Boeing 720B of Air Malta 35 60

1974.
529*   7c.5 Balloon and Boeing 747-100.............. 35 20

1978.
605   5c. Boeing 707.................................... 20 10
606   7c. Boeing 720B of Air Malta 20 10
607   11c. Boeing 747.................................... 25 10
608   17c. Boeing 707.................................... 35 30
609   20c. Boeing 720B of Air Malta 40 40
610   75c. Boeing 747-200............................. 1·25 2·75
605/610 *Set of 6* .... 2·40 3·25

1979.
625*   7c. Tailfin of Air Malta Boeing 707............. 20 10

1981.
682*   £3 Boeing 707 of Air Malta..................... 13·00 18·00

1984.
729   7c. Boeing 737 9H-ABA of Air Malta........ 50 30
730   8c. Boeing 720B of Air Malta 60 35
731   16c. Vickers 953 Vanguard G-APED
       Defiance of B.E.A................................. 1·25 70
732   23c. Vickers Viscount 700 of Alitalia........... 1·50 70
733   27c. Douglas DC-3 G-AGHH of B.O.A.C ..... 1·75 80
734   38c. Armstrong Whitworth A.W.15
       Atalanta G-ABTJ *Artemis* of Imperial
       Airways.. 2·25 2·75
735   75c. Marina Fiat MF.5 flying boat I-AZDL.... 3·25 5·00
729/735 *Set of 7* .... 10·00 9·50

1988.
827*   10c. Airliner.. 1·25 75

1992. Opening of International Air Terminal.
917   4c. Airliners of Air Malta over Malta
       International Airport............................. 75 30
918   10c. Malta International Airport................. 1·25 70

1994. Aviation Anniversaries and Events.
969   5c. Falcon Trophy, Piper PA30 Twin
       Comanche and Auster J-5 Autocar ... 50 20
970   14c. Aerospatiale (Sud) Alouette, display
       teams and logo (Malta International
       Air Show)... 1·75 85
971   20c. de Havilland DH.104 Dove, *City of
       Valetta* and Avro Type 685 York with
       logo (50th Anniversary, ICAO) .... 1·90 1·75
972   25c. Airbus A320 *Nicolas Cottoner* and de
       Havilland DH.106 Comet with logo
       (50th Anniversary of ICAO) .... 1·90 1·90
969/972 *Set of 4* .... 5·50 4·25

1995.
989*   5c. Junkers Ju 87B Stukas 25 25

1998. 25th Anniv of Air Malta.
1089*	26c. Aircraft tailfins....................	2·40	2·50

2000. Centenary of Air Transport.
1176	6c. de Havilland DH.66 Hercules, 1928...	85	1·10
1177	6c. Zeppelin LZ-127 *Graf Zeppelin*, 1933	85	1·10
1178	16c. Douglas DC-3 Dakota of Air Malta Ltd, 1949	1·60	1·90
1179	16c. Airbus Industries Airbus A320 of Air Malta	1·60	1·90
1176/1179 *Set of 4*......................		4·50	5·50

2005.
1446*	5c. Savoia Marchetti S-73 Sparviero attacking warships................	65	25
1447*	25c. Anti aircraft guns................	1·75	95
1448*	51c. Hawker Hurricanes, Supermarine Spitfires and Gloster Sea Gladiators .	3·50	3·50

MANAMA

Arabian Peninsula

100 dirhams = 1 riyal

1967. Nos. 143 and 147 of Ajman overprinted **MANAMA** in English and Arabic.
8*	70d. Sikorsky S-58 helicopter..................	40	40
12*	5r. Boeing 707 (air).....................	3·50	3·50

MANCHUKUO

Eastern Asia

100 fen = 1 yuan

1936.
93*	18f. Airplane..........................	16·00	12·00
94*	19f. Airplane..........................	5·25	3·50
97*	38f. Nakajima-built Fokker F.VIIb/3m....	17·00	16·00
98*	39f. Nakajima-built Fokker F.VIIb/3m....	1·70	1·20

MARSHALL ISLANDS

North Pacific

100 cents = 1 dollar

1986. Mail Planes.
75	44c. Consolidated PBY-5A Catalina amphibian of Trans Ocean Airways ..	70	65
76	44c. Grumman SA-16 Albatross flying boat of Trust Territory Airlines....	70	65
77	44c. Douglas DC-6B of Air Micronesia.......	70	65
78	44c. Boeing 727-100 of Air Micronesia at Majuro International Airport...........	70	65
75/78 *Set of 4*........................		2·50	2·30
MS79 $1 Douglas C-54		2·30	2·00

1987. Aviators.
111*	33c. Lindbergh's Ryan NYP Special *Spirit of St. Louis*	60	50
112*	33c. Charles Lindbergh and Chance Vought F4U Corsair..................	60	50
113*	39c. William Bridgeman and Consolidated B-24 Liberator	65	55
114*	39c. William Bridgeman and Douglas Skyrocket	65	55
115*	44c. John Glenn and Chance Vought F4U Corsair............................	70	60

1987. 50th Anniv of Amelia Earhart's Round the World Flight Attempt.
117*	44c. Amelia Earhart's Lockheed 10E Electra	65	55
119*	44c. Wreckage of Amelia Earhart's Lockheed 10E Electra on Barre Island..............................	65	55
120*	44c. Amelia Earhart's Lockheed 10E Electra being recovered by Japanese patrol boat *Koshu*	65	55
MS121* $1 Amelia Earhart's Lockheed 10E Electra ..		1·90	1·70

1988.
201*	25c. Sikorsky S-61B SH-3 Sea King helicopter of the U.S. Navy.................	45	35

1989. Airplanes.
211	12c. Dornier Do-228 of Marshall Islands Airline............................	20	20
212	36c. Boeing 737 of Air Nauru..............	65	55
213	39c. Hawker Siddeley H.S.748 of Marshall Islands Airline..................	75	65
214	45c. Boeing 727 of Continental Airlines ...	85	75
211/214 *Set of 4*.....................		2·20	1·90

1989.
232*	25c. Consolidated PBY-5 Catalina flying boats	1·30	1·10
233*	25c. Nakajima A6M2 "Rufe" seaplane	1·30	1·10
235*	25c. Consolidated PBY-5A Catalina amphibian............................	1·30	1·10

1990.
320*	25c. Junkers Ju 87B Stukas..............	50	35
324*	25c. Junkers Ju 87B Stuka..............	45	35
335*	45c. Supermarine Spitfire Mk.1A............	85	65
336*	45c. Hawker Hurricane Mk.1 and Spitfire....	85	65
337*	45c. Messerschmitt Bf 109E..............	85	65
338*	45c. Junkers Ju 87B Stuka..............	85	65
342*	25c. Fairey Swordfish..................	50	35

1991.
364*	29c. Dornier Do-17z Bombers..............	50	45
369*	50c. Fairey Swordfish..................	85	75
376*	50c. American airplanes................	85	75
376b*	50c. American airplanes................	1·00	75
377*	50c. Japanese dive bombers	85	75
379*	50c. Japanese aircraft carrier (may show aircraft)............................	85	75
382*	50c. Curtiss P-40 Tomahawk fighters........	85	75
383*	50c. Mitsubishi Ki-21 'Sally' bombers........	85	75
384*	29c. Grumman F4F-4 Wildcat fighters and Mitsubishi G3M 'Nell' bombers ..	50	45

1991.
385*	50c. Boeing 747-123 Space Shuttle Carrier.........................	75	65
388*	50c. Shuttle landing (may show chase plane)............................	75	65

1991. Passenger Aircraft.
402	12c. Dornier Do-228	20	15
403	29c. Douglas DC-8	55	35
404	50c. Hawker Siddeley H.S.748	95	65
405	50c. Saab 2000	95	65
402/405 *Set of 4*.....................		2·40	1·60

1992.
418*	50c. North American B-25 Mitchell (Doolittle raid on Tokyo, 1942)...........	85	75
420*	50c. Grumman F4F-3 Wildcat............	85	75
420b*	50c. As 420 but with aircraft name inscribed	85	75
421*	50c. Aichi D3A1 'Val' and Nakajima B5N2 'Kate' bombers (Wrongly inscribed Mitsubisi A6M2 Zero)...............	85	75
421a*	50c. As 421, inscription corrected..........	85	75
422*	50c. Douglas TBD-1 Devastator torpedo bombers (Wrongly inscribed 'US Douglas SBD Dauntless')...............	85	75
422a*	50c. As 422, inscription corrected..........	85	75
423*	50c. Mitsubishi A6M2 Zero-Sen fighters ..	85	75
423a*	50c. As 423, inscribed with aircraft name	85	75
426*	50c. Douglas SBD Dauntless dive bombers...........................	85	75
427*	50c. Nakajima B5N2 'Kate' dive bombers .	85	75
436*	29c. Aircraft over carrier................	50	45

1993.
460*	50c. Mitsubishi A6M Zero-Sen fighters......	85	75
461*	50c. Lockheed P-38 Lightnings and Bristol Beaufighters................	85	75
463*	50c. Douglas A-20 Havoc and North American B-25 Mitchell bombers.......	85	75
471*	50c. Boeing B-17F Flying Fortress bombers and Messerschmitt Bf.109 fighter............................	85	75

1994.

526*	29c. Douglas SBD Dauntless dive bombers	50	45
528*	52c. Boeing B-17 Flying Fortress bombers	95	80
530*	75c. Airspeed A.S.51 Horsa gliders (inscribed Horsa Gliders)	1·40	1·10
530b*	75c. As 530 but inscribed 'Horsa Gliders, Parachute Troops'	2·75	1·10
531*	75c. Hawker Typhoon 1B and North American P-51B Mustang fighters (wrongly inscribed 'US P51B Mustangs, British Hurricanes')	1·40	1·10
531a*	75c. As 531 inscribed correctly	3·00	2·30
534*	50c. Fieseler Fi.103 (V-1 flying bomb)	85	75
536*	50c. Grumman F6F-3 Hellcat	85	75
543*	50c. Avro Type 683 Lancasters	85	75
547*	50c. Pilot, Republic P-47 Thunderbolt and Douglas C-47 Skytrain	85	75

1995.

576*	55c. Bombers over Dresden	95	80
591*	$1 Boeing B-29 Superfortress *Enola Gay* and mushroom cloud (Atomic bomb on Hiroshima, 1945)	1·90	1·50

1995.

603*	55c. US Boeing B-29 Superfortress	75	65

1995. Jet Fighters.

634	32c. Messerschmitt Me 262-Ia	55	45
635	32c. Gloster Meteor F Mk 8	55	45
636	32c. Lockheed F-80 Shooting Star	55	45
637	32c. North American F-86 Sabre	55	45
638	32c. Grumman F9F-2 Panther	55	45
639	32c. Mikoyan Gurevich MiG-15	55	45
640	32c. North American F-100 Super Sabre	55	45
641	32c. Convair TF-102A Delta Dagger	55	45
642	32c. Lockheed F-104 Starfighter	55	45
643	32c. Mikoyan Gurevich MiG-21 MT	55	45
644	32c. Vought F8U Crusader	55	45
645	32c. Republic F-105 Thunderchief	55	45
646	32c. Saab J35 Draken	55	45
647	32c. Fiat G-91Y	55	45
648	32c. McDonnell Douglas F-4 Phantom II	55	45
649	32c. Saab JA37 Viggen	55	45
650	32c. Dassault Mirage F1C	55	45
651	32c. Grumman F-14 Tomcat	55	45
652	32c. Boeing F-15 Eagle	55	45
653	32c. Lockheed Martin F-16 Fighting Falcon	55	45
654	32c. Panavia Tornado F Mk3	55	45
655	32c. Sukhoi Su-27UB	55	45
656	32c. Dassault Mirage 2000C	55	45
657	32c. Hawker Siddeley (BAe) Sea Harrier FRS Mk1	55	45
658	32c. Lockheed F-117A Nighthawk	55	45
634/658	*Set of 25*	12·50	10·00

1996. Biplanes.

746	32c. Curtiss JN-4 *Jenny*	55	45
747	32c. SPAD XIII	55	45
748	32c. Albatros	55	45
749	32c. Airco (de Havilland) DH-4 Liberty	55	45
750	32c. Fokker Dr-1	55	45
751	32c. Sopwith Camel	55	45
752	32c. Martin MB-2	55	45
753	32c. Martin MB-3A Tommy	55	45
754	32c. Curtiss TS-1	55	45
755	32c. Curtiss P-1 Hawk	55	45
756	32c. Boeing PW-9	55	45
757	32c. Douglas O-2-H	55	45
758	32c. Keystone LB-5 Pirate	55	45
759	32c. Vought O2U-1 Corsair	55	45
760	32c. Curtiss F8C Helldiver	55	45
761	32c. Boeing F4B-4	55	45
762	32c. Svenska (SAAB) J6B Gerfalcon	55	45
763	32c. Martin BM	55	45
764	32c. Grumman FF-1 'Fifi'	55	45
765	32c. Fiat CR32 Cricket	55	45
766	32c. Polikarpov I-15 Gull	55	45
767	32c. Fairey Swordfish	55	45
768	32c. Aichi D1A2	55	45
769	32c. Grumman F3F	55	45
770	32c. Curtiss SOC-3 Seagull	55	45
746/770	*Set of 25*	12·50	10·00

1997.

810*	60c. Wright Brothers *Flyer I*	1·00	90

1998. Aircraft of the United States Air Force.

835	32c. Douglas C-24 Skymaster	55	45
836	32c. Convair B-36 Peacemaker	55	45
837	32c. North American F-86 Sabre	55	45
838	32c. Boeing B-47 Stratojet	55	45
839	32c. Douglas C-124 Globemaster II	55	45
840	32c. Lockheed C-121 Constellation	55	45
841	32c. Boeing B-52 Stratofortress	55	45
842	32c. North American F-100 Super Sabre	55	45
843	32c. Lockheed F-104 Starfighter	55	45
844	32c. Lockheed C-130 Hercules	55	45
845	32c. Republic F-105 Thunderchief	55	45
846	32c. Boeing KC-135 Stratotanker	55	45
847	32c. Convair B-58 Hustler	55	45
848	32c. McDonnell Douglas F-4 Phantom II	55	45
849	32c. Northrop T-38 Talon	55	45
850	32c. Lockheed C-141 StarLifter	55	45
851	32c. General Dynamics F-111 Aardvark	55	45
852	32c. Lockheed SR-71 Blackbird	55	45
853	32c. Lockheed C-5A Galaxy	55	45
854	32c. Fairchild Republic A-10 Thunderbolt II	55	45
855	32c. Boeing (McDonnell Douglas) F-15 Eagle	55	45
856	32c. Lockheed Martin (General Dynamics) F-16 Fighting Falcon	55	45
857	32c. Lockheed F-117A Nighthawk	55	45
858	32c. Northrop Grumman B-2A Spirit	55	45
859	32c. Boeing (McDonnell Douglas) C-17 Globemaster III	55	45
835/859	*Set of 25*	12·50	10·00

1997.

884*	60c. Von Richthofen and Fokker Dr. 1	1·00	90

1998.

961*	60c. Zeppelin LZ-127 *Graf Zeppelin* above Mount Fuji	1·00	90

1998. 50th Anniv of Berlin Airlift.

971	60c. Douglas C-54 Skymaster	1·00	90
972	60c. Avro Type 685 York	1·00	90
973	60c. Crowd and buildings	1·00	90
974	60c. Crowd	1·00	90
971/974	*Set of 4*	3·50	3·25

1998.

981*	60c. Douglas DC-3	1·00	85
983*	60c. Zeppelin LZ-129 *Hindenburg*	1·00	85
988*	60c. Junkers Ju-87B Stuka	1·00	85

1998. Aircraft of the United States Navy.

998	32c. Curtiss NC-4	55	45
999	32c. Consolidated PBY-5 Catalina	55	45
1000	32c. Douglas TBD Devastator	55	45
1001	32c. Vought SB2U Vindicator	55	45
1002	32c. Grumman F4F Wildcat	55	45
1003	32c. Vought-Sikorsky OS2U Kingfisher	55	45
1004	32c. Douglas SBD Dauntless	55	45
1005	32c. Vought F4U Corsair	55	45
1006	32c. Curtiss SB2C Helldiver	55	45
1007	32c. Lockheed PV-1 Ventura	55	45
1008	32c. Grumman TBM Avenger	55	45
1009	32c. Grumman F6F Hellcat	55	45
1010	32c. Consolidated PB4Y-2 Privateer	55	45
1011	32c. Douglas A-1J Skyraider	55	45
1012	32c. McDonnell F2H-2P Banshee	55	45
1013	32c. Grumman F9F-2B Panther	55	45
1014	32c. Martin P5M Marlin	55	45
1015	32c. Vought F-8 Crusader	55	45
1016	32c. McDonnell Douglas F-4 Phantom II	55	45
1017	32c. Grumman A-6 Intruder	55	45
1018	32c. Lockheed P-3 Orion	55	45
1019	32c. Vought A-7 Corsair II	55	45
1020	32c. Douglas A-4 Skyhawk	55	45
1021	32c. Lockheed S-3 Viking	55	45
1022	32c. Boeing (McDonnell Douglas) F/A18 Hornet	55	45
998/1022	*Set of 25*	12·50	10·00

1998.

1067*	60c. Supermarine Spitfires, Messerschmitt Bf 109s and Junkers Ju87 Stukas	1·00	85
1068*	60c. Mitsubishi B5M		
1080*	60c. Douglas C-47 Skytrain	1·00	85

1999.

1178*	60c. de Havilland DH.106 Comet	1·00	90

1999. Legendary Aircraft.

1191	33c. Martin B-10B	55	45
1192	33c. Northrop A-17 Nomad	55	45

1193	33c. Douglas B-18 Bolo	55	45
1194	33c. Boeing B-17F Flying Fortress	55	45
1195	33c. Douglas A-20 Havoc	55	45
1196	33c. North American B-25 Mitchell	55	45
1197	33c. Consolidated B-24 Liberator	55	45
1198	33c. North American P-51B Mustang	55	45
1199	33c. Martin B-26 Marauder	55	45
1200	33c. Douglas A-26B Invader	55	45
1201	33c. Bell P-59 Airacomet	55	45
1202	33c. Boeing KC-97 Stratofreighter	55	45
1203	33c. Douglas A-1J Skyraider	55	45
1204	33c. Lockheed P2V-7 Neptune	55	45
1205	33c. North American B-45 Tornado	55	45
1206	33c. Boeing B-50 Superfortress	55	45
1207	33c. North American AJ-2 Savage (later, A2)	55	45
1208	33c. Grumman F9F Cougar	55	45
1209	33c. Douglas A-3 Skywarrior	55	45
1210	33c. Martin (English Electric) B-57E Canberra	55	45
1211	33c. Douglas EB-66 Destroyer	55	45
1212	33c. Grumman E-2A Hawkeye	55	45
1213	33c. Northrop F-5E Tiger II	55	45
1214	33c. McDonnell Douglas AV-8B Harrier II.	55	45
1215	33c. Rockwell B-1B Lancer	55	45
1191/1215 Set of 25		12·50	10·00

1999.

1231*	60c. Concorde	1·00	90

1999.

1239*	60c. Boeing 747	1·00	90

2000.

1260*	60c. British Aeropace Sea Harrier	1·00	90
1266*	60c. Northrop B-2A Spirit	1·00	90
1267*	60c. Boeing 747 wreckage	1·00	90

2000. Legendary Aircraft (2nd series).

1272	33c. Boeing P-26A 'Peashooter'	55	50
1273	33c. Stearman N2S-1 Kaydett	55	50
1274	33c. Seversky P-35A	55	50
1275	33c. Curtiss P-36A Hawk	55	50
1276	33c. Curtiss P-40B Warhawk	55	50
1277	33c. Lockheed P-38 Lightning	55	50
1278	33c. Bell P-39D Airacobra	55	50
1279	33c. Curtiss C-46 Commando	55	50
1280	33c. Republic P-47D Thunderbolt	55	50
1281	33c. Northrop P-61A Black Widow	55	50
1282	33c. Boeing B-29 Superfortress	55	50
1283	33c. Grumman F7F-3N Tigercat	55	50
1284	33c. Grumman F8F-2 Bearcat	55	50
1285	33c. North American F-82 Twin Mustang	55	50
1286	33c. Republic F-84G Thunderjet	55	50
1287	33c. North American FJ-1 Fury	55	50
1288	33c. Fairchild C-119C Flying Boxcar	55	50
1289	33c. Douglas F3D-2 Skynight	55	50
1290	33c. Northrop F-89D Scorpion	55	50
1291	33c. Lockheed F-94B Starfire	55	50
1292	33c. Douglas F4D Skyray	55	50
1293	33c. McDonnell F3H-2 Demon	55	50
1294	33c. McDonnell RF-101 AC Voodoo	55	50
1295	33c. Lockheed U-2F	55	50
1296	33c. Rockwell OV-10 Bronco	55	50
1272/1296 Set of 25		12·50	11·00

2000.

1304	60c. Boeing (McDonnell Douglas) F/A-18 Hornet	1·00	90

2000. Centenary of Zeppelin Airships.

1366	33c. LZ-1, 1900	60	50
1367	33c. LZ-127 *Graf Zeppelin I*, 1928	60	50
1368	33c. LZ-129 *Hindenburg*, 1936	60	50
1369	33c. LZ-130 *Graf Zeppelin II*, 1937	60	50
1366/1369 Set of 4		2·20	1·80

2001.

MS1514 80c. Marc Mitscher, Fleet Air Commander and Douglas SBD; 80c. Edward O'Hare, Naval pilot and Grumman F6F (other stamps in the miniature sheet do not show aircraft) .... 12·50 10·50

2001. Classic Aircraft.

1534	80c. Supermarine Sea Eagle	1·40	1·20
1535	80c. Gloster Sea Gladiator	1·40	1·20
1536	80c. de Havilland Canada DHC-6 Twin Otter	1·40	1·20
1537	80c. Shorts 350	1·40	1·20
1538	80c. Short S-25 Sandringham	1·40	1·20
1539	80c. de Havilland Canada DHC-7 Dash 7.	1·40	1·20
1540	80c. Beech Model B60 Duke	1·40	1·20
1541	80c. Fokker/Fairchild F27 Friendship	1·40	1·20
1542	80c. Consolidated B-24J Liberator	1·40	1·20
1543	80c. Vickers 953C Merchantman	1·40	1·20
1534/1543 Set of 10		12·50	11·00

2002.

1674*	80c. William Mitchell and de Havilland DH-4 (senior aviation officer)	1·40	1·20
1677*	80c. Eddie Rickenbacker (U.S. Flying ace) abd SPAD S.X.III	1·40	1·20

2003. Centenary of Powered Flight.

1709	37c. Wright *Flyer I*	1·40	1·20
1710	37c. Curtiss JN-3	1·40	1·20
1711	37c. Douglas World Cruiser	1·40	1·20
1712	37c. Ryan NYP Special *Spirit of St.Louis*	1·40	1·20
1713	37c. Lockheed Vega 5	1·40	1·20
1714	37c. Boeing 314 Clipper	1·40	1·20
1715	37c. Douglas C-47 Skytrain	1·40	1·20
1716	37c. Boeing B-50 Superfortress	1·40	1·20
1717	37c. Antonov An-225 Mriya	1·40	1·20
1718	37c. Northrop B-2A Spirit	1·40	1·20
1709/1718 Set of 10		15·00	13·00

2004.

1758	37c. Airspeed Horsa gliders	65	55
1759	37c. Hawker Typhoon 1B and North American P.51B Mustangs	65	55

2004.

1781	23c. Wright *Flyer I*	40	35
1782	23c. Bleriot XI	40	35
1783	23c. Curtiss *Golden Flyer*	40	35
1784	23c. Curtiss Flying Boat	40	35
1785	23c. Deperdussin Racer	40	35
1786	23c. Sikorsky Ilya Muromets	40	35
1787	23c. Fokker EI	40	35
1788	23c. Junkers JI	40	35
1789	23c. Royal Aircraft Factory S.E.5a	40	35
1790	23c. Handley Page O/400	40	35
1791	23c. Fokker D. VII	40	35
1792	23c. Junkers F.13	40	35
1793	23c. Lockheed Vega	40	35
1794	23c. Martin M-130 Clipper	40	35
1795	23c. Messerschmitt Bf.109	40	35
1796	23c. Supermarine Spitfire	40	35
1797	23c. Junkers Ju88	40	35
1798	23c. Mitsubishi A6M Zero-Sen	40	35
1799	23c. Ilyushin Il-2 Shturmovik	40	35
1800	23c. Heinkel He-178	40	35
1801	23c. Douglas C-47 Skytrain	40	35
1802	23c. Piper Cub	40	35
1803	23c. Avro Type 683 Lancaster	40	35
1804	23c. Boeing B-17 Flying Fortress	40	35
1805	23c. Messerschmitt Me-262	40	35
1806	23c. Boeing B-29 Superfortress	40	35
1807	23c. North American P-51 Mustang	40	35
1808	23c. Yakovlev Yak-9	40	35
1809	23c. Bell Model 47	40	35
1810	23c. Bell X-1	40	35
1811	23c. Beech Bonanza	40	35
1812	23c. Antonov An-225 Mriya	40	35
1813	23c. Boeing B-47 Stratojet	40	35
1814	23c. Mikoyan Gureyvich MiG 15	40	35
1815	23c. Saab J-33 Draken	40	35
1816	23c. Boeing B-52 Stratofortress	40	35
1817	23c. Boeing 367-80 (Boeing 707 protype)	40	35
1818	23c. Lockheed U-2	40	35
1819	23c. Lockheed C-130 Hercules	40	35
1820	23c. McDonnell Douglas F-4 Phantom II.	40	35
1821	23c. North American X-15	40	35
1822	23c. Sikorsky S-61	40	35
1823	23c. Learjet 23	40	35
1824	23c. Lockheed SR-71 Blackbird	40	35
1825	23c. Boeing 747	40	35
1826	23c. Concorde	40	35
1827	23c. Airbus A300	40	35
1828	23c. Mikoyan Gureyvich MiG-29	40	35
1829	23c. Lockheed F-117A Nighthawk	40	35
1830	23c. Lockheed Martin F/A-22A Raptor	40	35
1781/1830 Set of 30		18·00	16·00

2004.

1843*	37c. Aviator, Douglas C-47 Skytrain and Republic P-47 Thunderbolt	65	55

2007. 60th Anniv of United States Air Force.

2028	41c. Douglas C-54 Skymaster	75	75
2029	41c. Convair B-36 Peacemaker	75	75
2030	41c. North American F-86 Sabre	75	75
2031	41c. Boeing B-47 Stratojet	75	75
2032	41c. Douglas C-124 Globemaster II	75	75
2033	41c. Lockheed C-121 Constellation	75	75
2034	41c. Boeing B-52 Stratofortress	75	75
2035	41c. North American F-100 Super Sabre	75	75
2036	41c. Lockheed F-104 Starfighter	75	75
2037	41c. Lockheed C-130 Hercules	75	75
2038	41c. Republic F-105 Thunderchief	75	75
2039	41c. Boeing KC-135 Stratotanker	75	75
2040	41c. Convair B-58 Hustler	75	75
2041	41c. McDonnell Douglas F-4 Phantom II.	75	75
2042	41c. Northrop T-38 Talon	75	75

2043	41c. Lockheed C-141 StarLifter	75	75
2044	41c. General Dynamics F-III Aardvark	75	75
2045	41c. Lockheed SR-71 Blackbird	75	75
2046	41c. Lockheed C-5A Galaxy	75	75
2047	41c. Fairchild Republic A-10 Thunderbolt II	75	75
2048	41c. Boeing (McDonnell Douglas) F-15 Eagle	75	75
2049	41c. Lockheed Martin (General Dynamics) F-16 Fighting Falcon	75	75
2050	41c. Lockheed F-117A Nighthawk	75	75
2051	41c. Northrop Grumman B-2A Spirit	75	75
2052	41c. Boeing (McDonnell Douglas) C-17 Globemaster III	75	75
2028/2052 *Set of 25*		17·00	17·00

MARTINIQUE

West Indies

100 centimes = 1 franc

1945. As Nos. 207/13 of Cameroun.

222	50f. Fairey FC-1 airliner	40	1·70
223	100f. Fairey FC-1 airliner	35	4·25

1947.

248*	50f. Latecoere 611 flying boat	6·75	6·75
249*	100f. Airplane	5·75	7·75

MAURITANIA

West Africa

1940. 100 centimes = 1 franc

1973. 100 cents = 1 ouguiya (um)

1940. As Nos. 117/21 of Dahomey.

120	1f.90 Twin-engine airliner	1·20	4·25
121	2f.90 Twin-engine airliner	65	5·25
122	4f.50 Twin-engine airliner	65	4·50
123	4f.90 Twin-engine airliner	1·20	4·25
124	6f.90 Twin-engine airliner	80	4·00
120/124 *Set of 5*		4·00	20·00

1942. As No. 143k of Dahomey.

124k*	50f. Twin-engine airliner	2·50	6·00

1962. Air Afrique Airline. As No. 307 of Cameroun.

150	100f. Boeing 707 airliners of Air Afrique	3·00	1·60

1963. Creation of National Airline.

162	500f. Douglas DC-3 of Air Mauritania over Nouakchott Airport	45	40

1966. Early Aircraft.

239	50f. Breguet 14T2 Salon	1·20	30
240	100f. Farman F.60 Goliath	2·20	70
241	150f. Couzinet 70 F-AMBV *Arc en Ciel*	4·75	2·20
242	200f. Latecoere 28-3 seaplane F-AJNQ *Comte de la Vaulx*	6·75	3·25
239/242 *Set of 4*		13·50	6·00

1966. Inauguration of Douglas DC-8F Air Services. As No. 438 of Cameroun.

249	30f. Douglas DC-8F Jet Trader of Air Afrique	75	45

1970.

364	100f. Montgolfier balloon (first manned free flight, 1783)	1·50	80

1973.

425*	40f. Concorde	70	25

1974. No. 425 surcharged **8 UM**.

448*	8um. on 40f. Concorde	75	25

1974.

454*	70um. Biplane	7·25	7·25
456*	250um. Biplane	22·00	22·00

1976. 75th Anniv of Zeppelin Airship.

517	5um. Airship LZ-4	30	10
518	10um. Airship LZ-10 *Schwaben*	55	25
519	12um. Airship LZ-13 *Hansa*	75	40
520	20um. Airship LZ-120 *Bodensee*	1·40	55
521	50um. Airship LZ-127 *Graf Zeppelin* (air)	3·25	1·30
522	60um. Airship LZ-130 *Graf Zeppelin II*	4·25	1·60
517/522 *Set of 6*		9·50	3·75
MS523	100um. Airship LZ-129 *Hindenburg*	7·50	2·30

1977. History of Aviation.

554	12um. Charles Lindbergh and Ryan NYP Special *Spirit of St. Louis*	75	25
555	14um. Clement Ader and his monoplane *Eole*,1890	95	25
556	15um. Louis Bleriot and Bleriot XI	1·10	40
557	55um. General Italo Balbo and Savoia Marchetti S-55X flying boats	3·50	90
558	60um. Concorde	3·75	1·10
554/558 *Set of 5*		9·00	2·50
MS559	100um. Charles Lindbergh and Ryan NYP Special *Spirit of St. Louis*	7·25	2·10

1979. 75th Anniv of First Powered Flight.

601	15um. Wright *Flyer I* and Clement Ader's *Avion III*	95	55
602	40um. Wright *Flyer I* and Concorde	2·75	1·50

1979.

620*	30um. Jet airliner	3·25	1·90

1980.

655	12um. Jet fighters	60	25
656	14um. Jet fighters	95	40

1981.

MS694*	100um. Boeing 747 SCA of NASA releasing Space Shuttle *Enterprise*	6·00	1·60

1983. Bicentenary of Manned Flight.

752*	14um. Montgolfier balloon (first manned free flight, 1783)	1·00	25
753*	18um. Charles' hydrogen balloon, 1783	1·00	25
754*	19um. Goodyear Aerospace airship (wrongly inscribed "Zeppelin")	1·00	45
755*	55um. Nieuport 11 "Bebe" biplane of the R. A. F.	2·75	70
756*	63um. Concorde	3·00	80

1983. Bicentenary of Manned Flight.

768	10um. Jean-Francois Pilatre de Rozier and Montgolfier balloon (first manned free flight, 1783)	55	25
769	14um. John Wise and his balloon *Atlantic*, 1859	1·10	25
770	25um. Charles Renard and Krebs' airship *La France*, 1884	1·40	35
771	100um. Henri Juillot and Lebaudy-Juillot airship *Patrie* (air)	6·00	1·40
768/771 *Set of 4*		8·00	2·00
MS772	100um. Joseph Montgolfier and balloon	6·00	1·70

1986. 55th Anniv (1985) of First Commercial South Atlantic Flight.

843	18um. Latecoere 28-3 seaplane F-AJNQ *Comte de la Vaulx*	75	45
844	50um. Piper PA-30 Twin Commanche	2·20	1·40

1986. 25th Anniv of Air Afrique.
858   26um. Boeing 737 (top) and Douglas DC-10
      of Air Afrique... 1·20 60

MAURITIUS

Indian Ocean

100 cents = 1 rupee

1949. As Nos. 114/15 of Antigua.
272*   12c. Airplane.. 50 1·75
273*   20c. Jet-powered Vickers Viking.................. 2·25 2·50

1970. Inauguration of Lufthansa Flight, Mauritius-Frankfurt.
415   25c. Boeing 707 of Lufthansa...................... 20 10
416   50c. Boeing 707 of Lufthansa...................... 20 10

1971. 25th Anniv of Plaisance Airport.
432*   60c. Boeing 707 of Air France at Plaisance
      Airport 70 10
433*   1r. Boeing 707 of Air France and cabin
      crew at Plaisance Airport..................... 75 10
434*   2r.50 Farman F.190 F-ALHG *Roland Garros*
      at Choissey Airfield, 1937 .... 2·25 4·50

1977. Inaugural International Flight of Air Mauritius.
524   25c. de Havilland Canada DHC-6 Twin
      Otter 200/300 of Air Mauritius........... 60 10
525   50c. de Havilland Canada DHC-6 Twin
      Otter 200/300 of Air Mauritius........... 80 10
526   75c. Piper PA-31 Navajo 5A-MCW of Air
      Mauritius and Boeing 747-100 .... 95 20
527   5r. Boeing 707 of Air Mauritius............... 3·00 3·75
524/527 *Set of* 4................................... 4·75 3·75

1983.
660*   10r. Hot-air balloon, Mauritius, 1784 .... 80 2·75

1988.
784*   5r. Boeing 707 at Sir Seewoosagur
      Ramgoolam International Airport..... 1·40 1·60

1991.
854*   10r. Supermarine Spitfire *Mauritius II*....... 4·50 8·00

1993. 25th Anniv of Air Mauritius Ltd.
885   40c. Bell 206B JetRanger helicopter of Air
      Mauritius.................................... 1·25 40
886   3r. Boeing 747SP of Air Mauritius .... 1·75 1·25
887   4r. Aerospatiale/Aeritalia ATR 42 of Air
      Mauritius.................................... 2·00 1·75
888   10r. Boeing 767-200ER of Air Mauritius ... 5·00 7·50
885/888 *Set of* 4.................................... 9·00 10·00

1994. 50th Anniv of ICAO.
906*   10p. Control tower, SSR International
      Airport .... 2·25 3·00

1995.
922*   5r. Consolidated PBY-5 Catalina.............. 2·00 2·50

1999.
1011*   2r. Boeing 747 .... 1·25 25

2004.
1116*   2r. Plaine Corail Airport and Avions de
      Transport Régional ATR42................... 55 25

MAYOTTE

Indian Ocean

1997. 100 cents = 1 franc

1997. Inauguration of New Airport.
52   20f. Terminal building and silhouette of
      airliner....................................... 5·75 4·75

1997. 20th Anniv of First Mayotte-Reunion Flight.
74   5f. Douglas DC-3................................ 1·70 1·50

2001. Dzaoudzi Flying Club.
137   20f. Airplanes....................................... 5·50 4·00

MEXICO

Central America

100 centavos = 1 peso

1929. First Death Anniv of Carranza (airman).
463   5c. Captain Emilio Carranza and Farman
      F.190 .... 1·30 70
464   10c. Captain Emilio Carranza and Farman
      F.190 .... 1·40 80
465   15c. Captain Emilio Carranza and Farman
      F.190 .... 3·25 1·30
466   20c. Captain Emilio Carranza and Farman
      F.190 .... 1·30 80
467   50c. Captain Emilio Carranza and Farman
      F.190 .... 6·75 2·75
468   1p. Captain Emilio Carranza and Farman
      F.190 .... 13·50 5·00
463/468 *Set of* 6................................... 25·00 10·00

1929. Perforated or rouletted.
476a   5c. Farman F.190 .... 25 15
477   10c. Farman F.190 .... 25 15
478   15c. Farman F.190 .... 30 15
479   20c. Farman F.190 .... 55 15
480   25c. Farman F.190 .... 1·10 85
472   30c. Farman F.190 .... 20 15
473   35c. Farman F.190 .... 35 25
481   50c. Farman F.190 .... 1·10 85
474   1p. Farman F.190 .... 1·30 60
475   5p. Farman F.190 .... 4·00 3·75
476   10p. Farman F.190 .... 6·25 7·25

1929. Aviation Week.
482   20c. Airplane.................................... 1·30 1·00
483   40c. Airplane.................................... 90·00 80·00

1930. No. 477 overprinted **Primer Congreso Nacional de Turismo. Mexico. Abril 20-27 de 1930.**
492   10c. Farman F.190 .... 2·20 1·30

1930. Nos. 463 and 465 overprinted **HABILITADO 1930.**
496   5c. Captain Emilio Carranza and Farman
      F.190 .... 6·25 5·25
497   15c. Captain Emilio Carranza and Farman
      F.190 .... 11·00 8·50

1930. Nos. 463/8 overprinted **HABILITADO Aereo 1930–1931.**
498   5c. Captain Emilio Carranza and Farman
      F.190 .... 6·75 6·50
499   10c. Captain Emilio Carranza and Farman
      F.190 .... 3·75 4·00
500   15c. Captain Emilio Carranza and Farman
      F.190 .... 7·25 7·00
501   20c. Captain Emilio Carranza and Farman
      F.190 .... 7·50 5·50
502   50c. Captain Emilio Carranza and Farman
      F.190 .... 13·50 10·50
503   1p. Captain Emilio Carranza and Farman
      F.190 .... 4·00 3·00
498/503 *Set of* 6................................... 38·00 33·00

1931. Aeronautic Week.
506   25c. Fokker F.10A Super Trimotor over
      airfield....................................... 4·00 4·25

1931. No. 479 surcharged **HABILITADO Quince centavos.**
516   15c. on 20c. Farman F.190.................... 60 80

1932. Nos. 506 and 479/80 surcharged in figures and words.

517*	20c. on 25c. Fokker F.10A Super Trimotor over airfield	70	25
521*	30c. on 20c. Farman F.190	35	15
522*	80c. on 25c. Farman F.190	1·60	1·30

1932. Nos. 463/7 overprinted **HABILITADO AERO-1932**.

523	5c. Captain Emilio Carranza and Farman F.190	5·50	3·00
524	10c. Captain Emilio Carranza and Farman F.190	5·50	3·00
525	15c. Captain Emilio Carranza and Farman F.190	5·50	3·00
526	20c. Captain Emilio Carranza and Farman F.190	5·50	3·00
527	50c. Captain Emilio Carranza and Farman F.190	38·00	36·00
523/527 Set of 5		55·00	43·00

1934.

553*	20c. Airplane	4·00	3·00
554*	30c. Airplane	8·00	5·75
555*	50c. Airplane	9·00	9·50
556*	75c. Airplane	9·00	14·50
557*	1p. Airplane	11·00	10·50
558*	5p. Airplane	60·00	85·00
559*	10p. Airplane	£160	£170
560*	20p. Airplane	£1300	£1400
553/560 Set of 8		£1400	£1500

1934.

575*	15c. Airplane	1·30	15
579*	1p. Aircraft	3·75	15
580*	5p. Airplane	7·50	70

1936.

594*	10c. Airplane	20	15
595*	20c. Douglas DC-2	35	15
596*	40c. Airplane	55	50

1938.

608*	40c. Biplane	80	35

1939.

640*	20c. Martin M-130 flying boat	1·10	15

1947.

793*	10p. Captain Emilio Carranza and Farman F.190	1·90	1·60
794*	20p. Douglas DC-4	3·00	3·00

1950.

869*	25c. Airliner	40	20

1960. 50th Anniv of Mexican Aviation.

974	50c. Alberto Braniff's Voisin "Boxkite" and Bristol Type 175 Britannia	55	15
975	1p. Alberto Braniff's Voisin "Boxkite" and Bristol Type 175 Britannia	40	25

1960.

990*	50c. Douglas DC-8	50	20

1962. Centenary of First Mexican Balloon Flight.

1010	80c. Balloon over Mexico City, 1862	1·90	65

1967. 50th Anniv of First Mexican Airmail Flight.

1138*	2p. Captain Horacio Ruiz Gavino's de Havilland D.H.6A biplane, 1917	55	30

1974. 50th Anniv of Mexicana (Mexican airlines).

1310	80c. Lincoln Standard biplane	30	15
1311	2p. Boeing 727-200 of Mexicana	30	15

1978. 50th Anniv of First Mexican Airmail Route.

1430	1p.60 Fairchild FC-71 X-ABCI of Mexicana	30	20
1431	4p.30 Fairchild FC-71 X-ABCI of Mexicana	40	20

1978. 50th Anniv of Mexico-Washington Flight by Emilio Carranza.

1440	1p.60 Captain Emilio Carranza and Farman F.190 (on stamp No. 464)	30	20

1978. 75th Anniv of First Powered Flight.

1465	1p.60 Wilbur and Orville Wright and Wright Flyer III	30	15
1466	4p.30 Wright Flyer I	40	20

1991.

1990	700p. Airliner	70	45

1991.

2004*	1000p. Boeing 737	1·20	65
2005*	1000p. Boeing 737 landing	1·20	65
2017*	1500p. Boeing 737 and control tower	1·60	80

1994. 50th Death Anniv of Antoine de Saint-Exupery.

2232	2p. Antoine de Saint-Exupery (pioneer aviator)	1·90	85

1994. 50th Anniv of ICAO.

2240	2p. Abstract, no airplanes	1·60	95

1995.

2257	2p.70 Kite	1·50	85

1995.

2309	2p.70 Stylised airliner	1·20	85

1996. National Aviation Day.

2333	1p.80 Grumman Gulfstream III	1·10	70
2334	1p.80 Squadron 201, 1945	1·10	70
2335	2p.70 Ley Airport	1·70	1·00
2336	2p.70 Modern jetliner and biplane	1·70	1·00
2333/2336 Set of 4		5·00	3·00

1997. 50th Anniv of Mexican Air Pilots' College.

2462	2p.30 Douglas DC-3 and Douglas DC-10	90	50

151

1998. 25th Anniv of Latin American Civil Aviation.
2560	3p.40 Airbus A320	1·10	70

2002. 50th Anniv of Mexico City Airport.
2783	6p. Aviators	2·40	1·50
2784	6p. Aviators	2·50	1·70
2785	8p.50 Aviators	4·00	3·50
2783/2785 Set of 3		8·00	6·00

Nos. 2783/2785 form a composite design featuring "Man's Conquest of the Air" by Juan O'Gorman.

2003. Centenary of Powered Flight.
2793	8p.50 Wright *Flyer*	2·50	1·60

EXPRESS LETTER STAMPS

1956.
E956*	80c. Douglas DC-4	50	65
E1066*	1p.20 Douglas DC-4	3·50	1·10
E1346q*	5p. Douglas DC-4	2·75	1·20

OFFICIAL STAMPS

1929. Nos. 476a and 482 overprinted **OFICIAL**.
O501*	5c. Farman F.190	1·00	1·00
O502*	20c. Airplane	1·20	1·90

1930.
O503	20c. Stinson SM-1 Detroiter	7·25	7·00
O504	35c. Stinson SM-1 Detroiter	1·30	2·20
O505	40c. Stinson SM-1 Detroiter	1·50	2·10
O506	70c. Stinson SM-1 Detroiter	1·50	2·10
O503/506 Set of 4		10·50	12·00

1931. No. O503 surcharged **HABILITADO Quince centavos**.
O515	15c. on 20c. Stinson SM-1 Detroiter	45	55

1932. Nos. 478/9 overprinted **SERVICIO OFICIAL** in one line.
O532*	10c. Farman F.190	45	60
O533*	15c. Farman F.190	1·50	2·10
O534*	20c. Farman F.190	1·50	2·10

1933. Nos. 476a/7, 479 and 481 overprinted **SERVICIO OFICIAL** in two lines.
O548	5c. Farman F.190	45	60
O549	10c. Farman F.190	45	35
O550	20c. Farman F.190	80	1·10
O551	50c. Farman F.190	1·50	2·10
O548/551 Set of 4		2·75	3·75

MICRONESIA

Pacific Ocean

100 cents = 1 dollar

1984.
21	28c. Boeing 727-100 of Air Micronesia		45	40
22	35c. Grumman SA-16 Albatross flying boat of Pan Am		60	55
23	40c. Consolidated PBY-5A Catalina amphibian of Trans Ocean Airways		75	70
21/23 Set of 3			1·60	1·50

1988.
80*	44c. Tourists disembarking from Douglas DC-10		70	65

1989.
126*	25c. North American X-15		35	35

1990.
185	22c. Beech 18		30	30
186	36c. Boeing 727		50	45
187	39c. Britten-Norman BN-2 Islander		55	55
188	45c. Beech 80 Queen Air		60	60
185/188 Set of 4			1·70	1·70

1990.
196	25c. Airliner being loaded with mail at Pohnpei Airport		35	35
197	45c. Mitsubishi A6M Zero-Sen		90	90

1991.
219*	29c. Boeing E-3 Sentry		45	40
220*	29c. Grumman F-14 Tomcat		45	40

1992.
253	40c. Britten Norman Islander		50	50
254	50c. Boeing 727-200		60	60

1993. Pioneers of Flight (1st series).
267	29c. Eddie Rickenbacker and Sopwith Camel		45	40
268	29c. Manfred von Richthofen (Red Baron) and Fokker DR-1 Triplane		45	40
269	29c. Andrei Tupolev and Tupolev Tu-144.		45	40
270	29c. John Macready and Fokker T-2		45	40
271	29c. Sir Charles Kingsford-Smith and Fokker F. VII		45	40
272	29c. Igor Sikorsky and Sikorsky VS300 helicopter		45	40
273	29c. Lord Trenchard (Father of the Royal Air Force) and Handley Page 0/400		45	40
274	29c. Glenn Curtiss and Curtiss JN-4 'Jenny'		45	40
267/274 Set of 8			3·25	2·75

1993. Pioneers of Flight (2nd series).
322*	50c. Lawrence Sperry and Sperry Messenger		50	45
323*	50c. Alberto Santos-Dumont and *14 bis*		50	45
326*	50c. Orville Wright and *Flyer I*		50	45
327*	50c. Wilbur Wright and *Flyer I*		50	45
328*	50c. Otto Lilienthal and glider		50	45
329*	50c. Sir Thomas Sopwith and Sopwith Camel		50	45

1994. Pioneers of Flight (3rd series).
364*	29c. Octave Chanute and glider		55	50
365*	29c. T. Claud Ryan and Ryan PT-22 Recruit		55	50
368*	29c. Frank Whittle and Gloster E. 28/39		55	50
369*	29c. Waldo Waterman and Waterman Arrowbile		55	50

1994. Pioneers of Flight (4th series).
397*	50c. William Bishop and Nieuport 17		60	60
399*	50c. John Towers and Curtiss NC-4		60	60
401*	50c. Marcel Dassault and Dassault Mirage F.1C		60	60
402*	50c. Geoffrey de Havilland and de Havilland DH. 98 Mosquito		60	60

1995. Pioneers of Flight (5th series).
419*	32c. Leroy Grumman and Grumman F6F Hellcat		50	45
420*	32c. Louis-Charles Breguet and Breguet Bre.16		50	45
421*	32c. Juan de la Cierva and Cierva C-4		50	45
422*	32c. Hugo Junkers and Junkers Ju52/3m		50	45
424*	32c. Donald Douglas and Douglas DC-3.		50	45
425*	32c. Reginald Mitchell and Supermarine Spitfire		50	45

1995. Pioneers of Flight (6th series).
441*	60c. Frederick Rohr and Consolidated B-24 Liberator		85	80
442*	60c. Juan Trippe and Martin M-130 China Clipper		85	80
444*	60c. Count Ferdinand von Zeppelin and Zeppelin airship		85	80
445*	60c. Air Chief Marshall Hugh Dowding, Hawker Hurricane (top) and Supermarine Spitfire (below)		85	80
446*	60c. William Mitchell and Martin MB-2		85	80
447*	60c. John E. Northrop and Northrop Alpha		85	80
448*	60c. Frederick Handley Page and Handley Page Halifax		85	80

1995. Pioneers of Flight (7th series).

453	32c. James Doolittle and North American B-25 Mitchell	50	45
454	32c. Claude Dornier and Dornier Do-X	50	45
455	32c. Ira Eaker and Boeing B-17 Flying Fortress	50	45
456	32c. Jacob Ellehammer and Ellehammer semi-biplane	50	45
457	32c. Henry 'Hap' Arnold and Boeing B-17 Flying Fortress	50	45
458	32c. Louis Bleriot and Bleriot XI	50	45
459	32c. William Boeing and Boeing P-12	50	45
460	32c. Sydney Camm and Hawker Hurricane	50	45
453/460 *Set of 8*		3·50	3·25

1996. Pioneers of Flight (8th series).

514*	60c. Curtis Le May and Boeing B-52 Stratofortress	90	85
515*	60c. Grover Loening and Loening OA-1	90	85
516*	60c. Gianni Caproni and Caproni Ca5	90	85
517*	60c. Henri Farman and Henri Farman III (HFI)	90	85
518*	60c. Glenn Martin and Martin TT (with floats)	90	85
519*	60c. Alliot Verdon Roe and Avro 504 K	90	85
521*	60c. Isaac Laddon and Consolidated P2Y-2 Ranger	90	85

1999. Man's First Century of Flight.

870	33c. Wright *Flyer I*	50	45
871	33c. Bleriot XI	50	45
872	33c. Fokker D.VII	50	45
873	33c. Dornier Komet I	50	45
874	33c. Charles Lindbergh's Ryan NYP Special *Spirit of St. Louis*	50	45
875	33c. Mitsubishi A6M Zero-Sen	50	45
876	33c. Boeing B-29 Superfortress	50	45
877	33c. Messerschmitt Me 262A	50	45
878	33c. Bell X-1	50	45
879	33c. Mikoyan Gurevich MiG-19	50	45
880	33c. Lockheed U-2	50	45
881	33c. Boeing 707	50	45
882	33c. Concorde	50	45
883	33c. McDonnell Douglas DC-10	50	45
884	33c. Northrop B-2A Spirit	50	45
870/884 *Set of 15*		6·75	6·00
MS885 Two sheets. (a) $2 Dornier Do-X; (b) $2 Lockheed P-38 Lightning *Price for 2 sheets*		5·75	5·75

2000.

939*	20c. Lindbergh and Ryan NYP Special *Spirit of St. Louis*	30	30
946*	20c. Douglas World Cruisers	30	30

2000.

981*	33c. Howard Hughes, (aviator and businessman)	50	50

2000. Centenary of First Zeppelin Flight and Airship Development.

1031	33c. Zodiac airship *Capitaine Ferber*	50	45
1032	33c. Astra airship *Adjutant Reau*	50	45
1033	33c. Airship 1A, Italy	50	45

1034	33c. Astra-Torres No. 14	50	45
1033	33c. Front of Astra-Torres No 14, Schuttle-Lanz SL3 and front of Siemens-Shukert airship	50	45
1036	33c. Siemens-Shukert airship	50	45
1031/1036 *Set of 6*		2·75	2·40
MS1037 Two sheets. (a) $2 Zeppelin LZ-130 *Graf Zeppelin II*; (b) $2 Dupuy de Lome airship		5·75	5·75

2001. 60th Anniv of Attack on Pearl Harbour.

MS1174 Three sheets. (a) 60c. Attack on Wheeler Field; 60c. Japanese bomber; 60c. Bombing of USS *Arizona* (other stamps in the miniature sheet and the other miniature sheets do not show aircraft) *Price for 3 sheets* ... 5·75 5·75

2003. 75th Anniv of First Solo Trans-Atlantic Flight.

MS1218 60c. Lindbergh, Donald Hall, Ryan NYP Special, *Spirit of St. Louis;* 60c. Ryan NYP Special *Spirit of St. Louis;* 60c. Ryan NYP Special *Spirit of St. Louis* on Curtis Field; 60c. Ryan NYP Special *Spirit of St. Louis* airborne; 60c. Arriving in Paris; 60c. Ticker-tape parade, New York ... 5·25 5·00

2003.

MS1222* Two sheets. (a) 37c. Boeing B-52 Stratofortress; 37c. Lockheed Martin F-16 Fighting Falcon; 37c. Bell AH-1 Huey Cobra; 37c. Boeing (McDonnell Douglas/Hughes) AH-64 Apache. (b) 37c. Lockheed F-117A Nighthawk; 37c. Lockheed AC-130 Hercules; 37c. Sikorsky MH-53 Pave Low; 37c. General Atomics RQ-1 Predator (other stamps in the miniature sheets do not show aircraft) *Price for 2 sheets* ... 6·50 6·25

2003. Centenary of Powered Flight.

MS1226 Two sheets. (a) 55c. Concorde; 55c. Boeing 757; 55c. Junkers F. 13a; 55c. Martin M-130 China Clipper; 55c. Handley Page HP 42W; 55c. Wright *Flyer II*. (b) $2 Boeing 747 *Price for 2 sheets* ... 8·00 7·50

2005.

1318*	60c. Hawker Typhoon	90	90
1324*	60c. Paul Tibbets (pilot) and Boeing B-29 Superfortress *Enola* Gay	90	90
1325*	60c. Atomic cloud, Hiroshima	90	90

2005.

MS1331 $1 Hot air balloon (other stamps in the miniature sheet do not show aircraft) ... 4·75 4·50

2006.

1426	75c. Concorde in flight	75	70
1427	75c. Concorde on ground	75	70

MOLDOVA

South-east Europe

100 kopeks = 1 rouble

1992.

15	1r.75 Tupolev Tu-144	35	30
16	2r.50 Tupolev Tu-144	45	30
17	7r.75 Tupolev Tu-144	60	50
18	8r.50 Tupolev Tu-144	1·10	95
15/18 *Set of 4*		2·20	1·80

1992.

55*	10r. Douglas DC-10	1·10	55

1993. As Nos. 15/18 but values and colours changed.

70	25r. red	45	40
71	45r. brown	65	55
72	50r. green	75	65
73	90r. blue	1·70	1·40
70/73 *Set of 4*		3·50	2·75

1995.

193*	10b. Airplane in eye	45	35

2003. Airships.

452	40b. Tissandier Brothers' Airship (1883)	65	55
453	2l. *Uchebny* (Training Craft) (1908)	2·50	2·20
454	5l. Zeppelin LZ-127 *Graf Zeppelin* (1928)	6·50	6·00
452/454 *Set of 3*		8·75	8·00

MONACO

Southern Europe

1933. 100 centimes = 1 franc

2002. 100 cents = 1 euro

1933. No. 104 surcharged **1F.50** and Bleriot XI airplane.

143	1f.50 on 5f. Monaco	26·00	22·00

1942.

271*	5f. Caudron C-530 Rafale	10	40
272*	10f. Caudron C-530 Rafale	10	40
276*	100f. Airplane	3·00	3·75

1945. As No. 272 and 276, surcharged **1f.+4f.**

302*	1f. +4f. on 10f. Caudron C-530 Rafale	50	55
306*	1f. +4f. on 100f. Airplane	50	55

1946. Nos. 311/12 overprinted **POSTE AERIENNE** and Sud Ouest SO.90 Cassiopees airplane.

320	50f. Prince Louis II	4·50	3·50
321	100f. Prince Louis II	4·50	3·50

MONACO

1946.

323	40f. Sud Ouest SO.90 Cassiopees	1·10	95
324	50f. Sud Ouest SO.90 Cassiopees	1·90	1·90
325	100f. Sud Ouest SO.90 Cassiopees	2·50	1·80
326	200f. Sud Ouest SO.90 Cassiopees	3·50	5·00
326a	300f. Sud Ouest SO.90 Cassiopees	65·00	65·00
326b	500f. Sud Ouest SO.90 Cassiopees	45·00	45·00
326c	1000f. Sud Ouest SO.90 Cassiopees	75·00	65·00
323/326c	Set of 7	£170	£170

1946.

333*	5f. Sud Ouest SO.95 Corse II	60	60
334*	10f. Sud Ouest SO.95 Corse II	75	60

1947.

340*	10f. Sud Ouest SO.95 Corse II	3·75	2·75
341*	15f. Sud Ouest SO.95 Corse II	6·75	6·75

1948.

349*	6f. +9f. Airplane	15·00	11·00
350*	10f. +15f. Airplane	22·00	16·00
351*	15f. +25f. Airplane	34·00	24·00

1955.

529*	1f. Balloon from *Five weeks in a Balloon* by Jules Verne	10	15

1956. Nos. D484/5, D488 and D490/1 overprinted or surcharged with bars obliterating "TIMBRE TAXE". Nos. 575/6 additionally overprinted **POSTE AERIENNE**.

555*	2f. on 4f. Santos-Dumont's monoplane No. 20 *Demoiselle*	35	40
556*	2f. on 4f. de Havilland DH.106 Comet 1 jet airliner	35	40
559*	5f. on 4f. Santos-Dumont's monoplane No. 20 *Demoiselle*	75	75
560*	5f. on 4f. de Havilland DH.106 Comet 1 jet airliner	75	75
561*	10f. on 4f. Santos-Dumont's monoplane No. 20 *Demoiselle*	1·10	1·10
562*	10f. on 4f. de Havilland DH.106 Comet 1 jet airliner	1·10	1·10
565*	20f. Mail balloon, Paris, 1870	3·00	3·00
566*	20f. Airship LZ-127 *Graf Zeppelin*	3·00	3·00
567*	25f. on 20f. Mail balloon, Paris, 1870	4·50	5·50
568*	25f. on 20f. Airship LZ-127 *Graf Zeppelin*	4·50	5·50
569*	30f. on 10f. Leonardo da Vinci's drawing of a "flying machine"	7·50	9·25
575*	100f. on 20f. Mail balloon, Paris, 1870 (air)	10·50	8·00
576*	100f. on 20f. Airship LZ-127 *Graf Zeppelin*	10·50	8·00

1963. 50th Anniv of First Aerial Crossing of Mediterranean Sea.

769	2f. Roland Garros and Morane Saulnier Type I	1·10	75

1964. 50th Anniv of First Aerial Rally, Monte Carlo.

787	1c. Deperdussin Monocoque Racer	10	15
788	2c. Renaux's Farman M.F.7 floatplane	10	15
789	3c. Espanet's Nieuport 4 seaplane	10	15
790	4c. Moineau's Breguet HU-3 seaplane	10	15
791	5c. Roland Garros' Morane Saulnier Type I seaplane	10	15
792	10c. Hirth's WDD Albatros seaplane	10	15
793	15c. Prevost's Deperdussin Monocoque Racer	15	15
794	20c. Ross and Keith Smith's Vickers Vimy G-EAOU, 1919	20	25
795	25c. Douglas World Cruiser seaplane, 1924	20	25
796	30c. De Pinedo's Savoia Marchetti S-55M flying boat *Santa Maria*, 1925	35	40
797	45c. Admiral Richard E. Byrd's Fokker F.VIIa/3m *Josephine Ford*	75	70
798	50c. Lindbergh's Ryan NYP Special *Spirit of St. Louis*	75	80
799	65c. Breguet 19 Super Bidon TR *Point d'Interrogation*	1·50	80
800	95c. Latecoere 28-3 seaplane F-AJNQ *Comte de la Vaulx*	1·90	1·40
801	1f. Dornier Do-X flying boat	2·30	1·40
802	5f. Convair B-58A Hustler (air)	2·50	5·50
787/802	Set of 16	10·00	11·50

1970. 60th Anniv (1973) of First Mediterranean Crossing.

1001	40c. Henri Rougier and Voisin "Boxkite"	20	10

1972. Birth Centenary of Louis Bleriot.

1062*	30c. Louis Bleriot and Bleriot XI	10	25

1973. Birth Centenary of Sir George *Cayley*.

1080*	90c. Sir George Cayley and his "convertiplane", 1843	45	55

1974. Birth Centenary of Henri Farman.

1115	30c. Henri Farman, Farman F.60 Goliath (top) and Farman H.F.III	20	25

1976. 50th Anniv of First Flights over North Pole.

1276	85c. Admiral Richard E. Byrd, Roald Amundsen, Fokker F.VIIa/3m *Josephine Ford* and airship N.1 *Norge*	1·50	1·10

1977. 50th Anniv of Lindbergh's Trans-Atlantic Flight.

1297	1f.90 Charles Lindbergh and Ryan NYP Special *Spirit of St. Louis*	1·50	1·10

1978.

1331*	5c. Wrecked balloon from *L'Ile Mysterieuse* by Jules Verne	10	15

1983.

1613*	1f.80 Montgolfier balloon (first manned free flight, 1783)	1·10	55

1984.

1658*	2f.80 Piccard's stratosphere balloon *F.N.R.S.*, 1931	1·10	55

1990. 30th International Airports Association Congress, Monte Carlo.

1997	3f. Bell 206B JetRanger III helicopters at Monaco heliport	1·50	55
1998	5f. Aerospatiale AS-350 Ecureuil helicopters	3·00	1·20

1994. 50th Anniv of ICAO.

2200	5f. Bell 206 and heliport	2·20	1·10
2201	7f. Eurocopter AS365 Dauphin 2 over harbour	3·00	1·60

2000. First Non-stop Balloon Circumnavigation of Globe (1999).

2490	9f. Breitling Orbiter	3·00	2·75

2003. Centenary of Powered Flight.

2606	€1.80 Wright Brothers and *Flyer I*	2·30	1·50

2007. Centenary of First Flight of Leger Helicopter.
2809   €1.15 Léger helicopter and modern helicopter........................... 3·75   3·75

POSTAGE DUE STAMPS

1953.
D479*   1f. Sikorsky S-51 helicopter...................... 10   15
D484*   4f. Santos-Dumont's monoplane No. 20 *Demoiselle*.............................. 10   25
D485*   4f. de Havilland DH.106 Comet 1 jet airliner............................... 10   25
D488*   10f. Leonardo da Vinci's drawing of a "flying machine"....................... 9·75   8·00
D490*   20f. Mail balloon, Paris, 1870 .... 5·50   5·50
D491*   20f. Airship LZ-127 *Graf Zeppelin*............... 5·50   5·50

MONGOLIA

Central Asia

100 mung = 1 tugrik

1961.
231*   50m. Ilyushin Il-14M 75   20

1965.
MS355a 4t. Boeing 707 .... 3·25   3·25

1965.
362*   20m. Helicopter................................. 3·25   65

1969.
523*   30m. Mil Mi-4 helicopter........................ 95   20

1970.
MS591 4t. Sikorsky S-61B SH-3 Sea King helicopter.   5·75   5·75

1971.
620*   60m. Polikarpov Po-2 biplane.................... 1·20   30
621*   80m. Antonov An-24B of Aeroflot................. 1·30   45

1972.
671*   40m. Tupolev Tu-144............................ 1·20   20

1973.
742*   1t.50 Antonov An-24............................ 2·40   45

1974.
819*   50m. Engraving of a "sail-steered balloon", 1789......................... 1·90   45
820*   50m. Polikarpov Po-2 biplane.................... 2·40   45

Тээвэр—50
1975—7—15.

1975. Nos. 620/1 overprinted with Cyrillic text and **1975–7–15**.
922*   60m. Polikarpov Po-2 biplane.................... 3·25   3·25
923*   80m. Antonov An-24B of Aeroflot................. 4·25   4·25

1976. Aircraft.
1014   10m. R-1 biplane............................... 20   10
1015   20m. Polikarpov R-5 biplane 30   10
1016   30m. Kalinin K-5 40   10
1017   40m. Polikarpov Po-2 biplane.................... 50   15
1018   60m. Polikarpov I-16 fighter and airplane on fire................................. 70   25
1019   80m. Yakovlev Ya-6 Air 6 90   35
1020   1t. Junkers F-13 .... 1·10   50
1014/1020 *Set of 7* .... 3·75   1·40

1977. First Balloon Flight in Mongolia.
MS1061* 4t.+50m. Hot-air balloon.................... 7·75   6·75

1977.
1078*   1t. Mil Mi-8 fire-fighting helicopter......... 80   45

1977. Airships and Balloons.
1099   20m. Montgolfier balloon (first manned free flight, 1783) (wrongly dated "21.10.1783").......................... 20   10
1100   30m. Airship LZ-127 *Graf Zeppelin*............ 25   15
1101   40m. Airship Osoaviakhim CCCP-86.............. 30   20
1102   50m. Airship *Sever*........................... 40   25
1103   60m. Aereon 340 airship....................... 60   35
1104   80m. Airship design by Nestrenko.............. 80   45
1105   1t.20 "Flying Crane" airship .... 1·20   55
1099/1105 *Set of 7* .... 3·50   1·80
MS1106 4t. Airship LZ-127 *Graf Zeppelin* (on Russia stamp No. 584)........................ 3·00   3·00

1978. History of Aviation.
1121   20m. Aleksandr Mozhaisky and his monoplane, 1884 20   10
1122   30m. Henri Farman and Farman H.F.III biplane 30   15
1123   40m. Geoffrey de Havilland and de Havilland FE-1 biplane 40   20
1124   50m. Charles Lindbergh and Ryan NYP Special *Spirit of St. Louis*..... 50   25
1125   60m. Shagdarsuren, Demberel, biplane and glider 60   30
1126   80m. Chkalov, Baidukov, Belyakov and Tupolev ANT-25................. 80   35
1127   1t.20 A.N. Tupolev and Tupolev Tu-154 ...... 1·20   55
1121/1127 *Set of 7* .... 3·50   1·70
MS1128 4t. Wilbur and Orville Wright and Wright *Flyer III* .... 3·50   3·50

1978.
1147   1t. Tupolev Tu-134............................ 1·40   35

1979.
1205*   50m. Antonov An-12 of the Mongolian Air Force..................................... 50   20

1980. World Aerobatic Championship, Oshkosh, USA.
1274   20m. Zlin Z-526 AFS Akrobat Special 10   10
1275   30m. Socata RF-6B Sportsman (inscribed "RS-180")........................... 20   15
1276   40m. Grumman A-1 Yankee (inscribed "YANKI-ANU")......................... 30   20

1277	50m. MJ-2 Tempete	40	20
1278	60m. Pitts S-2A biplane (inscribed "PITS")..	50	25
1279	80m. Hirth Acrostar.......................	60	35
1280	1t.20 Yakovlev Yak-50	90	45
1274/1280 *Set of 7*		2·75	1·50
MS1281 4t. Yakovlev Yak-52		3·00	3·00

1980.

1322*	1t.20 Ilyushin Il-18B	4·00	1·10

1981.

1334	60m. Mikoyan Gurevich MiG-23 jet fighters	60	25

1981.

1360*	30m. Ilyushin Il-62M	30	15
1361*	40m. Mil Mi-8 helicopter	40	20

1981. 50th Anniv of *Graf Zeppelin* Polar Flight.

1391	20m. Airship LZ-127 *Graf Zeppelin* (also on Germany stamp No. 469)	40	20
1392	30m. Airship LZ-127 *Graf Zeppelin* (also on Germany stamp No. 470)	50	20
1393	40m. Airship LZ-127 *Graf Zeppelin* (also on Germany stamp No. 471)	60	25
1394	50m. Airship LZ-127 *Graf Zeppelin* (also on Russia stamp No. 584)	70	30
1395	60m. Airship LZ-127 *Graf Zeppelin* (also on Russia stamp No. 585)	1·10	35
1396	80m. Airship LZ-127 *Graf Zeppelin* (also on Russia stamp No. 586)	1·30	55
1397	1t.20 Airship LZ-127 *Graf Zeppelin* (also on Russia stamp No. 587)	1·50	60
1391/1397 *Set of 7*		5·50	2·20
MS1398 4t. Airship LZ-127 *Graf Zeppelin*		5·25	5·25

1982. Bicentenary of Manned Flight.

1494	20m. Montgolfier balloon (tethered flight, 1783)	10	10
1495	30m. Blanchard and Jeffries' balloon, 1785	20	10
1496	40m. Charles Green's balloon *Royal Vauxhall*, 1836..........................	30	15
1497	50m. Salomon Andree's balloon *Ornen*, 1897..................................	40	20

1498	60m. Balloons in first Gordon Bennett race, Paris, 1906.......................	50	25
1499	80m. Piccard's stratosphere balloon *F.N.R.S.*, 1931	60	30
1500	1t.20 Stratosphere balloon USSR-VR-62.....	1·00	35
1494/1500 *Set of 7*		2·75	1·30
MS1501 4t. Hot-air balloon, Ulan Bator, 1977.............		3·00	3·00

1983.

1524*	20m. Antonov An-24B of Aeroflot	20	10

1983.

1546*	80m. Jet airliner...........................	2·50	55

1984.

1581*	40m. Antonov An-24 of MIAT-Air Mongol .	40	25

1984.

MS1586* 4t. Tupolev Tu-154		4·00	4·00

1984. Civil Aviation.

1597	20m. Douglas DC-10	20	10
1598	30m. Airbus Industrie A300B2 of Swissair.	30	15
1599	40m. Concorde of Air France...................	40	25
1600	50m. Boeing 747-200........................	50	35
1601	60m. Ilyushin Il-62M of Interflug.................	60	40
1602	80m. Tupolev Tu-154 of Aeroflot	80	45
1603	1t.20 Ilyushin Il-86 of Aeroflot	1·20	50
1597/1603 *Set of 7*		3·50	2·00
MS1604 4t. Yakovlev Yak-42		4·00	4·00

1987. Helicopters.

1880	20m. Mil Mi-V12 helicopter..................	10	10
1881	30m. Westland WG-30 helicopter...........	20	15
1882	40m. Bell 206L LongRanger II helicopter ...	30	20
1883	50m. Kawasaki-Hughes 369HS helicopter	40	25
1884	60m. Kamov Ka-32 helicopter.................	50	30

1885	80m. Mil Mi-17 helicopter..................	70	30
1886	1t.20 Mil Mi-10K helicopter....................	80	35
1880/1886 *Set of 7*		2·75	1·50

1989.

MS2020 4t. Tupolev Tu-154		3·00	3·00

1989.

MS2034 20m. Concorde of Air France (sheet contains 2 other designs)		6·00	6·00

1989.

2043	60m. Fighter aircraft	85	45

1989. No. **MS**2034 overprinted **WORLD STAMP EXPO '89**.

MS2072 20m. Concorde of Air France (sheet contains 2 other designs)		6·00	6·00

1991.

2242	1t.20 Tupolev Tu-154	3·25	85

1992. 75th Death Anniv of Count Ferdinand von Zeppelin (airship pioneer).

MS2325 16t. Von Zeppelin wearing white cap..........		3·25	3·25

1993. Airship flight over Ulan Bator.
2415   80t. Hologram of airship.................................. 3·25   2·50

1994.
MS2435 600t. Boeing 727 .... 3·75   3·75

1998.
2676*   100t. Tupolev Tu-154 50   40
2681*   200t. Tupolev Tu-154 .... 1·10   85
2686*   200t. Tupolev Tu-154 .... 1·10   85
2691*   400t. Tupolev Tu-154 .... 2·10   1·60
2696*   400t. Tupolev Tu-154 .... 2·10   1·60

2001.
2929*   300t. Barrage balloon................................. 1·10   65

2001.
MS2952* 50t. Zeppelin airship (stylised); 100t. Air
balloon; 250t. Concorde (other stamps in the
miniature sheet do not show aircraft)....................... 11·00   11·00

2006.
3082*   200t. Aircraft 75   60
MS3084 Six sheets. (f) As Nos. 3082/3 (other
miniature sheets do not show aircraft) *Price for* 6
sheets... 9·75   9·75

MONTENEGRO

South-east Europe

Italian Occupation

1941. 100 paras = 1 dinar

1942. 100 centesimi = 1 lira

Montenegro

Црна Гора

17-IV-41-XIX

1941. Nos. 360/7 of Yugoslavia overprinted with Cyrillic characters
and **Montenegro 17-IV-41-XIX.**
15*   50p. Fokker F.VIIa/3m .... 3·50   3·00
16*   1d. Junkers G.31 .... 3·50   3·00
17*   2d. Fokker F.VIIa/3m .... 3·50   2·75
18*   2d.50 Fokker F.VIIa/3m .... 3·00   2·75
19*   5d. Fokker F.VIIa/3m .... 35·00   30·00
20*   10d. Junkers G.31 .... 3·50   2·75
21*   20d. Fokker F.VIIa/3m .... 4·50   4·25
22*   30d. Fokker F.VIIa/3m .... 11·00   8·00

1942. Nos. 360/7 of Yugoslavia overprinted **Governatorato del
Montenegro Valore LIRE.**
52b   0l.50 Fokker F.VIIa/3m 20   15
53b   1l. Junkers G.31 45   20
54b   2l. Fokker F.VIIa/3m 35   45
55b   2l.50 Fokker F.VIIa/3m 30   25
56b   5l. Fokker F.VIIa/3m 30   45
57b   10l. Junkers G.31 30   45
58b   20l. Fokker F.VIIa/3m £350   £350
59b   30l. Fokker F.VIIa/3m .... 90·00   60·00

1943.
70   50c. Fokker F.VIIa/3m .... 3·50   2·25
71   1l. Fokker F.VIIa/3m .... 3·50   2·25
72   2l. Junkers G.31 .... 22·00   4·00
73   5l. Fokker F.VIIa/3m .... 22·00   1·90
74   10l. Fokker F.VIIa/3m .... 25·00   1·90
75   20l. Junkers G.31 .... 12·00   2·25

German Occupation

1943. 100 centesimi = 1 lira

1944. 100 rentenpfennige = 1 rentenmark

1943. Nos. 70/4 overprinted **Nationaler Verwaltungsausschuss
10.XI.1943.**
90*   50c. Fokker F.VIIa/3m 30   1·00
91*   1l. Fokker F.VIIa/3m 30   1·00
92*   2l. Junkers G.31 30   1·00
93*   5l. Fokker F.VIIa/3m 30   1·00
94*   10l. Fokker F.VIIa/3m 30   1·00

1944. Nos. 52/4 surcharged **Fluchtlingshilfe Montenegro** and
value.
101*   15pf. +85pf. on 0l.50 Fokker F.VIIa/3m........ 1·00   1·50
102*   25pf. +1m.25 on 1l. Junkers G.31 30   30
103*   50pf. +1m.50 on 2l. Fokker F.VIIa/3m 30   30

1944. Nos. 70/2 surcharged+Crveni krst Montenegro and value.
108*   25pf. +1m.75 on 50c. Fokker F.VIIa/3m 35   35
109*   25pf. +2m.75 on 1l. Fokker F.VIIa/3m 50   50
110*   50pf. +2m. on 2l. Junkers G.31 75   1·50

MONTSERRAT

West Indies

1949. 12 pence = 1 shilling

20 shillings = 1 pound

1951. 100 cents = 1 dollar

1949. As Nos. 114/15 of Antigua.
117*   2½d. Airplane..................................... 15   1·25
118*   3d. Jet-powered Vickers Viking................ 1·75   75

1969.
229*   50c. Hawker Siddeley H.S.748 15   20

1971. 14th Anniv of Inauguration of LIAT (Leeward Islands Air
Transport).
280   5c. Piper PA-23 Apache of L.I.A.T 10   10
281   10c. Beech 50 Twin Bonanza VP-LIF
of L. A. T. 15   15
282   15c. de Havilland DH.114 Heron 2 VP-LIA
of L.I.A.T. 30   15
283   20c. Britten-Norman BN-2 Islander VP-
LAE of L. I. A. T. 35   15
284   40c. de Havilland Canada DHC-6 Twin
Otter 100 VP-LIR of L.I.A.T. 50   45
285   75c. Hawker Siddeley H.S.748 VP-LIP
of L. I. A. T. .... 1·40   2·25
280/285 *Set of* 6 .... 2·50   3·00

1980.
461*   55c. Hawker Siddeley H.S.748 of L.I.A.T 25   25
465* $1.20 Aeronca Champion 17 30   55

1981. 50th Anniv of Montserrat Airmail Service.
519   50c. Fairey IIIF Firefly seaplane................ 30   30
520   65c. Beech 50 Twin Bonanza VP-LIF
of L. I. A. T. 40   30
521    $1.50 de Havilland DH.89 Dragon Rapide
G-AFEZ *Lord Shaftesbury* of B.E.A 60   1·75
522    $2.50 Hawker Siddeley H.S.748 VP-LAZ
of L. I. A. T. 80   3·00
519/522 *Set of* 4.. 1·90   4·75

1983. Bicentenary of Manned Flight.
586   35c. Montgolfier balloon (first manned
free flight, 1783)............................. 15   15
587   75c. de Havilland Canada DHC-6 Twin
Otter 200/300 VP-LMO of Montserrat
Aviation Services 25   30
588    $1.50 Wiley Post's Lockheed Vega V
NR-105-W *Winnie Mae* 40   75
589    $2 Beardmore airship R-34.................... 60   1·25
586/589 *Set of* 4.. 1·30   2·20
Nos. 586/9 were later issued overprinted **INAUGURAL FLIGHT
Montserrat-Nevis-St. Kitts.**

1990. No. 461 surcharged **90c** and Stamp World London 90
emblem.
819*   90c. on 55c. Hawker Siddeley H.S.748 of
L.I.A.T.. 90   90

1993. 75th Anniv of Royal Air Force.
922   15c. Boeing E-3 Sentry of the R.A.F............ 45   20
923   65c. Vickers Valiant B Mk 1 of the R.A.F...... 65   40
924    $1.15 Handley Page H.P.67 Hastings C Mk 2
of the R.A.F .... 1·25   65
925    $3 Lockheed PV-1 Ventura of the R.A.F . 2·50   4·25
922/925 *Set of* 4.. 4·25   5·00
MS926 $1.50 Felixstowe F5 flying boat of the R.A.F.;
$1.50 Armstrong Whitworth Atlas of the R.A.F.;
$1.50 Fairey Gordon of the R.A.F.; $1.50 Boulton
& Paul Overstrand of the R.A.F .... 4·50   6·00

1995.
971* $1.50 Junkers Ju-88G 7a .... 1·90   2·00
972* $1.50 Boeing E6 A.W.A.C.S.................... 1·90   2·00
973* $1.50 Gloster G.41 Meteor Mk III .... 1·90   2·00
974* $1.50 Concorde.................................. 1·90   2·00

1996.
993* $3 Handley Page Type W.8f Hamilton .... 2·25   3·50

1998.
1074* $1.50 Charles Lindbergh........................ 1·25   1·25

2000. 60th Anniv of Battle of Britain.
1156   70c. Supermarine Spitfire squadron
taking off .... 1·00   50
1157 $1.15 Overhauling Hawker Hurricane........ 1·25   65
1158 $1.50 Hawker Hurricane Mk I attacking ...... 1·50   1·25
1159 $1.50 Flt. Lt. Frank Howell's Supermarine
Spitfire Mk IA .... 3·50   5·00
1156/1159 *Set of* 4.. 6·50   6·75
MS1160 $6 Hawker Hurricane .... 4·50   5·50

2003. Centenary of Powered Flight.
MS1234 $2 Wright *Flyer II* (blue); $2 Wright *Flyer II* (brown); $2 Orville and Wilbur Wright; $2 Wright *Flyer I* .... 5·00 5·50
MS1235 $6 Wright *Flyer II* .... 5·00 5·50

2004.
1266* $1.15 Martin B-26 Marauder............................ 1·25 75

2005.
MS1284* $2 Blackburne Airport; $2 Eurocopter EC 155 (other stamps in the miniature sheet do not show aircraft) .... 16·00 18·00

MOROCCO

North-west Africa

A. Northern Zone

100 centimos = 1 peseta

1956.
9   25c. Lockheed L.1049 Super Constellation   45   45
10   1p.40 Lockheed L.1049 Super Constellation   1·10   1·10
11   3p.40 Lockheed L.1049 Super Constellation   2·40   2·40
12   4p.80 Lockheed L.1049 Super Constellation   4·25   4·25
9/12 *Set of 4* .... 7·50 7·50

C. General Issues

1961. 100 centimes = 1 franc

1962. 100 francs = 1 dirham

1961.
97*   90f. Sud Aviation SE 210 Caravelle............ 1·20 80

1966.
193*   3d. Sud Aviation SE 210 Caravelle of Royal Air Maroc .... 5·00 2·10

1973.
366   25f. Aircraft.. 75 25

1981. First Anniv of Mohammed V Airport.
589   1d.30 Boeing 727 airliners at Mohammed V Airport and Boeing 707 taking off.   95   45

1983.
655   2d. Boeing 747 .... 1·20 45

1992.
830   3d.40 Boeing 737 .... 1·60 55

1992. Al Massira Airport, Agadir.
840   3d.40 Two Douglas DC-9 airliners and Boeing 727 of Royal Air Moroc at Al Massira Airport, Agadir........................ 1·60 65

1994. 50th Death Anniv of Antoine de Saint-Exupery (aviator).
870   4d.80 Saint-Exupery, map and Breguet 393T.. 2·30 55

2000.
961   6d. Helicopters.. 2·10 55

2000. Birth Centenary of Antoine de Saint-Exupery (aviator).
981   6d.50 Saint-Exupery and Breguet 393T....... 2·30 55

2007. 50th Anniv of Royal Air Maroc.
1186   7d.80 Boeing 757 .... 1·10 1·10

MOZAMBIQUE

South-east Africa

1938. 100 centavos = 1 escudo

1980. 100 centavos = 1 metical

1938. As Nos. 401/9 of Angola.
369*   10c. Airplane.............................. 35   35
370*   20c. Airplane.............................. 35   35
371*   50c. Airplane.............................. 45   35
372*   1e. Airplane............................... 45   35
373*   2e. Airplane............................... 75   35
374*   3e. Airplane............................... 1·60   35
375*   5e. Airplane............................... 2·75   60
376*   9e. Airplane............................... 5·00   1·00
377*   10e. Airplane.............................. 8·75   1·90
369/377 *Set of 9* .... 18·00   5·00

1946. No. 375 surcharged **3$00**.
389*   3e. on 5e. Airplane .... 15·00 10·00

1946.
391   1e.20 Lockheed L.18 Lodestar .... 3·00   1·00
392   1e.60 Lockheed L.18 Lodestar .... 3·00   1·10
393   1e.70 Lockheed L.18 Lodestar .... 5·00   1·50
394   2e.90 Lockheed L.18 Lodestar .... 8·00   3·00
395   3e. Lockheed L.18 Lodestar .... 8·75   3·00
391/395 *Set of 5* .... 25·00   8·75

1947. As Nos. 391/5, overprinted **Taxe percue**.
397   50c. Lockheed L.18 Lodestar .... 1·30   55
398   1e. Lockheed L.18 Lodestar .... 1·30   55
399   3e. Lockheed L.18 Lodestar .... 2·20   70
400   4e.50 Lockheed L.18 Lodestar .... 3·75   1·20
401   5e. Lockheed L.18 Lodestar .... 5·25   1·30
402   10e. Lockheed L.18 Lodestar .... 15·00   3·50
403   20e. Lockheed L.18 Lodestar .... 39·00   9·50
404   50e. Lockheed L.18 Lodestar .... 80·00 24·00
397/404 *Set of 8* .... £130 37·00

1949. As Nos. 445/9 of Angola.
432   50c. Boeing 377 Stratocruiser, Douglas DC-3 and other aircraft..................... 65   20
433   1e.20 Boeing 377 Stratocruiser, Douglas DC-3 and other aircraft............... 1·30   40
434   4e.50 Boeing 377 Stratocruiser, Douglas DC-3 and other aircraft............... 2·75   65
435   5e. Boeing 377 Stratocruiser, Douglas DC-3 and other aircraft..................... 10·00   85
436   20e. Boeing 377 Stratocruiser, Douglas DC-3 and other aircraft............... 14·50   4·25
432/436 *Set of 5* .... 26·00   5·75

1952.
468   1e.50 Lockheed Constellation 85 45

1953.
492   1e. Lockheed Constellation (on stamp No. 468).. 1·30 35
493   3e. Lockheed Constellation (on stamp No. 468).. 5·00 90

1962. 25th Anniv of DETA (Mozambique Airline).

| 539 | 3e. Fokker F.27 Friendship (top) and de Havilland DH.89 Dragon Rapide of DETA | 60 | 20 |

1962.

541	1e.50 Lockheed L.1049 Super Constellation	65	20
542	2e. Fokker F.27 Friendship	55	20
543	3e.50 de Havilland DH.89 Dragon Rapide..	55	20
544	4e.50 Fokker F.27 Friendship	55	20
545	5e. Fokker F.27 Friendship	55	20
546	20e. Fokker F.27 Friendship	2·40	70
541/546 Set of 6		4·75	1·50

1963. 10th Anniv of TAP Airline (Portuguese Airline). As No. 611 of Angola.

| 548 | 2e.50 Boeing 707 and Lockheed L.1049G Super Constellation of T.A.P. | 40 | 20 |

1969.

| 598 | 70c. Admiral Gago Coutinho Airport, Lourenco Marques | 25 | 10 |

1972. 50th Anniv of First Flight, Lisbon-Rio de Janeiro.

| 619 | 1e. Fairey IIID seaplane *Santa Cruz* | 15 | 10 |

1975. Nos. 543/6 overprinted with ornamental device and **INDEPENDENCIA 25 JUN 75.**

646*	3e.50 de Havilland DH.89 Dragon Rapide..	35	25
647*	4e.50 Fokker F.27 Friendship	40	25
648*	5e. Fokker F.27 Friendship	1·25	50
649*	20e. Fokker F.27 Friendship	2·00	4·25

1981.

| 846* | 3m.50 Jet airliner | 2·00 | 75 |

1981. Mozambique Aviation History.

870	50c. de Havilland DH.89 Dragon Rapide CR-AAD (inscribed "DRAGON FLY")...	10	10
871	1m.50 Junkers Ju 52/3m CR-AAL of DETA (inscribed "JUNKER")	10	10
872	3m. Lockheed 14-H2 Super Electra (inscribed "LOCKEED LODSTAR 18-08")	20	15
873	7m.50 de Havilland DH.104 Dove CR-ADD of DETA	35	30
874	10m. Douglas DC-3 CR-ABO of DETA	50	35
875	12m.50 Fokker F.27 Friendship of DETA	75	50
870/875 Set of 6		1·80	1·40

1981.

| 876* | 2m. Helicopter | 30 | 15 |

1987. History of Aviation in Mozambique.

1168	20m. Piper PA-31 Navajo CR-ABL	15	10
1169	40m. de Havilland DH.87B Hornet Moth....	25	10
1170	80m. Boeing 737 over Maputo Airport	50	20
1171	120m. Beech C90 King Air	75	20
1172	160m. Piper PA-23 Aztec	1·00	35
1173	320m. Douglas DC-10	2·00	75
1168/1173 Set of 6		4·25	1·50

1992.

| 1344* | 500m. Airplane dropping parachutists | 25 | 10 |

1994. 50th Anniv of ICAO.

1381	300m. Air Tractor AT-500	10	10
1382	500m. Airport	10	10
1383	2000m. Air Transport	40	20
1384	3500m. Ayres S2B Turbo-Thrush	75	35
1381/1384 Set of 4		1·20	70

2002.
MS1648 22000m. Antoine de St-Exupery (aviator); 22000m. Charles Lindbergh and Ryan NYP Special *Spirit of St. Louis;* 22000m. Charles Lindbergh and light aircraft; 22000m. Concorde .... 2·30 2·40

2002.
MS1676* 17000m. Concorde taking off right; 17000m. Concorde flying left; 17000m. Concorde taking off left (other stamps in the miniature sheet do not show aircraft) .... 4·75 5·00

2002. Count Ferdinand von Zeppelin Commemoration.
MS1681 Two sheets. (a) 28000m. Count Ferdinand von Zeppelin; 28000m. Zeppelin LZ-2 (1905); 28000m. Zeppelin LZ-10 (1911); 28000m. Zeppelin LZ-1 (1900). (b) 28000m. Zeppelin LZ-1 over water; 28000m. Zeppelin LZ-2 over water; 28000m. Zeppelin LZ-10 over field of sheep; 28000m. Ferdinand von Zeppelin holding binoculars.......... 10·00 10·50
MS1682 Two sheets. (a) 50000m. Von Zeppelin wearing shirt and tie. (b) 50000m. Von Zeppelin wearing army uniform *Price for 4 sheets* .... 5·00 5·25

MOZAMBIQUE COMPANY

South-east Africa

100 centavos = 1 escudo

1935. Inauguration of Blantyre-Beira-Salisbury Air Route.

261	5c. Armstrong Whitworth A.W.15 Atalanta G-ABPI	75	50
262	10c. Armstrong Whitworth A.W.15 Atalanta G-ABPI	75	50
263	15c. Armstrong Whitworth A.W.15 Atalanta G-ABPI	75	50
264	20c. Armstrong Whitworth A.W.15 Atalanta G-ABPI	75	50
265	30c. Armstrong Whitworth A.W.15 Atalanta G-ABPI	75	50
266	40c. Armstrong Whitworth A.W.15 Atalanta G-ABPI	1·00	65
267	45c. Armstrong Whitworth A.W.15 Atalanta G-ABPI	1·00	65
268	50c. Armstrong Whitworth A.W.15 Atalanta G-ABPI	1·00	65
269	60c. Armstrong Whitworth A.W.15 Atalanta G-ABPI	1·70	1·00
270	80c. Armstrong Whitworth A.W.15 Atalanta G-ABPI	1·70	1·00
261/270 Set of 10		9·25	5·75

1935.

271	5c. Armstrong Whitworth A.W.15 Atalanta G-ABPI	20	20
272	10c. Armstrong Whitworth A.W.15 Atalanta G-ABPI	20	20
273	15c. Armstrong Whitworth A.W.15 Atalanta G-ABPI	20	20
274	20c. Armstrong Whitworth A.W.15 Atalanta G-ABPI	20	20
275	30c. Armstrong Whitworth A.W.15 Atalanta G-ABPI	20	20
276	40c. Armstrong Whitworth A.W.15 Atalanta G-ABPI	20	20
277	45c. Armstrong Whitworth A.W.15 Atalanta G-ABPI	20	20
278	50c. Armstrong Whitworth A.W.15 Atalanta G-ABPI	20	20
279	60c. Armstrong Whitworth A.W.15 Atalanta G-ABPI	20	20
280	80c. Armstrong Whitworth A.W.15 Atalanta G-ABPI	20	20
281	1e. Armstrong Whitworth A.W.15 Atalanta G-ABPI	20	20
282	2e. Armstrong Whitworth A.W.15 Atalanta G-ABPI	50	45
283	5e. Armstrong Whitworth A.W.15 Atalanta G-ABPI	85	70
284	10e. Armstrong Whitworth A.W.15 Atalanta G-ABPI	1·10	85
285	20e. Armstrong Whitworth A.W.15 Atalanta G-ABPI	2·20	1·10
271/285 Set of 15		6·25	4·75

MUSCAT

Arabia

12 pies = 1 anna

16 annas = 1 rupee

آل بوسعيد ١٣٦٣

1944. No. 277 of India overprinted with Arabic text.

| 13* | 14a. Armstrong Whitworth A.W.27 Ensign I | 4·00 | 12·00 |

NABHA

Indian sub-continent

12 pies = 1 anna

16 annas = 1 rupee

1938. No. 258 of India overprinted **NABHA STATE**.
88*	12a. Armstrong Whitworth A.W.27 Ensign I	2·50	25·00

NAMIBIA

South West Africa

1991. 100 cents = 1 rand

1993. 100 cents = 1 Namibia dollar

1991.
568*	20c. Radiosonde Weather Balloon	20	20

1999. Gliding.
833	$1.60 Zogling glider, 1928	40	50
834	$1.80 Schleicher glider, 1998	60	70

2001. Civil Aviation.
882	(–) Cessna Model 210 Turbo Centurian	40	15
883	$2.20 Douglas DC-6B	70	50
884	$2.50 Pitts S2A	75	55
885	$13.20 Bell 407	4·00	4·25
882/885	Set of 4	5·25	5·00

NANKING AND SHANGHAI

See Japanese Occupation of China

NAURU

Pacific

100 cents = 1 dollar

1974.
118*	15c. Fokker F.28 Fellowship *Nauru Chief* of Air Nauru	65	30

1976.
152*	20c. Boeing 737 and Fokker F.28 Fellowship, both of Air Nauru	40	30

1979. Flight Anniversaries.
200	10c. Wright *Flyer I*	25	15
201	15c. Fokker F.VIIa/3m G-AUSU *Southern Cross* superimposed on nose of Boeing 737	35	20
202	15c. Fokker F.VIIa/3m G-AUSU *Southern Cross* above front view of Boeing 737	35	20
203	30c. Wright *Flyer I* over Nauru Airfield	60	30
200/203	Set of 4	1·40	75

1980. 10th Anniv of Air Nauru.
220	15c. Dassault Breguet Mystere Falcon 50 of Air Nauru	35	15
221	20c. Fokker F.28 Fellowship of Air Nauru	40	15
222	25c. Boeing 727-100 of Air Nauru	40	15
223	30c. Boeing 737 of Air Nauru	40	15
220/223	Set of 4	1·40	55

1981.
254*	30c. Boeing 737 of Air Nauru	25	25

1983.
284*	10c. Boeing 727	20	15
287*	40c. Boeing 727	90	45

1984.
309*	25c. Boeing 727 of Air Nauru at Nauru Airport	80	55
311*	40c. Tail of Boeing 727 of Air Nauru	90	55

1985. 15th Anniv of Air Nauru.
318	20c. Boeing 737 C2-RN8 of Air Nauru at Nauru Airport	50	35
319	30c. Boeing 727 of Air Nauru and cabin crew	60	60
320	40c. Fokker F.28 Fellowship of Air Nauru	75	75
321	50c. Boeing 727 C2-RN7 of Air Nauru	85	85
318/321	Set of 4	2·40	2·30

1994. 50th Anniv of ICAO.
424	55c. Emblems and Boeing 737	50	55
425	65c. Control tower, Nauru International Airport	60	65
426	80c. DVOR equipment	70	1·00
427	$1 Crash tenders	90	1·10
424/427	Set of 4	2·40	3·00

2002.
MS555	$5 Boeing 737	8·00	8·50

2003. Centenary of Powered Flight. Airships.
570	50c. Santos-Dumont's *Ballon No. 6*	80	85
571	50c. USS *Shenandoah*	80	85
572	50c. R101, 1929	80	85
573	50c. Beardmore R34, 1919	80	85
574	50c. Zeppelin LZ-1, 1900	80	85
575	50c. USS *Los Angeles*	80	85
576	50c. Goodyear C-71	80	85
577	50c. LZ-130 *Graf Zeppelin II*	80	85
578	50c. Zeppelin over Alps	80	85
570/578	Set of 9	6·50	7·00
MS579	$2 LZ-127 *Graf Zeppelin* over Mount Fuji; $2 LZ-127 *Graf Zeppelin* over San Francisco; $2 LZ-127 *Graf Zeppelin* over Franz Josef Land	8·50	9·00

2005.
593*	75c. Consolidated B-24 Liberator	1·10	1·10
595*	75c. North American B-25G Mitchell *Coral Princess*	1·10	1·10
596*	75c. Supermarine Spitfires	1·10	1·10

2006. 30th Anniv of Inaugural Flight of Concorde.
643	$1 Concorde G-BOAF of British Airways	1·50	1·50
644	$1 First flight of Concorde 002, 9 April 1969	1·50	1·50
645	$1 Concorde at take-off	1·50	1·50
646	$1 Concorde and BAe Hawks of Red Arrows display team (Golden Jubilee flypast, 4 June 2002)	1·50	1·50
647	$1 Concorde and Supermarine Spitfire (Battle of Britain 50th Anniversary, 6 June 1990)	1·50	1·50
648	$1 Concorde at 60,000ft and Mach 2	1·50	1·50
649	$1 Extreme conditions testing	1·50	1·50
650	$1 Concorde on runway	1·50	1·50
651	$1 First commercial flight, 21 January, 1976	1·50	1·50
652	$1 Concorde above Earth	1·50	1·50
653	$1 Concorde G-BOAF of British Airways at take-off	1·50	1·50
654	$1 Two Concordes on ground	1·50	1·50
643/654	Set of 12	16·00	16·00

2008. 90th Anniv of Royal Air Force.
664	70c. Air Vice Marshall 'Johnnie' Johnson (fighter ace)	1·25	1·25
665	70c. R. J. Mitchell (Spitfire designer)	1·25	1·25
666	70c. Sir Sydney Camm (Hurricane designer)	1·25	1·25
667	70c. Sir Frank Whittle (jet engine pioneer)	1·25	1·25
668	70c. Sir Douglas Bader (flying legend)	1·25	1·25
664/668	Set of 5	5·50	5·50
MS669	$3 Avro Type 698 Vulcan	4·00	4·50

NEGRI SEMBILAN

South-east Asia

100 cents = 1 dollar

1949. As Nos. 114/15 of Antigua.
63*	10c. Airplane	20	20
64*	15c. Jet-powered Vickers Viking	1·40	3·00

NEPAL

Central Asia

100 paisa = 1 rupee

1968. 10th Anniv of Royal Nepal Airlines.
228*   2r.50 Convair CV 440 Metropolitan of Royal Nepal Airlines...............................   2·50   2·20

1978. 75th Anniv of First Powered Flight.
373   2r.30 Boeing 727-100 of Royal Nepal Airlines and Wright Flyer I   90   75

1983. 25th Anniv of Royal Nepal Airlines.
431   1r. Boeing 727 of Royal Nepal Airlines...   45   20

1994.
572   1r.50 Boeing 727   15   15

1994. 50th Anniv of ICAO.
584   11r. Boeing 757-200..................................   80   50

NETHERLANDS

North-west Europe
100 cents = 1 gulden

1931.
394*   36c. Fokker F.XII monoplanes......................   14·50   80

1933. Special Flights.
417   30c. Nose of Pander S.4 Postjager   85   80

1954. National Aviation Fund.
802*   2c. +2c. Boy with model glider.................   1·50   90

1959. 40th Anniv of KLM (Royal Dutch Airlines).
884   12c. Douglas DC-8 of KLM   25   10
885   30c. Douglas DC-8 of KLM...........................   1·70   1·20

1968. Dutch Aviation Anniversaries.
1058   12c. Wright Type A (top) and Cessna 150F..   20   15
1059   20c. Fokker F.II H-NABC (top) and Fokker F.28 Fellowship of KLM   25   20
1060   45c. Airco (de Havilland) D.H.9B biplane H-NABE and Douglas DC-9 of KLM ...   1·30   1·20
1058/1060 *Set of 3* ....   1·60   1·40

1971.
1135*   25c. Boeing 747 (top left) and Fokker F.27 Friendship   30   15

1980.
1334*   45c. Avro Type 683 Lancaster of the R.A.F. dropping food parcels   45   20

1981.
1367*   60c. Airport runways   60   40

1985.
1462*   60c. Fighters   65   15

1994. 75th Anniv of Aircraft Industry.
1723   80c. KLM (Royal Dutch Airlines) Fokker F.28 airliner...   90   25
1724   80c. Plan and outline of aircraft (Royal Netherlands Fokker Aircraft Industries)   90   25
1725   80c. Airplane and clouds (National Aerospace Laboratory).........................   90   25
1723/1725 *Set of 3* ....   2·40   70

1994.
1739*   90c. Douglas C-47 dropping paratroops..   1·00   70

NETHERLANDS ANTILLES

West Indies
100 cents = 1 gulden

1959. 25th Anniv of KLM Netherlands-Curacao Air Service.
413   10c. Fokker F.XVIII PH-AIS *De Snip*............   50   35
414   20c. Fokker F.XVIII PH-AIS *De Snip*..............   50   35
415   25c. Douglas DC-7C "Seven Seas"................   50   15
416   35c. Douglas DC-8 at Aruba Airport   50   55
413/416 *Set of 4*..   1·80   1·30

1964. 35th Anniv of First US-Curacao Flight.
452*   25c. Sikorsky S-38 flying boat and Boeing 707   35   35

1968. Dutch Antillean Airlines.
510   10c. Fokker F.27 Friendship 500 of Royal Netherlands Antillean Airline..............   30   30
511   20c. Douglas DC-9 of Royal Netherlands Antillean Airline   30   30
512   25c. Fokker F.27 Friendship 500 and Douglas DC-9   30   30
510/512 *Set of 3*   80   80

1975. 40th Anniv of Aruba Airport.
606   15c. Fokker F.XVIII PH-AIS *De Snip* and old control tower at Aruba Airport..........   35   25
607   30c. Douglas DC-9-30 and new control tower at Aruba Airport   50   35
608   40c. Tail of Boeing 727-200 and buildings at Aruba Airport...................................   50   45
606/608 *Set of 3* ....   1·20   95

1983.
807   1g. Fokker F.28 Fellowship.........................   1·40   1·25

1984. 40th Anniv of ICAO.
851*   100c. Fokker F.XVIII PH-AIS *De Snip*..............   1·60   1·25

1987.
933*   85c. Douglas DC-10   90   80

1991.
1031   20g. Douglas DC-10 .... 23·00   22·00

1993. 50th Anniv of Princess Juliana International Airport, St. Maarten.
1092*   65c. de Havilland Canada DHC-6 Twin Otter 200/300 and flight paths........... 70   70
1094*   90c. de Havilland Canada DHC-6 Twin Otter 200/300 at Princess Juliana International Airport .... 1·00   1·00

1999.
1334*   85c. Fokker F.XVIII PH-AIS *De Snip* (first Amsterdam-Curacao flight, 1934) ..... 1·10   1·10

2004.
1601*   95c. Wright *Flyer I*, 1903.................... 60   50

NETHERLANDS INDIES

South-east Asia

100 cents = 1 gulden

1928. Nos. 273, 221, 281 and 224/5 surcharged **LUCHTPOST**, Fokker F.VII airplane and value.
303   10c. on 12½c. Queen Wilhelmina .... 1·25   1·25
304   20c. on 25c. Queen Wilhelmina .... 2·75   2·75
305   40c. on 80c. Queen Wilhelmina .... 2·10   2·10
306   75c. on 1g. Queen Wilhelmina .... 1·10   1·10
307   1½g. on 2½g. Queen Wilhelmina .... 7·25   7·25
303/307 *Set of 5*.................. 13·00   13·00

1928.
308   10c. Fokker F.VIIa 35   35
309   20c. Fokker F.VIIa 90   75
310   40c. Fokker F.VIIa .... 1·10   75
311   75c. Fokker F.VIIa .... 2·40   35
312   1g.50 Fokker F.VIIa .... 4·25   75
308/312 *Set of 5*............... 8·00   2·75

1930. No. 310 surcharged **30**.
313   30c. on 40c. Fokker F.VIIa .... 1·10   40

1932. No. 312 surcharged **50** on Fokker F.VIIa/3m airplane.
328   50c. on 1g.50 Fokker F.VIIa .... 3·25   55

1933. Special Flights.
360   30c. Nose of Pander S.4 Postjager 1 .... 1·50   1·50

1934. Nos. 308/9 and 311/12 surcharged with new value.
365*   2c. on 10c. Fokker F.VIIa 35   50
366*   2c. on 20c. Fokker F.VIIa 35   30
368*   42½c. on 75c. Fokker F.VIIa .... 4·75   35
369*   42½c. on 1g.50 Fokker F.VIIa .... 4·75   50

1938. Air Service Fund. 10th Anniv of Royal Netherlands Indies Air Lines.
394   17½c. +5c. Douglas DC-2 of Royal Netherlands Indies Air Lines............... 90   90
395   20c. +5c. Douglas DC-2 of Royal Netherlands Indies Air Lines............... 90   90

1945.
471*   7½c. Douglas DC-2.................................... 75   15

NETHERLANDS NEW GUINEA

South-east Asia

100 cents = 1 gulden

1959.
59   55c. Helicopter.. 1·25   90

NEVIS

West Indies

100 cents = 1 dollar

1980. No. 403 of St. Kitts-Nevis overprinted with bars obliterating "St. Christopher" and "Anguilla".
46*   55c. Jet airliner on runway at Golden Rock................................ 60   15

1983. Bicentenary of Manned Flight.
122   10c. Montgolfier balloon (first manned free flight, 1783)................ 10   10
123   45c. Sikorsky S-38 flying boat............... 15   10
124   50c. Beech 50 Twin Bonanza V2-LAL of Carib Airways................ 15   10
125    $2.50 Hawker Siddeley Sea Harrier............... 30   1·25
122/125 *Set of 4*................ 65   1·40

1986. 50th Anniv of Supermarine Spitfire.
372    $1 Supermarine Spitfire prototype K-5054................ 20   50
373    $2.50 Supermarine Spitfire IA................ 30   75
374    $3 Supermarine Spitfire Mk XII and V-1 flying bomb................ 30   75
375    $4 Supermarine Spitfire Mk *IV 30   1·25
372/375 *Set of 4*................ 1·00   3·00
MS376 $6 Supermarine Seafire Mk III .... 1·10   3·75

1993. 75th Death Anniv of Count Ferdinand von Zeppelin.
721*   50c. Airship LZ-129 *Hindenburg* on fire at Lakehurst, New Jersey, 1937........... 1·00   65
732* $5 Lebaudy-Juillot airship No. 1 *La Jaune*, 1902................ 3·25   3·75
MS734* Five sheets. (b) $6 Airship LZ-5 damaged after crash (other sheets do not show aircraft) *Set of 5 sheets* .... 18·00   19·00

CLARK GABLE

1995.
904* $1.25 Douglas C-47 and Clark Gable........... 1·00   1·00
908* $1.25 Jimmy Doolittle and North American B-25 Mitchell................ 1·00   1·00
911* $1.25 Bombers and James Stewart............. 1·00   1·00
MS912* $6 Jimmy Doolittle and North American B-52 Mitchell .... 4·00   4·50

F4F-WILDCAT

1995.
928    $2 Grumman F4F Wildcat.................... 1·40   1·40
929    $2 Vought F4U-1A Corsair.................... 1·40   1·40
930    $2 Vought SB2U Vindicator.................... 1·40   1·40
931    $2 Grumman F6F Hellcat.................... 1·40   1·40
932    $2 Douglas SBD Dauntless.................... 1·40   1·40
933    $2 Grumman TBF-1 Avenger.................... 1·40   1·40
928/933 *Set of 6*............. 7·50   7·50
MS934 $6 Vought F4U-1A Corsair (different)............. 5·50   6·50

1995. 10th Anniv of American Eagle Air Services to the Caribbean.
MS945 80c. Logo; $3 Avions de Transport Régional ATR72 over Nevis beach................ 2·40   2·50

1998.
1195   10c. Boeing 747-200B (USA) 30   30
1196   90c. Cessna 185 Skywagon (USA).............. 65   40
1197 $1 Northrop B-2A Spirit (USA).............. 70   80
1198 $1 Lockheed SR-71A Blackbird (USA)....... 70   80
1199 $1 Beechcraft T-44A (USA)............... 70   80
1200 $1 Sukhoi Su-27UB (USSR)................ 70   80
1201 $1 BAe (Hawker Siddeley) Harrier GR. Mk1 (Great Britain)............... 70   80
1202 $1 Boeing E-3A Sentry (USA)............... 70   80
1203 $1 Convair B-36H Peacemaker (USA) 70   80
1204 $1 IAI Kfir C2 (Israel)............... 70   80
1205 $1.80 McDonnell Douglas DC-9 SO (USA)..... 1·40   1·40
1206 $5 Airbus A-300 B4 (European consortium)................ 3·50   4·00
1195/1206 *Set of 12*................ 10·50   11·50
MS1207 Two sheets. (a) $5 Lockheed F-117A Nighthawk (USA); $5 Concorde (Britain/France) *Set of 2 sheets* .... 7·50   7·50

1998. 80th Anniv of the Royal Air Force.
1246 $2 Panavia Tornado F Mk3.................... 1·50   1·60
1247 $2 Panavia Tornado F Mk3 firing Skyflash missile................ 1·50   1·60
1248 $2 Lockheed Tristar Mk1 tanker refueling Panavia Tornado GR1 .... 1·50   1·60
1249 $2 Panavia Tornado GR1 firing AIM-9L missile................ 1·50   1·60
1246/1249 *Set of 4*................ 5·50   5·75
MS1250 Two sheets. (a) $5 Bristol F2B fighter; (b)$5 Westland Wessex and Eurofighter EF-2000 Typhoon................ 8·00   8·00

2000. Centenary of First Zeppelin Flight.
1516 $3 LZ-129 *Hindenburg* 1929.............. 2·00   2·25
1517 $3 LZ-1, 1900................ 2·00   2·25
1518 $3 LZ-11, *Viktoria Luise*, 1912.............. 2·00   2·25
1516/1518 *Set of 3*................ 5·50   6·00
MS1519 $5 LZ-127 *Graf Zeppelin* 1928 .... 3·50   3·75
No. 1516 is inscribed *Hindenberg* in error.

2003. 75th Anniv of First Solo Trans-Atlantic Flight.
MS1789 $2 Ryan Airlines crew attaching wing to Ryan NYP Special *Spirit of St. Louis*; $2 Charles Lindbergh with Donald Hall (designer) and Benjamin F. Mahoney (President of Ryan Airlines); $2 Lindbergh planning flight; $2 Donald Hall (Chief Engineer of Ryan Airlines) working on plans of aircraft...................... 5·00 5·50
MS1790 $2 Donald Hall and drawing of Ryan NYP Special *Spirit of St. Louis*; $2 Charles Lindbergh; $2 Ryan NYP Special *Spirit of St. Louis* being towed from factory; $2 Ryan NYP Special *Spirit of St. Louis* at Curtis Field before flight...................... 5·00 5·50

2003. Centenary of Powered Flight and Commemoration of A.V. Roe (aircraft designer).
MS1805 $1.80 Avro Type 547A Triplane 1920 (wrongly inscribed Avroplane Triplane, 1909); $1.80 Avro Type 504D with floats (wrongly inscribed AV Roe's Type D biplane, 1911); $1.80 Avro Type 584 Avocet, 1921 (wrongly inscribed Avro Type F); $1.80 Avro Type 504M, 1928 (wrongly inscribed Avro Type 504 in service unit 1933)...................... 4·75 5·00
MS1806 $5 Avro Type 604 Antelope, 1927 (wrongly inscribed Avro Type 561, 1924)...................... 3·25 3·50

2005.
1891 $2 Boeing B-29 Superfortress *Enola Gay* and flight crew...................... 1·75 1·75
1892 $2 A-bomb exploding over Hiroshima.. 1·75 1·75

2007. Concorde.
2026 $1.20 Concorde 02 on ground...................... 70 75
2027 $1.20 Concorde 02 flying over snowy mountains (pale new blue inscriptions)...................... 70 75
2028 $1.20 Concorde 02 on ground (lemon inscriptions)...................... 70 75
2029 $1.20 As no 2027 (lemon inscriptions) 70 75
2030 $1.20 Concorde 02 on ground (pale new blue inscriptions)...................... 70 75
2031 $1.20 As No 2027 (white inscriptions) 70 75
2026/2031 *Set of 6* .... 3·75 4·00
MS2032 All Concorde F-BTSD, as follows: $1.20 Flying to right, dark blue background (over upper left part of globe); $1.20 Flying to left, azure background (over map 'MERICA'); $1.20 Flying to right, dark blue background (over upper right part of globe); $1.20 Flying to left, azure background (over equator line); $1.20 Flying to right, dark blue background (over map of islands); $1.20 Flying to left, azure background (equator line at lower right)...................... 4·25 4·50
Nos. 2026/31 were printed together, *se-tenant*, in sheetlets of six stamps with enlarged illustrated margins. They commemorate the Washington to Paris record flight of Concorde 02, the second pre-production aircraft, on September 26, 1973.

2007. Centenary of First Helicopter Flight.
MS2050 $3 Westland Sea King; $3 Schweizer N330TT; $3 Sikorsky R4/R5; $3 PZL Swidnik W-3 Sokol...................... 7·00 7·25
MS2051 $6 Mil V-12...................... 3·50 3·75

OFFICIAL STAMPS

1980. No. 46 further overprinted **OFFICIAL**.
O7* 55c. Jet airliner on runway at Golden Rock...................... 15 20

NEW CALEDONIA

South Pacific

100 centimes = 1 franc

1932. Nos. 148 and 151 overprinted **PARIS-NOUMEA Verneilh-Deve-Munch 5 Avril 1932** and Couzinet 33 airplane.
183 40c. Chief's hut...................... £350 £350
184 50c. Chief's hut...................... £350 £325

1933. Nos. 137/8, 140/9, 151, 155/9, 161, 165, 168, 170, 172 and 175/8 overprinted **PARIS-NOUMEA Premiere Liaison aerienne 5 Avril 1932** and Couzinet 33 airplane.
185 1c. Pointe des Paletuviers...................... 8·00 20·00
186 2c. Pointe des Paletuviers...................... 9·00 18·00
187 4c. Pointe des Paletuviers...................... 7·75 18·00
188 5c. Pointe des Paletuviers...................... 8·50 19·00
189 10c. Pointe des Paletuviers...................... 9·00 19·00
190 15c. Pointe des Paletuviers...................... 7·50 18·00
191 20c. Pointe des Paletuviers...................... 7·50 18·00
192 25c. Pointe des Paletuviers...................... 10·50 20·00
193 30c. Chief's hut...................... 8·25 19·00
194 35c. Chief's hut...................... 9·00 19·00
195 40c. Chief's hut...................... 8·50 12·50
196 45c. Chief's hut...................... 9·00 19·00
197 50c. Chief's hut...................... 6·75 19·00
198 70c. Chief's hut...................... 8·50 21·00
199 75c. Chief's hut...................... 10·00 16·00
200 85c. Chief's hut...................... 8·50 16·00
201 90c. Chief's hut...................... 8·50 16·00
202 1f. La Perouse, De Bougainville and L'Astrolabe...................... 10·50 23·00
203 1f.25 La Perouse, De Bougainville and L'Astrolabe...................... 10·50 22·00
204 1f.50 La Perouse, De Bougainville and L'Astrolabe...................... 13·50 22·00
205 1f.75 La Perouse, De Bougainville and L'Astrolabe...................... 6·25 13·00
206 2f. La Perouse, De Bougainville and L'Astrolabe...................... 10·50 26·00
207 3f. La Perouse, De Bougainville and L'Astrolabe...................... 10·50 25·00
208 5f. La Perouse, De Bougainville and L'Astrolabe...................... 14·50 26·00
209 10f. La Perouse, De Bougainville and L'Astrolabe...................... 8·50 25·00
210 20f. La Perouse, De Bougainville and L'Astrolabe...................... 7·75 26·00
185/210 *Set of 26* £225 £475

1938.
217 65c. Breguet Br 530 Saigon flying boat .... 85 4·75
218 4f.50 Breguet Br 530 Saigon flying boat .... 3·00 4·50
219 7f. Breguet Br 530 Saigon flying boat .... 50 4·00
220 9f. Breguet Br 530 Saigon flying boat .... 4·25 5·25
221 20f. Breguet Br 530 Saigon flying boat .... 3·25 3·25
222 50f. Breguet Br 530 Saigon flying boat .... 3·25 7·25
217/222 *Set of 6* .... 13·50 26·00

1942. As Nos. 207/13 of Cameroun.
281* 1f. Fairey FC-1 airliner...................... 15 4·50
282* 1f.50 Fairey F-1 airliner...................... 20 4·25
283* 5f. Fairey FC-1 airliner...................... 35 2·75
284* 10f. Fairey FC-1 airliner...................... 40 3·75
285* 25f. Fairey FC-1 airliner...................... 40 1·90
286* 50f. Fairey FC-1 airliner...................... 50 80
287* 100f. Fairey FC-1 airliner...................... 85 1·50

1948.
325* 50f. Sud Est SE 161 Languedoc...................... 2·50 3·00
326* 100f. Sud Est SE 161 Languedoc...................... 6·50 2·50
327* 200f. Sud Est SE 161 Languedoc...................... 4·25 4·25

1949. As No. 254 of Cameroun.
328 10f. Lockheed Constellation...................... 1·50 8·50

1954. As No. 264 of Cameroun.
335 3f. Bomber...................... 8·50 8·75

1955.
339* 14f. Airplane...................... 70 75

1959.
357* 200f. Airliner...................... 9·25 10·00

1969. 30th Anniv of First Noumea-Paris Flight by Martinet and Klein.
465 29f. Caudron C-600 Aiglon...................... 3·50 2·75

1969. First Flight of Concorde. As No. 83 of Comoro Islands.
466 100f. Concorde of Air France...................... 16·00 32·00

1969. 20th Anniv of Regular Noumea-Paris Air Service.
475 50f. Douglas DC-4...................... 13·00 8·25

1970. 10th Anniv of French Around the World Air Service.
477 200f. Douglas DC-6B (lower left), Boeing 707 (top left) and other airliners........ 26·00 10·50

1971. 40th Anniv of First New Caledonia-Australia Flight.
495 90f. de Havilland DH.60G Gipsy Moth *Golden Eagle*...................... 10·00 11·50

1972. 40th Anniv of First Paris-Noumea Flight.
499 110f. Couzinet 33 F-ALMV *Le Biarritz*.......... 2·75 2·50

1973.
515* 23f. Concorde...................... 13·00 8·75

1973. Inauguration of Noumea-Paris Douglas DC-10 Service.
518 100f. Douglas DC-10...................... 16·00 7·75

NEW CALEDONIA – NEWFOUNDLAND

1976. First Commercial Flight of Concorde.
560   147f. Concorde of Air France .... 19·00 12·50

1977. Airports.
588   24f. Magenta Airport .... 4·00 4·00
589   57f. La Tontouta International Airport...... 6·75 5·50

1977. No. 560 overprinted **22.11.77 PARIS NEW-YORK**.
590   147f. Concorde of Air France .... 29·00 27·00

1980. Coral Sea Air Rally.
637   31f. Scintex CP 1310 Super Emeraude ..... 3·00 3·50

1981. 50th Anniv of First New Caledonia-Australia Airmail Flight.
667   37f. Victor Roffey and de Havilland
     DH.60G Gipsy Moth *Golden Eagle*...... 3·00 3·25

1982. New Caledonian Aircraft (1st series).
670   38f. Biplane *La Roussette* .... 3·00 3·00
671   51f. Monoplane *Le Cagou* .... 3·00 3·25

1982. 50th Anniv of First Flight from Paris to Noumea.
674   250f. De Verneilh, Deve, Munch and
     Couzinet 33 F-ALMV *Le Biarritz*........... 11·50 8·25

1983. New Caledonian Aircraft (2nd series).
712   46f. Mignet HM14 *Pou du Ciel*........... 3·75 3·25
713   61f. Caudron C-600 Aiglon .... 4·00 3·50

1985.
763   17f. Boeing 737 .... 2·30 2·75

1985. 30th Anniv of First Regular Internal Air Service.
774   80f. de Havilland DH.89 Dragon Rapide
     of Transpac Airlines........................ 4·25 4·00

1986. 30th Anniv of Scheduled Paris-Noumea Flights.
779   72f. Tail fins of Sud Aviation Caravelle
     and Boeing 747 .... 3·50 3·75

1986. Inaugural Flight of ATR 42.
792   18f. Avions de Transport Régional ATR 42
     F-ODG of Air Caledonie..................... 2·50 2·75

1992.
948*   50f. Bell P-39 Airacobra (top left),
     Grumman F4F Wildcat and barrage
     balloon .... 2·30 2·30

1993. 10th Anniv of Air Cal (National Airline).
976   85f. Boeing 737-300/500 of Air Cal
     International............................... 2·75 2·50

1993. 25th Anniv of Chamber of Commerce and Industry's
  Management of La Tontouta Airport, Noumea.
979   90f. Douglas DC-3 and tailfins of Boeing
     737s, hangar and jet engine, La
     Tontouta Airport.......................... 2·75 2·30

1994. First Paris-Noumea Flight.
997   90f. Airbus A-340........................ 3·25 2·50

1994.
1016*   30f. Dassault Falcon 200 over frigate........ 1·90 1·70

1997. 50th Anniv of Establishment by TRAPAS of First Commercial
  Air Routes in South Pacific.
1103   95f. Consolidated PBY-5 Catalina .... 2·30 2·50
1104   95f. Republic Rc-3 Seabee seaplane .... 2·30 2·50

1999.
1181   135f. Aeritalia G. 222 transport and
     Aerospatiale SA330 Puma helicopter 2·50 1·70

1999. 50th Anniv of First Paris-Noumea Scheduled Flight.
1188   100f. Boeing 747 and Douglas DC-4 .... 2·00 1·80

2000. Birth Centenary of Antoine de Saint-Exupery (pilot and
  writer).
1204   130f. Lockheed P-38 Lightning .... 2·50 1·50

2001. First Anniv of Noumea-Osaka Passenger Service.
1238   110f. Airbus A310-300 of Air International
     Caledonie .... 1·50 1·40

2003. 20th Anniv of Aircalin.
1302   100f. Airbus A330-200 .... 1·40 1·20

2006.
1385   85f. Cartoon aircraft........................ 2·75 2·20

NEWFOUNDLAND

North Atlantic

100 cents = 1 dollar

1928.
175*   15c. Vickers FB-27 Vimy .... 6·00 35·00

1931.
192*	15c. Westland Limousine III	9·00	17·00
193*	50c. Vickers FB-27 Vimy	32·00	55·00

1933. No. 192 overprinted **L. & S. Post.**
229	15c. Westland Limousine III	4·25	15·00

1933.
230	5c. Westland Limousine II	20·00	22·00
231	10c. Seaplane	16·00	35·00
232	30c. Westland Limousine II	32·00	48·00
233	60c. Seaplane	50·00	£110
234	75c. Aircraft	50·00	£110
229/234 Set of 5		£160	£300

1943.
291	7c. Lockheed L.18 Lodestar	50	1·00

NEW GUINEA

Australasia

12 pence = 1 shilling

20 shillings = 1 pound

1931. Nos. 125/36 overprinted **AIR MAIL** and biplane.
137	½d. Native village	1·50	7·50
138	1d. Native village	1·60	5·00
139	1½d. Native village	1·25	5·00
140	2d. Native village	1·25	7·00
141	3d. Native village	1·75	13·00
142	4d. Native village	1·25	9·00
143	6d. Native village	1·75	14·00
144	9d. Native village	3·00	17·00
145	1s. Native village	3·00	17·00
146	2s. Native village	7·00	42·00
147	5s. Native village	20·00	65·00
148	10s. Native village	80·00	£110
149	£1 Native village	£140	£250
137/149 Set of 13		£250	£500

1931. Nos. 150/62 (with commemorative dates "1921 1931") and similar ½d. value overprinted **AIR MAIL** and biplane.
163	½d. Raggiana Bird of Paradise	3·25	3·25
164	1d. Raggiana Bird of Paradise	4·00	4·75
165	1½d. Raggiana Bird of Paradise	3·75	10·00
166	2d. Raggiana Bird of Paradise	3·75	3·00
167	3d. Raggiana Bird of Paradise	6·00	6·50
168	4d. Raggiana Bird of Paradise	6·00	6·00
169	5d. Raggiana Bird of Paradise	6·00	11·00
170	6d. Raggiana Bird of Paradise	7·00	26·00
171	9d. Raggiana Bird of Paradise	8·00	15·00
172	1s. Raggiana Bird of Paradise	7·50	15·00
173	2s. Raggiana Bird of Paradise	16·00	48·00
174	5s. Raggiana Bird of Paradise	42·00	70·00
175	10s. Raggiana Bird of Paradise	70·00	£120
176	£1 Raggiana Bird of Paradise	£120	£250
163/176 Set of 14		£275	£550

1932. Nos. 177/89 (without commemorative dates) and similar ½d. value overprinted **AIR MAIL** and biplane.
190	½d. Raggiana Bird of Paradise	60	1·50
191	1d. Raggiana Bird of Paradise	1·25	1·50
192	1½d. Raggiana Bird of Paradise	1·75	7·50
193	2d. Raggiana Bird of Paradise	1·75	30
193a	2½d. Raggiana Bird of Paradise	6·50	2·50
194	3d. Raggiana Bird of Paradise	3·25	3·00
194a	3½d. Raggiana Bird of Paradise	4·50	3·25
195	4d. Raggiana Bird of Paradise	4·50	10·00
196	5d. Raggiana Bird of Paradise	7·00	7·50
197	6d. Raggiana Bird of Paradise	4·50	15·00
198	9d. Raggiana Bird of Paradise	6·00	9·00
199	1s. Raggiana Bird of Paradise	6·00	9·00
200	2s. Raggiana Bird of Paradise	10·00	48·00
201	5s. Raggiana Bird of Paradise	48·00	60·00
202	10s. Raggiana Bird of Paradise	90·00	85·00
203	£1 Raggiana Bird of Paradise	80·00	55·00
190/203 Set of 16		£250	£275

1935.
204	£2 Junkers G.31F	£275	£140
205	£5 Junkers G.31F	£600	£400

1939. As Nos. 204/5, but inscribed "AIR MAIL POSTAGE".
212	½d. Junkers G.31F	3·75	7·00
213	1d. Junkers G.31F	3·25	4·50
214	1½d. Junkers G.31F	4·00	11·00
215	2d. Junkers G.31F	8·00	3·50
216	3d. Junkers G.31F	14·00	18·00
217	4d. Junkers G.31F	14·00	8·50
218	5d. Junkers G.31F	13·00	4·00
219	6d. Junkers G.31F	28·00	22·00
220	9d. Junkers G.31F	28·00	28·00
221	1s. Junkers G.31F	29·00	23·00
222	2s. Junkers G.31F	65·00	50·00
223	5s. Junkers G.31F	£140	£110
224	10s. Junkers G.31F	£425	£275
225	£1 Junkers G.31F	£100	£110
212/225 Set of 14		£800	£600

NEW HEBRIDES

South Pacific

1949. 100 gold centimes = 1 gold franc

1977. 100 centimes = 1 franc

I. Stamps inscribed in English

1949. As Nos. 114/15 of Antigua.
64*	10c. Airplane	30	1·00
65*	15c. Jet-powered Vickers Viking	30	1·00

1967.
128*	1f. Boeing B-17 Flying Fortress	50	80

1968. Anglo-French Concorde Project.
133	25c. Concorde	35	30
134	60c. Concorde	40	45

1972.
154	20c. de Havilland Australia DHA.3 Drover 3 of Air Melanesia	30	15
155	25c. Short S.25 Sandringham 4 flying boat VH-EBX of QANTAS	30	15
156	30c. de Havilland DH.89 Dragon Rapide	30	15
157	65c. Sud Aviation SE 210 Caravelle of U.T.A.	75	1·25
154/157 Set of 4		1·50	1·50

1976. First Commercial Flight of Concorde.
207	5f. Concorde of British Airways	4·00	5·00

1978. Concorde Commemoration.
258	10f. Concorde of British Airways	1·00	75
259	20f. Concorde of British Airways	1·00	1·00
260	30f. Concorde of British Airways	1·25	1·40
261	40f. Concorde of British Airways	1·50	1·60
258/261 Set of 4		4·25	4·25

II. Stamps inscribed in French

1949. As Nos. 64/5.
F77*	10c. Airplane	3·00	6·50
F78*	15c. Jet-powered Vickers Viking	4·25	10·00

1967. As No. 128.
F144*	1f. Boeing B-17 Flying Fortress	2·00	2·75

1968. As No. 133/4.
F148	25c. Concorde	1·90	2·40
F149	60c. Concorde	2·25	4·25

1972. As Nos. 154/7.
F169	20c. de Havilland Australia DHA.3 Drover 3 of Air Melanesia	1·00	1·60
F170	25c. Short S.25 Sandringham 4 flying boat VH-EBX of QANTAS	1·00	1·60
F171	30c. de Havilland DH.89 Dragon Rapide	1·10	1·60
F172	65c. Sud Aviation SE 210 Caravelle of U.T.A.	2·75	5·00
F169/172 Set of 4		5·25	8·75

1976. As No. 207.
F221	5f. Concorde of Air France	13·00	12·00

1978. As Nos. 258/61.
F272	10f. Concorde of Air France	2·50	1·50
F273	20f. Concorde of Air France	2·75	1·75
F274	30f. Concorde of Air France	3·25	2·25
F275	40f. Concorde of Air France	3·75	3·50
F272/275 Set of 4		11·00	8·00

NEW ZEALAND

Australasia

1931. 12 pence = 1 shilling

20 shillings = 1 pound

1967. 100 cents = 1 dollar

1931.
548	3d. Airplane	22·00	15·00
549	4d. Airplane	22·00	21·00
550	7d. Airplane (orange)	22·00	9·00
548/550 Set of 3		60·00	40·00

1931. No. 548 surcharged **FIVE PENCE.**
551	5d. on 3d. Airplane	10·00	9·50

1931. No. 550 in changed colour overprinted **TRANS-TASMAN AIR MAIL. "FAITH IN AUSTRALIA".**
554	7d. Airplane (blue)	35·00	40·00

1935.
570	1d. de Havilland DH.86 Dragon Express VH-URN *Miss Hobart* of Holyman's Airways over Bell Block Aerodrome	1·00	70
571	3d. de Havilland DH.86 Dragon Express VH-URN *Miss Hobart* of Holyman's Airways over Bell Block Aerodrome	5·00	3·00
572	6d. de Havilland DH.86 Dragon Express VH-URN *Miss Hobart* of Holyman's Airways over Bell Block Aerodrome	9·50	3·00
570/572 Set of 3		14·00	6·00

1940.
619*	4d. Short S.30 modified "G" Class flying boat	13·00	1·50

1946.
671*	3d. Avro Type 683 Lancaster (top left), Supermarine Spitfire Mk I (lower left), Short S.30 modified "G" Class flying boat and Avro Type 685 York	30	15

1950.
707*	1s. Lockheed 10 Electra	60	1·10

1955.
741* 4d. Douglas DC-3 ZK-URI of New Zealand National Airways..................... 60 1·00

1958. 30th Anniv of First Air Crossing of Tasman Sea.
766 6d. Sir Charles Kingsford Smith and Fokker F.VIIa/3m G-AUSU *Southern Cross* (incorrect registration "VH-USU" shown)... 50 75

1960.
794* 1s.9d de Havilland Canada DHC-2 Beaver spraying crops (brown) .... 10·00 15
795* 1s.9d de Havilland Canada DHC-2 Beaver spraying crops (multicoloured) .... 3·00 1·00

1968.
885* 10c. Pilots, Fairey Firefly (top right) and English Electric Canberra...................... 35 70

1970.
934* $2 Bell 47G Trooper helicopter................. 2·50 1·75

1972. 25th Anniv of National Airways Corporation.
980* 5c. de Havilland DH.89 Dragon Rapide (foreground) and Boeing 737 .... 25 10

1974. History of New Zealand Airmail Transport.
1050 3c. Boeing and Westervelt Model 1 seaplane, 1919......................... 25 10
1051 4c. Lockheed 10 Electra ZK-AFD *Kauha* of Union Airways 30 10
1052 5c. Bristol Type 170 Freighter Mk 31 ZK-AYG of Safe Air 30 30
1053 23c. Short S.30 modified "G" Class flying boat ZK-AMA *Aotearoa* of Tasman Empire Airways........................ 1·40 2·00
1050/1053 *Set of 4*... 2·00 2·25

1978.
1174* 12c. Bell 212 helicopter 15 15

1985.
1382* 75c. Westland AS.1 Wasp helicopter.......... 1·40 2·25

1987.
1412* 70c. Pilatus PC-6 Turbo Porter...................... 60 60

1987.
1421* 40c. Boeing 737.. 1·00 1·25

1987. 50th Anniv of Royal New Zealand Air Force.
1423 40c. Avro Type 626 trainer over Wigram Airfield, 1937.................................... 65 15
1424 70c. Curtiss P-40E Klttyhawk I fighters of the Royal New Zealand Air Force...... 90 1·75
1425 80c. Short S.25 Sunderland flying boat .... 1·00 1·75
1426 85c. Douglas A-4F Skyhawk jet bombers 1·10 1·75
1423/1426 *Set of 4*..................................... 3·25 4·75

1990. 50th Anniv of Air New Zealand.
1539 80c. Boeing 747-200 of Air New Zealand and Short S.30 modified "G" Class flying boat ZK-AMA *Aotearoa* of Tasman Empire Airways .... 1·40 1·10

1990.
1549* 50c. Jean Batten and Percival D.3 Gull Six G-ADPR.................................. 65 85
1551* 80c. Richard Pearse and early flying machine .... 90 1·50

1992.
1712* $1.80 Pilots and biplane.................................. 2·00 2·75

1993.
1772* 50c. de Havilland DH.82 Tiger Moth dusting crops.............................. 85 60

1994.
1782* $1.80 Heli-skiing with Bell 206B JetRanger III helicopter............................ 1·50 2·00

1996.
1981* $1 Air-sea rescue.. 1·10 1·10
1982* $1.50 Air ambulance and rescue helicopter............................... 1·60 2·50

1997.
2071* 40c. Aircraft letter box................................. 50 50

1998.
2145* $1.80c. Boeing 747................................. 1·60 1·60

1999.
2305* 80c. Richard Pearse's aircraft (first New Zealand aircraft)........................... 75 55

2001.
2408 40c. Douglas DC-3......................... 35 30
2409 80c. Fletcher FU24 Topdresser................. 65 55
2410 90c. de Havilland DH.82A Tiger Moth 70 60
2411 $1.30 Fokker F.VIIb/3m *Southern Cross* .... 90 1·10
2412 $1.50 de Havilland DH.100 Vampire .... 1·00 1·25
2413 $2 Boeing and Westervelt seaplane .... 1·25 1·25
2408/2413 *Set of 6*................................. 4·50 4·50

2003.

2587*	40c. Pilot serving with RAF Bomber Command, Europe, 1943	45	40
2588*	40c. Fighter pilot, No. 1 (Islands) Group, Royal New Zealand Air force, Pacific, 1943	45	40
2593*	40c. Canberra pilot with RAF Far East Command, Malaya, 1960	45	40

OFFICIAL STAMPS

1940. No. 619 overprinted **Official.**

O147*	4d. Short S.30 modified "G" Class flying boat	40·00	1·50

NICARAGUA

Central America

100 centavos = 1 cordoba

1929.

629	15c. Airco (de Havilland) DH.4 biplanes (purple)	20	20
630	20c. Airco (de Havilland) DH.4 biplanes (green)	35	35
631	25c. Airco (de Havilland) DH.4 biplanes (olive)	45	35
632	50c. Airco (de Havilland) DH.4biplanes (sepia)	75	70
633	1cor. Airco (de Havilland) DH.4 biplanes (red)	95	90
629/633	Set of 5	2·40	2·30

1930. No. 631 surcharged **Vale** and value.

634	15c. on 25c. Airco (de Havilland) DH.4 biplanes	45	35
635	20c. on 25c. Airco (de Havilland) DH.4 biplanes	75	70

1932. Nos. 632/3 surcharged **Vale** and value.

688	30c. on 50c. Airco (de Havilland) DH.4 biplanes	1·50	1·50
689	35c. on 50c. Airco (de Havilland) DH.4 biplanes	1·50	1·50
690	40c. on 1cor. Airco (de Havilland) DH.4 biplanes	1·70	1·60
691	55c. on 1cor. Airco (de Havilland) DH.4 biplanes	1·70	1·60
688/691	Set of 4	5·75	5·50

1932. No. 629 overprinted **Semana Correo Aereo Internacional 11-17 Septiembre 1932.**

692	15c. Airco (de Havilland) DH.4 biplanes	75·00	70·00

1932. No. 633 surcharged **Inauguracion Interior 12 Octubre 1932 Vale C$0.08.**

693	8c. on 1cor. Airco (de Havilland) DH.4 biplanes	20·00	20·00

1933. Nos. 632/3 surcharged Vale and value.

791	30c. on 50c. Airco (de Havilland) DH.4 biplanes	30	20
792	35c. on 50c. Airco (de Havilland) DH.4 biplanes	45	20
793	40c. on 1cor. Airco (de Havilland) DH.4 biplanes	45	20
794	55c. on 1cor. Airco (de Havilland) DH.4 biplanes	55	20
791/794	Set of 4	1·60	70

1934. Nos. 630/1 surcharged **Servicio Centroamericano Vale 10 centavos.**

814	10c. on 20c. Airco (de Havilland) DH.4 biplanes	35	25
815	10c. on 25c. Airco (de Havilland) DH.4 biplanes	30	25

1935. Overprinted **RESELLO - 1935** in rectangular frame.

(a) On Nos. 629/33

853A	15c. Airco (de Havilland) DH.4 biplanes	55	20
873A	20c. Airco (de Havilland) DH.4 biplanes	35	25
855A	25c. Airco (de Havilland) DH.4 biplanes	65	55
856A	50c. Airco (de Havilland) DH.4 biplanes	65	55
857A	1cor. Airco (de Havilland) DH.4 biplanes	55	55

(b) On Nos. 791/4

858A	30c. on 50c. Airco (de Havilland) DH.4 biplanes (orange)	55	55
859A	35c. on 50c. Airco (de Havilland) DH.4 biplanes (blue)	55	55
860A	40c. on 1cor. Airco (de Havilland) DH.4 biplanes (yellow)	55	55
861A	55c. on 1cor. Airco (de Havilland) DH.4 biplanes (green)	55	55

(c) On Nos. 814/15

862A	10c. on 20c. Airco (de Havilland) DH.4 biplanes	£550	£500
863A	10c. on 25c. Airco (de Havilland) DH.4 biplanes	55	45

1936. No. 631 surcharged **RESELLO - 1935** in rectangular frame and **Servicio Centroamericano Vale diez centavos.**

871	10c. on 25c. Airco (de Havilland) DH.4 biplanes	30	25

1936. Nos. 632/3 surcharged **1936 Vale Quince Centavos.**

906	15c. on 50c. Airco (de Havilland) DH.4 biplanes	20	20
907	15c. on 1cor. Airco (de Havilland) DH.4 biplanes	20	20

1937. As Nos. 629/33, but colours changed.

926	15c. (de Havilland) DH.4 biplanes (orange)	20	20
927	20c. Airco (de Havilland) DH.4 biplanes (red)	20	20
928	25c. Airco (de Havilland) DH.4 biplanes (black)	30	20
929	50c. Airco (de Havilland) DH.4 biplanes (violet)	30	20
930	1cor. Airco (de Havilland) DH.4 biplanes (orange)	65	25
926/930	Set of 5	1·50	95

1937. As Nos. 929/30, but colours changed, surcharged **Vale** and value.

931	30c. on 50c. Airco (de Havilland) DH.4 biplanes (red)	30	20
932	35c. on 50c. Airco (de Havilland) DH.4 biplanes (olive)	30	20
933	40c. on 1cor. Airco (de Havilland) DH.4 biplanes (green)	30	20
934	55c. on 1cor. Airco (de Havilland) DH.4 biplanes (blue)	30	20
931/934	Set of 4	1·10	70

1937. No. 857 surcharged **Servicio Centroamericano Vale Diez Centavos.**

949	10c. on 1cor. Airco (de Havilland) DH.4 biplanes	30	20

1937.

965	1c. Ryan B-5 Brougham	20	20
966	2c. Ryan B-5 Brougham	20	20
967	3c. Ryan B-5 Brougham	20	20
968	4c. Ryan B-5 Brougham	20	20
969	5c. Ryan B-5 Brougham	20	20
970	6c. Ryan B-5 Brougham	20	20
971	8c. Ryan B-5 Brougham	20	20
972	16c. Ryan B-5 Brougham	20	20
973	24c. Ryan B-5 Brougham	20	20
974	25c. Ryan B-5 Brougham	30	20
965/974	Set of 10	1·90	1·80

1937.

975	10c. Ryan B-5 Brougham	20	20
976	15c. Ryan B-5 Brougham	20	20
977	20c. Ryan B-5 Brougham	20	20
978	25c. Ryan B-5 Brougham	20	20
979	30c. Ryan B-5 Brougham	30	20
980	50c. Ryan B-5 Brougham	35	20
981	1cor. Ryan B-5 Brougham	70	55
975/981	Set of 7	1·90	1·60

1937.

982	10c. Douglas DC-3	1·90	1·10
983	15c. Douglas DC-3 (?)	1·90	1·30
984	20c. Douglas DC-3 (?)	1·10	1·10
985	25c. Douglas DC-3 (?)	1·10	1·10
986	30c. Douglas DC-3 (?)	1·10	1·10
987	35c. Douglas DC-3 (?)	60	60
988	40c. Douglas DC-3 (?)	50	50
989	45c. Douglas DC-3 (?)	50	45
990	50c. Douglas DC-3 (?)	50	45
991	55c. Douglas DC-3 (?)	50	45
992	75c. Douglas DC-3 (?)	50	45
993	1cor. Douglas DC-3 (?)	1·10	60
982/993	Set of 12	10·50	8·25

1937. Perf or imperf.

993a	1c. Douglas DC-2	20	20
993b	4c. Douglas DC-2	20	20
993c	5c. Douglas DC-2	30	25
993d	8c. Douglas DC-2	30	20
993e	10c. Douglas DC-2 (international airmail)	20	20
993f	15c. Douglas DC-2	20	20
993g	20c. Douglas DC-2	30	25
993a/993g	Set of 7	1·50	1·40

1938. Perf or imperf.

999a	1c. Douglas DC-2	25	25
999b	5c. Douglas DC-2	25	25
999c	8c. Douglas DC-2	35	35
999d	16c. Douglas DC-2	35	35
999e	10c. Douglas DC-2 (international airmail)	35	25
999f	15c. Douglas DC-2	35	35
999g	25c. Douglas DC-2	50	50
999h	50c. Douglas DC-2	60	60
999a/999h	Set of 8	2·75	2·50

1939.

1029	1c. Ford "Tin Goose" over Managua Airport	25	25
1030	2c. Ford "Tin Goose" of Pan Am	25	25
1031	3c. Ford "Tin Goose"	25	25
1032	4c. Ford "Tin Goose"	25	25
1033	5c. Ford "Tin Goose"	25	25
1029/1033	Set of 5	1·10	1·10

1940.

1046	1cor.25 Douglas DC-2	95	80

1941. No. 1029 surcharged **Servicio ordinario Vale Diez Centavos de Cordoba.**

1050	10c. on 1c. Ford "Tin Goose" over Managua Airport	25	25

1943. No. 1029 surcharged **Servicio ordinario Vale Diez Centavos.**

1056	10c. on 1c. Ford "Tin Goose" over Managua Airport	4·75	25

1947.

1113*	35c. Mercedes Airport, Managua	30	30

1954. National Air Force.

1210*	2c. North American F-86 Sabre	20	20
1211*	3c. Douglas A-20G Boston	20	20
1212*	4c. Consolidated B-24 Liberator	20	20
1213*	5c. North American T-6 Texan trainer	20	20
1217*	15c. North American F-86 Sabre (air)	20	20
1219*	25c. Hangars at airfield	20	20
1221*	50c. North American T-6 Texan trainers	50	50
1222*	1cor. Lockheed P-38 Lightning	40	30

1964.

1505*	15c. Airplane	20	20

1967.
1595*	20c. Sikorsky S-61B SH-3 Sea King helicopter of the U.S. Navy...............	30	30
1599*	1cor. Sikorsky S-61B SH-3 Sea King helicopter of the U.S. Navy...............	40	40

1974.
1937*	4c. de Havilland DH.4 biplanes (on stamp No. 814)	15	15

1976.
2065*	5c. Boeing 747-100	10	10

1976.
2091*	5c. Curtiss JN-4 "Jenny" (on United States of America stamp No. A548 with centre inverted).....................	10	10

1977. 75th Anniv of First Zeppelin Flight.
2104	1c. Airship LZ-127 *Graf Zeppelin*...............	15	15
2105	2c. Airship LZ-127 *Graf Zeppelin*...............	15	15
2106	3c. Henri Giffard's steam-powered dirigible airship, 1852..................	15	15
2107	4c. Airship LZ-127 *Graf Zeppelin*...............	15	15
2108	5c. Airship LZ-127 *Graf Zeppelin*...............	15	15
2109	35c. Astra airship *Ville de Paris* (air)	20	20
2110	70c. Airship LZ-10 *Schwaben*......................	30	20
2111	3cor. Airship LZ-127 *Graf Zeppelin*...............	1·00	80
2112	10cor. Airship LZ-2..................................	3·25	2·50
2104/2112 *Set of 9*		5·00	4·00
MS2113 20cor. Airship LZ-127 *Graf Zeppelin*		7·25	5·00

1977. 50th Anniv of Lindbergh's Trans-Atlantic Flight.
2115*	2c. Lindbergh's Ryan NYP Special *Spirit of St. Louis*......................	15	15
2117*	4c. Lindbergh's Ryan NYP Special *Spirit of St. Louis*......................	15	15
2118*	5c. Charles Lindbergh and Ryan NYP Special *Spirit of St. Louis*........	15	15
2119*	20c. Lindbergh's Ryan NYP Special *Spirit of St. Louis*......................	15	15
2120*	55c. Lindbergh's Ryan NYP Special *Spirit of St. Louis* over airfield in Nicaragua (air)..........................	20	20
2121*	80c. Lindbergh's Ryan NYP Special *Spirit of St. Louis*......................	30	20
2122*	2cor. Lindbergh's Ryan NYP Special *Spirit of St. Louis*......................	50	30
2123*	10cor. Lindbergh's Ryan NYP Special *Spirit of St. Louis*......................	2·50	2·00
MS2124* 20cor. Lindbergh's Ryan NYP Special *Spirit of St. Louis*		6·25	5·00

1978.
2168*	4c. Balloon from *Five Weeks in a Balloon* by Jules Verne	10	10
2170*	10cor. Balloon from the film *Around the World in Eighty Days* (air)	2·10	1·80

1978. History of Aviation. 75th Anniv of First Powered Flight.
2172	1c. Wright Glider No. IV	10	10
2173	2c. Montgolfier balloon (first manned free flight, 1783) and Wright Glider No. IV............................	10	10
2174	3c. Wright *Flyer I* and Wright Glider No. IV............................	10	10
2175	4c. Orville Wright in Wright Type A and Wright Glider No. IV................	10	10
2176	55c. Igor Sikorsky in Vought-Sikorsky VS-300 helicopter prototype, and Wright Glider No. IV (air)	30	20
2177	10cor. Wright Glider No. IV	1·60	1·20
2172/2177 *Set of 6* 2,50		2·10	1·60
MS2178 20cor. Wright *Flyer III* and Wright Glider No. IV...................................		6·25	5·00

1979.
2211*	2cor.20 Concorde and model aircraft.............	12·50	12·00

1980.
2219*	5cor. Airco (de Havilland) DH.4 biplanes and airship LZ-127 *Graf Zeppelin* (on cover bearing Nicaragua stamps Nos. 631/2 and United States of America stamp No. A688).....................	23·00	22·00

1982.
2358*	10cor. Boeing 727-100 of Aeronica	1·50	90

1982.
MS2367 15cor. Balloon *Ville d'Orleans*, Paris, 1870.....		3·00	2·00

1983.
MS2495 10cor. Boeing 727-100		2·50	1·30

1984.
2607	15cor. Boeing 727.............................	3·25	1·70
MS2608 15cor. Airship LZ-120 *Bodensee*		4·00	2·20

1984.
2626*	1cor. Red Cross Douglas DC-4	30	15

1985.
2656*	7cor. Casa C-212 Aviocar of Aeronica..........	2·50	50

1985.
2700*	15cor. Ilyushin Il-86 (top) and Tupolev Tu-154 with Red Cross markings	1·10	60

1986.
2783	1cor. Lockheed L-1011 TriStar 500	20	10
2784	1cor. Yakovlev Yak-40.....................	20	10
2785	3cor. B.A.C. One Eleven	30	15
2786	3cor. Boeing 747-100	30	15
2787	9cor. Airbus Industrie A300 (air)	45	25
2788	15cor. Tupolev Tu-154	65	35
2789	100cor. Concorde	3·25	1·50
2783/2789 *Set of 7*		4·75	2·30
MS2790 100cor. Saab-Fairchild SF-340		3·75	1·70

1988. Helicopters.
2971	4cor. Bell 206B JetRanger III helicopter and autogyro	35	10
2972	12cor. MBB-Kawasaki BK-117A-3 helicopter and autogyro	35	15
2973	16cor. Boeing-Vertol B-360 helicopter and autogyro	55	20
2974	20cor. Agusta A.109 MR11 helicopter and autogyro	70	25
2975	24cor. Sikorsky S-61N helicopter and autogyro	85	30
2976	28cor. Aerospatiale SA.365 Dauphin 2 helicopter and autogyro	95	35
2977	56cor. Sikorsky S-76 Spirit helicopter and autogyro	2·00	70
2971/2977 *Set of 7*		5·25	1·80
MS2978 120cor. Nardi NH 90 helicopter.....................		4·25	3·25

1994. Zeppelin Airships.
3376	1cor.50 Hugo Eckener and Count Ferdinand von Zeppelin	45	25
3377	1cor.50 *Graf Zeppelin* over New York, 1928....	45	25
3378	1cor.50 *Graf Zeppelin* over Tokyo, 1929	45	25

3379	1cor.50 *Graf Zeppelin* over Randolph Hearst's villa, 1929	45	25
3380	1cor.50 Charles Lindbergh, Hugo Eckener and *Graf Zeppelin* at Lakehurst, 1929	45	25
3381	1cor.50 *Graf Zeppelin* over St. Basil's Cathedral Moscow (wrongly inscribed *Santra Sofia*	45	25
3382	1cor.50 *Graf Zeppelin* over Paris, 1930	45	25
3383	1cor.50 *Graf Zeppelin* over Cairo, Egypt, 1931	45	25
3384	1cor.50 *Graf Zeppelin* over Arctic Sea	45	25
3385	1cor.50 *Graf Zeppelin* over Rio de Janeiro, 1932	45	25
3386	1cor.50 *Graf Zeppelin* over St. Paul's Cathedral, London, 1935	45	25
3387	1cor.50 *Graf Zeppelin* over St. Peter's Cathedral, Rome	45	25
3388	1cor.50 *Graf Zeppelin* over Swiss Alps	45	25
3389	1cor.50 *Graf Zeppelin* over Brandenburg Gate, Berlin	45	25
3390	1cor.50 Hugh Eckener piloting *Graf Zeppelin*	45	25
3391	1cor.50 Captain Ernest Lehman, *Graf Zeppelin* and Dornier Do-X	45	25
3376/3391 *Set of 16*		6·50	3·50
MS3392 Two sheets. (a)10cor. Hugo Eckener and *Graf Zeppelin*. (b) 10cor. Count and Ferdinand von Zeppelin and airship *Set of 2 sheets*		6·50	4·25

NICARAGUA ₡3.00

1994.

3452*	3cor. Hawker Typhoon 1B	1·10	70
3453*	3cor. Douglas C-47 Skytrain	1·10	70

3 Correos 95

1995.

3554*	30cor. Short S.29 Stirling bombers	85	50

1996.

MS3580* 10cor. Messerschmitt Bf.109		3·75	3·75

NICARAGUA ₡12.00

1999. Ballooning.

3864	12cor. Tiberius Cavallo (early researcher into gases)	2·50	1·80
3865	12cor. *Breitling Orbiter 3* (1990)	2·50	1·80
3866	12cor. Bertrand Piccard and Brian Jones (balloonists)	2·50	1·80
3867	12cor. Brian Jones (captain)	2·50	1·80
3868	12cor. *Breitling Orbiter 3* (first non-stop circumnavigation of world, 1999)	2·50	1·80
3869	12cor. Bertrand Piccard (co-pilot)	2·50	1·80
3870	12cor. *Breitling Orbiter 3* over alps	2·50	1·80
3871	12cor. Leonardo da Vinci (experiments with heavier air)	2·50	1·80
3872	12cor. Bertrand Piccard and Brian Jones (different)	2·50	1·80
3873	12cor. *Solo Spirit 3* (first crossing of South Atlantic, 1998)	2·50	1·80
3874	12cor. *Breitling Orbiter 3* emblem	2·50	1·80
3875	12cor. ICO Global (1998)	2·50	1·80
3864/3875 *Set of 12*		27·00	19·00
MS3876 Three sheets. (a) 25cor. Pilatre de Rozier (first manned flight); (b) 25cor. Madame Thible (first woman solo balloon flight); (c) 25cor. J.A.C. Charles (early balloon producer)		17·00	17·00
MS3877 25cor. Jean Pierre Blanchard (balloon pioneer) *Set of 4 sheets*		5·50	5·50

₡7.50

2000.

3913	7cor.50 Montgolfier balloon	1·90	1·30
3914	7cor.50 Bristol F2B	1·90	1·30
3915	7cor.50 Hunting (Percival) P.84 Jet Provost	1·90	1·30
3916	7cor.50 Hawker Hunter. Inscribed Hunter	1·90	1·30
3917	7cor.50 Westland Wessex	1·90	1·30
3918	7cor.50 Inscribed "Redwing II trainer"	1·90	1·30
3919	7cor.50 Montgolfier balloon (different)	1·90	1·30
3920	7cor.50 Hawker Hart	1·90	1·30
3921	7cor.50 Westland Lysander	1·90	1·30
3922	7cor.50 BAe Harrier	1·90	1·30
3923	7cor.50 Vickers VC 10	1·90	1·30
3924	7cor.50 Bleriot XI and de Havilland DH.83 Fox Moth	1·90	1·30
3913/3924 *Set of 12*		21·00	14·00
MS3925 Two sheets. (a) 25cor. Spartan Arrow and de Havilland DH.82 Tiger Moth; (b) 25cor. de Havilland DH.82 Tiger Moth and Spartan Arrow *Set of 2 sheets*		13·00	13·00
No. 3915 is inscribed Provest Jet in error.			

2000.

3959*	5cor. Helicopter rescue of Alan Shepard	1·30	95

OFFICIAL STAMPS

1937. Nos. 926/30 overprinted **SERVICIO OFICIAL Republica de Nicaragua C.A.** in circular emblem.

O944	15c. Airco (de Havilland) DH.4 biplanes	1·10	55
O945	20c. Airco (de Havilland) DH.4 biplanes	1·10	55
O946	25c. Airco (de Havilland) DH.4 biplanes	1·10	70
O947	50c. Airco (de Havilland) DH.4 biplanes	1·10	70
O948	1cor. Airco (de Havilland) DH.4 biplanes	1·10	70
O944/948 *Set of 5*		5·00	3·00

1947.

O1120*	5c. Buildings and control tower at Mercedes Airport, Managua	30	30

NIGER

West Africa

100 centimes = 1 franc

1940. As Nos. 117/21 of Dahomey.

94	1f.90 Twin-engine airliner	1·30	3·50
95	2f.90 Twin-engine airliner	75	3·50
96	4f.50 Twin-engine airliner	1·20	3·75
97	4f.90 Twin-engine airliner	65	4·75
98	6f.90 Twin-engine airliner	2·30	5·00
94/98 *Set of 5*		4·25	17·00

1942. As No. 143k of Dahomey.

98k	50f. Twin-engine airliner	2·30	5·00

1961.

119	25f. Lockheed L.1049 Super Constellation, Boeing 707 and another airliner	65	35
120	100f. Lockheed L.1049 Super Constellation, Boeing 707 and another airliner	2·40	1·20

1962. As No. 307 of Cameroun.

121	100f. Boeing 707 airliners of Air Afrique	1·90	95

1963. Nos. 119/20 overprinted with cross and **Centenaire de la Croix-Rouge.**

142	25f. Lockheed L.1049 Super Constellation, Boeing 707 and another airliner	90	60
143	100f. Lockheed L.1049 Super Constellation, Boeing 707 and another airliner	2·20	1·10

1966. As No. 438 of Cameroun.

233	30f. Douglas DC-8F Jet Trader of Air Afrique	75	40

1967.

259	45f. Jet airliner	75	45

1968. 35th Anniv of First France-Niger Airmail Service.

281	45f. Breguet 27	1·20	45
282	80f. Potez 25 TOE	1·80	70
283	100f. Potez 25 TOE	2·75	95
281/283 *Set of 3*		5·25	1·90

1969.

311	50f. Boeing 707	95	55

1969. 10th Anniv of ASECNA. As No. 552 of Cameroun.

333	100f. Airliner over airport	1·60	85

1970. Aviation Pioneers.

347*	50f. Clement Ader's *Avion III* and Fokker F.27	1·00	45
348*	100f. Joseph and Etienne Montgolfier and Montgolfier balloon (unmanned flight, 1783)	2·10	70
351*	250f. Leonardo da Vinci's drawing of a "flying machine" and Chanute's glider	4·50	1·90

1970. No. 348 overprinted **Solidarite Spatiale Apollo XIII 11-17 Avril 1970.**

355*	100f. Joseph and Etienne Montgolfier and Montgolfier balloon (unmanned flight, 1783)	1·50	70

1970. No. 351 surcharged **200F LUNA 16-Sept. 1970 PREMIERS PRELEVEMENTS AUTOMATIQUES SUR LA LUNE.**

368*	200f. on 250f. Leonardo da Vinci's drawing of a "flying machine" and Chanute's glider	4·00	1·60

1972. Milestones in Aviation History.

431	50f. Bleriot XI	1·20	45
432	75f. Lindbergh's Ryan NYP Special *Spirit of St. Louis*	1·80	70
433	100f. Concorde	3·50	1·60
431/433 *Set of 3*		5·75	2·50

1972.

447*	150f. Fokker F.27 Friendship at airport	2·50	90

1973.

480	100f. Douglas DC-8 of Air Afrique	2·00	75

1974.
543* 50f. Douglas DC-8 airliners 95   40

1976. 75th Anniv of Zeppelin Airships.
624 40f. Airship LZ-129 *Hindenburg* 55   20
625 50f. Airship LZ-3 75   25
626 150f. German Navy airship L-9 (LZ-36) ...... 2·20   60
627 200f. Airship LZ-2 .... 2·75   80
628 300f. Airship LZ-130 *Graf Zeppelin II* .... 3·75   95
624/628 *Set of 5* .... 9·00 2·50
MS629 500f. Airship LZ-127 *Graf Zeppelin* .... 6·00 2·00

1976.
630 100f. Concorde .... 1·50   70

1979.
763* 150f. Model glider .... 1·80   60

1979.
766* 150f. Douglas DC-3 of Air Niger .... 1·80   45

1979. 60th Anniv of First Trans-Atlantic Flight.
771 100f. Vickers FB-27 Vimy, 1919, and statue
        of Alcock and Brown .... 1·30   45

1979. 20th Anniv of ASECNA.
781 150f. Douglas DC-10 .... 1·20   40

1981.
846* 150f. Boeing 747-123 of NASA carrying
        Space Shuttle .... 1·40   45

1983. Bicentenary of Manned Flight.
926* 65f. Montgolfier balloon (first manned
        free flight, 1783) 55   25
927* 85f. Charles' hydrogen balloon, 1783 55   25
928* 200f. Goodyear Aerospace airship
        (wrongly inscribed "Zeppelin") 95   25
929* 250f. Farman H.F.III biplane .... 1·50   40
930* 300f. Concorde of Air France .... 1·80   70

1985.
1037 110f. Boeing 737 .... 1·20   60

1985.
1054* 150f. Aerospatiale SA316 Alouette III .... 1·50   75

1991.
1248* 500f. Lockheed F-117A Nighthawk and
        Concorde .... 4·50 1·10

NIGERIA

West Africa

1949 12 pence = 1 shilling
20 shillings = 1 pound
1973 100 kobo = 1 naira

1949. As Nos. 114/15 of Antigua.
64* 1d. Airplane 15   30
65* 3d. Jet-powered Vickers Viking .... 1·25 3·50

1961.
100* 10s. Buildings at Kano Airport .... 3·50 4·25

1961.
104* 1s.3d. Bristol 175 Britannia 80   20

1962.
118* 1s.3d. Airplane spraying crops 20   10

1974.
326* 18k. Boeing 727 (?) .... 2·00   60

1978. 75th Anniv of Powered Flight.
393 5k. Wilbur and Orville Wright and Wright
        Type A 20   10
394 18k. SEPECAT Jaguars 60   20

1979. Opening of Murtala Muhammed Airport.
395 5k. Boeing 727 over Murtala Muhammed
        Airport 40   30

1980.
418* 25k. Jet airliner 30   10

1984. 40th Anniv of ICAO.
488 10k. Boeing 747 at airport 40   10
489 45k. Boeing 707 .... 1·50 2·25

1988.
553* 20k. Boeing 737 65   30

NIUAFO'OU

South Pacific

100 seniti = 1 pa'anga

1983. Inauguration of Niuafo'ou Airport. As Nos. 843/4 of Tonga.
17 29s. de Havilland Canada DHC-6 Twin
        Otter 300 of South Pacific Island
        Airways .... 1·50 1·00
18 1p. de Havilland Canada DHC-6 Twin
        Otter 300 of South Pacific Island
        Airways .... 3·00 3·25

1987. Air Pioneers of the South Pacific.
99 42s. Captain E.C. Musick and Sikorsky
        S-42A flying boat *Samoan Clipper* ..... 2·00 1·40

100	57s. Captain J.W. Burgess and Short S.30 modified "G" Class flying boat ZK-AMA *Aotearoa* of Tasman Empire Airways.................		2·25	1·75
101	1p.50 Sir Charles Kingsford Smith and Fokker F.VIIa/3m G-AUSU *Southern Cross*		4·00	4·25
102	2p. Amelia Earhart and Lockheed 10E Electra		4·25	5·50
99/102	*Set of 4*		11·50	11·50

1988. Fifth Anniv of Niuafo'ou Airport.

105*	1p. de Havilland Canada DHC-6 Twin Otter 300 of South Pacific Island Airways (on stamp No. 17) and Concorde		5·00	3·25
106*	2p. de Havilland Canada DHC-6 Twin Otter 300 of South Pacific Island Airways (on stamp No. 17) and Concorde		5·50	4·00

1988.

MS107*	42s. Flying Doctor de Havilland Australia DHA.3 Drover (sheet contains 11 other 42s, designs)		38·00	35·00

1990.

151*	2p.50 de Havilland Canada DHC-6 Twin Otter 200/300		3·25	4·00

1992.

166*	42s. Wrecked Douglas B-18 Bolo		1·60	1·60
167*	42s. Mitsubishi A6M Zero-Sen		1·60	1·60
170*	42s. Douglas SBD Dauntless dive bomber		1·60	1·60
176*	42s. Boeing B-29 Superfortress		1·60	1·60

1993. 10th Anniv of First Flight to Niuafo'ou.

188	1p. de Havilland Canada DHC-6 Twin Otter 200/300 of South Pacific Island Airways		1·50	2·00
189	2p.50 de Havilland Canada DHC-6 Twin Otter 200/300 of Friendly Islands Airways		3·50	4·50

1993.

193*	80s. de Havilland Canada DHC-6 Twin Otter 200/300		1·25	1·75

1995.

239*	60s. Concorde		1·25	1·75

2002. Mail Planes.

MS323	80s. CASA C-212 Aviocar; 1p.40 Britten-Norman BN-2 Islander; 2p.50 de Havilland Canada DHC-6 Twin Otter		6·00	6·50

NIUE

South Pacific

100 cents = 1 dollar

1970. Opening of Niue Airport.

155	3c. Fokker F.27 Friendship		10	20
156	5c. Fokker F.27 Friendship		15	20
157	8c. Fokker F.27 Friendship over airport ..		15	30
155/157	*Set of 3*		35	65

1979.

302*	60c. Sikorsky S-61B SH-3 Sea King helicopter of the U.S. Navy and aircraft carrier		90	40

1980. No. 302 surcharged **HURRICANE RELIEF Plus 2c.**

326*	60c. +2c. Sikorsky S-61B SH-3 Sea King helicopter of the U.S. Navy and aircraft carrier		50	75

1983. Bicentenary of Manned Flight.

496*	25c. Montgolfier balloon (first manned free flight, 1783) and another balloon		55	25
497*	40c. Wright Flyer I		1·40	45
498*	58c. Airship LZ-127 *Graf Zeppelin*		1·50	60
499*	70c. Boeing 247		1·75	85
MS502*	25c., 40c., 58c., 70c. as Nos. 496/9, but inscribed "AIRMAIL" (sheet contains two other designs)		3·00	3·25

2003. Centenary of Powered Flight.

MS926	80c. Boeing 737-200; 80c. Boeing Model 377 Stratocruiser; 80c. Boeing Model SA-307B; 80c. Douglas DC-2; 80c. Wright *Flyer I*; 80c. Airco (de Havilland) DH.4A		6·00	6·50
MS927	$4 Boeing 767 *Set of 2 sheets*		6·00	6·50

2004.

MS934*	$1.50 North American B-25 Mitchell bombers; $1.50 Paratroopers		4·75	5·50

2005.

942*	$1.25 Paratroopers		2·00	2·00
944*	$1.25 Hawker Typhoon		2·00	2·00

2007. Concorde.

1004	$1 Final landing of Concorde F-BVFC at Toulouse (olive-bistre frame)		2·00	2·00
1005	$1 Crew waving to crowd from cockpit (brownish grey frame)		2·00	2·00
1006	$1 As No. 1004 with grey-olive frame		2·00	2·00
1007	$1 As No. 1005 with light brown frame.		2·00	2·00
1008	$1 As No. 1004 with olive-grey frame		2·00	2·00
1009	$1 As No. 1005 with turquoise blue frame		2·00	2·00
1010	$1 Concorde G-BOAD on ground (grey background, blue tint to aircraft)		2·00	2·00
1011	$1 Concorde G-BOAD in flight (natural colours)		2·00	2·00
1012	$1 As No. 1010 with orange-brown background		2·00	2·00
1013	$1 As No. 1011 but lilac tint		2·00	2·00
1014	$1 As No. 1010 but drab background		2·00	2·00
1015	$1 As No. 1011 but turquoise blue tint..		2·00	2·00
1004/1015	*Set of 12*		22·00	22·00

Nos. 1004/9 show the last flight of Concorde F-BVFC from Paris to Toulouse on 27 June 2003.

Nos. 1010/15 show the final flight of Concorde G-BOAD from London Heathrow Airport to New York on 10 November 2003.

NORFOLK ISLAND

Australasia

1953. 12 pence = 1 shilling

20 shillings = 1 pound

1966. 100 cents = 1 dollar

1953.

14*	6½d. Douglas DC-3		2·25	3·25

1968. 21st Anniv of QANTAS Air Service, Sydney-Norfolk Island.

96	5c. Avro Type 691 Lancastrian VH-EAT and Douglas DC-4 VH-EDB of QANTAS		15	10
97	7c. Avro Type 691 Lancastrian VH-EAT and Douglas DC-4 VH-EDB of QANTAS		15	10

1974. First Aircraft Landing on Norfolk Island.

151	14c. Sir Francis Chichester's de Havilland DH.60G Gipsy Moth seaplane ZK-AKK *Madame Elijah*, 1931		75	70

1976.
174*   40c. Boeing B-17 Flying Fortress............... 30   85

1980. Airplanes.
236   1c. Hawker Siddeley H.S.748 of the
            Royal Australian Air Force.................... 15   20
237   2c. de Havilland DH.60G Gipsy Moth
            seaplane ZK-AKK *Madame Elijah*........ 15   20
238   3c. Two Curtiss P-40E Kittyhawk I
            fighters and Douglas DC-3 Dakota of
            the Royal Australian Air Force............ 15   20
239   4c. Vought F4U-1 Corsair of the Royal
            Australian Air Force........................... 15   30
240   5c. Grumman TBF Avengers of the Royal
            New Zealand Air Force....................... 15   30
241   15c. Douglas SBD-5 Dauntless dive
            bombers of the Royal New Zealand
            Air Force.. 30   30
242   20c. Cessna 172D Skyhawk VH-DOW........ 30   30
243   25c. Lockheed 414 Hudson of the Royal
            New Zealand Air Force....................... 30   35
244   30c. Lockheed PV-1 Ventura of the Royal
            New Zealand Air Force....................... 40   2·00
245   40c. Avro Type 685 York...................... 50   55
246   50c. Douglas DC-3 ZK-APA of New
            Zealand National Airways.................. 65   65
247   60c. Avro Type 691 Lancastrian VH-EAT.... 75   75
248   80c. Douglas DC-4 of QANTAS.............. 1·00   1·00
249      $1 Beech 200 Super King Air VH-IBC of
            Norfolk Island Airways...................... 1·00   1·00
250      $2 Fokker F.27 Friendship 500............ 2·00   3·00
251      $5 Lockheed C-130 Hercules.............. 2·25   2·00
236/251 *Set of 16* .... 9·25   12·00
Nos. 236/51 each have a panel at right showing a de Havilland
DH.60G Gipsy Moth seaplane and part of a Fokker F.27 Friendship.

1982. 40th Anniv of First Supply Plane Landing on Norfolk Island.
293   27c. Lockheed 414 Hudson of the Royal
            New Zealand Air Force....................... 75   35
294   40c. Lockheed 414 Hudson of the Royal
            New Zealand Air Force....................... 95   65
295   75c. Lockheed 414 Hudson of the Royal
            New Zealand Air Force....................... 1·10   1·40
293/295 *Set of 3* .... 2·50   2·20

1983. Bicentenary of Manned Flight.
304   10c. Beech 18...................................... 15   15
305   27c. Fokker F.28 Fellowship of East West
            Airlines.. 25   35
306   45c. Douglas C-54 of the French Air
            Force.. 40   60
307   75c. Sikorsky S-61N helicopter.............. 60   95
304/307 *Set of 4* .... 1·30   1·80

1988.
444*   37c. Turbo-prop airliner 75   1·25

1991.
523*   70c. Boeing B-17 Flying Fortress on
            jungle airstrip................................... 2·25   2·75

1992.
532*   70c. Consolidated PBY-5 Catalina flying
            boat... 2·00   2·50
533* $1.05 Japanese aircraft carrier on fire
            and Douglas SBD Dauntless dive
            bomber.. 2·75   3·50

1995.
602*   5c. Servicing Curtiss P-40 ....

1996. 75th Anniv of Royal Australian Air Force.
615   45c. Sopwith Pup................................. 60   60
616   45c. Commonwealth Aircraft CA-1
            Wirraway.. 60   60
617   75c. General Dynamics F-111 Aardvark.... 1·00   1·50
618   85c. Boeing (McDonnell Douglas) F/A-18
            Hornet.. 1·10   1·60
615/618 *Set of 4* .... 3·00   3·75

1999.
690   5c. Short S.23 Sandringham................ 25   40
691   5c. Douglas DC-4 *Norfolk Trader* 25   40

1999.
MS716* $3 General Aircraft Monospar ST-25
            Jubilee, Amy Johnson (flight to Australia, 1930)
            and Queen Elizabeth, the Queen Mother............... 3·50   3·75

2003. Centenary of Powered Flight.
855   50c. Sir Francis Chichester's de Havilland
            DH.60G Gipsy Moth (first aircraft at
            Norfolk Island, 1931) 85   55
856      $1.10 Boeing 737 (Norfolk Island-Australia
            service).. 1·60   1·50
857      $1.65 Douglas DC-4 (passenger service
            1949–1977).. 2·50   3·25
855/857 *Set of 3* .... 4·50   4·75
MS858 $1.65 Wright *Flyer I*....................... 3·25   3·75

NORTH BORNEO

South-east Asia

100 cents = 1 dollar

1949. As Nos. 114/15 of Antigua.
352*   8c. Airplane....................................... 60   30
353*   10c. Jet-powered Vickers Viking.............. 3·25   1·75

NORTH KOREA

See under Korea

NORTHERN RHODESIA

Central Africa

12 pence = 1 shilling

20 shillings = 1 pound

1949. As Nos. 114/15 of Antigua.
50*   2d. Airplane....................................... 20   30
51*   3d. Jet-powered Vickers Viking................ 2·00   2·50

NORWAY

Northern Europe

100 ore = 1 krone

1925. Amundsen's Polar Flight.
167   2ore Dornier Do-J Wal flying boat.............. 3·00   3·00
168   3ore Dornier Do-J Wal flying boat.............. 6·00   4·00
169   5ore Dornier Do-J Wal flying boat.............. 12·50   11·50
170   10ore Dornier Do-J Wal flying boat............ 15·00   14·50
171   15ore Dornier Do-J Wa flying boat............. 16·00   19·00
172   20ore Dornier Do-J Wal flying boat............ 18·00   21·00
173   25ore Dornier Do-J Wal flying boat............ 7·25   5·00
167/173 *Set of 7* .... 70·00   70·00

1927.
199a   45ore Airplane (with frame lines).................... 8·75   2·75
323   45ore Airplane (without frame lines)............... 1·10   30

1944.
361*   15ore +10ore Bristol Type **142** Blenheim
            Mk IV.. 70   5·75

1944. 30th Anniv of First North Sea Flight by Tryggve Gran.
363   40ore Tryggve Gran's Bleriot XI *Nordsjoen*,
            1914.. 50   3·00

1960. 10th Anniv of Scandinavian Airlines (SAS).
507   90ore Douglas DC-8 of Scandinavian
            Airlines System................................ 75   60

1962. 50th Anniv of Norwegian Aviation.
524   1k.50 Etrich/Rumpler Taube monoplane
            Start.. 2·30   50

1978.
819*   1k.25 Dornier Do-J Wal flying boat (on
            stamp No. 170).................................... 65   65

820*	1k.25 Dornier Do-J Wal flying boat (on stamp No. 171)	65	65
823*	1k.25 Dornier Do-J Wal flying boat (on stamp No. 172)	65	65
825*	1k.25 Dornier Do-J Wal flying boat (on stamp No. 173)	65	65

1979. Arctic Aviation.
MS847 1k.25 Dornier Do-J Wal flying boat N-25; 2k. Airship N.1 Norge; 2k.80 Loening OA-2 amphibian *Leiv Eiriksson*; 4k. Douglas DC-7C *Reidar Viking* of Scandinavian Airlines System .... 4·75 4·50

1980.
MS862 4k. Boeing 737 and Douglas DC-9 (sheet contains 3 other designs) .... 4·75 4·50

1990.
1074* 3k.20 Consolidated PBY-5 Catalina flying boat of the Norwegian Air Force........ 1·10 25

1996.
1240* 3k.50 Loading mail on Junkers W-34 seaplane... 95 65

1998. Inauguration of Oslo Airport, Gardermoen.
1323	3k.80 Boeing 747, Douglas DC-3 and Junkers Ju 52/3m	1·00	50
1324	6k. Boeing 737 and map	1·50	70
1325	24k. Terminal building, control tower and drawing of wings by Leonardo da Vinci	5·75	2·75
1323/1325 *Set of* 3		7·50	3·50

NYASALAND PROTECTORATE

Central Africa

12 pence = 1 shilling

20 shillings = 1 pound

1949. As Nos. 114/15 of Antigua.
163*	1d. Airplane	30	20
164*	3d. Jet-powered Vickers Viking	2·25	4·00

OCEANIC SETTLEMENTS

East Pacific
100 centimes = 1 franc

1934.
120   5f. Flying boat .... 1·50 4·00

1941. No. 120 overprinted **FRANCE LIBRE**.
146*   5f. Flying boat .... 1·80 4·50

1942. As Nos. 207/13 of Cameroun.
161* 1f. Fairey FC-1 airliner .... 1·70 4·00
162* 1f.50 Fairey FC-1 airliner .... 1·80 4·50
163* 5f. Fairey FC-1 airliner .... 1·80 5·25
164* 10f. Fairey FC-1 airliner .... 2·50 6·00
165* 25f. Fairey FC-1 airliner .... 3·00 7·00
166* 50f. Fairey FC-1 airliner .... 4·00 7·00
167* 100f. Fairey FC-1 airliner .... 3·75 7·00

1948.
208* 100f. Airplane .... 25·00 18·00

1949. As No. 254 of Cameroun.
210   10f. Lockheed Constellation .... 3·25 34·00

1954. As No. 264 of Cameroun.
214   3f. Bomber .... 9·25 6·75

OMAN

Arabia
1000 baizas = 1 rial saidi

1973.
173* 50b. Boeing 747 at Seeb International Airport .... 5·75 1·50

1976.
202* 40b. Lockheed C-130 Hercules .... 2·30 55
203* 75b. Agusta-Bell AB-212 helicopters .... 4·50 1·20

1979.
227* 40b. SEPECAT Jaguar International (top left) and Hawker Hunter .... 3·75 1·20

1981.
255* 100b. Lockheed C-130 Hercules transport aircraft .... 3·75 1·90

1982.
277   50b. Aircraft .... 6·25 2·75
278   100b. Aircraft .... 4·50 2·30

1983.
287   100b. Lockheed F-104G Starfighters and Agusta-Bell AB-212 helicopters ...... 6·25 2·30

1984.
298   100b. SEPECAT Jaguars .... 6·25 2·75

1985.
299   100b. Bell 214ST helicopter .... 6·25 2·75

1985.
312* 200b. Douglas DC-10 .... 3·50 2·30

1985.
314   100b. Westland WG-13 Lynx helicopters ..... 6·25 1·50

1990. 40th Anniv of Gulf Air.
381   80b. Douglas DC-10 of Gulf Air .... 2·30 75

1991.
394   100b. Sepecat Jaguar of the Omani Air Force .... 1·50 75

1993.
405   100b. Helicopter .... 1·50 75

1994. 50th Anniv of ICAO.
418   100b. Boeing 737 .... 3·00 1·50

1999. 40th Anniv of Royal Air Force of Oman.
488   100b. SEPECAT Jaguar and BAe Hawk ...... 1·50 90

2000. 50th Anniv of Gulf Air.
518   100b. Boeing 767-300 ER .... 1·00 75

2005.
654* 100b. Airbus A320 .... 75 60
655* 100b. Bell 205 and cavalry 75 60
658* 100b. SEPECAT Jaguars, ship and tanks 75 60

PAHANG

South-east Asia

100 cents = 1 dollar

1949. As Nos. 114/15 of Antigua.
49*	10c. Airplane	30	25
50*	15c. Jet-powered Vickers Viking	1·10	1·50

PAKISTAN

Indian sub-continent

1947. 12 pies = 1 anna

16 annas = 1 rupee

1961. 100 paisa = 1 rupee

1947. No. 277 of India overprinted **PAKISTAN**.
13*	14a. Armstrong Whitworth A.W.27 Ensign I	3·25	3·50

1948.
21*	2½a. Douglas DC-3 over entrance to Karachi Airport	1·25	20

1948. Designs show crescent pointing right.
31*	3a. Karachi Airport	7·50	1·00
36*	10a. Karachi Airport	6·00	9·00

1949. As Nos. 31 and 36, but crescent pointing left.
47*	3a. Karachi Airport	15·00	1·00
50*	10a. Karachi Airport	23·00	3·25

1957.
92	1½a. Lockheed Constellation	30	30
93	4a. Lockheed Constellation	45	1·50
94	12a. Lockheed Constellation	45	50
92/94 Set of 3		1·10	2·10

1962. No. 87 surcharged **FIRST JET FLIGHT KARACHI-DACCA 13 Paisa** and Boeing 720B airliner.
155	13p. on 2½a. Karnaphuli Paper Mill, East Bengal	1·75	1·25

1965.
228*	50p. Pilot and Lockheed F-104C Starfighters of the Pakistan Air Force	2·50	30

1968.
268*	50p. Dassault Mirage IIIC (left), Mikoyan Gurevich MiG-15 (top) and Lockheed F-104C Starfighter	2·00	20

1969. 50th Anniv of First England-Australia Flight.
287	50p. Ross and Keith Smith's Vickers Vimy G-EAOU, 1919, and Karachi Airport	70	35

1974.
379*	2r.25 Boeing 707	55	1·40

1978. 75th Anniv of Powered Flight.
483	65p. Panavia MRCA Tornado, de Havilland DH.89 Dragon Rapide and Wright Flyer I	1·00	1·70
484	1r. McDonnell Douglas F-4A Phantom II, Lockheed L-1011 TriStar 500 and Wright Flyer I	1·10	1·75
485	2r. North American X-15, Tupolev Tu-104 and Wright Flyer I	1·25	2·00
486	2r.25 Mikoyan Gurevich MiG-15, Concorde and Wright Flyer I	1·25	2·25
483/486 Set of 4		4·25	7·00

1980. 25th Anniv of Pakistan International Air Lines.
512	1r. Douglas DC-3 (on ground) and Boeing 747-200 of Pakistan International Airlines	1·75	90

1981. 50th Anniv of Airmail Service.
548	1r. Stylised airliner	60	20

1984. 20th Anniv of Pakistan International Airways Service to China.
624	3r. Boeing 707 of Pakistan International Airlines	5·00	5·50

1987.
707*	5r. Lockheed Martin (General Dynamics) F-16 Fighting Falcon	1·10	1·25

1987. Air Force Day. Military Aircraft.
715	3r. Hawker Tempest Mk II	1·25	1·25
716	3r. Hawker Fury	1·25	1·25
717	3r. Supermarine Attacker	1·25	1·25
718	3r. North American F-86 Sabre	1·25	1·25
719	3r. Lockheed F-104C Starfighter of the Pakistan Air Force	1·25	1·25
720	3r. Lockheed C-130 Hercules of the Pakistan Air Force	1·25	1·25
721	3r. Shenyang/Tianjin F-6 of the Pakistan Air Force	1·25	1·25
722	3r. Dassault Mirage III of the Pakistan Air Force	1·25	1·25
723	3r. NAMC (Nanchang) A-5C Fantan	1·25	1·25
724	3r. Lockheed Martin (General Dynamics) F-16 Fighting Falcon	1·25	1·25
715/724 Set of 10		11·00	12·50

1998. 50th Anniv (1997) of Armed Forces.
1034	7r. Servicemen, including fighter pilot	1·00	1·00

1998.
1056*	2r. Boeing 727	35	40

2003. 32nd Death Anniv of Pilot Officer Rashid Minhas.
1193	2r. Pilot Officer Minhas and North American F-86 Sabre	75	35

2003. Centenary of Powered Flight. Pakistan Air Force.
1222	2r. Dassault Falcon Mystere 20	65	65
1223	2r. North American F-86 Sabre and North American P-51 Mustang	65	65

2005. Air Force.
1281	5r. Hawker Tempest II	65	65
1282	5r. Lockheed Martin F-16 Fighting Falcon	65	65
1283	5r. Lockheed Martin F-16 Fighting Falcon and airbase	65	65
1284	5r. Roundel and Lockheed Martin F-16 Fighting Falcon	65	65
1281/1284 Set of 4		2·30	2·30

2007. Pakistan Air Force Defense Day.
1350	5r. Pakistan Aeronautical complex (PAC) JF-17 Thunder	15	10

PALAU

PALAU

North Pacific

100 cents = 1 dollar

1985. 50th Anniv of First Trans-Pacific Airmail Flight.

89	44c. Consolidated PBY-5A Catalina amphibian of Trans Ocean Airways ..	75	65
90	44c. Douglas DC-6B of Air Micronesia.......	75	65
91	44c. Grumman SA-16 Albatross flying boat of Trust Territory Airlines............	75	65
92	44c. Douglas DC-4 of Pan Am	75	65
89/92	Set of 4	2·75	2·30
MS93	$1 Martin M-130 flying boat NC14716 of Pan Am................	2·20	1·90

1987.

210*	33c. Nakajima-built Douglas DC-2 (on Japan stamp No. 336), airliner (in postmark) and Douglas DC-2 of Japan Air Lines (inscribed "JAPAN AIRWAYS")	55	50

1988.

MS241	45c. Martin M-130 flying boat NC14716 of Pan Am (on original artwork for No. **MS**93)(sheet contains five other 45c. designs)	3·75	3·25

1989.

261	36c. Cessna 207 Stationair 7 of Aero Belau (inscribed "SKYWAGON")	55	50
262	39c. Embraer EMB-110 Bandeirante of Island Air..........................	55	50
264	45c. Boeing 727 of Continental Airlines ...	55	50
261/264	Set of 3	1·50	1·30

1989.

289*	25c. Sikorsky S-61B SH-3 Sea King helicopter	40	30

1990.

340*	25c. Vincenzo Lunardi's balloon (over London, 1785)....................	65	50

1990.

380	45c. Consolidated PBY-5A Catalina amphibian (on illustrated cover)	85	75
381	45c. Boeing 727 of Continental Airlines ...	85	75

1990.

387*	45c. Consolidated B-24S Liberator bombers of the U.S.A.F	75	65

1991. Operation Desert Storm.

458*	20c. McDonnell Douglas F-4G Phantom II Wild Weasel fighters	30	30
459*	20c. Lockheed F-117A Nighthawk.............	30	30
460*	20c. Boeing (McDonnell Douglas/ Hughes) AH-64 Apache helicopter ...	30	30

1991.

499*	29c. Kawasaki H6K "Mavis" flying boat......	40	35

1991.

501*	29c. Mitsubishi A6M Zero-Sen	45	40
504*	29c. Douglas SBD Dauntless dive bombers attacking Japanese aircraft carrier *Akagi*..............	45	40

1992.

574	50c. Grumman TBF Avenger	85	75
575	50c. Curtiss P-40C of the Flying Tigers	85	75
576	50c. Mitsubishi A6M Zero-Sen	85	75
577	50c. Hawker Hurricane Mk I	85	75
578	50c. Consolidated PBY-5 Catalina flying boat	85	75
579	50c. Curtiss Hawk 75 of the Royal Netherlands Indies Air Force	85	75
580	50c. Boeing B-17E Flying Fortress...............	85	75
581	50c. Brewster F2A Buffalo.......................	85	75
582	50c. Vickers Supermarine Walrus flying boat	85	75
583	50c. Curtiss P-40E Kittyhawk I of the Royal New Zealand Air Force..................	85	75
574/583	Set of 10	7·50	6·75

1993.

606*	29c. Douglas SBD Dauntless dive bombers	50	45
609*	29c. North American B-25 Mitchell bombers over Rabaul......................	50	45
610*	29c. Bombers over Kwajelein	50	45

1994.

682*	29c. Aerial bombardment of Japanese air base, Truk......................	45	40
685*	29c. Shooting down Japanese Mitsubishi A6M Zero-Sen bombers, Mariana Islands (Turkey Shoot)	45	40

1994.

691*	50c. Douglas C-47 Skytrain dropping paratroops......................	75	65
696*	50c. Aircraft attacking German positions	75	65
697*	50c. Gliders dropping paratroops...............	75	65

1995. Research and Experimental Jet Aircraft.

887	50c. Fairey Delta 2................................	75	65
888	50c. North American B-70 Valkyrie.............	75	65
889	50c. Douglas X-3 Stilletto	75	65
890	50c. Northrop/NASA HL-10	75	65
891	50c. Bell X-1(incorrectly inscribed XS-1)...	75	65
892	50c. Tupolev Tu-144..............................	75	65
893	50c. Bell X-1A (incorrectly inscribed X-1) .	75	65
894	50c. Boulton Paul P.111.........................	75	65
895	50c. EWR VJ 101C...................................	75	65
896	50c. Handley Page HP-115	75	65
897	50c. Rolls Royce TMR *Flying Bedstead*	75	65
898	50c. North American X-15	75	65
887/898	Set of 12	8·00	7·00
MS899	$2 Concorde............	3·00	2·75

1995.

933*	32c. Grumman F6F Hellcats	50	45
934*	32c. Douglas SBD Dauntless dive bombers	50	45
935*	32c. Grumman F6F Hellcats and Douglas SBD Dauntless	50	45
MS949*	$3 Nose art on Boeing B-29 Superfortress *Bock's car* (dropped second atom bomb. Nagasaki, 9 August, 1945)	4·25	3·75

1996. Circumnavigators.

MS985	Two sheets. (b) $3 Bob Martin, Mark Sullivan and Troy Bradley and helium balloon *Odyssey* (other miniature sheet does not show aircraft)	9·50	8·25

1996. Circumnavigators (air).

986*	60c. Lowell Smith and Douglas World Cruisers.........................	95	85
987*	60c. Ernst Lehmann and LZ-127 *Graf Zeppelin*.........................	95	85
988*	60c. Wiley Post and Lockheed Vega 5B *Winnie Mae*.........................	95	85
990*	60c. Jerrie Mock and Cessna 180 *Spirit of Columbus*.........................	95	85
991*	60c. H. Ross Perot Jnr. and Bell LongRanger III *Spirit of Texas*.............	95	85
992*	60c. Brooke Knapp and Gulfstream Aerospace Gulfstream III *The American Dream*.........................	95	85
993*	60c. Jeanna Yeager, Dick Rutan and Rutan *Voyager*.........................	95	85
994*	60c. Fred Lasby and Piper PA-24 Commanche.........................	95	85

176

1996. Spy Planes.
1085	40c. Lockheed U-2	70	60
1086	40c. General Dynamics EF-111A	70	60
1087	40c. Lockheed YF-12A	70	60
1088	40c. Lockheed SR-71A Blackbird	70	60
1089	40c. Teledyne Ryan Tier II Plus (UAV)	70	60
1090	40c. Lockheed XST 'Have Blue' project	70	60
1091	40c. Lockheed ER-2	70	60
1092	40c. Lockheed F-117A Nighthawk	70	60
1093	40c. Lockheed EC-130E	70	60
1094	40c. Ryan Firebee (UAV)	70	60
1095	40c. Lockheed Martin/Boeing Darkstar (UAV)	70	60
1096	40c. Boeing E-3A Sentry	70	60
1085/1096 Set of 12		7·50	6·50
MS1097 $3 Northrop B-2A Spirit		5·25	4·50

1996.
1118	60c. Northrop XB-35	1·00	90
1119	60c. Leduc O.21	1·00	90
1120	60c. Convair Model 118 Flying Car	1·00	90
1121	60c. Blohm und Voss BV141	1·00	90
1122	60c. Vought V-173	1·00	90
1123	60c. McDonnell XF-85 Goblin	1·00	90
1124	60c. North American F-82B Twin Mustang	1·00	90
1125	60c. Lockheed XFV-1 (Salmon)	1·00	90
1126	60c. Northrop XP-79B	1·00	90
1127	60c. Saunders Roe (Saro) SR/A1	1·00	90
1128	60c. Sokolov A-90 Orlyonok (Eaglet) ekranoplane (incorrectly inscribed Caspian Sea Monster)	1·00	90
1129	60c. Grumman X-29	1·00	90
1118/1129 Set of 12		11·00	9·75
MS1130 $3 Martin Marieeta X-24B lifting body research aircraft		5·25	4·50

1997. Bicentenary of the Parachute.
1147	32c. Apollo 15 command module splash down under three canopies	55	50
1148	32c. Sky diving team in formation	55	50
1149	32c. Cargo drop from airplane	55	50
1150	32c. Parasailing	55	50
1151	32c. Parachutist falling to earth	55	50
1152	32c. Parachute demonstration team	55	50
1153	32c. Parachuting falling into sea	55	50
1154	32c. Drag racing car	55	50
1147/1154 Set of 8		4·00	3·50
MS1155 Two sheets. (a) $2 Training tower, Fort Benning, Georgia; (b) $2 Funny Car safety parachute Set of 2 sheets		7·00	6·00

1999.
1156	60c. Parachuting demonstration (air)	1·00	90
1157	60c. The Blue Flame (world land-speed record attempt)	1·00	90
1158	60c. Atmospheric Re-entry Demonstrator (capsule with 3 canopies)	1·00	90
1159	60c. Spies parachuting behind enemy lines during Second World War	1·00	90
1160	60c. André Jacques Garnerin's first successful parachute descent (from balloon), 1797	1·00	90
1161	60c. Lockheed C-130E Hercules demonstrating Low Altitude Parachute Extraction System (airplane and capsule with four canopies)	1·00	90
1162	60c. U.S. Army parachutist flying parafoil	1·00	90
1163	60c. Parachute (one canopy) slowing McDonnell Douglas F4 Phantom II	1·00	90
1156/1163 Set of 8		7·25	6·50

2000.
1643*	33c. Wilbur and Orville Wright (aviation pioneers)	55	50

2000. Centenary of First Zeppelin Flight and Airship Development.
1729	55c. Lebaudy-Juillot airship Le Jaune	90	80
1730	55c. Forlanini airship Leonardo daVinci	90	80
1731	55c. Thomas Baldwin's airship, US Military No. 1 (1908)	90	80
1732	55c. Astra-Torres 1	90	80
1733	55c. Rear of Astra-Torres 1 and Parseval PL VII	90	80
1734	55c. Rear of Parseval PL VII and Lebaudy airship Liberte	90	80
1729/1734 Set of 6		5·00	4·25
MS1735 Two sheets. (a) $2 Santos-Dumont's airship 'Ballon No. 9, La Badaleuse'; (b) $2 Santos-Dumont's airship Ballon No. 6 circling Eiffel Tower		13·00	11·50

2003. 75th Anniv of First Solo Trans-Atlantic Flight.
1962	60c. Charles Lindbergh, Donald Hall and Ryan NYP Special Spirit of St. Louis	1·10	95
1963	60c. Ryan NYP Special Spirit of St. Louis	1·10	95
1964	60c. Ryan NYP Special Spirit of St. Louis at Curtis Field	1·10	95
1965	60c. Ryan NYP Special Spirit of St. Louis airborne	1·10	95
1966	60c. Arriving in Paris (may show aircraft)	1·10	95
1967	60c. Ticker-tape Parade, New York City (including Lindbergh)	1·10	95
1962/1967 Set of 6		6·00	5·25

2003.
1971*	37c. Northrop B-2A Spirit	70	60
1972*	37c. Boeing (McDonnell Douglas) F/A-18 Hornet	70	60

2003. Centenary of Powered Flight.
MS1986 Two sheets. (a) 55c. Fokker 70; 55c. Boeing 747-217B; 55c. Curtiss T-32 Condor II; 55c. Vickers Type 630 Viscount; 55c. Wright Flyer III; 55c. Avro Type 618 Ten Achilles. (b) $2 Wright Flyer III (different) Set of 2 sheets ... 3·25 3·00

2005. Dambusters' Raid (May 1945).
2096*	80c. Pilots reviewing route	1·40	1·20
2097*	80c. 'Dambuster' flight crew	1·40	1·20
2098*	80c. Ground crew	1·40	1·20
2099*	80c. Avro Type 683 Lancaster bomber over Mohne dam	1·40	1·20
MS2104* Two sheets. (a) $2 Squadron Leader Guy Gibson of 617 'Dambusters' Squadron and bouncing bomb (other miniature sheet does not show aircraft) Price for 2 sheets		6·50	6·50

2006. 10th Anniv of Concorde's Record Flight from New York to London.
2233	75c. Concorde over New York	2·60	2·60
2234	75c. Concorde over London	2·60	2·60
2235	75c. Tail bumper wheel	2·60	2·60
2236	75c. Drop-down nose	2·60	2·60
2233/2236 Set of 4		9·50	9·50

2007. Centenary of First Helicopter Flight.
2260	10c. Bell 206B JetRanger III	20	20
2261	19c. Boeing (McDonnell Douglas Helicopters/Hughes) MD500	40	40
2262	20c. Boeing (McDonnell Douglas Helicopters/Hughes) AH-64A Apache	45	45
2263	22c. Aerospatiale (Eurocopter) AS332 Super Puma	50	50
2264	75c. Aerospatiale AS 335F-1 Twin Squirrel	1·50	1·50
2265	84c. MBB Eurocopter BO105 DB/4	2·00	2·00
2266	$1 Sikorsky MH-53J Pave Low III	2·40	2·40
2260/2266 Set of 7		6·75	6·75
MS2267 $2 Boeing Yertol 234LR Chinook		5·00	5·00

PALESTINIAN AUTHORITY

Western Asia

1999. 1,000 fils = £P1

1999. Inauguration of Gaza International Airport.
PA123	80f. Control tower	15	15
PA124	300f. Fokker F-27 Friendship	70	70
PA125	700f. Terminal building	1·90	1·90
PA123/125 Set of 3		2·50	2·50

PANAMA

Central America

100 centesimos = 1 balboa

1928. Lindbergh's Flying Tour.
222	2c. Ryan NYP Special Spirit of St. Louis (overprinted HOMENAJE A LINDBERGH)	40	30
223	5c. Ryan NYP Special Spirit of St. Louis	60	45

1929. Nos. E3 and 182 overprinted CORREO AEREO 25 VEINTICINCO CENTESIMOS and Fokker Universal (No. 225) or CORREO AEREO and airplane (No. 239).
225*	25c. on 10c. Cyclist messenger	1·20	95
239*	1b. Nereus in San Pedro Miguel Locks	21·00	16·00

1930.
231	5c. Ryan B-5 Brougham (blue)	25	20
232	5c. Ryan B-5 Brougham (orange)	30	30
233	7c. Ryan B-5 Brougham	30	30
234	8c. Ryan B-5 Brougham	30	30
235	15c. Ryan B-5 Brougham	40	30
236	20c. Ryan B-5 Brougham	60	30
237	25c. Ryan B-5 Brougham	75	75
231/237 Set of 7		2·50	2·20

1930.
244	5c. Biplane	30	30
245	10c. Biplane	40	30
246	30c. Biplane	6·25	4·25
247	50c. Biplane	1·70	55
248	1b. Biplane	6·25	4·25
244/248 Set of 5		13·50	8·50

1931. Opening of Service between Panama City and Western Provinces.
250	5c. Consolidated Commodore flying boat	95	1·10

1932. No. 237 surcharged **HABILITADA 20 c.**
260*	20c. on 25c. Ryan B-5 Brougham	6·75	80

1938. Nos. 246 and 235 surcharged **NORMAL DE SANTIAGO JUNIO 5 1938** and value.
341*	7c. on 30c. Biplane	60	55
342*	8c. on 15c. Ryan B-5 Brougham	60	55

1938.
348*	7c. Douglas DC-3	40	35
349*	8c. Douglas DC-3	60	55
350*	15c. Douglas DC-3	75	55
351*	50c. Douglas DC-3	8·75	7·00
352*	1b. Douglas DC-3	8·75	7·00

1941. Nos. 236 and 247/8 overprinted **CONSTITUCION 1941.**
390*	20c. Ryan B-5 Brougham	2·10	2·00
391*	50c. Biplane	6·25	4·00
392*	1b. Biplane	14·00	10·00

1947. Nos. 234/5 surcharged **AEREO 1947** and value.
449*	5c. on 8c. Ryan B-5 Brougham	30	30
451*	10c. on 15c. Ryan B-5 Brougham	60	55

1947. No. 234 surcharged **HABILITADA CORREOS B/. 0.0½.**
460*	½c. on 8c. Ryan B-5 Brougham	10	10

1949. No. 234 overprinted **1849–1949 CHIRIQUI CENTENARIO.**
493*	5c. Ryan B-5 Brougham	40	20

1949. No. 232 overprinted **1874 1949 U.P.U.**
500*	5c. Ryan B-5 Brougham	95	65

1950. Nos. 232 and 237 overprinted **CENTENARIO del Gral. Jose de San Martin 17 de Agosto de 1950.**
513*	5c. Ryan B-5 Brougham	70	45
515*	25c. Ryan B-5 Brougham	70	55

1960.
700	5c. Boeing 707	25	20
701	10c. Boeing 707	30	20
702	20c. Boeing 707	50	30
700/702 Set of 3		95	65

1961. No. 701 surcharged **1c "Rehabilitacion de Menores".**
710*	1c. on 10c. Boeing 707	25	20

1975.
1075*	33c. Tocumen International Airport	1·10	75

1982.
1304*	41c. General Omar Torrijos Herrera Airport	1·10	60

1997. 50th Anniv of Panamanian Aviation Company.
1603	35c. Douglas DC-3	1·00	85
1604	35c. Martin 4-0-4 (wrongly inscribed 404)	1·00	85

1605	35c. Avro (Hawker Siddeley) HS-748	1·00	85
1606	35c. Lockheed L-188 Electra	1·00	85
1607	35c. Boeing 727-100	1·00	85
1608	35c. Boeing 737-200 Advanced	1·00	85
1603/1608 Set of 6		5·25	4·50

PAPUA

Australasia

12 pence = 1 shilling

20 shillings = 1 pound

1930. Nos. 98 and 101/2 overprinted **AIR MAIL** on wings of airplane.
118	3d. Lakatoi (canoe)	1·00	6·00
119	6d. Lakatoi (canoe)	5·50	8·00
120	1s. Lakatoi (canoe)	4·25	13·00
118/120 Set of 3		9·50	25·00

1938.
158	2d. de Havilland DH.86B Dragon Express	3·00	3·00
159	3d. de Havilland DH.86B Dragon Express	3·00	2·25
160	5d. de Havilland DH.86B Dragon Express	3·00	3·50
161	8d. de Havilland DH.86B Dragon Express	6·00	16·00
162	1s. de Havilland DH.86B Dragon Express	19·00	17·00
158/162 Set of 5		31·00	38·00

1939.
163	2d. de Havilland DH.86B Dragon Express	3·00	5·00
164	3d. de Havilland DH.86B Dragon Express	3·00	10·00
165	5d. de Havilland DH.86B Dragon Express	3·00	2·20
166	8d. de Havilland DH.86B Dragon Express	8·00	3·50
167	1s. de Havilland DH.86B Dragon Express	10·00	9·00
168	1s.6d. de Havilland DH.86B Dragon Express	30·00	35·00
163/168 Set of 6		50·00	60·00

PAPUA NEW GUINEA

Australasia

1963. 12 pence = 1 shilling

20 shillings = 1 pound

1966. 100 cents = 1 dollar

1975. 100 toea = 1 kina

1963.
48*	2s.3d. Piaggio P-166B Portofino VH-PAP	30	30

1967.
117*	2c. Curtiss P-40K Kittyhawk II of the Royal Australian Air Force	10	50
119*	20c. Mitsubishi Ki-67 Hiryu	25	10
120*	50c. Aichi D3A "Val" bomber	80	70

1970. Australian and Newar Guinea Air Services.
177	5c. Douglas DC-6B of Trans Australian Airways ("TAA" in red on tail)	25	30
178	5c. Lockheed L.188 Electra (red and blue stripes on tail)	25	30
179	5c. Boeing 727-100 of Trans Australian Airways (white "T" on tail)	25	30
180	5c. Fokker F.27 Friendship (red and white emblem on tail)	25	30
181	25c. Douglas DC-3	35	40
182	30c. Boeing 707	35	60
177/182 Set of 6		1·50	2·00

1972. 50th Anniv of Aviation.
220	7c. Curtiss MF-6 Seagull flying boat	40	10
221	14c. de Havilland DH.37 G-AUAA of Guinea Gold	60	1·25
222	20c. Junkers G.31 VH-UOV	70	1·25
223	25c. Junkers F-13 VH-UTM	70	1·25
220/223 Set of 4		2·20	3·50

1973.
232*	7c. Sud Aviation SE 3160 Alouette III helicopter	15	20

1976. 50th Anniv of Survey Flights.
310*	10t. de Havilland DH.50A seaplane of the Royal Australian Air Force	15	20
312*	60t. de Havilland DH.50A seaplane of the Royal Australian Air Force	60	3·00

1980.
381*	25t. Douglas DC-3	25	25

1981.
409*	15t. Douglas DC-3 and crew	25	25

1981. Mission Aviation.
412	10t. Cessna 205 Super Skywagon P2-MFQ of Mission Aviation	20	10
413	15t. British Aircraft Swallow VH-UUR St. Paulus	25	15
414	20t. Hiller 12E helicopter P2-SIF	25	25
415	30t. Junkers F-13 SE-AEC	35	40
416	35t. Piper PA-23 Aztec VH-SDM of the Seventh Day Adventist Church	35	55
412/416 Set of 5		1·20	1·30

1983. Papua New Guinea.
468*	10t. Boeing 707 tailfin	30	10
471*	60t. Cessna 206 Stationair 6	1·10	90

1984. 50th Anniv of First Airmail Australia-Papua New Guinea.
478	20t. Avro Type 618 Ten VH-U* *Faith in Australia* of Australian National Airways	40	30
479	25t. de Havilland DH.86B Dragon Express VH-UYU *Carmania* of W.R. Carpenter	40	45
480	40t. Westland Widgeon VU-UGI	50	80

481	60t. Consolidated PBY-5 Catalina flying boat NC-777 *Guba*	70	1·25
478/481 *Set of 4*		1·80	2·50

1985.

509*	40t. Airplane being loaded with mail	1·75	2·25

1987. Aircraft in Papua New Guinea.

567	15t. Cessna 206 Stationair 6 P2-DWL of Divine World Airways	1·25	25
568	35t. Britten-Norman BN-2 Islander P2-ATS of Douglas Airways	2·00	90
569	45t. de Havilland Canada DHC-6 Twin Otter 100 of Talair	2·00	1·00
570	70t. Fokker F.28 Fellowship P2-ANE of Air Nuigini	3·00	6·50
567/570 *Set of 4*		7·50	7·75

1992.

674*	90t. Lockheed P-38 Lightning	2·50	3·75

1993. 20th Anniv of Air Niugini.

696	21t. Douglas DC-3	75	25
697	45t. Fokker F.27 Friendship	1·75	70
698	60t. de Havilland Canada DHC-7 Dash Seven	2·00	2·25
699	90t. Airbus A310	2·75	4·25
696/699 *Set of 4*		6·50	6·75

1995.

749*	50t. on 45t. Fokker F-28 Friendship	1·40	1·25

1996.

789*	25t. Air traffic controller	10	15

1997. Inaugural Air Niugini Flight, Port Moresby to Osaka.

MS820 3k. Airbus A310		1·00	1·10

2001. 50th Anniv of Mission Aviation Fellowship.

896	35t. Cessna 170	25	15
897	70t. Auster Autocar	50	35
898	90t. Cessna 260	75	50
899	1k.40 de Havilland Canada DHC-6 Twin Otter	1·25	1·40
896/899 *Set of 4*		2·50	2·20

2003. Centenary of Powered Flight.

983	65t. Orville Wright in Wright *Flyer* circling Fort Myer, Virginia, 1908	20	25
984	1k.50 Orville Wright piloting *Baby Grand* biplane, Belmont, New York, 1910	50	55
985	2k.50 Wilbur Wright holding anemometer, Pau, France, 1909	75	80
986	4k. Wilbur Wright piloting Wright 'Model A', Pau, France, 1909	1·40	1·50
983/986 *Set of 4*		2·50	2·75
MS987	2k.50 Wright *Flyer I* outside hangar, Kitty Hawk, North Carolina, 1903; 2k.50 Wright *Flyer I* rolled out from hangar; 2k.50 Wright *Flyer I* being prepared for take-off; 2k.50 Wright *Flyer I* taking off, 1903	3·50	3·75
MS988	10k. Wright *Flyer I*, 1903	3·50	3·75

2006.

1118*	3k.25 Rural people and Cessna A185 (Summer Institute of Linguistics Aviation)	2·50	2·75

PARAGUAY

South America

1929. 100 centavos = 1 peso

1944. 100 centimos = 1 guarani

1929.

355*	11p.30 Airplane (purple)	70	55
356*	11p.30 Airplane (blue)	35	35

1930.

374	95c. Airplane (blue on blue)	40	35
375	95c. Airplane (red on pink)	40	35
376	1p.90 Airplane (purple on blue)	40	35
377	1p.90 Airplane (red on pink)	40	35
378	6p.80 Airplane (black on blue)	40	35
379	6p.80 Airplane (green on pink)	40	35
374/379 *Set of 6*		2·20	1·90

1931.

397	1p. Three aircraft (red)	25	20
398	1p. Three aircraft (blue)	25	20
399	2p. Three aircraft (orange)	30	25
400	2p. Three aircraft (brown)	30	25
401	3p. Three aircraft (green)	65	40
402	3p. Three aircraft (blue)	65	45
403	3p. Three aircraft (red)	60	40
404	6p. Three aircraft (green)	75	60
405	6p. Three aircraft (mauve)	95	65
406	6p. Three aircraft (blue)	70	50
407	10p. Three aircraft (red)	2·00	1·40
408	10p. Three aircraft (green)	2·50	1·90
409	10p. Three aircraft (green)	1·40	1·00
410	10p. Three aircraft (brown)	2·25	1·60
411	10p. Three aircraft (pink)	2·00	1·40
397/411 *Set of 15*		14·00	10·00

1931.

414*	5c. Fokker F.7 Trimotor (blue)	15	10
415*	5c. Fokker F.7 Trimotor (green)	15	10
416*	5c. Fokker F.7 Trimotor (red)	20	10
417*	5c. Fokker F.7 Trimotor (purple)	15	10
422*	20c. Fokker F.7 Trimotor (red)	15	10
423*	20c. Fokker F.7 Trimotor (blue)	20	10
424*	20c. Fokker F.7 Trimotor (green)	20	15
425*	20c. Fokker F.7 Trimotor (brown)	15	10
426*	40c. Fokker F.7 Trimotor (green)	20	10
426a*	40c. Fokker F.7 Trimotor (green)	15	10
426b*	40c. Fokker F.7 Trimotor (red)	20	10

1931. No. 270 overprinted **Correo Aereo "Graf Zeppelin"** and *Graf Zeppelin* (airship) or surcharged also.

429	3p. on 4p. Map	7·75	6·25
430	4p. Map	7·75	6·25

1932.

435	4p. Airship LZ-127 *Graf Zeppelin*	1·40	1·75
436	5p. Airship LZ-127 *Graf Zeppelin*	2·40	2·00
437	12p. Airship LZ-127 *Graf Zeppelin*	1·90	1·75
438	16p. Airship LZ-127 *Graf Zeppelin*	3·75	3·00
439	20p. Airship LZ-127 *Graf Zeppelin*	4·00	3·75
435/439 *Set of 5*		12·00	11·00

1932. Nos. 435/9 surcharged **CORREOS FELIZ AND NUEVO 1933** and value.

446	50c. on 4p. Airship LZ-127 *Graf Zeppelin*	35	30
447	1p. on 8p. Airship LZ-127 *Graf Zeppelin*	35	30
448	1p.50 on 12p. Airship LZ-127 *Graf Zeppelin*	35	30
449	2p. on 16p. Airship LZ-127 *Graf Zeppelin*	35	30
450	5p. on 20p. Airship LZ-127 *Graf Zeppelin*	1·25	75
446/450 *Set of 5*		2·40	1·70

1933. *Graf Zeppelin.*

451	4p.50 Airship LZ-127 *Graf Zeppelin*	1·25	75
452	9p. Airship LZ-127 *Graf Zeppelin*	2·50	1·90
453	13p.50 Airship LZ-127 *Graf Zeppelin*	2·50	1·90
454	22p.50 Airship LZ-127 *Graf Zeppelin*	6·00	4·50
455	45p. Airship LZ-127 *Graf Zeppelin*	8·25	6·75
451/455 *Set of 5*		18·00	14·00

1934. *Graf Zeppelin.* Nos. 451/5 overprinted **1934**.

469	4p.50 Airship LZ-127 *Graf Zeppelin*	1·75	1·75
470	9p. Airship LZ-127 *Graf Zeppelin*	2·25	2·25
471	13p.50 Airship LZ-127 *Graf Zeppelin*	6·50	6·50
472	22p.50 Airship LZ-127 *Graf Zeppelin*	5·25	5·25
473	45p. Airship LZ-127 *Graf Zeppelin*	11·00	11·00
469/473 *Set of 5*		24·00	24·00

1935. *Graf Zeppelin.* Nos. 451/5 overprinted **1935**.

474	4p.50 Airship LZ-127 *Graf Zeppelin*	2·25	2·25
475	9p. Airship LZ-127 *Graf Zeppelin*	3·25	3·25
476	13p.50 Airship LZ-127 *Graf Zeppelin*	9·25	9·25
477	22p.50 Airship LZ-127 *Graf Zeppelin*	8·75	8·75
478	45p. Airship LZ-127 *Graf Zeppelin*	23·00	23·00
474/478 *Set of 5*		42·00	42·00

1935.

479	17p. Fokker F.7 Trimotor (brown)	3·75	3·00
480	17p. Fokker F.7 Trimotor (red)	6·75	5·00
481	17p. Fokker F.7 Trimotor (blue)	4·25	3·50
482	17p. Fokker F.7 Trimotor (green)	2·10	1·75
479/482 *Set of 4*		15·00	12·00

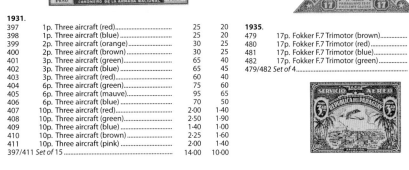

1939.

502	3p.40 Airplane (blue)	75	45
503	3p.40 Airplane (green)	75	45
504	3p.40 Airplane (brown)	75	45
502/504 Set of 3		2·00	1·20

1961.

908*	36g. Boeing 707	60	50

1973.

1163*	100g. Lockheed L.188C Electra	80	40

1980. Inauguration of Paraguayan Airlines Boeing 707 Service.

1222	20g. Boeing 707 of Lineas Aereas de Paraguay	30	10
1223	100g. Boeing 707 of Lineas Aereas de Paraguay (air)	1·40	70

APPENDIX

The following stamps have either been issued in excess of postal needs or have not been made available to the public in reasonable quantities at face value. Miniature sheets, imperforate stamps, etc are excluded from this section.

1964

Red Cross Centenary. 10g. (Westland Wessex helicopter).

1966

German Space Research. 10g. (airship LZ-127 *Graf Zeppelin*, on Paraguay stamp No. 478 and Germany stamp No. 469).

1967

50th Birth Anniversary of President Kennedy. 10g. (helicopter).

1969

International Projects in Outer Space. 18g.15 (airship LZ-127 *Graf Zeppelin* and Boeing 707).

1973

"Apollo" Moon Missions and Future Space Projects. 20g. (helicopter).

1974

UPU Centenary. 5g. (Montgolfier balloon and Boeing 707).

1975

Various Commemorations. 4g. (airship).
Various Commemorations. 4g. (Concorde), 5g. (Junkers Ju 52/3m).

1976

Bicentenary of American Revolution (4th issue) and U.S. Postal Service. 5g. (Curtiss JN-4 "Jenny").

1977

Luposta 77 Stamp Exhibition. Postage 1g., 2g., 3g., 4g., 5g. Air 10g., 15g., 20g. (airships).
History of Aviation. Postage 1g., 2g., 3g., 4g., 5g. Air 10g., 15g., 20g.

1979

History of Aviation. Postage 3g., 4g., 5g., 6g., 7g., 8g., 20g., Air 10g., 25g.
Death Centenary of Sir Rowland Hill (1st issue) Postage 4g., 6g., 7g., 8g., 20g. Air 10g., 25g. (stamps showing aircraft and airships).

1980

Death Centenary of Sir Rowland Hill (2nd issue). Military Aircraft. Postage 3g., 4g., 5g., 6g., 7g., 8g., 20g. Air 10g., 25g.
Death Centenary of Sir Rowland Hill (3rd issue). Stamps. 10g., 25g. (stamps showing airships).

1983

Bicentenary of Manned Flight. 5g., 10g., 30g. (balloons).
Aircraft Carriers. 25c., 50c., 1g., 3g., 4g., 5g. (aircraft).

1984

Bicentenary of Manned Flight. 25c., 50c., 1g., 2g., 3g., 4g., 5g.
50th Anniversary of First Lufthansa Europe-South America Direct Mail Flight. 5g., 10g., 30g. (aircraft).

1984

Lufthansa Europe-South America Flight stamp overprinted. 10g.
Bicentenary of Manned Flight stamp overprinted. 5g.

1985

International Federation of Aero-philatelic Societies Congress, Stuttgart.
Lupo 85 Stamp Exhibition, Lucerne.

1987

National Topics. 100g (Boeing 707).
750th Anniversary of Berlin (1st issue) and Luposta 87 Air Stamps Exhibition, Berlin. 1g. (Lilienthal glider, on West Berlin stamp No. B548).

1987

750th Anniversary of Berlin stamp overprinted. 1g.
Lupo Wien 88 Stamp Exhibition, Vienna.
National Topics stamp overprinted. 100g.

1988

Aeropex 88 Air Stamps Exhibition, Adelaide.

PATIALA

Indian sub-continent

12 pies = 1 anna

16 annas = 1 rupee

1937. No. 258 of India overprinted **PATIALA STATE**.

91*	12a. Armstrong Whitworth A.W.27 Ensign I	25·00	70·00

PENANG

South-east Asia

100 cents = 1 dollar

1949. As Nos. 114/15 of Antigua.

23*	10c. Airplane	20	10
24*	15c. Jet-powered Vickers Viking	2·25	3·50

PENRHYN ISLAND

South Pacific

100 cents = 1 dollar

1983. Bicentenary of Manned Flight. Wrongly inscribed "NORTHERN COOK ISLANS".

320A	36c. Sir George Cayley's airship design, 1837	1·00	80
321A	48c. Dupuy de Lome's airship, 1872	1·25	90
322A	60c. Santos-Dumont's airship *Ballon No. 6*. 1901	1·50	1·25
323A	96c. Lebaudy-Juillot airship No. 1 *La Jaune*, 1902	2·25	1·75
324A	$1.32 Airship LZ-127 *Graf Zeppelin*	3·00	2·50
320A/324A Set of 5		8·00	6·50

1983. Bicentenary of Manned Flight. Nos. 320A/4A overprinted **NORTHERN COOK ISLANDS**.

320B	36c. Sir George Cayley's airship design, 1837	35	30
321B	48c. Dupuy de Lome's airship, 1872	40	45
322B	60c. Santos-Dumont's airship *Ballon No. 6*, 1901	45	50
323B	96c. Lebaudy-Juillot airship No. 1 *La Jaune*, 1902	75	80
324B	$1.32 Airship LZ-127 *Graf Zeppelin*	1·00	1·10
320B/324B Set of 5		2·75	2·75

1995.

514*	$3.75 Boeing B-29 Superfortress *Enola Gay* over Hiroshima	8·00	8·00

PERAK

South-east Asia

100 cents = 1 dollar

1949. As Nos. 114/15 of Antigua.

124*	10c. Airplane	15	10
125*	15c. Jet-powered Vickers Viking	1·50	2·00

PERLIS

South-east Asia

100 cents = 1 dollar

1949. As Nos. 114/15 of Antigua.

3*	10c. Airplane	30	1·75
4*	15c. Jet-powered Vickers Viking	1·25	4·00

PERU

South America

1934. 100 centavos = 1 sol

1985. 100 centimos = 1 inti

1991. 100 centimos = 1 sol

1934.

534	2s. Hawker Hart	4·50	35
535	5s. Hawker Hart	9·50	70

1935.

560*	35c. Airplane	75	35
561*	50c. Airplane	1·25	70
562*	1s. Airplane	1·75	75

1936. Nos. 534/5 surcharged **Habilitado** and value.

583*	5c. on 2s. Hawker Hart	35	15
584*	25c. on 5s. Hawker Hart	70	25

1936.

630*	70c. Tri-motor Ford "Tin Goose"	1·25	50
603*	80c. Biplanes (black)	14·00	7·00
631*	80c. Biplanes (green)	4·50	1·00
605*	1s.50 Las Palmas Aerodrome, Lima (brown)	9·00	5·50
633*	1s.50 Las Palmas Aerodrome, Lima (orange)	5·50	40
606*	2s. Douglas DC-2 (blue)	15·00	6·50
634*	2s. Douglas DC-2 (green)	11·00	70
607*	5s. Tri-motor Ford "Tin Goose"	20·00	3·25

1937. Nos. 630, 603 and 606 surcharged **Habilit.** and value.

613*	15c. on 70c. Tri-motor Ford "Tin Goose"	3·50	2·25
614*	25c. on 80c. Biplanes	7·50	6·00
615*	1s. on 2s. Douglas DC-2	5·50	3·00

1937. Pan-American Aviation Conference.
635*	10c. Juan Bielovucic's Voisin "Boxkite" over Lima, 1911	40	10
637*	25c. Stinson-Faucett F.19 at Lima-Tambo Airport	40	10
638*	1s. Stinson-Faucett F.19	1·90	1·00

1938.
653*	25c. Tri-motor Ford "Tin Goose"	20	10

1942. No. 653 surcharged **Habilit. 0.15.**
675	15c. on 25c. Tri-motor Ford "Tin Goose"	85	10

1942. No. 653 surcharged **Habilitada S/o.** and value.
722*	5c. on 25c. Tri-motor Ford "Tin Goose"	10	10
723*	10c. on 25c. Tri-motor Ford "Tin Goose"	30	10

1951. Overprinted **U.P.U. 1874–1949.**
745*	5c. Airplane	10	10
747*	55c. Douglas Super DC-3 (?)	15	10
748*	95c. Douglas DC-4	20	15
749*	1s.50 Airplane	30	25
750*	2s. Airplane	35	30

1952.
784*	40c. Seaplanes	65	10
786*	1s.25 Corpac-Lima-Tambo Airport	25	10

1968. 12th Anniv of APSA (Peruvian Airlines).
962*	5s.60 Stylised Boeing 707 of Aerolineas Peruanas	45	20

1969. First APSA (Peruvian Airlines) Flight to Europe.
987	2s.50 Boeing 707 of Aerolineas Peruanas	20	10
988	3s. Boeing 707 of Aerolineas Peruanas (air)	30	10
989	4s. Boeing 707 of Aerolineas Peruanas	40	10
990	5s.50 Boeing 707 of Aerolineas Peruanas	50	15
991	6s.50 Boeing 707 of Aerolineas Peruanas	60	25
987/991	Set of 5	1·80	60

1973.
1218*	8s. B.A.C. One Eleven 200 of Aerolineas Peruanas	1·00	25

1977. No. 962 surcharged.
1346*	10s. on 5s.60 Stylised Boeing 707 of Aerolineas Peruanas	50	25

1978. 50th Anniv of Faucett Aviation.
1411	40s. Elmer J. Faucett, Stinson-Faucett F-19 OA-BBO and Boeing 727-200 of Faucett Aviation	50	30

1983. 25th Anniv of Lima-Bogota Airmail Service.
1556	150s. Boeing 747-200 of Avianca	60	25

1985. 40th Anniv of ICAO.
1621	1100s. Curtiss JN-4 "Jenny"	40	15

1986. 75th Anniv of Trans-Alpine Flight by Jorge Chavez Dartnell.
1648	5i. Jorge Chavez Dartnell and Bleriot XI, 1911	1·00	35

1990. Surcharged **I/. 110 000.**
1744*	110,000i. on 200i. Helicopter	1·25	25

1998. 25th Anniv of Aeroperu.
1939*	2s.70 Airbus A320	2·25	50

2000.
2047	1s.30 Airplane	45	25

2002.
2106	3s.80 Lockheed C-5A Galaxy	1·20	75

2003. Centenary of Powered Flight.
2171	4s.80 Wright *Flyer I*, Orville and Wilbur Wright	1·60	95
2172	4s.80 Caption in Spanish	1·60	95

2005. Armed Forces.
2306	1s.80 Dassault Mirage 2000	30	35
2303	3s.20 Mikoyan MiG29 Fulcrum Sukhoi aircraft	1·10	65

2005.
2331	5s. Paper plane	1·60	90

2006. National Air Force.
2429	6s. Beech Model 45T Turbo Mentor and Mikoyan MiG-29 'Fulcrum'	2·00	1·10
2430	6s. Pilot and Mikoyan MiG29	2·00	1·10

PHILIPPINES

South-east Asia

1928. 100 centavos = 1 peso

1962. 100 sentimos = 1 piso

1928. London-Orient Flight by British Squadron of Seaplanes. Nos. 337/47 and 363a overprinted **L.O.F. 1928** and Fairey IIID seaplane.
402	2c. Rizal	40	25
403	4c. McKinley	50	40
404	6c. Magellan	1·70	1·50
405	8c. Legaspi	2·00	1·50
406	10c. Lawton	2·00	1·70
407	12c. Lincoln	2·75	2·50
408	16c. Dewey	2·00	1·70
409	20c. Washington	2·75	2·50
410	26c. Carriedo	8·25	5·50
411	30c. Franklin	8·25	5·50
412	1p. Arms	41·00	31·00
402/412	Set of 11	65·00	50·00

1932. Nos. 424/30 overprinted **ROUND-THE-WORLD FLIGHT VON GRONAU 1932** and Dornier Do-J II 8-t Wal flying boat D-2053 Gronland Wal.
433	2c. Mayon Volcano	35	35
434	4c. Post Office, Manila	35	35
435	12c. Freighters, Manila Bay	50	50
436	18c. "Pagsanjan Falls"	3·00	3·00
437	20c. Rice plantation	1·50	1·50
438	24c. Rice terraces	1·50	1·50
439	32c. Baguio Zigzag	1·50	1·50
433/439	Set of 7	8·00	8·00

1933. Nos. 337 and 425/30 overprinted **AIR MAIL** on wings of airplane.
450	2c. Rizal	40	40
451	4c. Post Office, Manila	15	15
452	12c. Freighters, Manila Bay	25	15
453	20c. Rice plantation	25	15
454	24c. Rice terraces	35	25
455	32c. Baguio Zigzag	40	35
450/455	Set of 6	1·60	1·30

1935. China Clipper Trans-Pacific Airmail Flight. Nos. 463 and 468 overprinted **P.I.U.S. INITIAL FLIGHT December-1935** and Martin M-130 flying boat China Clipper.
488	10c. Fort Santiago	25	15
489	30c. Blood Compact	40	40

1941.
566	8c. Boeing 314 flying boat	85	50
567	20c. Boeing 314 flying boat	1·00	40
568	60c. Boeing 314 flying boat	1·20	85
569	1p. Boeing 314 flying boat	65	40
566/569	Set of 4	3·25	1·90

1955. Air Force Heroes.

781	20c. Lieutenant J. Gozar and Boeing P-26A "Peashooter"	80	15
782	30c. Lieutenant C.F. Basa and Boeing P-26A "Peashooter"	1·30	30
783	50c. Lieutenant J. Gozar and Boeing P-26A "Peashooter"	1·10	20
784	70c. Lieutenant C.F. Basa and Boeing P-26A "Peashooter"	1·90	1·30
781/784 Set of 4		4·50	1·70

1959.

827*	70c. +30c. Model airplane	1·30	1·30

1960. 25th Anniv of Philippine Air Force.

850	10c. North American F-86 Sabre and Boeing P-12 biplane	15	15
851	20c. North American F-86 Sabre and Boeing P-12 biplane	45	30

1961. No. 850 surcharged **6c PAAF GOLDEN JUBILEE 1911–1961**.

886	6c. on 10c. North American F-86 Sabre and Boeing P-12 biplane	20	20

1971.

1210	10s. Airliner	15	15
1211	30s. Airliner	30	20
1212	1p. Airliner	75	60
1210/1212 Set of 3		1·10	85

1973. Col. J. Villamor (P.A.F. pilot) Commemoration.

1297	10s. Colonel Jesus Villamor, Boeing P-26A "Peashooter" and Mitsubishi A6M Zero-Sen fighters	15	10
1298	2p. Colonel Jesus Villamor, Boeing P-26A "Peashooter" and Mitsubishi A6M Zero-Sen fighters	1·30	1·30

1974. No. 1297 surcharged with Lions International emblem and **PHILIPPINE LIONISM 1949–1974 15s**.

1338*	15s. Colonel Jesus Villamor, Boeing P-26A on "Peashooter" and Mitsubishi A6M 10s. Zero-Sen fighters	15	10

1975. 40th Anniv of First Trans-Pacific China Clipper Airmail Flight.

1385	60s. Martin M-130 flying boat and Boeing 747-100 of Pan Am	45	20
1386	1p.50 Martin M-130 flying boat and Boeing 747-100 of Pan Am	1·20	60

1976. 30th Anniv of Philippine Airlines (PAL).

1398	60s. Douglas DC-3 (left) and Douglas DC-10 of Philippine Airlines	30	15
1399	1p.50 Douglas DC-3 (left) and Douglas DC-10 of Philippine Airlines	1·20	65

1976.

1412	80s. Survey airplane	25	25

1977. 50th Anniv of First Pan-Am International Air Service.

1445	2p.30 Fokker F.7 Trimotor *General New* of Pan Am	95	60

1979. 25th Anniv of Air France Service to the Philippines.

1552	1p.05 Concorde of Air France	50	20
1553	2p.20 Concorde of Air France	1·30	60

1985. 50th Anniv of First Trans-Pacific Commercial Flight (San Francisco-Manila).

1934	3p. Martin M-130 flying boat *China Clipper*	35	20
1935	3p.60 Martin M-130 flying boat *China Clipper*	50	20

1986. 45th Anniv of Philippine Airlines.

1947	60s. Douglas DC-3, 1946	15	15
1948	60s. Douglas DC-4, 1946	15	15
1949	60s. Douglas DC-6, 1948	15	15
1950	60s. Vickers Viscount 784, 1957	15	15
1951	2p.40 Fokker F-27 Friendship, 1960	50	20
1952	2p.40 Douglas DC-8.50, 1962	80	35
1953	2p.40 B.A.C. One Eleven 500, 1964	50	20
1954	2p.40 Douglas DC-10-30, 1974	50	20
1955	3p.60 Beech 18, 1941	75	35
1956	3p.60 Boeing 747-200, 1980	75	35
1947/1956 Set of 10		4·00	2·00

1986.

1967*	1p.20 Helicopter	20	15

1987. As No. 1956 but smaller, 32×22 mm.

2013*	5p.50 Boeing 747-200, 1980	1·10	20

1991. 50th Anniv of Philippine Airlines.

2232	1p. Boeing 747 tailplane and Stewardess	15	15
2233	5p.50 Boeing 747 tailplane and Stewardess (air)	95	60

1991.

2298*	2p. Air Corps	20	15
2302*	2p. Air Corps	20	15

1993.

2599*	6p. Boeing 747	65	45

1994.

2632	2p. Stylised Boeing 747	20	15

1994. 50th Anniv of ICAO.

2688*	7p. Airplane and symbols of flight	30	1·70

1998.

3088	15p. Clark International Airport and Boeing 747 taking off	1·10	1·10

1999.

3290*	5p. Bell UH-1 Iroquois	45	45

2000.

3361	5p. Boeing 747	50	50

2004. Centenary (2003) of Powered Flight.

3655	6p. Dornier Do-24TT	15	15
3656	6p. Dornier Do-24TT	15	15

PITCAIRN ISLANDS

South Pacific

1949. 12 pence = 1 shilling
20 shillings = 1 pound
1967. 100 cents = 1 dollar

1949. As Nos. 114/15 of Antigua.
13*	2½d. Airplane	1·00	4·25
14*	3d. Jet-powered Vickers Viking	8·00	4·25

1989.
348	20c. Lockheed P-3 Orion of the Royal New Zealand Air Force	1·50	60
349	80c. Beech 80 Queen Air	2·75	1·25
350	$1.05 Boeing-Vertol CH-47 Chinook helicopter of the U.S. Navy	3·00	1·50
351	$1.30 Lockheed C-130 Hercules of the Royal New Zealand Air Force	3·00	1·75
348/351	Set of 4	9·25	4·50

1993.
429*	$3 Westland Dragonfly helicopter	5·75	5·50

1995.
486*	$3 Lockheed L-1011 TriStar	3·50	3·75

2000.
MS581	$2.50 Sikorsky SH-3 Sea King (other stamp in the miniature sheet does not show aircraft)	8·00	8·50

POLAND

Eastern Europe

100 groszy = 1 zloty

1925.
252	1g. L.V.G. Schneider biplane	45	4·75
253	2g. L.V.G. Schneider biplane	45	4·75
254	3g. L.V.G. Schneider biplane	45	4·75
255	5g. L.V.G. Schneider biplane	45	55
256	10g. L.V.G. Schneider biplane	1·40	65
257	15g. L.V.G. Schneider biplane	1·60	75
258	20g. L.V.G. Schneider biplane	12·50	4·75
259	30g. L.V.G. Schneider biplane	6·50	1·75
260	45g. L.V.G. Schneider biplane	8·50	3·50
252/260	Set of 9	29·00	23·00

1933. Victory in Flight Around Europe Air Race, 1932.
292	30g. F. Zwirco, S. Wigura and RWD-6 SP-AHN	16·00	1·75

1934. International Air Tournament. Nos. 258 and 292 overprinted **Challenge 1934.**
301	20g. L.V.G. Schneider biplane	12·00	10·00
302	30g. F. Zwirco, S. Wigura and RWD-6 SP-AHN	7·50	2·50

1941.
484*	1z. Vickers-Armstrong Wellington and Hawker Hurricanes Mk I	5·75	6·50

1943.
486*	5g. Vickers-Armstrong Wellington	85	1·10

1944. No. 484 surcharged **MONTE CASSINO 18. V. 1944 Gr80.**
496*	80g. on 1z. Vickers-Armstrong Wellington and Hawker Hurricanes Mk I	13·00	16·00

1946.
555	5z. Lisunov Li-2	35	10
556	10z. Lisunov Li-2	45	25
557	15z. Lisunov Li-2	2·75	25
558	20z. Lisunov Li-2	1·10	25
559	25z. Lisunov Li-2	2·10	35
560	30z. Lisunov Li-2	3·50	50
555/560	Set of 6 8	9·25	1·50

1948.
604	15z. Airliner	1·60	25
605	25z. Airliner	1·10	20
606	30z. Airliner	1·10	45
607	50z. Airliner	2·25	45
608	75z. Airliner	2·25	55
609	100z. Airliner	2·25	55
604/609	Set of 7	9·50	2·20

1949.
654*	80z. Lisunov Li-2	4·25	4·75

1950.
664	500z. Airplane, hangar and mechanic	4·50	6·50

1952.
738	55g. Ilyushin Il-12	35	30
739	90g. Ilyushin Il-12	35	30
740	1z.40 Ilyushin Il-12	45	45
741	5z. Ilyushin Il-12	1·40	55
738/741	Set of 4	2·30	1·40

1952. Aviation Day.
778*	30g. +15g. Pilot and glider	1·25	10
779*	45g. +15g. Pilot and Yakovlev Yak-18U	2·00	70

1954.
MS855a	5z.+(2z.50) Lisunov Li-2	26·00	21·00

1954.
856	40g. Glider	65	15
857	60g. Glider (violet)	1·90	70
858	60g. Glider (brown)	1·25	15
859	1z.35 Glider	2·00	25
856/859	Set of 4	5·25	1·10

1954. Polish Airlines (LOT).
860	60g. Ilyushin Il-12	25	10
861	80g. Ilyushin Il-12	35	10
862	1z.15 Ilyushin Il-12	1·75	1·60
863	1z.50 Ilyushin Il-12	80	10
864	1z.55 Ilyushin Il-12	80	10
865	1z.95 Ilyushin Il-12	1·00	10
860/865	Set of 6	4·50	1·90

1957.
1035	90g. Ilyushin Il-14P SP-LAG	15	10
1036	1z.50 Ilyushin Il-14P SP-LAG	15	10
1037	3z.40 Ilyushin Il-14P SP-LAG	45	10
1038	3z.90 Ilyushin Il-14P SP-LAG	90	60
1039	4z. Ilyushin Il-14P SP-LAG	45	10
1039a	5z. Ilyushin Il-14P SP-LAG	55	10
1039b	10z. Ilyushin Il-14P SP-LAG (brown and turquoise)	90	35
1040	15z. Ilyushin Il-14P SP-LAG	1·50	45
1040a	20z. Ilyushin Il-14P SP-LAG	1·60	80
1040b	30z. Ilyushin Il-14P SP-LAG	2·75	1·10
1040c	50z. Ilyushin Il-14P SP-LAG	8·25	1·10
1035/1040c	Set of 11	16·00	4·50

1959. As No. 1039b, but colour changed.
1095	10z. Ilyushin Il-14P SP-LAG (purple)	3·25	3·75

1963.
1413*	60g. Mikoyan Gurevich MiG-21C	10	10

1966.
1631	60g. PZL-106A Kruk	10	10

1968. 11th World Gliding Championships, Leszno. Gliders.

1826	60g.	Zephyr glider SP-1127	10	10
1827	90g.	Stork glider SP-1135	10	10
1828	1z.50	Swallow glider SP-1050	15	10
1829	3z.40	Fly glider	35	20
1830	4z.	Seal glider SP-1201	80	30
1831	5z.50	Pirate glider SP-250	95	30
1826/1831	*Set of 6*		2·20	1·00

1968.

1833*	60g.	Balloon	10	10

1968.

1861*	60g.	Mikoyan Gurevich MiG-17	30	10

1971. Polish Aircraft of World War II.

2100	90g.	PZL P-11C fighter	10	10
2101	1z.50	PZL 23A Karas fighter	20	10
2102	3z.40	PZL P-37 Los bomber	30	20
2100/2102	*Set of 3*		55	35

1973.

2261*	1z.	Mikoyan Gurevich MiG-21D	10	10

1975. 50th Anniv of First Polish Airmail Stamps.

2386	2z.40	Albatros biplane	15	15
2387	4z.90	Tail of Ilyushin Il-62M of LOT	40	15

1976. Contemporary Aviation.

2424	5z.	Jantar glider	35	10
2425	10z.	Mil Mi-6 helicopter	75	10
2425a	20z.	PZL-106A Kruk spraying crops	1·50	10
2425b	50z.	PZL-Mielec TS-11 Iskra jet trainer	3·50	60
2424/2425b	*Set of 4*		5·50	80

1978. Aviation History and 50th Anniv of Polish Aero Club.

2538	50g.	Czeslaw Tanski and glider, 1896	10	10
2539	1z.	F. Zwirco, S. Wigura and RWD-6 SP-AHN	10	10
2540	1z.50	Stanislaw Skarzynski and RWD-5 bis SP-AJU	10	10
2541	4z.20	Mil Mi-2 helicopter SP-WXA	25	10
2542	6z.90	PZL-104 Wilga	75	25
2543	8z.40	SZD-45 Ogar powered glider	60	25
2538/2543	*Set of 6*		1·70	80

1979. 50th Anniv of LOT Polish Airlines.

2590	6z.90	Ilyushin Il-62M (top) and Fokker F.VIIb/3m P-POZM of LOT	55	25

1980.

2707*	6z.	Airliner being loaded with mail	45	10

1981. Balloons.

2721	2z.	Jean-Francois Pilatre de Rozier and Jules Romain in hydrogen/hot-air balloon, 1785 (inscribed "Pilatre de Rozier D'Arlandes 1783")	20	10
2722	2z.	Blanchard and Jeffries' balloon, 1785	20	10
2723	2z.50	Eugene Godard's quintuple "acrobatic" balloon, 1850	25	10
2724	3z.	F. Hynek and Z. Burzynski in balloon SP-ADS *Kosciusko*, 1933	25	10
2725	6z.	Z. Burzynski and N. Wyescki in balloon *Polonia II*, 1935	45	25
2726	6z.50	Ben Abruzzo, Max Anderson, Larry Newman and balloon *Double Eagle II*, 1978	45	25
2721/2726	*Set of 6*		1·60	80
MS2727	10z.50	Balloon SP-BCU *L.O.P.P.*, 1938	80	95

1981.

2764*	1z.	Model airplane	15	10
2767*	4z.20	Model gliders	30	10

1982. 50th Anniv of Polish Victory in Tourist Aircraft Challenge Competition.

2808	27z.	RWD-6 SP-AHN	75	25
2809	31z.	RWD-9 SP-ORO	1·00	30

1982.

2845	27z.	Helicopter	1·10	40

1984. Polish Aviation.

2955	5z.	Balloon over Warsaw, 1784	25	10
2956	5z.	Michal Scipio del Campo and biplane, 1911	25	10
2957	6z.	Balloon *Polonez*, 1983	25	10
2958	10z.	PWS 101 and Jantar gliders	30	10
2959	16z.	PZL-104 Wilga SP-APV, 1983	40	15
2960	27z.	Jan Nagorski and Farman M.F.7 floatplane	90	30
2961	31z.	PZL P-37 Los and PZL P-7	1·10	50
2955/2961	*Set of 7*		3·00	1·20

1985. Polish World Championship Successes.

3054*	5z.	PZL-106A Kruk SP-AGS	15	10
3056*	10z.	Glider KUBUZ-3	30	10

1986.

3064	40z.	Airliner	75	30

1987.

3128*	15z.	Colonel Stefan Pawlikowski and PZL P-7	30	10

1988. 60th Anniv of Polish State Aircraft Works.

3171	45z.	PZL P-37 Los	30	10

1988.

3172*	15z.	PZL P-11 of the Polish Air Force	25	10

1988. 60th Anniv of Military Institute of Aviation Medicine.
3177   20z. Hanriot XIV hospital aircraft 15   10

1990. 50th Anniv of Battle of Britain.
3327   1500z. Hawker Hurricane Mk I of 303 Squadron, Polish Fighter Wing, R.A.F   60   30

1993. The Polish Rangers (Second World War Air Troop).
3494   1500z. Handley Page H.P.61 Halifax A.IX 30   30

2004. 75th Anniv of LOT.
4110   1z.25 Boeing 767 40   10

PORTUGAL

South-west Europe
1923. 100 centavos = 1 escudo
2002. 100 cents = 1 euro

1923. Portugal–Brazil Trans-Atlantic Flight.
578   1c. Admiral Gago Coutinho, Sacadura Cabral and Fairey IIID seaplane 15   70
579   2c. Admiral Gago Coutinho, Sacadura Cabral and Fairey IIID seaplane 15   70
580   3c. Admiral Gago Coutinho, Sacadura Cabral and Fairey IIID seaplane 15   70
581   4c. Admiral Gago Coutinho, Sacadura Cabral and Fairey IIID seaplane 15   70
582   5c. Admiral Gago Coutinho, Sacadura Cabral and Fairey IIID seaplane 15   70
583   10c. Admiral Gago Coutinho, Sacadura Cabral and Fairey IIID seaplane 15   70
584   15c. Admiral Gago Coutinho, Sacadura Cabral and Fairey IIID seaplane 15   70
585   20c. Admiral Gago Coutinho, Sacadura Cabral and Fairey IIID seaplane 15   70
586   25c. Admiral Gago Coutinho, Sacadura Cabral and Fairey IIID seaplane 15   70
587   30c. Admiral Gago Coutinho, Sacadura Cabral and Fairey IIID seaplane 65   2·00
588   40c. Admiral Gago Coutinho, Sacadura Cabral and Fairey IIID seaplane 15   70
589   50c. Admiral Gago Coutinho, Sacadura Cabral and Fairey IIID seaplane 35   90
590   75c. Admiral Gago Coutinho, Sacadura Cabral and Fairey IIID seaplane 35   1·10
591   1e. Admiral Gago Coutinho, Sacadura Cabral and Fairey IIID seaplane 35   2·10
592   1e.50 Admiral Gago Coutinho, Sacadura Cabral and Fairey IIID seaplane 70   2·40
593   2e. Admiral Gago Coutinho, Sacadura Cabral and Fairey IIID seaplane 70   6·25
578/593 Set of 16 .... 4·25   20·00

1960. 50th Anniv of Portuguese Aero Club.
1169   1e. Glider 20   10
1170   1e.50 Light monoplane 70   25
1171   2e. Airplane and parachutes .... 1·40   65
1172   2e.50 Model glider .... 2·75   1·30
1169/1172 Set of 4 .... 4·50   2·10

1963. 10th Anniv of TAP (Portuguese Airline).
1237   1e. Airplane.............. 15   10
1238   2e.50 Airplane.............. 1·30   65
1239   3e.50 Airplane.............. 1·80   1·20
1237/1239 Set of 3 .... 3·00   1·80

1965. 50th Anniv of Portuguese Air Force.
1279   1e. Outline of North American F-86 Sabre 20   10
1280   2e. Outline of North American F-86 Sabre .... 1·50   75
1281   5e. Outline of North American F-86 Sabre .... 2·75   1·70
1279/1281 Set of 3 .... 4·00   2·30

1969. Birth Centenary of Admiral Gago Coutinho (aviator).
1370*   1e. Admiral Gago Coutinho and Fairey IIID seaplane 15   10
1372*   3e.30 Admiral Gago Coutinho and Fairey IIID seaplane .... 2·50   1·90

1972. 50th Anniv of First Lisbon-Rio de Janeiro Flight.
1489   1e. Admiral Gago Coutinho, Sacadura Cabral and Fairey IIID seaplane 10   10
1490   2e.50 Fairey IIID seaplane and map of flight from Lisbon to Rio de Janeiro, 1922 . 85   40
1491   2e.80 Admiral Gago Coutinho, Sacadura Cabral and Fairey IIID seaplane .... 1·10   90
1492   3e.50 Fairey IIID seaplane and map of flight from Lisbon to Rio de Janeiro, 1922 . 1·80   1·40
1489/1492 Set of 4 .... 3·50   2·50

1973.
1509*   1e. B.A.C. One Eleven 10   10

1975. 26th International Astronautical Federation Congress, Lisbon.
1580*   2e. Lilienthal glider 45   10

1978.
1692*   6e.50 B.A.C. One Eleven and monoplane ... 20   10

1979.
1743*   14e. Airport lounge and tail of Douglas DC-10 20   10

1982.
1896   10e. Fairey IIID seaplane *Lusitania* 35   10
1897   19e. Dornier Do-J Wal flying boat *Argus* ... 1·40   75
1898   33e.50 Douglas DC-7C "Seven Seas" .... 2·00   75
1899   50e. Boeing 747-282B of Air Portugal ...... 2·50   1·10
1896/1899 Set of 4 .... 5·50   2·50

1983. Bicentenary of Manned Flight.
1937   16e. Bartolomeu de Gusmao and balloon, 1709 75   10
1938   51e. Montgolfier balloon (first manned free flight, 1783) .... 2·00   90

1983. Air Force Uniforms.
1948   16e. Pilot and Hawker Hurricane Mk II of the Portuguese Air Force 55   10
1949   35e. Pilot and Republic F-84G Thunderjet of the Portuguese Air Force .... 2·10   55
1950   40e. Pilot and Nord 2501D Noratlas of the Portuguese Air Force .... 2·00   65
1951   51e. Pilot and Vought A-70 Corsair II of the Portuguese Air Force .... 2·50   90
1948/1951 Set of 4 .... 6·50   2·00

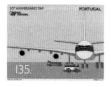

1995.
2485   135e. Airbus A340/300 .... 1·20   65

1999. 25th Anniv of Sarmento de Beires and Brito Pais's Portugal-Macao Flight.
2703   140e. Breguet Bre 16 Bri 2 *Patria* .... 1·20   55
2704   140e. Airco (de Havilland) DH.9 .... 1·20   55

1999. 75th Anniv of Military Aviation.
2719   51e. de Havilland DH.82A Tiger Moth 40   20
2720   51e. Supermarine Spitfire V6 40   20
2721   85e. Breguet Bre XIV-A2 70   35
2722   85e. SPAD VII-C1 70   35
2723   95e. Caudron G-3 85   45
2724   95e. Junkers Ju 52/3m 85   45
2719/2724 Set of 6 .... 3·50   1·80

2000.
MS2768 52e. Early airplanes.................................... 10·50   10·50

2000. Inauguration of Madeira Airports' Second Runway Extension.
2808   140e. Airbus A310 .... 1·10   55

2002. 50th Anniv of Portuguese Air Force.
2952   28c. Lockheed Martin (General Dynamics)
            F-16 Fighting Falcon 40   20
2953   43c. Sud Aviation SA300 Puma.................. 65   30
2954   54c. Dassault Dornier Alphajet A 80   40
2955   70c. Lockheed C-130 Hercules.................. 1·00   55
2956   €1.25 Lockheed P-3P Orion .... 1·80   90
2957   €1.75 Fiat G-91 .... 2·50   1·30
2952/2957 *Set of 6* .... 6·50   3·25
MS2958 €1.15 Four Cessna T-37; €1.75 Aerospatiale
    TB30 Epsilon and Cessna T-37 .... 4·25   4·25

2002.
MS2970 43c. Stylised Boeing 737 (other stamps in
    the miniature sheet do not show aircraft)............... 3·75   3·75

PORTUGUESE GUINEA

West Africa

100 centavos = 1 escudo

1938. As Nos. 401/9 of Angola.
288   10c. Airplane................................ 85   60
289   20c. Airplane................................ 85   60
290   50c. Airplane................................ 85   60
291   1e. Airplane................................ 85   60
292   2e. Airplane................................ 7·25   3·75
293   3e. Airplane................................ 2·40   1·20
294   5e. Airplane................................ 5·25   1·60
295   9e. Airplane................................ 7·50   4·00
296   10e. Airplane................................ 13·00   4·50
288/296 *Set of 9* .... 35·00   16·00

1963. As No. 611 of Angola.
364   2e.50 Boeing 707 and Lockheed L.1049G
            Super Constellation of T.A.P................ 60   25

1972. 50th Anniv of First Lisbon-Rio de Janeiro Flight.
424   1e. Fairey IIID seaplane *Lusitania* 20   10

PORTUGUESE INDIA

Indian Sub-continent

12 reis = 1 tanga

16 tangas = 1 rupia

1938. As Nos. 401/9 of Angola.
534   1t. Airplane................................ 1·40   65
535   2½t. Airplane................................ 1·40   65
536   3½t. Airplane................................ 1·40   65
537   4½t. Airplane................................ 1·40   65
538   7t. Airplane................................ 1·60   65
539   7½t. Airplane................................ 1·80   65
540   9t. Airplane................................ 6·25   1·90
541   11t. Airplane................................ 6·75   1·90
534/541 *Set of 8* .... 20·00   7·00

PORTUGUESE TIMOR

Australasia

1938. 100 avos = 1 pataca

1960. 100 centavos = 1 escudo

1938. As Nos. 401/9 of Angola.
270   1a. Airplane................................ 45   45
271   2a. Airplane................................ 50   45
272   3a. Airplane................................ 50   45
273   5a. Airplane................................ 60   60
274   10a. Airplane................................ 75   75
275   20a. Airplane................................ 1·60   95
276   50a. Airplane................................ 3·25   2·75
277   70a. Airplane................................ 4·00   3·50
278   1p. Airplane................................ 8·75   4·00
270/278 *Set of 9*.................................... 18·00   12·50

1946. Nos. 371/2, 374/5 and 377 of Mozambique surcharged
    TIMOR and value.
285*   8a. on 50c. Airplane .... 3·25   2·75
286*   12a. on 1e. Airplane .... 3·25   2·75
287*   40a. on 3e. Airplane .... 3·25   2·75
288*   50a. on 5e. Airplane .... 3·25   2·75
289*   1p. on 10e. Airplane .... 3·75   2·75

1947. Nos. 270/8 overprinted **LIBERTACAO**.
301   1a. Airplane................................ 15·00   4·00
302   2a. Airplane................................ 15·00   4·00
303   3a. Airplane................................ 15·00   4·00
304   5a. Airplane................................ 15·00   4·00
305   10a. Airplane................................ 3·75   1·30
306   20a. Airplane................................ 3·75   1·30
307   50a. Airplane................................ 3·75   1·30
308   70a. Airplane................................ 15·00   3·75
309   1p. Airplane................................ 6·25   1·50
301/309 *Set of 9*.................................... 85·00   22·00

1966.
388*   4e.50 Sacadura Cabral and Fairey IIID
            seaplane *Lusitania*........................... 1·50   80

1972.
417   1e. Admiral Gago Coutinho and
            Sacadura Cabral in Fairey IIID
            seaplane.. 35   30

QATAR

Arabia

1966. 100 naye paise = 1 rupee

1966. 100 dirhams = 1 riyal

1966.
177*	10np. Hawker Siddeley Comet 4 at Doha Airport	65	15
184*	70np. Hawker Siddeley Comet 4 at Doha Airport	3·75	1·30

1969.
278*	5d. Airliner over Doha Airport....................	35	10

1969.
284*	3d. Military helicopter...................................	35	15

1970.
307*	1d. Douglas DC-8 of Middle East Airlines being loaded with mail at Doha Airport	15	15

1970. First Gulf Air Vickers VC-10 Flight, Doha-London.
317*	1d. Vickers VC-10....................................	20	10
318*	2d. Vickers VC-10....................................	45	10
319*	3d. Tail view of Vickers VC-10..................	45	10
321*	1r.25 Vickers VC-10..................................	6·00	1·10
322*	2r. Tail of Vickers VC-10..........................	9·50	3·75

1972.
437*	3d. Helicopter..	75	15
442*	1r. Airliner at airport	13·50	1·80

1973.
465*	2d. de Havilland Canada DHC-2 Beaver spraying crops	30	15

1973.
473*	4d. Hawker Siddeley H.S.125......................	30	15
475*	10d. Meteorological airplane......................	95	20

1974.
504*	35d. Handley Page H.P.42 and Vickers VC-10...	1·30	30

1974. Arab Civil Aviation Day.
525*	20d. Vickers VC-10 of Gulf Aviation............	1·20	20
526*	25d. Vickers VC-10 and other airliners at Doha Airport	1·80	20

1990. 40th Anniv of Gulf Air.
840	50d. Anniversary Emblem............................	60	20
841	75d. Anniversary Emblem............................	90	35
842	4r. Anniversary Emblem............................	4·50	1·80
840/842 Set of 3		5·50	2·10

1994. 50th Anniv of ICAO.
949	25d. Boeing 777 and emblem	65	15
950	75d. Emblem..	1·60	35

2003. Centenary of Powered Flight.
MS1134 50d. Wright *Flyer I*; 50d. Otto Lilienthal's glider; 50d. Airbus A340; 50d. Douglas DC-5.........		1·00	80

QU'AITI STATE IN HADHRAMAUT

See Aden Protectorate States

RAS AL KHAIMA

Arabian Peninsula

100 dirhams = 1 riyal

APPENDIX

The following stamps have either been issued in excess of postal needs or have not been made available to the public in reasonable quantities at face value. Miniature sheets, imperforate stamps, etc are excluded from this section.

1969

"Apollo 11" Astronauts. 4r.25 (helicopter).

1970

Space Programmes. 4r. (helicopter).

REDONDA

West Indies

100 cents = 1 dollar

APPENDIX

The following stamps have either been issued in excess of postal needs or have not been made available to the public in reasonable quantities at face value. Miniature sheets, imperforate stamps, etc are excluded from this section.

1979

Antigua 1976 issue overprinted **REDONDA**. $10 Boeing 747 over Coolidge International Airport.

1983

Bicentenary of Manned Flight. 10c., 50c., 90c., $2.50.

REUNION

Indian Ocean

100 centimes = 1 franc

1938.
181	3f.65 Caudron C-600 *Aiglon*	95	95
182	6f.65 Caudron C-600 *Aiglon*	1·10	4·75
183	9f.65 Caudron C-600 *Aiglon*	65	5·00
184	12f.65 Caudron C-600 *Aiglon*	1·40	6·00
181/184 *Set of 4*		3·75	15·00

1943. Nos. 181/4 overprinted **France Libre**.
241	3f.65 Caudron C-600 *Aiglon*	2·30	8·25
242	6f.65 Caudron C-600 *Aiglon*	2·30	7·75
243	9f.65 Caudron C-600 *Aiglon*	1·60	7·75
244	12f.65 Caudron C-600 *Aiglon*	2·50	8·25
241/244 *Set of 4*		8·00	29·00

1944. As Nos. 207/13 of Cameroun.
259	1f. Fairey FC-1 airliner	35	55
260	1f.50 Fairey FC-1 airliner	45	35
261	5f. Fairey FC-1 airliner	70	1·10
262	10f. Fairey FC-1 airliner	1·40	4·00
263	25f. Fairey FC-1 airliner	2·00	3·50
264	50f. Fairey FC-1 airliner	1·90	1·50
265	100f. Fairey FC-1 airliner	2·25	3·25
259/265 *Set of 7*		8·00	13·00

1947.
304*	100f. Douglas DC-4	10·50	24·00

1949. Nos. 967/70 of France surcharged **CFA** and value.
326*	20f. on 40f. Lockheed 14 Super Electra	90	55
327*	25f. on 50f. Sud Ouest SO.30P Bretagne	1·60	30
328*	50f. on 100f. Sud Ouest SO.95 Corse IL	2·75	1·30
329*	100f. on 200f. Sud Ouest SO.30P Bretagne	10·00	10·00

1954. Nos. 1194/7 of France surcharged **CFA** and value.
365	50f. on 100f. Dassault Mystere IVA	2·75	70
366	100f. on 200f. Nord 2501 Noratlas	2·30	2·50
367	200f. on 500f. Air Fouga CM-170 Magister	19·00	26·00
368	500f. on 1000f. Breguet Br 763 Provence	10·00	30·00
365/368 *Set of 4*		31·00	55·00

1957. Nos. 1319/20 of France surcharged **CFA** and value.
393*	200f. on 500f. Sud Aviation SE 210 Caravelle	6·50	11·50
394*	500f. on 1000f. Sud Aviation SE 3130 Alouette II helicopter	10·00	34·00

1960. Nos. 1457, 1457b and 1459/60 of France surcharged **CFA** and value.
402	100f. on 2f. Nord 2501 Noratlas	5·00	1·50
403	100f. on 2f. Dassault Falcon/Mystere 20	1·40	1·50
404	200f. on 5f. Sud Aviation SE 210 Caravelle	5·25	5·00
405	500f. on 10f. Sud Aviation SE 3130 Alouette II helicopter	17·00	11·50
402/405 *Set of 4*		26·00	17·00

1968. No. 1806 of France surcharged **20F CFA**.
452	20f. on 40c. Nord 2501 Noratlas and Sud Aviation SE 3130 Alouette II helicopter	2·30	3·75

1972. No. 1890 of France surcharged **200F CFA**.
482	200f. on 5f. Didier Daurat, Raymond Vanier and Douglas DC-4	4·25	4·25

RHINELAND PALATINATE

See under Germany (Allied Occupation)

RHODESIA

Central Africa

1966. 12 pence = 1 shilling

20 shillings = 1 pound

1970. 100 cents = 1 dollar

1966. 20th Anniv of Central African Airways.
393	6d. de Havilland DH.89 Dragon Rapide VP-YBK of Central African Airways	75	35
394	1s.3d. Douglas DC-3 of Central African Airways	1·00	40
395	2s.6d. Vickers Viscount 748 VP-YNB *Matopos* of Central African Airways	1·50	1·50
396	5s. B.A.C. One Eleven 200 VP-YXA of Central African Airways	3·25	4·50
393/396 *Set of 4*		6·00	6·00

1970.
450*	50c. Vickers Viscount 810	1·25	55
451*	$1 Sud Aviation SE 3160 Alouette III helicopter	3·75	1·50

1970.
454*	3½c. Vickers Viscount 782 VP-WAS of Air Rhodesia being loaded with mail at Salisbury Airport	40	50

1978. 75th Anniv of Powered Flight.
570	4c. Wright Flyer I	10	10
571	5c. Bleriot XI	10	10
572	7c. Van Ryneveld and Brand's Vickers Vimy *Silver Queen II*, 1920	10	10
573	9c. Armstrong Whitworth A.W.15 Atalanta G-ABTI	10	10
574	17c. Vickers Viking 1B VP-YEW *Zambezi* of Central African Airways	10	10
575	25c. Boeing 720B of Air Rhodesia	15	50
570/575 *Set of 6*		60	90

RHODESIA AND NYASALAND

Central Africa

12 pence = 1 shilling

20 shillings = 1 pound

1955.
16*	3d. de Havilland DH.106 Comet	55	30

1959.
28*	2s.6d. Vickers Viscount 748 VP-YND *Mweru* of Central African Airways at Salisbury Airport	4·50	40

1962. 30th Anniv of First London-Rhodesian Airmail Service.
40	6d. de Havilland DH.66 Hercules G-AAJH *City of Basra*	35	50
41	1s.3d. Short S.23 flying boat G-ADHL *Canopus*	1·50	50
42	2s.6d. Hawker Siddeley Comet 4 of B.O.A.C. at Salisbury Airport	4·00	5·50
40/42 *Set of 3*		5·25	9·00

ROMANIA

South-east Europe

100 bani = 1 leu

1928.
1099	1l. Bleriot SPAD 33 C-RAIU of C.F.R.N.A.	6·25	4·00
1100	2l. Bleriot SPAD 33 C-RAIU of C.F.R.N.A.	6·25	4·00
1101	5l. Bleriot SPAD 33 C-RAIU of C.F.R.N.A.	6·25	4·00
1099/1101 *Set of 3*		17·00	11·00

1930. Nos. 1099/1101 overprinted **8 IUNIE 1930**.
1147b	1l. Bleriot SPAD 33 C-RAIU of C.F.R.N.A.	12·00	6·00
1148b	2l. Bleriot SPAD 33 C-RAIU of C.F.R.N.A.	12·00	6·00
1149b	5l. Bleriot SPAD 33 C-RAIU of C.F.R.N.A.	12·00	6·00
1147b/1149b *Set of 3*		32·00	16·00

1931.
1226	2l. Farman F.121 Jaribu	1·30	65
1227	3l. Farman F.300 and biplane	1·60	1·00
1228	5l. Farman F.60 Goliath	1·20	1·30
1229	10l. Fokker F.XII	4·25	2·75
1230	20l. Three aircraft	15·00	4·25
1226/1230 *Set of 5*		21·00	9·00

1945.
1743*	200l. +1000l. Airplane	12·00	14·00

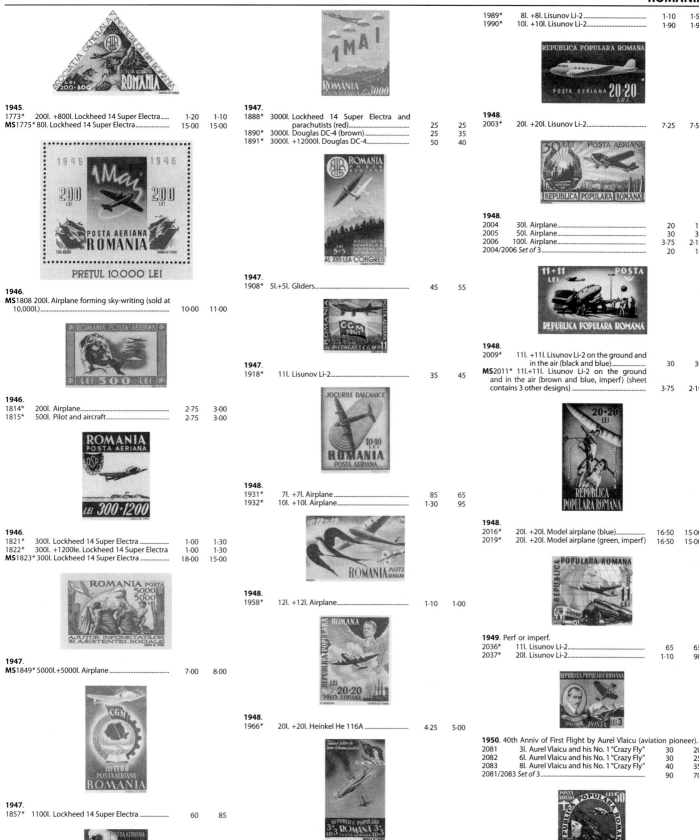

1945.
1773*	200l. +800l. Lockheed 14 Super Electra.....		1·20	1·10
MS1775*	80l. Lockheed 14 Super Electra..................		15·00	15·00

1946.
MS1808	200l. Airplane forming sky-writing (sold at 10,000l.)...	10·00	11·00

1946.
1814*	200l. Airplane...	2·75	3·00
1815*	500l. Pilot and aircraft..................................	2·75	3·00

1946.
1821*	300l. Lockheed 14 Super Electra	1·00	1·30
1822*	300l. +1200le. Lockheed 14 Super Electra	1·00	1·30
MS1823*	300l. Lockheed 14 Super Electra	18·00	15·00

1947.
MS1849*	5000l.+5000l. Airplane	7·00	8·00

1947.
1857*	1100l. Lockheed 14 Super Electra	60	85

1947.
1858	3000l. +7000l. Lockheed 14 Super Electra...	85	85

1947.
1882*	15000l. +15000l. Lisunov Li-2........................	75	65

1947.
1888*	3000l. Lockheed 14 Super Electra and parachutists (red)................................	25	25
1890*	3000l. Douglas DC-4 (brown)	25	35
1891*	3000l. +12000l. Douglas DC-4......................	50	40

1947.
1908*	5l.+5l. Gliders...	45	55

1947.
1918*	11l. Lisunov Li-2..	35	45

1948.
1931*	7l. +7l. Airplane..	85	65
1932*	10l. +10l. Airplane......................................	1·30	95

1948.
1958*	12l. +12l. Airplane......................................	1·10	1·00

1948.
1966*	20l. +20l. Heinkel He 116A	4·25	5·00

1948.
1972*	3l.+3l. Ilyushin Il-2M3 Shturmovik.................	3·75	4·50
1973*	5l.+5l. Petlyakov Pe-2 dive bomber	6·75	6·75

1948. Air Force Day.
1987*	2l. +2l. Monimoa gliders	75	95
1988*	5l. +5l. Vlaicu's No. 1 "Crazy Fly".................	75	95

1989*	8l. +8l. Lisunov Li-2......................................	1·10	1·50
1990*	10l. +10l. Lisunov Li-2..................................	1·90	1·90

1948.
2003*	20l. +20l. Lisunov Li-2..................................	7·25	7·50

1948.
2004	30l. Airplane...	20	10
2005	50l. Airplane...	30	30
2006	100l. Airplane...	3·75	2·10
2004/2006	Set of 3	20	10

1948.
2009*	11l. +11l. Lisunov Li-2 on the ground and in the air (black and blue)................	30	30
MS2011*	11l.+11l. Lisunov Li-2 on the ground and in the air (brown and blue, imperf) (sheet contains 3 other designs)	3·75	2·10

1948.
2016*	20l. +20l. Model airplane (blue).................	16·50	15·00
2019*	20l. +20l. Model airplane (green, imperf)	16·50	15·00

1949. Perf or imperf.
2036*	11l. Lisunov Li-2..	65	65
2037*	20l. Lisunov Li-2..	1·10	90

1950. 40th Anniv of First Flight by Aurel Vlaicu (aviation pioneer).
2081	3l. Aurel Vlaicu and his No. 1 "Crazy Fly"	30	20
2082	6l. Aurel Vlaicu and his No. 1 "Crazy Fly"	30	25
2083	8l. Aurel Vlaicu and his No. 1 "Crazy Fly"	40	35
2081/2083	Set of 3	90	70

1951.
2135*	50l. Lisunov Li-2..	6·00	4·25

1952. Nos. 2004/6, 2081/3 and 2135 surcharged with new value.
2157a*	3b. on 30l. Airplane......................................	6·25	4·75
2158*	3b. on 50l. Airplane......................................	1·80	1·40
2159*	3b. on 100l. Airplane....................................	6·25	3·00
2191*	10b. on 3l. Aurel Vlaicu and his No. 1 "Crazy Fly"...	1·50	70
2192*	10b. on 6l. Aurel Vlaicu and his No. 1 "Crazy Fly"2	1·60	70
2193*	10b. on 8l. Aurel Vlaicu and his No. 1 "Crazy Fly"..	1·60	30
2217*	1l. on 50l. Lisunov Li-2..................................	13·50	4·25

1952. Nos. 2032/3 surcharged **AERIANA**, airplane and new value.
2162*	3l. on 20l. Globe and posthorn......................	30·00	21·00
2163*	5l. on 30l. Forms of transport......................	45·00	24·00

1953.
2290* 55b. Model gliders .... 1·30 20

1953. Aerial Sports.
2308* 10b. Model gliders .... 1·90 35
2310* 55b. Glider .... 10·00 45
2311* 1l.75 Zlin Z-22 (?) .... 12·00 70

1953. 40th Death Anniv of Aurel Vlaicu (aviation pioneer).
2320 50b. Aurel Vlaicu and his No. 1 "Crazy Fly" 85 25

1954. Aviation Day.
2346 55b. Pilot and Mikoyan Gurevich MiG-15
jet fighters .... 2·50 25

1956. 50th Anniv of First Flight by Trajan Vuia (aviation pioneer).
2442 55b. Traian Vuia, Vuia No. 1 (on ground),
biplane and Yakovlev Yak-25 jet
fighters .... 1·10 35

1956.
2486 20b. Ilyushin Il-18 .... 50 40
2487 55b. Ilyushin Il-18 .... 75 40
2488 1l.75 Ilyushin Il-18 .... 3·50 60
2489 2l.55 Ilyushin Il-18 .... 4·00 1·20
2486/2489 Set of 4 .... 8·00 2·30

1958.
2603* 3l.30 Pilot and Mikoyan Gurevich MiG-17
jet fighters .... 1·30 45

1960.
2751* 3l.20 Ilyushin Il-18 at Baneasa Airport and
tail of airliner of TAROM .... 4·50 10

1960. 50th Anniv of First Flight by Aurel Vlaicu and Aviation Day.
2752 10b. Aurel Vlaicu and his No. 1 "Crazy Fly" 15 10
2753 20b. Aurel Vlaicu and his No. 2 .... 20 10
2754 35b. I.A.R. 817 flying ambulance............... 30 10
2755 40b. Antonov An-2 biplane YR-ANF
spraying crops 35 10
2756 55b. Pilot and Mikoyan Gurevich MiG-17
jet fighters 50 10
2757 1l.60 Ilyushin Il-18 of TAROM and Baneasa
Airport, Bucharest .... 1·30 20
2758 1l.75 Airplane and parachutists .... 1·70 35
2752/2758 Set of 7 .... 4·00 95

1960.
2794 55b. (+45b.) Ilyushin Il-18.......................... 60 35

1961.
2900* 20b. Ilyushin Il-18 .... 25 10
2901* 40b. Ilyushin Il-18 .... 90 15
2902* 55b. Ilyushin Il-18 .... 40 10
2903* 75b. Ilyushin Il-18 .... 45 10
2904* 1l. Helicopter 60 15
2905* 1l.20 Ilyushin Il-18 .... 65 35

1963.
2998 30b. Ilyushin Il-18 .... 25 10
2999 40b. Ilyushin Il-18 .... 25 15
3000 55b. Ilyushin Il-18 .... 40 10
3001 1l. Ilyushin Il-18 .... 60 15
3002 1l.55 Ilyushin Il-18 .... 85 20
3003 1l.75 Ilyushin Il-18 .... 85 25
2998/3003 Set of 6 .... 3·00 85

1963.
3031 40b. Ilyushin Il-18 .... 50 15
3032 55b. Ilyushin Il-18 .... 50 15
3033 75b. Ilyushin Il-18 .... 50 15
3034 1l.35 Ilyushin Il-18....................................... 1·30 30
3035 1l.75 Ilyushin Il-18 YR-IME of TAROM .... 1·40 20
3031/3035 Set of 5 .... 3·75 85

1963. No. 2752 surcharged **1913–1963 50 ani de la moarte 1,75
lei.**
3049 1l.75 on 10b. Aurel Vlaicu and his No. 1
"Crazy Fly".. 2·20 90

1966.
3420 55b. +45b. Ilyushin Il-18.......................... 65 30

1967.
3512* 35b. Zlin Z-226A Akrobat 20 15
3519* 1l.35 Mil Mi-4 helicopter (29×23 mm) 70 15
3526* 3l.20 Ilyushin Il-18 of TAROM (29×23 mm) 1·40 15

1968. Romanian Aviation.
3539 40b. Antonov An-2 biplane spraying
crops... 10 10
3540 55b. I.A.R. 817 flying ambulance................ 25 10
3541 1l. Airliner 30 10
3542 2l.40 Mircea Zorileanu and biplane............. 80 40
3539/3542 Set of 4 .... 1·30 60

1968.
3556* 55b. Model airplane 20 10

1970. 50th Anniv of Romanian Civil Aviation.
3717* 60b. B.A.C. One Eleven 475 YR-BCA of
TAROM and silhouettes of Lilienthal
glider (top left), Vlaicu's No. 1 "Crazy
Fly" (top centre), Henri Coanda's
turbine-powered model airplane
(top right), Mil Mi-4 helicopter, I.A.R.
817 flying ambulance (lower centre)
and Zlin Z-226A Akrobat.................... 25 10
3718* 2l. B.A.C. One Eleven 475 YR-BCA of
TAROM and control tower at Otopeni
Airport, Bucharest 55 25

1970.
3766* 60b. Kamov Ka-26 helicopter...................... 35 10

1970. 60th Anniv of First Experimental Turbine-powered Airplane.
3776 60b. Henri Coanda's turbine-powered
model airplane, 1910 .... 55 20

1971. As Nos. 3519 and 3526, but 23×17 mm.
3844* 1l.35 Mil Mi-4 helicopter 75 15
3851* 3l.20 Ilyushin Il-18 of TAROM 50 15

1972. Romanian Aviation Pioneers.
3927* 60b. Aurel Vlaicu, his No. 1 "Crazy Fly" and
silhouette of Boeing 707.................... 15 10
3928* 3l. Traian Vuia, Vuia No. 1 and silhouette
of Boeing 707.. 80 40

1972.
3948* 14l.60 Otopeni Airport, Bucharest.................. 3·00 30

1974.
4077* 55b. Tupolev Tu-134 being loaded with mail 10 15

1976.
4214* 3l.35 I.A.R. 817 flying ambulance 55 20

1976. 50th Anniv of Romanian Airline (TAROM).
4218 20b. Airco (de Havilland) D.H.9C CV-AAB . 10 10
4219 40b. I.C.A.R. Comercial YR-ACS 15 10
4220 60b. Douglas DC-3 YR-PAF 25 10
4221 1l.75 Antonov An-24 YR-AMB of TAROM ... 40 10
4222 2l.75 Ilyushin Il-62 YR-IRA of TAROM 60 20
4223 3l.60 Boeing 707 YR-ABA of TAROM 90 20
4218/4223 Set of 6 .... 2·20 70

1977. Romanian Gliders.
4278 20b. I.C.A.R.1 glider YR-210 .... 10 10
4279 40b. IS-3d glider YR-915 .... 10 10
4280 55b. RG-5 glider YR-977 .... 10 10
4281 1l.50 IS-11 glider YR-918 .... 25 10
4282 3l. IS-29D glider YR-1004 and light airplane 50 20
4283 3l.40 IS-28B glider YR-1007 .... 90 35
4278/4283 Set of 6 .... 1·80 85

1977.
MS4303 10l. Boeing 707 YR-ABB of TAROM over Otopeni Airport, Bucharest .... 4·00 4·00

1977.
4304* 20l. Tupolev Tu-154 .... 3·00 1·00
4305* 30l. Tupolev Tu-154 of TAROM and control tower at Otopeni Airport, Bucharest .... 4·50 1·70

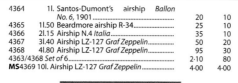

1978. Airships.
4363 60b. Airship LZ-1 .... 10 10

4364 1l. Santos-Dumont's airship *Ballon No. 6*, 1901 .... 20 10
4365 1l.50 Beardmore airship R-34 .... 25 10
4366 2l.15 Airship N.4 *Italia* 35 10
4367 3l.40 Airship LZ-127 *Graf Zeppelin* 50 20
4368 4l.80 Airship LZ-127 *Graf Zeppelin* 95 30
4363/4368 Set of 6 .... 2·10 80
MS4369 10l. Airship LZ-127 *Graf Zeppelin* .... 4·00 4·00

1979. Pioneers of Aviation.
4426 55b. Wilbur and Orville Wright and Wright Type A 10 10
4427 1l. Louis Bleriot and Bleriot XI 15 10
4428 1l.50 Anthony Fokker and Fokker F.VIIa/3m *Josephine Ford* 20 10
4429 2l.15 A.N. Tupolev and Tupolev ANT-25 ..... 30 10
4430 3l. Otto Lilienthal and Lilienthal monoplane glider 35 15
4431 3l.40 Traian Vuia and Vuia No. 1, 1906 .... 40 20
4432 4l.80 Aurel Vlaicu and his No. 1 "Crazy Fly" 50 30
4426/4432 Set of 7 .... 1·80 95
MS4433 10l. Henri Coanda and his turbine-powered model airplane, 1910 .... 4·25 4·50

1979.
4451* 3l.40 Boeing 707 of TAROM 65 35

1981.
4675* 4l.80 Model gliders 70 75

1982.
4709* 4l. Helicopter spraying crops 65 35

1982. Hang Gliders.
4711 50b. Vladimir Nicolae's Standard 1 hang-glider 10 10
4712 1l. Excelsior D hang-glider 20 10
4713 1l.50 Dedal-1 hang-glider 25 10
4714 2l.50 Entuziast hang-glider 40 15
4715 4l. AK-22 hang-glider 60 30
4716 5l. Grifrom hang-glider 85 35
4711/4716 Set of 6 .... 2·20 1·00

1982. Birth Centenary of Aurel Vlaicu (aviation pioneer).
4727 50b. Vlaicu's glider, 1909 .... 10 10
4728 1l. Aircraft and Vlaicu monument 20 10
4729 2l.50 Aircraft and Air Heroes' Monument .. 45 20
4730 3l. Vlaicu's No. 1 "Crazy Fly" 50 15
4727/4730 Set of 4 .... 1·10 50

1983. First Romanian Built Jetliner.
4776 11l. Rombac One Eleven 500 of TAROM .. 2·00 50

1983.
4794 2l. Boeing 707 of TAROM being loaded with mail 55 10

1983.
MS4809* 10l. Rombac One Eleven 500 of TAROM at Otopeni Airport, Bucharest .... 4·50 4·50

1984. 40th Anniv of ICAO.
4878 50b. Lockheed 14 Super Electra YR-LIS 15 10
4879 1l.50 Britten-Norman BN-2 Islander YR-BNC over Baneasa Airport 30 10
4880 3l. Rombac One Eleven 500 leaving Otopeni Airport, Bucharest and airliner on ground 60 20
4881 6l. Boeing 707 of TAROM .... 1·10 30
4878/4881 Set of 4 .... 1·90 60

1985.
5006* 1l. Orville and Wilbur Wright and Wright Flyer I 15 10
5008* 2l. Amelia Earhart and Fokker F.VIIb/3m seaplane *Friendship*, 1928 .... 35 10
5009* 3l. Charles Lindbergh and Ryan NYP Special *Spirit of St. Louis* 45 20
5012* 5l. Admiral Richard E. Byrd and Fokker F.VIIa/3m *Josephine Ford* .... 1·20 40

1986.
MS5044 10l. Alexandru Papana's Bucker Bu 133 Jungmeister biplane YR-PAX *Gilmore* .... 4·00 3·50

1987.

5122	50b. Henri August's glider, 1909	10	10
5123	1l. IS-28 B2 glider and sky diver	15	10
5124	2l. IS-29 D2 glider	25	15
5125	3l. IS-32 glider	50	15
5126	4l. I.A.R. 35 light airplane	65	25
5127	5l. IS-28 M2 aircraft	90	30
5122/5127 *Set of* 6		2·30	95

1987.

5151	2l. (+1l.) Ilyushin Il-86	50	30

1988.

MS5179 Two sheets (a) 3l. Airbus Industrie A320 (sheets contain 7 other 3l. designs) *Set of* 2 sheets 10·50 10·50

1988.

5206	2l. (+1l.) Ilyushin Il-62M	50	40

1992.

5462*	30l. Vuia No. 1, 1906	35	10

1993. Balloons.

5498	30l. Parseval Sigsfeld kite-type observation balloon, 1898	15	15
5499	90l. Caquot observation balloon, 1917	50	15

1994.

MS5614 2100l. Henri Coanda (aircraft designer) (other stamp in the miniature does not show aircraft) 2·75 2·75

1994. 50th Anniv of ICAO.

5639	110l. Traian Vuia's Airplane No 1, 1906	15	30
5640	350l. Rombac One Eleven	45	30
5641	500l. Boeing 737-300	70	30
5642	635l. Airbus A310	85	30
5639/5642 *Set of* 4		1·90	1·10

1995. 75th Anniv of Founding of Franco-Romanian Air Company.

5694	60l. Tailfins of Boeing 737 Tarom and Boeing 737 Air France aircraft (Romanian and French State Airlines)	55	10
5695	960l. Potez IX and Paris-Bucharest route map	60	20

1995.

5719*	285l. IAR 80 (70th Anniversary Romanian aeronautical industry)	15	10
5720*	715l. IAR 316 Red Cross Helicopter	45	10
5721*	965l. Aerospatiale SA 330 Puma	55	10
5722*	1575l. IAR 818H seaplane	95	15
5723*	3410l. Boeing 737-300 (75th Anniversary Romanian air transport)	1·90	1·60

1995. 75th Anniv of Institute of Aeronautics Medicine.

5759	960l. General Dr. Victor Anastasiu	50	10

1998.

5932*	3900l. Iraian Vuia, first flight, 1906	1·50	60

1998. Nos. 5402 and 5403 overprinted with helicopter and airplane and additionally surcharged.

5980*	50l. on 5l.	15	15
5981*	50l. on 9l.	15	15

1998.

5992*	1100l. Henri Coanda and his turbine powered model airplane, 1910	50	30
5993*	1600l. Louis Bleriot and his *Bleriot XI* airplane (first powered flight over English Channel 1909)	65	30

2000. Centenary of First Zeppelin Flight.

6127	2100l. Count Ferdinand von Zeppelin and Zeppelin (probably LZ-1)	35	20

2000. No. 5695 overprinted with a Potez IX and additionally surcharged.

6149	2000l. on 960l.	25	50
6150	4200l. on 960l.	60	50
6151	4600l. on 960l.	65	50
6152	6500l. on 960l.	95	50
6149/6152 *Set of* 4		2·20	1·80

2001. No. 5720 additionally surcharged.

6225*	2500l. on 715l. IAR Red Cross helicopter	10	10

2004. 50th Anniv of TAROM (national airline).

6429	16000l. Airbus A310 and emblem	60	15

2004. 75th Anniv of Zeppelin LZ-127's Flight over Brasov.

6437	31000l. Zeppelin LZ-127	1·20	30

2005. 125th Birth Anniv of G. V. Bibescu (aviation pioneer).

6483*	77000l. G.V. Bibescu	2·70	70

2006. Centenary of Traian Vuia's First Powered Flight.

6633	70b. Traian Vuia and drawing	50	15
6634	80b. *Vuia I* (aircraft)	60	15
6635	1l.60 *Vuia II* (aircraft)	1·40	35
6633/6635 *Set of* 3		2·30	60
MS6637 4l.70. Traian Vuia seated on *Vuia I*		4·00	4·00

2008. Centenary of First 1000m Closed Circuit Flight in One Minute.

6863	5l. *Voisin-Farman I* and Henri Farman	4·25	4·25

POSTAL TAX STAMPS

1931.

T1216	50b. Airplane	65	10
T1217	1l. Airplane	1·10	10
T1218	2l. Airplane	1·10	25
T1216/1218 *Set of* 3		2·50	40

ROSS DEPENDENCY

Antarctica

100 cents = 1 dollar

1972.

10a*	4c. Lockheed C-130 Hercules at Williams Field	15	1·60

1995.

37*	$1.80 Ford 4-AT-B Trimotor *Floyd Bennett*	2·00	2·00

2000.

66*	40c. Lockheed C-130 Hercules	90	50

2007.
104*   50c. de Havilland Canada DHC-2 Beaver..   85   60

RUSSIA

Eastern Europe and Northern Asia
100 kopeks = 1 rouble

1922. No. 283 overprinted with airplane.
284   45r. Worker ....   17·00   42·00

1922.
288*   20r. +5r. Airplane ....   2·40   11·50

1924. Surcharged.
417   5k. on 3r. Fokker F.III of Deutsche
        Russische Luftverkehrs ....   3·25   1·50
418   10k. on 5r. Fokker F.III of Deutsche
        Russische Luftverkehrs ....   2·50   1·00
419   15k. on 1r. Fokker F .III of Deutsche
        Russische Luftverkehrs ....   3·25   1·50
420   20k. on 10r. Fokker F.III of Deutsche
        Russische Luftverkehrs ....   3·25   1·50
417/420 *Set of 4* ....   11·00   5·00

1926.
499   10k. Tupolev ANT-3 ....   22·00   6·75
500   15k. Tupolev ANT-3 ....   26·00   10·00

1930. *Graf Zeppelin* Flight to Moscow.
574   40k. Airship LZ-127 *Graf Zeppelin* ....   44·00   21·00
575   80k. Airship LZ-127 *Graf Zeppelin* ....   35·00   13·50

1931. Airship Construction Fund. Imperf or perf.
579c   10k. Airship LZ-127 *Graf Zeppelin* ....   7·00   5·00
580b   15k. Airship LZ-127 *Graf Zeppelin* (blue)...   44·00   18·00
581c   20k. Airship LZ-127 *Graf Zeppelin* ....   7·00   6·75
582b   50k. Airship LZ-127 *Graf Zeppelin* ....   10·50   7·50
583c   1r. Airship construction ....   13·00   12·50
579c/583c *Set of 5* ....   75·00   45·00

1931. *Graf Zeppelin* North Pole Flight. Imperf or perf.
584   30k. Airship LZ-127 *Graf Zeppelin* ....   31·00   18·00
585b   35k. Airship LZ-127 *Graf Zeppelin* ....   31·00   21·00
586   1r. Airship LZ-127 *Graf Zeppelin* ....   39·00   25·00
587   2r. Airship LZ-127 *Graf Zeppelin* ....   31·00   18·00
584/587 *Set of 4* ....   £120   75·00

1932.
E591   50k. Kalinin K-4 ....   50·00   21·00
E592   1r. Kalinin K-4 ....   85·00   50·00

1933.
634   5k. Stratosphere balloon *U.S.S.R.-1* ....   £120   30·00
635   10k. Stratosphere balloon *U.S.S.R.-1* ....   65·00   10·00
636   20k. Stratosphere balloon *U.S.S.R.-1* ....   32·00   6·25
634/636 *Set of 3* ....   £200   42·00

1934. 10th Anniv of Soviet Civil Aviation and USSR Airmail
Service.
643   5k. Tupolev ANT-9 PS9 ....   16·00   4·75
644   10k. Tupolev ANT-9 PS9 ....   16·00   4·75
645   20k. Tupolev ANT-9 PS9 ....   29·00   6·00
646   50k. Tupolev ANT-9 PS9 ....   55·00   18·00
647   80k. Tupolev ANT-9 PS9 ....   31·00   7·50
643/647 *Set of 5* ....   £130   37·00

1934. Stratosphere Balloon "Osoaviakhim" Disaster Victims.
659A   5k. I. D. Usyskin and stratosphere
        balloon *Osoaviakhim* ....   26·00   6·25
660A   10k. A. V. Vasenko and stratosphere
        balloon *Osoaviakhim* ....   75·00   8·75
661A   20k. P. F. Fedoseenko and stratosphere
        balloon *Osoaviakhim* ....   50·00   6·25
1042   1r. I. D. Usyskin and stratosphere
        balloon *Osoaviakhim* (slate-green)...   8·75   3·25
1043   1r. A. V. Vasenko and stratosphere
        balloon *Osoaviakhim* (light green)....   8·75   3·25
1044   1r. P. F. Fedoseenko and stratosphere
        balloon *Osoaviakhim* (blue)................   8·75   3·25
659/661 and 1042/1044 *Set of 6* ....   £160   28·00

1934. Airship Travel Propaganda.
662   5k. Airship *Pravda* emerging from
        hangar ....   22·00   6·75
663   10k. Airship ....   22·00   6·75
664   15k. Airship *Voroshilov* ....   38·00   17·00
665   20k. Airship gondola and mooring mast .   44·00   11·50
666   30k. Airship *Lenin* ....   85·00   30·00
662/666 *Set of 5* ....   £190   65·00

1935.
678   1k. Airplane ....   6·25   1·40
679   3k. Tupolev ANT-4 TB-1 fitted with skis ..   6·25   1·70
680   5k. Lyapidevsky and Tupolev ANT-4 TB-1
        fitted with skis ....   7·00   1·40
681   10k. Levanevsky and Tupolev ANT-4 TB-1
        fitted with skis ....   12·00   2·10
682   15k. Slepnev and Tupolev ANT-4 TB-1
        fitted with skis ....   13·50   2·75
683   20k. Doronin and Junkers W.33 fitted
        with skis ....   19·00   3·50
684   25k. Polikarpov R-5 biplane fitted with
        skis ....   55·00   21·00
685   30k. Polikarpov R-5 biplane fitted with
        skis ....   70·00   28·00
686   40k. N.P. Kamanin and Polikarpov R-5
        biplanes fitted with skis ....   39·00   4·00

687   50k. Polikarpov R-5 biplanes fitted with
        skis ....   47·00   14·00
678/687 *Set of 10* ....   £250   70·00

1935. No. 681 surcharged.
706   1r. on 10k. Levanevsky and Tupolev
        ANT-4 TB-1 fitted with skis £350   £450

1937. Air Force Exhibition.
746   10k. Yakovlev Ya-7 Air 7 ....   2·50   60
747   20k. Tupolev ANT-9 ....   2·50   60
748   30k. Tupolev ANT-6 ....   4·25   65
749   40k. O.S.G.A. 101 flying boat ....   8·75   1·30
750   50k. Tupolev ANT-4 TB-1 ....   10·50   3·00
751   80k. Tupolev ANT-20 *Maksim Gorky* ....   13·00   3·00
752   1r. Tupolev ANT-14 CCCP N1001 Pravda   26·00   5·50
746/752 *Set of 7* ....   60·00   13·00

1938. North Pole Flight.
769   10k. Tupolev ANT-6 ....   1·70   35
770   20k. Tupolev ANT-6 ....   3·50   65
771   40k. Tupolev ANT-6 ....   7·75   2·30
772   80k. Tupolev ANT-6 ....   2·50   1·40
769/772 *Set of 4* ....   14·00   4·25

1938. First Flight over North Pole.
780   10k. Tupolev ANT-25 ....   2·20   60
781   20k. Tupolev ANT-25 ....   2·20   60
782   40k. Tupolev ANT-25 ....   4·00   1·80
783   50k. Tupolev ANT-25 ....   7·50   3·25
780/783 *Set of 4* ....   14·00   5·50

1938. Second Flight over North Pole.
784   10k. Tupolev ANT-25 ....   4·00   60
785   20k. Tupolev ANT-25 ....   4·00   1·30
786   50k. Tupolev ANT-25 ....   7·00   1·70
784/786 *Set of 3* ....   13·50   3·25

1938.
796*   50k. Model airplane ....   5·75   1·80
797*   80k. Model airplane ....   7·50   2·10

1938. Aviation.
810*   5k. Model of a Tupolev ANT-6 ....   3·00   85
811*   10k. Glider ....   2·00   85
812*   15k. Captive observation balloon ....   2·50   1·00
813*   20k. Airship *Osoaviakhim* ....   2·50   1·00

815*	40k. Yakovlev VT-2 seaplane	7·25	2·00
816*	50k. Balloon	13·00	2·30
817*	80k. Stratosphere balloon	8·25	3·25
818*	1r. Tupolev ANT-6	14·00	3·50

1938.

829*	80k. Tupolev ANT-6	6·75	1·40

1939. Women's Moscow–Far East Flight.

845	15k. Paulina Osipenko and Tupolev ANT-37 *Rodina*	1·50	85
846	30k. Marina Raskova and Tupolev ANT-37 *Rodina*	1·50	1·10
847	60k. Valentina Grizodubova and Tupolev ANT-37 *Rodina*	3·00	1·70
845/847 *Set of 3*		5·50	3·25

18 АВГУСТА
ДЕНЬ АВИАЦИИ СССР

1939. Nos. 811, 815/16 and 818 overprinted with two lines of type.

866*	10k. Glider	1·20	65
868*	40k. Yakovlev VT-2 seaplane	2·50	90
869*	50k. Balloon	3·25	1·10
870*	1r. Tupolev ANT-6	7·00	3·75

1941.

945*	20k. Lisunov Li-2	1·70	85
948*	60k. Airliners	1·70	85

1942.

987*	20k. Lavochkin LaGC-3 and Junkers Ju 88	60	35
988*	70	40
1048c*	30k. Lavochkin LaGC-3 and Junkers Ju 88	1·30	60
1048d*	30k. Polikarpov I-16 (blue)	1·30	60

1942.

1001*	20k. Bomber	1·90	1·00

1943.

1038	30k. Fighter aircraft	1·00	60
1039	60k. Fighter aircraft	1·00	65

АВИАПОЧТА
1944 г.
1 РУБЛЬ

1944. Nos. 1048c/d surcharged.

1049	1r. on 30k. Lavochkin LaGC-3 and Junkers Ju 88	2·20	65
1050	1r. on 30k. Polikarpov I-16	2·20	65

1944.

1076*	60k. Aerial battle	1·60	50

1945.

1108	60k. Bomber	3·00	1·00

1945.

1111*	1r. Heinkel He 111H in aerial battle over Moscow	1·50	90

1945. Aviation Day.

1123	1r. Petlyakov Pe-2 dive bombers (brown, vert)	3·50	1·20
1124	1r. Ilyushin Il-2M3 Shturmovic fighters (brown, horiz)	3·50	1·20
1125	1r. Lavochkin La-7 fighters and tail of Focke Wulf Fw 190 (red)	3·50	1·20
1126	1r. Ilyushin Il-4 DB-3 bombers (black)	3·50	1·20
1127	1r. Tupolev ANT-60 Tu-2 bombers (blue)	3·50	1·20
1128	1r. Polikarpov Po-2 biplane (green)	3·50	1·20
1129	1r. Petlyakov Pe-8 TB-7 bomber (grey)	3·50	1·20
1130	1r. Yakovlev Yak-3 fighter (right) and Messerschmitt Bf 109 (brown)	3·50	1·20
1131	1r. Yakovlev Yak-9 shooting down Henschel Hs 129B (red)	3·50	1·20
1123/1131 *Set of 9*		28·00	9·75

1945.

1150*	60k. Aircraft designers and aircraft	3·50	1·30

1946. Aviation Day. As Nos. 1123/31, but different face values.

1163	5k. Yakovlev Yak-3 fighter (right) and Messerschmitt Bf 109	60	40
1164	10k. Petlyakov Pe-2 dive bombers	60	40
1165	15k. Ilyushin Il-2M3 Shturmovic fighters (red)	65	45
1166	15k. Petlyakov Pe-8 TB-7 bomber (green)	65	45
1167	20k. Tupolev ANT-60 Tu-2 bombers	65	45
1168	30k. Ilyushin Il-4 DB-3 bombers (violet)	1·30	90
1169	30k. Polikarpov Po-2 biplane (brown)	1·30	90
1170	50k. Lavochkin La-7 fighters and tail of Focke Wulf Fw 190	2·10	1·50
1171	60k. Yakovlev Yak-9 shooting down Henschel Hs 129B	3·50	1·50
1163/1171 *Set of 9*		10·00	6·25

1946.

1220*	15k. Tupolev ANT-6	2·20	1·10

1947. Air Force Day.

1268	30k. Yakovlev Yak-9	95	35
1269	1r. Yakovlev Yak-9	2·40	85

1948.

1347*	30k. Petlyakov Pe-2 bomber	1·30	50

1948. Air Force Day. Nos. 1268/9 overprinted with three lines of type.

1386	30k. Yakovlev Yak-9	5·25	3·25
1387	1r. Yakovlev Yak-9	6·00	5·00

1948.

1423*	30k. Model aircraft	8·75	3·25

1948. Air Force Day.

1445a	1r. Yakovlev Yak-9 fighters	8·75	2·50

1949.

1523	40k. Airliner	2·20	40
1524	50k. Airliner	2·50	60

1949.

1541	50k. Ilyushin Il-12	2·20	1·10
1542	60k. Ilyushin Il-12	3·25	85
1543	1r. Ilyushin Il-12 (horiz)	4·25	1·90
1544	1r. Ilyushin Il-12, facing left (vert)	4·25	1·90
1545	1r. Ilyushin Il-12, facing right (vert)	4·25	1·90
1546	1r. Three Ilyushin Il-12 airliners and map	10·50	4·25
1547	2r. Ilyushin Il-12	13·00	7·25
1548	3r. Ilyushin Il-12	26·00	10·00
1541/1548 *Set of 8*		60·00	26·00

1951. Aviation Development.
1725   40k. Yakovlev Yak-18U trainers and badge
        showing glider.................................... 1·30   15
1726   60k. Model glider, glider in flight and
        badge showing glider......................... 2·40   50
1727   1r. Airplane, parachutists and badge
        showing glider.................................... 3·25   85
1728   2r. Yakovlev Yak-18U trainers .... 6·00   1·50
1725/1728 *Set of 4* .... 11·50   2·75

1955.
1881   1r. Ilyushin Il-12 .... 1·70   40
1882   2r. Ilyushin Il-12 .... 3·75   60

1955.
1893   2r. Ilyushin Il-12 (brown) .... 3·50   1·30
1894   2r. Ilyushin Il-12 (blue) .... 3·50   1·30

„Сев. полюс"
— Москва
1955 г.

1955. Nos. 1881/2 overprinted.
1921   1r. Ilyushin Il-12 .... 13·00   8·50
1922   2r. Ilyushin Il-12 .... 18·00   10·00

1955.
1924   40k. Mil Mi-4 helicopter.................... 3·25   35
1925   60k. Mil Mi-4 helicopter.................... 3·50   65
1926   1r. Mil Mi-4 helicopter...................... 5·25   1·00
1924/1926 *Set of 3* .... 11·00   1·80

1956.
1965   1r. Airplane...................................... 4·75   2·10

1956. 225th Anniv of First Balloon Flight by Kryakutni.
2034   40k. Kryakutni's balloon, 1731 .... 1·90   70

1958.
2202   40k. Airliner...................................... 2·40   35

1958.
2207*   25k. Model airplane 50   20

1958. Civil Aviation. Imperf or perf.
2224   20k. Ilyushin Il-14M CCCP 21120 of
        Aeroflot... 50   10
2225   40k. Tupolev Tu-104 of Aeroflot (green
        background)....................................... 80   15
2226   40k. Tupolev Tu-114 Rossiya of Aeroflot
        (blue background) 80   15
2227   60k. Tupolev Tu-104 (blue background)... 90   20
2228   60k. Tupolev Tu-110 of Aeroflot (red
        background)....................................... 90   20
2229   1r. Antonov An-10 Ukrainia of Aeroflot. 2·00   45
2230   2r. Ilyushin Il-18B of Aeroflot.................. 3·00   60
2224/2230 *Set of 7* .... 8·00   1·70

1958.
2241*   40k. Tupolev Tu-104.......................... 90   35
2244*   1r. Tupolev Tu-104 at airport .... 2·30   80
2245*   1r. Tupolev Tu-114 Rossiya CCCP 5611
        over ship and train .... 2·30   80

1959.
2373   40k. Ilyushin Il-14M .... 1·50   30

1959.
2380   40k. Tupolev Tu-104.......................... 60   15
2381   60k. Tupolev Tu-104.......................... 80   25

1959.
2389*   10k. Mil Mi-1 helicopter.................... 30   10

1960.
2419*   40k. Timur Frunze, Lavochkin LaGC-3
        and Junkers Ju-87B "Stuka" dive
        bombers .... 4·00   2·30

1960.
2421   60k. Mil Mi-4 helicopter.................... 1·30   25

1961.
2530   16k. Airliner...................................... 5·00   95

1961.
2602*   4k. Gliders.. 40   15

1961.
2617*   4k. Fighters 60   25

1961.
2625   4k. Tupolev Tu-104 and Mil Mi-4
        helicopter.. 80   25

1961. No. 2421 surcharged 1961 r. 6 kon.
2656   6k. on 60k. Mil Mi-4 helicopter.......... 30   15

1962.
2664*   4k. Yakovlev Yak-9T fighters.............. 95   35

1962.
2738   4k. Tupolev Tu-104............................ 40   15

1962.
2773*   4k. Airliner.. 95   45

1962.
2790   6k. Yakovlev Yak-9 fighters................ 80   25

1963.

2814*	10k. Ilyushin Il-62	95	45
2816*	16k. Tupolev Tu-124	1·50	80

1963. Aviation Celebrities.

2886	6k. Aleksandr Mozhaisky and his monoplane, 1884	60	15
2887	10k. Pyotr Nesterov and diagram (incorrect in detail) of his airplane making "loop the loop" manoeuvre, 1913	90	35
2888	16k. N.E. Zhukovsky and model airplane in wind tunnel	1·50	60
2886/2888 Set of 3		2·75	1·00

1963.

2896*	6k. Aircraft and helicopter	95	45

1963.

2898	4k. Ilyushin Il-62	40	15

1965.

3086*	4k. Air Force General I.S. Polbin and Ilyushin Il-2M3 Stormovik fighters shooting down German bomber	40	15

1965.

3172*	12k. Airplane	1·10	35

1965.

3195*	4k. Antonov An-2 biplane	50	15
3196*	6k. Airplane	70	20
3198*	16k. Helicopter, airliner and airport buildings	1·50	50

1965. Soviet Civil Aviation.

3233	6k. Tupolev Tu-134 of Aeroflot and airliner at airport	70	15
3234	10k. Antonov An-24 of Aeroflot and aircraft at airport	95	25
3235	12k. Mil Mi-10 helicopter of Aeroflot and helicopter at airport	1·20	35
3236	16k. Beriev Be-10 flying boat of Aeroflot and riverside air terminal	1·60	45
3237	20k. Antonov An-22 Anteus CCCP-46191 of Aeroflot and airliner at airport	1·90	50
3233/3237 Set of 5		5·75	1·50

1965. No. 3198 overprinted with three lines of type.

3265	16k. Helicopter, airliner and airport buildings	4·75	2·30

1966.

3338*	4k. Tupolev Tu-144	30	15

1966.

3351*	6k. Antonov An-10A Ukrainia	40	10
3357*	50k. Airliner (ultramarine, blue and grey)	2·40	60
3568*	50k. Airliner (blue)	6·00	1·40

1966.

3362	4k. Tupolev Tu-144	50	20

1966.

3366*	4k. Fighters	30	10

1967. 25th Anniv of French "Normandie-Nieman" Fighter Squadron.

3466	6k. Yakovlev Yak-9	40	15

1967.

3495*	6k. Airliner and light airplane	50	15

1967.

3506*	4k. Jet airliner	40	25

1968.

3572*	6k. Helicopter and airliner	45	25

1968.

3596*	4k. Airliner	25	10

1968.

3617*	10k. Mil Mi-2 helicopter	85	25

1969.

3735*	4k. Sergei Gritsevets, Polikarpov I-16 and airplane being shot down	30	10

1969. 30 Years of MiG Aircraft.

3761	6k. Mikoyan Gurevich MiG-3 (top) and Mikoyan Gurevich MiG-23	80	25

1969. Development of Soviet Civil Aircraft.

3763	2k. Tupolev ANT-2	20	10
3764	3k. Polikarpov Po-2	25	10
3765	4k. Tupolev ANT-9	25	10
3766	6k. TsAGI 1-EA helicopter	30	20
3767	10k. Tupolev ANT-20 Maksim Gorky	60	25
3768	12k. Tupolev Tu-104 of Aeroflot	70	35
3769	16k. Mil Mi-10 helicopter	90	45
3770	20k. Ilyushin Il-62 of Aeroflot	1·10	55
3763/3770 Set of 8		4·00	1·90
MS3771 50k. Tupolev Tu-144		4·00	2·00

1969.

3772*	3k. Model gliders	20	10

1969.

3796*	10k. Silhouettes of aircraft being refueled in flight	50	25

1970.
3865* 4k. Mil Mi-3 helicopter...................................... 30 10

1971.
3944 6k. Airliner.. 80 30
3945 10k. Tupolev Tu-104................................. 1·10 45

1971.
3960 4k. Airplane... 30 10

1971.
3977* 4k. Mil Mi-8 helicopter.................................. 30 15

1972.
4079 6k. Roald Amundsen and airship N.1
Norge... 1·50 90

1972.
4087* 6k. Jet fighters 30 15

1972.
4103 4k. Tupolev Tu-144.. 30 10

1973. 50th Anniv of Soviet Civil Aviation.
4137 6k. Tupolev Tu-154 of Aeroflot (in
foreground), Tupolev Tu-144 (left), Mil
Mi-8 helicopter, Mil Mi-4 helicopter
(lower left) and Tupolev ANT-2 biplane 60 25

1974.
4305* 6k. Kamov Ka-25 helicopter and
helicopter carrier.............................. 50 25

1974.
MS4332 30k. Ilyushin Il-62M (sheet contains 2 other
designs) .... 14·00 9·00

1974. Early Russian Aircraft (1st series).
4357 6k. Mozhaisky's monoplane, 1884 .... 40 25
4358 6k. Grizodubov No. 2 biplane, 1910
(blue border) 40 25
4359 6k. Sikorsky *Russia A*, 1910 (mauve
border).. 40 25
4360 6k. Sikorsky *Russky Vityaz*, 1913 .... 40 25
4361 6k. Grigorovich M-5 flying boat, 1914 .... 40 25
4357/4361 *Set of 5*... 1·80 1·10

1975. 150th Birth Anniv of Aleksandr Mozhaisky (aircraft designer).
4375 6k. Aleksandr Mozhaisky and his
monoplane, 1884, and Tupolev
Tu-144 jet airliner.................................. 40 15

1975.
4376 6k. Tupolev Tu-144............................... 30 10

1976.
4537 6k. Tupolev Tu-154............................... 45 10

1976.
4559* 4k. Ilyushin Il-62M 20 10

1976. Early Russian Aircraft (2nd series).
4580 3k. Gakkel VII biplane, 1911 .... 10 10
4581 6k. Gakkel IX monoplane, 1912 .... 20 15
4582 12k. Steglau No. 2, 1912 .... 40 20
4583 14k. Dybovsky Dolphin, 1913................. 55 25
4584 16k. Sikorsky Ilya Muromets, 1914 .... 60 35
4580/4584 *Set of 5*... 1·70 95

1977. Early Russian Aircraft (3rd series).
4661 4k. Porokhovshchikov P-IV bis biplane
trainer, 1917....................................... 20 10
4662 6k. Kalinin AK-1, 1924............................ 25 15
4663 10k. Tupolev ANT-3 R-3, 1925................. 30 25
4664 12k. Tupolev ANT-4 TB-1 bomber, 1925 ... 40 35
4665 16k. Polikarpov R-5 biplane, 1929........... 50 45
4666 20k. Shavrov Sh-2 flying boat, 1930......... 70 55
4661/4666 *Set of 6*... 2·10 1·70

1976.
4673* 6k. Tupolev Tu-154............................... 30 10
4680* 32k. Ilyushin Il-76................................. 1·60 50

1977.
4716* 4k. Mil Mi-4 helicopter and Tupolev
Tu-154.. 20 10

1978. Early Russian Aircraft (4th series).
4791 4k. Polikarpov Po-2 biplane, 1928........... 15 10
4792 6k. Kalinin K-5, 1929 .... 25 20
4793 10k. Tupolev ANT-6 TB-3, 1930 .... 45 25
4794 12k. Putilov Stal-2, 1931......................... 55 35
4795 16k. Beriev Be-2 MBR-2 reconnaissance
seaplane, 1932................................... 70 45
4796 20k. Polikarpov I-16, 1934...................... 95 55
4791/4796 *Set of 6*... 2·75 1·70

1978.
4806 6k. Ilyushin Il-62................................... 30 20

1979. Soviet Aircraft.
4883 2k. Antonov An-28 of Aeroflot............... 10 10
4884 3k. Yakovlev Yak-42 of Aeroflot 20 15
4885 10k. Tupolev Tu-154 of Aeroflot 50 25
4886 15k. Ilyushin Il-76 of Aeroflot................. 75 30
4887 32k. Ilyushin Il-86 of Aeroflot................. 1·40 65
4883/4887 *Set of 5*... 2·75 1·30

1980. Helicopters.
4998	1k. Yakovlev Yak-24 helicopter of Aeroflot, 1953	10	10
4999	2k. Mil Mi-8 helicopter of Aeroflot, 1962	10	10
5000	3k. Kamov Ka-26 helicopter of Aeroflot, 1965	20	10
5001	6k. Mil Mi-6 helicopter of Aeroflot, 1957	30	20
5002	15k. Mil Mi-10K helicopter of Aeroflot, 1965	80	55
5003	32k. Mil Mi-V12 helicopter of Aeroflot, 1969	1·90	1·10
4998/5003	Set of 6	3·00	1·90

1980.
5061*	5k. Tupolev Tu-154	20	10
5067*	2r. Kamov Ka-25 helicopter	75	55

1981.
5084*	6k. Jet airliner	50	30
5085*	15k. Mil Mi-4 helicopter	1·50	65

1981.
5149*	4k. Helicopter	20	10
5151*	4k. Airliner	20	10

1982. Gliders (1st series).
5256	4k. Mastyazhart glider, 1923	20	10
5257	6k. Red Star glider, 1930	25	20
5258	10k. TsAGI-2 glider, 1934	50	40
5259	20k. Stakhonovets glider, 1939	1·00	55
5260	32k. Paratroops boarding GR-29 glider, 1941	1·50	95
5256/5260	Set of 5	3·00	2·00

1982.
5280*	10k. Ilyushin Il-86 of Aeroflot	35	25

1983. 60th Anniv of Aeroflot (state airline).
MS5300	50k. Ilyushin Il-86 of Aeroflot	2·00	1·10

1983. Gliders (2nd series).
5301	2k. A-9 gliders, 1948	10	10
5302	4k. KAI-12 glider, 1957	20	15
5303	6k. A-15 glider, 1960	30	20
5304	20k. SA-7 glider, 1970	90	75
5305	45k. LAK-12 glider, 1979	1·90	1·30
5301/5305	Set of 5	3·00	2·20

1983.
5325	4k. Antonov An-24	25	10

1983. 50th Anniv of Stratosphere Balloon's Record Altitude Flight.
5346	20k. Stratosphere balloon *U.S.S.R.-1*, 1933	1·00	65

1984.
5431*	45k. Tupolev ANT-4 and Polikarpov R-5 biplane	1·80	95

1984.
5493	5k. Kamov Ka-26 helicopter	25	10

1984. 60th Anniv of M.V. Frunze Central House of Aviation and Cosmonautics, Moscow.
5500	5k. Ilyushin Il-86	20	10

1985.
5548*	5k. Ilyushin Il-2M3 Shturmovic fighters	25	20
5549*	5k. Ilyushin Il-2M3 Shturmovic fighters under construction	25	20

1985.
5612*	45k. Ilyushin Il-62M	1·60	75

1986.
5693*	5k. Mil Mi-4 helicopter	25	10

1986. Sports Aircraft designed by Aleksandr Yakovlev.
5707	4k. Yakovlev Ya-1, 1927	20	10
5708	5k. Yakovlev UT-2 trainer, 1935	20	10
5709	10k. Yakovlev Yak-18, 1946	40	25
5710	20k. Yakovlev Yak-50, 1972	80	45
5711	30k. Yakovlev Yak-55, 1981	1·30	75
5707/5711	Set of 5	2·50	1·50

1988.
6077*	7k. Ilyushin Il-86 and Mil Mi-2 helicopter	30	15

1991. Airships.
6270	1k. Airship *Albatros*, 1910	10	10
6271	3k. Airship GA-42, 1987	15	10
6272	4k. Airship N.1 *Norge*	15	10
6273	5k. Airship *Pobeda*, 1944	20	10
6274	20k. Airship LZ-127 *Graf Zeppelin*, 1928	55	30
6270/6274	Set of 5	1·00	65

1994.
6479*	100r. Ilyushin Il-2 Shturmovics	20	15

1995.
6523*	250r. Petlyakov Pe-2	30	25

1996.
6618*   1000r. *Admiral Kuznetsov* aircraft carrier....... 50   30
MS6619* 1000r. *Admiral Kuznetsov* aircraft carrier
(other stamps in the miniature sheet do not show
aircraft) .... 2·00   1·40

1997. Helicopters.
6676   500r. Mil Mi-14 (amphibian) 25   15
6677   1000r. Mil Mi-24 (gunship) 40   20
6678   1500r. Mil Mi-26 (transport) 60   30
6679   2000r. Mil Mi-28 (gunship) 80   45
6680   2500r. Mil Mi-34 (patrol) .... 1·20   55
6676/6680 *Set of 5* .... 3·00   1·40

1998.
6792*   1r. Sukhoi Su-27 'Flanker' Ilyushin
Il-96-400 and Wright *Flyer I* 40   20

2000.
6891*   2r. P.A. Gordienko (polar explorer) and
airplane 40   20

2000.
6970*   3r. Sukhoi Su-25, Tupolev Tu-124 and
Farman M.F.7 (?) 40   20

2002. Birth Centenary of Nikolai Kamov (helicopter designer and
manufacturer).
7107   1r. Kamov KA-10 10   10
7108   1r.50 Kamov KA-22 20   15
7109   2r. Kamov KA-26 30   20
7110   2r.50 Kamov KA-27 (naval helicopter) 35   25
7111   5r. Kamov KA-50 Black Shark (army
helicopter) 55   35
7107/7111 *Set of 5* .... 1·40   95

2003.
7191   5r. Airplane... 70   40

2003.
7224   4r. Airship *Count Zeppelin* (?) 50   25

2004. Birth Centenary of Valery Chkalov (test pilot).
7235   3r. Tupolev ANT-25.................................... 50   30

2004. Birth Centenary of Vladimir Kokkinaki (test pilot).
7276   3r. Ilyushin Il-18 (top) Ilyushin DB-3
(mid) and Ilyushin Il-2 Shturmovik
(lower), with Vladimir Kokkinaki 40   30

2005. Birth Centenary of Artem Ivanovich Mikoyan (aircraft
designer).
7363   5r. Mikoyan Gureyvich MiG-3.................... 90   45
7364   5r. Mikoyan Gureyvich MiG-15 90   45
7365   5r. Mikoyan Gureyvich MiG-21 90   45
7366   5r. Mikoyan Gureyvich MiG-25 90   45
7367   5r. Mikoyan MiG-29................................ 90   45
7363/7367 *Set of 5*.. 4·00   2·00

2006. Birth Centenary of Oleg Konstantinovich Antonov (aircraft
designer).
7378   5r.60 Antonov An-12.. 70   45
7379   5r.60 Antonov An-24.. 70   45
7380   5r.60 Antonov An-124...................................... 70   45
7381   5r.60 Antonov An-74.. 70   45
7382   5r.60 Antonov An-3T.. 70   45
7378/7382 *Set of 5*.. 3·25   2·00

2006.
7388*   7r. Ilyushin Il-76 90   55

2006. Birth Centenary of Alexandr Sergevich Yakovlev (aircraft
designer).
7403   5r. AIR 1 70   45
7404   5r. Yakovlev Yak-54 70   45
7405   5r. Yakovlev Yak-141 70   45
7406   5r. Yakovlev Yak-42 'Clobber' 70   45
7407   5r. Yakovlev Yak-130 70   45
7403/7407 *Set of 5*.. 3·25   2·00

RWANDA

Central Africa

100 centimes = 1 franc

1966.
168   20c. Boeing B-52 Stratofortress bombers   10   10
169   30c. Boeing B-52 Stratofortress bombers   10   10
170   50c. Boeing B-52 Stratofortress bombers   10   10
171   6f. Boeing B-52 Stratofortress bombers   10   10
172   15f. Boeing B-52 Stratofortress bombers   65   30
173   18f. Boeing B-52 Stratofortress bombers   65   40
168/173 *Set of 6*.. 1·50   1·00

1970.
390*   80f. Sikorsky S-61B Sea King helicopter...   10   10

1972.
445*   15f. Sud Aviation SE 3160 Alouette III
helicopter 40   20

1975.
704*   20c. Douglas DC-8F Jet Trader   10   10

1977.
783*   54f. Sikorsky S-61B Sea King helicopter...   2·25   1·25

1977. No. 783 overprinted **in memoriam WERNHER VON BRAUN
1912–1977.**
848*   54f. Sikorsky S-61B Sea King helicopter...   2·50   1·50

1978. Aviation History.
889   20c. Orville and Wilbur Wright and Wright
Flyer I, 1903...   10   10
890   30c. Alberto Santos-Dumont and his
biplane *14 bis*, 1906.............................   10   10
891   50c. Henri Farman and Farman Voisin
No. 1 bis, 1908.......................................   10   10
892   1f. Jan Olieslagers and Bleriot XI.............   10   10
893   3f. General Italo Balbo and Savoia S-17
flying boat, 1919....................................   10   10
894   10f. Lindbergh and Ryan NYP Special
Spirit of St. Louis, 1927..........................   15   10
895   55f. Hugo Junkers and Junkers Ju 52/3m
OO-AGV, 1932...   1·10   55
896   60f. Igor Sikorsky and Vought-Sikorsky
VS-300 helicopter prototype.............   1·60   85
889/896 *Set of 8*.. 3·00   1·80
MS897 130f. Concorde .... 3·00   3·00

1981.
1059*   2f. Airliner..   10   10
1063*   70f. Helicopter.......................................   1·90   70

1984.
1191*   50f. Sud Aviation SE210 Caravelle.............   1·10   45

1984. Bicentenary of Manned Flight.
1194	20c.	Montgolfier balloon *Le Martial* and unmanned balloon.................................	10	10
1195	30c.	Montgolfier balloon (first manned free flight, 1783).......................................	10	10
1196	50c.	Charles' hydrogen balloon, 1783, and Jean-Pierre Blanchard's balloon with oars, 1784	10	10
1197	9f.	Jean-Pierre and Madame Blanchard and balloon with oars, 1784	20	10
1198	10f.	Blanchard and Jeffries' balloon, 1785..	20	10
1199	50f.	Demuyter's balloon *Belgica*, 1937, and Piccard's stratosphere balloon *F.N.R.S.*, 1931....................................	1·10	10
1200	80f.	Hot-air balloons	2·75	40
1201	200f.	Balloon *Double Eagle II*, 1978, and early hydrogen balloon.........................	3·50	1·90
1194/1201		*Set of 8*...	7·25	2·50

1986.
1257*   80f. Kigali Airport..   1·75   1·25

RYUKYU ISLANDS

Northern Pacific
100 cents = 1 dollar

1963.
147	5½c. Convair 880..	35	25
148	7c. Convair 880...	45	35

SAAR

Western Europe
100 centimes = 1 franc

1928.
126   50c. Breguet Bre.14 biplane .... 4·50 3·50
127   1f. Breguet Bre.14 biplane .... 7·00 4·50

1932.
157   60c. Focke Wulf A-17 Mowe over
       Saarbrucken Airport .... 7·00 5·25
158   5f. Focke Wulf A-17 Mowe over
       Saarbrucken Airport .... 48·00 £110

1934. Nos. 126/7 and 157/8 overprinted **VOLKSABSTIMMUNG 1935.**
192*   50c. Breguet Bre.14 biplane .... 4·50 8·00
193*   60c. Focke Wulf A-17 Mowe over
       Saarbrucken Airport .... 3·50 3·00
194*   1f. Breguet Bre.14 biplane .... 6·25 10·50
195*   5f. Focke Wulf A-17 Mowe over
       Saarbrucken Airport .... 7·00 16·00

ST. HELENA

South Atlantic
1949. 12 pence = 1 shilling
20 shillings = 1 pound
1971. 100 pence = 1 pound

1949. As Nos. 114/15 of Antigua.
145*   3d. Airplane .... 25 1·00
146*   4d. Jet-powered Vickers Viking .... 3·00 1·60

1993.
651*   25p. Model airplane .... 1·25 1·50

1995.
693*   12p. Gloster Gladiator .... 1·50 1·60

1996.
721*   12p. Westland Whirlwind (helicopter) ... 65 45
723*   53p. Loading Lockheed L-1011 TriStar,
       Wideawake Airfield, Ascension
       Island .... 1·50 2·00

1999.
793*   80p. Queen Mother with BAe (Hawker
       Siddeley) Hawk Mk 1s of Red Arrows ... 2·50 3·50

2002.
861*   15p. Aircraft carrier and Sea Harrier .. 70 70

2003. Centenary of Powered Flight.
905   10p. Westland WG-13 Lynx 70 60
906   15p. Douglas C-124 Globemaster II 75 60
907   20p. BAe Nimrod AEW Mk 3 .... 80 60
908   25p. Lockheed C-130 Hercules 90 70
909   30p. Lockheed L-1011 TriStar .... 1·10 1·10
910   50p. Wright *Flyer* .... 1·75 2·00
905/910 Set of 6 .... 5·50 5·00
MS911 £1.80 Supermarine *Walrus* .... 5·00 5·50

2005.
955*   30p. Hawker Hurricane .... 1·00 1·10

2006.
974*   25p. USA 24c stamp of 1918 showing
       inverted Curtiss JN-4 'Jenny' .... 1·10 85

2008. 90th Anniv of Royal Air Force.
1047   15p. Airco (de Havilland) D.H.9 .... 50 50
1048   25p. Hawker Hurricane 90 90
1049   35p. Handley Page Hastings .... 1·00 1·00
1050   40p. English Electric Lightning ...... 1·40 1·40
1051   50p. Hawker Siddeley (BAe) Harrier GR7 .. 1·60 1·60
1047/1051 Set of 5 .... 5·00 5·00
MS1052 £1.50 Berlin Airlift (will show aircraft) .. 5·00 5·00

ST. KITTS

West Indies
100 cents = 1 dollar

1980. No. 403 of St. Kitts-Nevis overprinted **St. Kitts.**
38*   55c. Jet airliner on runway at Golden
       Rock 15 15

1983. Bicentenary of Manned Flight.
129   10c. Montgolfier balloon (first manned
       free flight, 1783) 10 10
130   45c. Sikorsky *Russky Vityaz* biplane .. 15 10
131   50c. Lockheed L-1011 TriStar 500 9Y-TGJ
       Flamingo of B.W.I.A. 15 15
132    $2.50 Bell X-1 .... 1·00 90
129/132 Set of 4 .... 1·30 1·10

1987. Aircraft Visiting St. Kitts.
237   40c. Lockheed L-1011 TriStar 500 of
       B.W.I.A 75 30
238   60c. Hawker Siddeley Super 748 of L.I.A.T .. 95 60
239    $1.20 de Havilland Canada DHC-6 Twin
       Otter 300 PJ-WIF of Windward
       Islands Airways .... 1·50 2·75
240    $3 Avions de Transport Régional ATR 42
       of American Eagle .... 2·75 4·75
237/240 Set of 4 .... 5·25 7·50

1990. 50th Anniv of Battle of Britain.
MS311 $3 Supermarine Spitfire Mk Vb *St. Kitts Nevis I* of 71 Squadron, R.A.F.; $3 Supermarine Spitfire Mk Vb *St. Kitts Nevis II* of 345 Squadron, R.A.F. .... 14·00 14·00

1993. 75th Anniv of Royal Air Force.
369   25c. Short Singapore III flying boat of the
       R.A.F., 1934 .... 85 20
370   50c. Bristol Type 152 Beaufort Mk II of the
       R.A.F., 1938 .... 1·40 30
371   80c. Westland Whirlwind Series 3 H.A.R.10
       helicopter of the R.A.F., 1960 .... 3·00 1·50
372    $1.60 English Electric Canberra T.11 of the
       R.A.F .... 3·00 3·50
369/372 Set of 4 .... 7·50 5·00
MS373 $2 Handley Page 0/400 of the R.A.F., 1917; $2 Fairey Long Range monoplane of the R.A.F.; $2 Vickers Wellesley of the R.A.F., 1935; $2 SEPECAT Jaguar G.R.1 of the R.A.F., 1972 .... 11·00 11·00

1993.
384*   20c. Hawker Siddeley HS748 .... 1·00 15

1995.
436*   50c. Grumman TBF Avenger 35 35
437* $2 Supermarine Spitfire Mk Vb .... 1·25 1·50

2001.
648* $1.40 Gloster Gamecock (?) .... 2·00 2·00

201

2002. 75th Anniv of First Solo Trans-Atlantic Flight.
MS720 $1.50 Charles Lindbergh; $1.50 Lindbergh holding propeller of Ryan NYP Special *Spirit of St. Louis*; $1.50 Charles Lindbergh; $1.50 Charles Lindbergh and Ryan NYP Special *Spirit of St. Louis*; $1.50 Lindbergh wearing flying helmet; $1.50 Charles Lindbergh .... 6·75 7·00

2003. Centenary of Powered Flight.
MS738 $2 Voisin LA-5; $2 Gotha G.V; $2 Polikarpov I-16; $2 Bell YFM-1 Airacuda .... 5·50 6·50
MS739 $5 Bristol Type 142 Blenheim Mk I *Price for 2 sheets* .... 3·50 3·75

2005.
809* $2 Lockheed PBO-1 Hudson .... 1·75 1·75

2007. Concorde.
930 $1.60 Concorde in flight 90 90
931 $1.60 Concorde in flight (side view) 90 90
932 $1.60 Concorde over Singapore (panel yellow-olive at left, bright yellow-green at right) 90 90
933 $1.60 Concorde at Melbourne Airport, Australia ('Austria' in panel) 90 90
934 $1.60 As No. 932 .... 90 90
935 $1.60 As No. 933 ('Spain' at left of panel) 90 90
936 $1.60 As No. 932 (bright yellow-green (Italy) in centre of panel) 90 90
937 $1.60 As No. 933 (bright yellow-green at left and yellow-olive (Black Sea) at right of panel) 90 90
930/937 Set of 8 .... 6·50 6·50

OFFICIAL STAMPS
1980. No. 38 additionally overprinted **OFFICIAL**.
O7* 55c. Jet airliner on runway at Golden Rock 15 15

ST. KITTS-NEVIS

West Indies
1949. 12 pence = 1 shilling
20 shillings = 1 pound
1951. 100 cents = 1 dollar

1949. As Nos. 114/15 of Antigua.
82* 2½d. Airplane 15 30
83* 3d. Jet-powered Vickers Viking .... 2·10 2·50

1968.
188 25c. Handley Page H.P.R.7 Dart Herald VP-BCG of Bahamas Airways 40 10
189 50c. Handley Page H.P.R.7 Dart Herald VP-BCG of Bahamas Airways 40 20

1978.
403* 55c. Jet airliner on runway at Golden Rock .... 1·25 10

OFFICIAL STAMPS
1980. No. 403 overprinted **OFFICIAL**.
O6* 55c. Jet airliner on runway at Golden Rock .... 1·25 50

ST. LUCIA

West Indies
100 cents = 1 dollar

1949. As Nos. 114/15 of Antigua.
160* 5c. Airplane 15 70
161* 6c. Jet-powered Vickers Viking .... 1·60 2·25

1970.
281* 10c. Hawker Siddeley H.S.748 at Vigie Airport .... 2·00 10

1971. Opening of Beane Field Airport.
309 5c. de Havilland DH.104 Dove 50 15
310 25c. Boeing 727-200 at Beane Field Airport 50 15

1973.
358* 15c. Rockwell Thrush Commander spraying banana plantation 15 10

1979. 50th Anniv of Lindbergh's Inaugural Airmail Flight via St. Lucia.
500* 10c. Charles Lindbergh and Sikorsky S-38A flying boat NC 9776 .... 50 10
501* 30c. Sikorsky S-38A flying boat and route map 60 10
502* 50c. Sikorsky S-38A flying boat 60 10

1980.
537* 5c. Hawker Siddeley H.S.748 VP-LAZ of L.I.A.T. at airport 30 30
538* 10c. Douglas DC-10-30 of Wardair 65 30
541* 25c. Britten-Norman BN-2 Islander VP-LAE of L.I.A.T. 65 30
543* 50c. Boeing 727-200 of Eastern Airlines .... 1·00 60
545* $1 Lockheed L-1011 TriStar 500 of B.W.I.A. .... 85 1·40
547* $5 Boeing 707-420 of British Airways .... 5·00 6·00

1980. No. 543 surcharged **1980 $1.50 HURRICANE RELIEF**.
566* $1.50 on 50c. Boeing 727-200 of Eastern Airlines 30 40

1983.
642* 50c. Boeing 747-200 and Britten-Norman BN-2 Islander 40 15

1985. Military Aircraft.
812 5c. Messerschmitt Bf 109E of the Luftwaffe 10 15

813 5c. Technical drawings of Messerschmitt Bf 109E 10 15
814 55c. Avro Type 683 Lancaster Mk I of the R.A.F. 25 40
815 55c. Technical drawings of Avro Type 683 Lancaster Mk I 25 40
816 60c. North American P-51D Mustang of the U.S.A.A.F. 25 40
817 60c. Technical drawings of North American P-51D Mustang 25 40
818 $2 Supermarine Spitfire Mk II of the R.A.F. 40 75
819 $2 Technical drawings of Supermarine Spitfire Mk II 40 75
812/819 Set of 8 .... 1·80 3·00

1987.
949* $1 Concorde .... 2·75 1·50
950* $5 Flying boat .... 3·00 5·50

1995.
1116* $1.10 Supermarine Spitfire Mk V *St. Lucia* .... 1·75 2·00

1995.
1118* 10c. Sud Aviation SE 330 Puma 15 10
1120* $1.35 Transall C-160 .... 95 1·40
1121* $5 Douglas DC-3 .... 3·75 6·00

1999.
1217* 65c. Sikorsky S.38 .... 90 45
1219* $3 Douglas DC-10 .... 2·25 3·25

2003. Centenary of Powered Flight.
1290 20c. Sikorsky S-38 .... 45 20
1291 70c. Consolidated PBY-5A Catalina 75 45
1292 $1 Lockheed 18 Lodestar .... 1·10 75
1293 $3 Supermarine Spitfire Mk V *St. Lucia* .... 4·25 5·00
1290/1293 Set of 4 .... 6·00 6·00

2004.
1299* 95c. Aircraft .... 1·00 55

2006. 50th Anniv of LIAT (Leeward Islands Air Transport) Airline.
1352 30c. BAe Hawker Siddeley Super 748 of LIAT in flight 40 20
1353 75c. Bombardier de Havilland Canada DHC-8 Dash 8 of LIAT on ground 85 90

OFFICIAL STAMPS
1983. Nos. 537/8, 541, 543, 545 and 547 overprinted **OFFICIAL**.
O1* 5c. Hawker Siddeley H.S.748 VP-LAZ of L.I.A.T. at airport 20 20
O2* 10c. Douglas DC-10-30 of Wardair 30 20
O5* 25c. Britten Norman Islander VP-LAE of L.I.A.T. 60 30
O7* 50c. Boeing 727-200 of Eastern Airlines 90 40
O9* $1 Lockheed L-1011 TriStar 500 of B.W.I.A. .... 1·50 85
O11* $5 Boeing 707-420 of British Airways .... 3·50 3·75

ST. PIERRE ET MIQUELON

North Atlantic

100 centimes = 1 franc

1942. As Nos. 207/13 of Cameroun.
336	1f. Fairey FC-1 airliner	65	4·00
337	1f.50 Fairey FC-1 airliner	1·10	2·50
338	5f. Fairey FC-1 airliner	75	2·75
339	10f. Fairey FC1 airliner	1·30	3·00
340	25f. Fairey FC-1 airliner	1·40	5·25
341	50f. Fairey FC-1 airliner	95	5·50
342	100f. Fairey FC-1 airliner	1·20	6·75
336/342	Set of 7	6·50	27·00

1947.
382*	50f. Airplane	5·00	8·50
383*	100f. Douglas DC-4	8·75	15·00
384*	200f. Airplane	9·50	19·00

1949. As No. 254 of Cameroun.
395	25f. Lockheed Constellation	3·50	20·00

1954. As No. 264 of Cameroun.
398	15f. Bomber	5·25	3·75

1955.
410*	50f. Boeing 707	26·00	44·00
411*	100f. Sud Aviation SE 210 Caravelle	9·75	22·00
412*	200f. Douglas DC-3	50·00	50·00

1964. First St. Pierre-New York Airmail Flight.
435	100f. Potez 842	5·50	16·00

1967. Opening of St. Pierre Airport.
445	30f. Runway and control tower at Saint Pierre Airport and airliners on map of air routes	3·25	5·25

1969. First Flight of Concorde. As No. 83 of Comoro Islands.
456	34f. Concorde of Air France	22·00	30·00

1973.
523	10f. Transall C-160	60·00	55·00

1976. Concorde's First Commercial Flight.
543	10f. Concorde of Air France	23·00	24·00

1987.
592	5f. Hawker Siddeley H.S.748 F-OSPM of Air Saint-Pierre	3·25	3·75
593	10f. Latecoere 522 flying boat F-ARAF *Ville de Saint-Pierre*	5·50	5·25

1988.
601	5f. Airship LZ-129 *Hindenburg*	3·00	3·75
602	10f. Douglas DC-3 of Air Saint-Pierre over control tower	5·50	5·25

1989.
614	20f. Piper PA-23 Aztec over airport	7·00	6·25

1990.
646	5f. Mignet HM14 Pou du Ciel	1·40	3·50

1991.
667	10f. Piper PA-38-112 Tomahawk F-OCEY	3·75	4·25

1992.
681	20f. Model airplane and remote control handset	4·75	6·00

1997. 70th Anniv of Disappearance of Charles Nungesser and Francois Coli (aviators) on attempted Non-stop Flight between Paris and New York (9 May, 1927).
759	14f. Levasseur PL-8 *L'Oiseau Blanc*	3·25	3·50

2000.
851*	2f. Runway extension, Pointe Blanche Airport, 1999	1·70	1·60

2001. St. Pierre Pointe Blanche Airport.
869	5f. Aircraft taking off from Pointe Blanche Airport	1·30	90

ST. THOMAS AND PRINCE ISLANDS

In Atlantic off West Africa

1938. 100 centavos = 1 escudo

1977. 100 centimos = 1 dobra

1938. As Nos. 401/9 of Angola, but inscribed "S. TOME".
362	10c. Airplane	£100	70·00
363	20c. Airplane	48·00	34·00
364	50c. Airplane	2·30	2·20
365	1e. Airplane	7·50	5·25
366	2e. Airplane	6·00	4·00
367	3e. Airplane	7·50	5·50
368	5e. Airplane	12·50	10·00
369	9e. Airplane	13·50	10·00
370	10e. Airplane	13·50	10·00
362/370	Set of 9	£190	£130

1939. As Nos. 401/9 of Angola, but inscribed "S. TOME e PRINCIPE".
392	10c. Airplane	45	35
393	20c. Airplane	45	35
394	50c. Airplane	45	35
395	1e. Airplane	45	35
396	2e. Airplane	1·00	60
397	3e. Airplane	1·40	85
398	5e. Airplane	4·00	2·20
399	7e. Airplane	7·75	4·25
400	10e. Airplane	8·00	5·50
392/400	Set of 9	22·00	13·50

1954.
427	15c. Airliner and map of presidential tour	10	10
428	5e. Airliner and map of presidential tour	1·10	75

1963. As No. 611 of Angola.
441	1e.50 Boeing 707 and Lockheed L.1049G Super Constellation of T.A.P.	65	30

1972.
469	2e.50 Fairey IIID seaplane *Lusitania*	35	20

APPENDIX

The following stamps have either been issued in excess of postal needs or have not been made available to the public in reasonable quantities at face value. Miniature sheets, imperforate stamps, etc are excluded from this section.

1977

60th Anniversary of Russian Revolution. 30d. (Tupolev Tu-144).

1978

Centenary of U.P.U. 15d. (Concorde and balloon); 15d. (Zeppelin airship).

1979

History of Aviation. 50c., 1d., 5d., 7d., 8d.

1980

Balloons. 50c., 1d., 3d., 7d., 8d., 25d.
Airships. 50c., 1d., 3d., 7d., 8d., 17d.

ST. VINCENT

West Indies

100 cents = 1 dollar

1949. As Nos. 114/15 of Antigua.
178*	5c. Airplane	20	20
179*	6c. Jet-powered Vickers Viking	1·50	2·25

1965.
233*	3c. Terminal building at Arnos Vale Airport	60	10

203

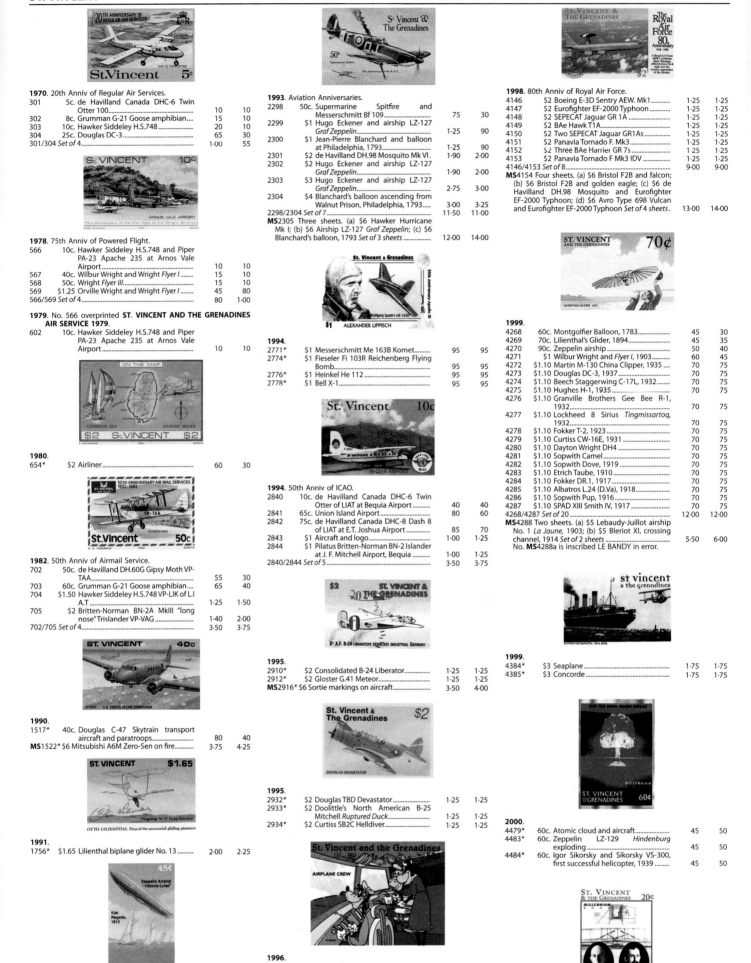

1970. 20th Anniv of Regular Air Services.

301	5c. de Havilland Canada DHC-6 Twin Otter 100	10	10
302	8c. Grumman G-21 Goose amphibian....	15	10
303	10c. Hawker Siddeley H.S.748	20	10
304	25c. Douglas DC-3	65	30
301/304	Set of 4	1·00	55

1978. 75th Anniv of Powered Flight.

566	10c. Hawker Siddeley H.S.748 and Piper PA-23 Apache 235 at Arnos Vale Airport	10	10
567	40c. Wilbur Wright and Wright *Flyer I*	15	10
568	50c. Wright *Flyer III*	15	10
569	$1.25 Orville Wright and Wright *Flyer I*	45	80
566/569	Set of 4	80	1·00

1979. No. 566 overprinted **ST. VINCENT AND THE GRENADINES AIR SERVICE 1979**.

602	10c. Hawker Siddeley H.S.748 and Piper PA-23 Apache 235 at Arnos Vale Airport	10	10

1980.

654*	$2 Airliner	60	30

1982. 50th Anniv of Airmail Service.

702	50c. de Havilland DH.60G Gipsy Moth VP-TAA	55	30
703	60c. Grumman G-21 Goose amphibian....	65	40
704	$1.50 Hawker Siddeley H.S.748 VP-LIK of L.I A.T	1·25	1·50
705	$2 Britten-Norman BN-2A MkIII "long nose" Trislander VP-VAG	1·40	2·00
702/705	Set of 4	3·50	3·75

1990.

1517*	40c. Douglas C-47 Skytrain transport aircraft and paratroops	80	40
MS1522*	$6 Mitsubishi A6M Zero-Sen on fire	3·75	4·25

1991.

1756*	$1.65 Lilienthal biplane glider No. 13	2·00	2·25

1992.

2158*	45c. Airship LZ-11 *Viktoria Luise*	1·25	35
2170*	$6 Airship LZ-1	5·00	5·50
MS2171*	Five sheets. (a) $6 Cabin of airship LZ-127 *Graf Zeppelin*; (b) $6 Douglas DC-6 on Berlin Airlift (other sheets do not show aircraft) *Price for 5 sheets*	20·00	23·00

1993. Aviation Anniversaries.

2298	50c. Supermarine Spitfire and Messerschmitt Bf 109	75	30
2299	$1 Hugo Eckener and airship LZ-127 *Graf Zeppelin*	1·25	90
2300	$1 Jean-Pierre Blanchard and balloon at Philadelphia, 1793	1·25	90
2301	$2 de Havilland DH.98 Mosquito Mk VI.	1·90	2·00
2302	$2 Hugo Eckener and airship LZ-127 *Graf Zeppelin*	1·90	2·00
2303	$3 Hugo Eckener and airship LZ-127 *Graf Zeppelin*	2·75	3·00
2304	$4 Blanchard's balloon ascending from Walnut Prison, Philadelphia, 1793	3·00	3·25
2298/2304	Set of 7	11·50	11·00
MS2305	Three sheets. (a) $6 Hawker Hurricane Mk I; (b) $6 Airship LZ-127 *Graf Zeppelin*; (c) $6 Blanchard's balloon, 1793 *Set of 3 sheets*	12·00	14·00

1994.

2771*	$1 Messerschmitt Me 163B Komet.	95	95
2774*	$1 Fieseler Fi 103R Reichenberg Flying Bomb.	95	95
2776*	$1 Heinkel He 112	95	95
2778*	$1 Bell X-1	95	95

1994. 50th Anniv of ICAO.

2840	10c. de Havilland Canada DHC-6 Twin Otter of LIAT at Bequia Airport	40	40
2841	65c. Union Island Airport	80	60
2842	75c. de Havilland Canada DHC-8 Dash 8 of LIAT at E.T. Joshua Airport	85	70
2843	$1 Aircraft and logo	1·00	1·25
2844	$1 Pilatus Britten-Norman BN-2 Islander at J. F. Mitchell Airport, Bequia	1·00	1·25
2840/2844	Set of 5	3·50	3·75

1995.

2910*	$2 Consolidated B-24 Liberator	1·25	1·25
2912*	$2 Gloster G.41 Meteor	1·25	1·25
MS2916*	$6 Sortie markings on aircraft	3·50	4·00

1995.

2932*	$2 Douglas TBD Devastator	1·25	1·25
2933*	$2 Doolittle's North American B-25 Mitchell *Ruptured Duck*	1·25	1·25
2934*	$2 Curtiss SB2C Helldiver	1·25	1·25

1996.

3198*	50c. Disney characters as aircrew	50	50
3204*	50c. Disney characters as air traffic controllers	50	50

1996. Designs as Nos. 3198 and 3204.

3517*	10c. Disney characters as aircrew	25	30
3521*	10c. Disney characters as air traffic controllers	25	30

1998. 80th Anniv of Royal Air Force.

4146	$2 Boeing E-3D Sentry AEW. Mk1	1·25	1·25
4147	$2 Eurofighter EF-2000 Typhoon	1·25	1·25
4148	$2 SEPECAT Jaguar GR 1A	1·25	1·25
4149	$2 BAe Hawk T1A	1·25	1·25
4150	$2 Two SEPECAT Jaguar GR1As	1·25	1·25
4151	$2 Panavia Tornado F. Mk3	1·25	1·25
4152	$2 Three BAe Harrier GR 7s	1·25	1·25
4153	$2 Panavia Tornado F Mk3 IDV	1·25	1·25
4146/4153	Set of 8	9·00	9·00
MS4154	Four sheets. (a) $6 Bristol F2B and falcon; (b) $6 Bristol F2B and golden eagle; (c) $6 de Havilland DH.98 Mosquito and Eurofighter EF-2000 Typhoon; (d) $6 Avro Type 698 Vulcan and Eurofighter EF-2000 Typhoon *Set of 4 sheets*	13·00	14·00

1999.

4268	60c. Montgolfier Balloon, 1783	45	30
4269	70c. Lilienthal's Glider, 1894	45	35
4270	90c. Zeppelin airship	50	40
4271	$1 Wilbur Wright and *Flyer I*, 1903	60	45
4272	$1.10 Martin M-130 China Clipper, 1935	70	75
4273	$1.10 Douglas DC-3, 1937	70	75
4274	$1.10 Beech Staggerwing C-17L, 1932	70	75
4275	$1.10 Hughes H-1, 1935	70	75
4276	$1.10 Granville Brothers Gee Bee R-1, 1932	70	75
4277	$1.10 Lockheed 8 Sirius *Tingmissartoq*, 1932	70	75
4278	$1.10 Fokker T-2, 1923	70	75
4279	$1.10 Curtiss CW-16E, 1931	70	75
4280	$1.10 Dayton Wright DH4	70	75
4281	$1.10 Sopwith Camel	70	75
4282	$1.10 Sopwith Dove, 1919	70	75
4283	$1.10 Etrich Taube, 1910	70	75
4284	$1.10 Fokker DR.1, 1917	70	75
4285	$1.10 Albatros L.24 (D.Va), 1918	70	75
4286	$1.10 Sopwith Pup, 1916	70	75
4287	$1.10 SPAD XIII Smith IV, 1917	70	75
4268/4287	Set of 20	12·00	12·00
MS4288	Two sheets. (a) $5 Lebaudy-Juillot airship No. 1 *La Jaune*, 1903; (b) $5 Bleriot XI, crossing channel, 1914 *Set of 2 sheets*	5·50	6·00

No. **MS**4288a is inscribed LE BANDY in error.

1999.

4384*	$3 Seaplane	1·75	1·75
4385*	$3 Concorde	1·75	1·75

2000.

4479*	60c. Atomic cloud and aircraft	45	50
4483*	60c. Zeppelin LZ-129 *Hindenburg* exploding	45	50
4484*	60c. Igor Sikorsky and Sikorsky VS-300, first successful helicopter, 1939	45	50

2000.

4487*	20c. Orville and Wilbur Wright construction of *Flyer III*, 1903	25	30

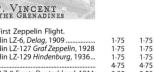

2000. Centenary of First Zeppelin Flight.
4586	$3 Zeppelin LZ-6, *Delag*, 1909	1·75	1·75
4587	$3 Zeppelin LZ-127 *Graf Zeppelin*, 1928	1·75	1·75
4588	$3 Zeppelin LZ-129 *Hindenburg*, 1936...	1·75	1·75
4586/4588 *Set of 3*		4·75	4·75
MS4589 $5 Zeppelin LZ-9 *Ersatz Deutschland*, 1911		3·25	3·50
No. 4588 is inscribed (129) *Hindenberg* in error.			

2000.
4682*	$1 Consolidated B-24 Liberators..............	75	75
4685*	$1 North American F-86 Sabre	75	75
4686*	$1 Aircraft carrier- may show aircraft.....	75	75
4687*	$1 Boeing B-52 Stratofortress................	75	75
4689*	$1 McDonnell Douglas F-4 Phantom IIs	75	75
4693*	$1 Aircraft carrier – may show aircraft...	75	75
4694*	$1 BAe Harriers................................	75	75
MS4697 Two sheets. (a) $5 Boeing B-52 Stratofortress; (b) $5 McDonnell Douglas F-4 Phantom II *Set of 2 sheets*		7·50	7·50

2000. 60th Anniv of Battle of Britain.
4739	80c. Supermarine Spitfires	75	75
4740	90c. Supermarine Spitfire over countryside.............................	75	75
4741	90c. Dornier Do 217 on fire	75	75
4742	90c. Gloster Gladiators........................	75	75
4743	90c. Hawker Hurricanes attacking German fighters........................	75	75
4744	90c. Junkers Ju 87 Stuka (face value bottom left)...........................	75	75
4745	90c. Supermarine Spitfires (different)	75	75
4746	90c. Junkers Ju88 on fire.......................	75	75
4747	90c. Junkers Ju87 Stuka (face value bottom right)	75	75
4748	90c. Westland Lysander and Gloster Gladiator............................	75	75
4749	90c. Messerschmitt Bf 109.....................	75	75
4750	90c. Heinkel He 111 under attack............	75	75
4751	90c. Hawker Hurricanes from below	75	75
4752	90c. Bristol Type 142 Blenheim...............	75	75
4753	90c. Supermarine Spitfires over fields......	75	75
4754	90c. Messerschmitt Bf 110.....................	75	75
4739/4754 *Set of 16*		11·00	11·00
MS4755 Two sheets. (a) $5 Supermarine Spitfire; (b) $5 Hawker Hurricane *Set of 2 sheets*		7·50	8·00

2001. 60th Anniv of Japanese Attack on Pearl Harbour.
5042	$1.40 Aircraft.......................................	1·00	1·00
5043	$1.40 Aircraft.......................................	1·00	1·00
5044	$1.40 Aircraft.......................................	1·00	1·00
5045	$1.40 Aircraft.......................................	1·00	1·00
5046	$1.40 Aircraft.......................................	1·00	1·00
5047	$1.40 Aircraft.......................................	1·00	1·00
5048	$1.40 Aircraft.......................................	1·00	1·00
5049	$1.40 Aircraft.......................................	1·00	1·00
5050	$1.40 Aircraft.......................................	1·00	1·00
5051	$1.40 Aircraft.......................................	1·00	1·00
5052	$1.40 Aircraft.......................................	1·00	1·00
5053	$1.40 Aircraft.......................................	1·00	1·00
5042/5053 *Set of 12*		11·00	11·00
MS5054 Two sheets. (a) $5 Aircraft; (b) $5 Aircraft *Set of 2 sheets*		7·50	8·00

2003. Centenary of Powered Flight.
MS5260 $2 Handley Page Heyford; $2 Heinkel He 111 B; $2 Gloster Gauntlet; $2 Curtiss BF 2C-1.......		5·00	5·50
MS5261 $2 Mitsubishi A6M Reisen; $2 Dewoitine D-520; $2 Messerschmitt Bf 109E; $2 Republic P-47 Thunderbolt.................		5·00	5·50
MS5262 Two sheets. (a) $5 Fairey Flycatcher; (b) $5 Bristol Type 142 Blenheim IV *Set of 2 sheets*		6·50	7·00

2003.
MS5269* $1 Boeing (McDonnell Douglas) Grumman F-14Tomcats; $1 Helicopter; $1 Bomber; $1 Fighter		4·75	5·50
MS5270* $1.50 Gunship; $1.50 Aircraft carrier; $1.50 Aircraft carrier (other stamps in the miniature sheets do not show aircraft)................		5·50	6·50

2004. Last Flight of Concorde.
MS5311 $3 Concorde; $3 Concorde; $3 Concorde ...		6·00	6·00

2004.
5323*	70c. Air Chief Marshall Sir Trafford Leigh-Mallory of Royal Air Force....................	65	40

2005.
5497*	$2 Douglas SBD-3 Dauntless*..................	1·60	1·60
5498*	$2 Mitsubishi A6M5 Zero-Sen.................	1·60	1·60

2006. 50th Death Anniv of Ludwig Durr (Zeppelin engineer).
5553	$4 ZRS-4, USS *Akron*	2·25	2·50
5554	$4 A-170 airship	2·25	2·50
5555	$4 Altair-Z experimental airship	2·25	2·50
5553/5555 *Set of 3*		6·00	6·75

2006. 50th Anniv of LIAT (Leeward Islands Air Transport).
5560	20c. LIAT emblem..............................	30	15
5561	50c. de Havilland Canada DHC-8 Dash 8 in flight	50	35
5562	70c. Hawker Siddeley HS-748 on ground	60	50
5563	90c. de Havilland Canada DHC-8 Dash 8 in flight	80	65
5560/5563 *Set of 4*		2·00	1·50
MS5564 $5 Beech Model 50 Twin Bonanza		3·25	3·50

2006. Last Flights of Concorde.
5588	$1.40 Captains waving Union Jack flags from cockpit..........................	1·50	1·50
5589	$1.40 Concorde landing at Heathrow Airport...............................	1·50	1·50
5590	$1.40 Filton flypast by Concord G-BOAF......	1·50	1·50
5591	$1.40 Concorde comes home to Filton	1·50	1·50
5588/5591 *Set of 4*		5·50	5·50

SAMOA

West Pacific
1962. 12 pence = 1 shilling
20 shillings = 1 pound
1967. 100 sene = 1 tale

1962.
244*	8d. Airplane at airport....................	80	10

1966. No. 244 surcharged **HURRICANE RELIEF 6d.**
273*	8d. +6d. Airplane at airport..................	10	10

1970.
345	3s. Sir Gordon Taylor's Short S.25 Sandringham 7 flying boat VH-APG *Frigate Bird III*	45	10
346	7s. Douglas DC-3 of Polynesian Airlines	55	10
347	20s. Sikorsky S-42A flying boat *Samoan Clipper* of Pan Am	75	60
348	30s. Britten-Norman BN-2 Islander 5W-FAF of Air Samoa....................	75	1·75
345/348 *Set of 4*		2·30	2·30

1973.
409	8s. Hawker Siddeley H.S.748 SW-FAN of Polynesian Airlines over Faleolo Airport	45	15
410	10s. Hawker Siddeley H.S.748 SW-FAN of Polynesian Airlines over runway........	55	15
411	12s. Hawker Siddeley H.S.748 of Polynesian Airlines being refuelled ..	60	35
412	22s. B.A.C. One Eleven (in foreground), Hawker Siddeley H.S.748 of Polynesian Airlines and Britten-Norman BN-2 Islander (in background) at Faleolo Airport..........	85	60
409/412 *Set of 4*		2·20	1·10

1974.
430*	8s. Hawker Siddeley H.S.748 of Polynesian Airlines being loaded with mail at Faleolo Airport...............	35	10

1975.
448*	50s. Douglas DC-4...............................	50	1·25

1977. 50th Anniv of Lindbergh's Trans-Atlantic Flight.
483	22s. Ryan NYP Special *Spirit of St. Louis*.....	25	10
484	24s. Ryan NYP Special *Spirit of St. Louis*.....	35	15
485	26s. Ryan NYP Special *Spirit of St. Louis*.....	35	15
486	50s. Charles Lindbergh and Ryan NYP Special *Spirit of St. Louis*..............	80	75
483/486 *Set of 4*		1·60	1·00

1978. Aviation Progress.

501	12s. Boeing 737 of Polynesian Airlines on runway	15	10
502	24s. Wright *Flyer I*	30	20
503	26s. Fokker F.VIIa/3m *Southern Cross*	30	20
504	50s. Concorde of British Airways	75	85
501/504 *Set of 5*		1·40	1·20

1981.

595*	18s. Boeing 737	25	15

1982.

617*	23s. Boeing 737 of Polynesian Airlines	1·25	30

1983. Bicentenary of Manned Flight and 50th Anniv of Douglas Commercial Aircraft.

MS638	32s. Douglas DC-1 X223Y of Trans World Airlines; 32s. Douglas DC-2; 32s. Douglas DC-3; 32s. Douglas DC-4; 32s. Douglas DC-5; 32s. Douglas DC-6; 32s. Douglas DC-7; 32s. Douglas DC-8-63; 32s. Douglas DC-9.10; 32s. Douglas DC-10	3·25	3·25

1984.

MS683	$2.50 Government Aircraft Factory N24A Nomad SW-FAT of Polynesian Airlines	4·75	6·00

1986.

732*	56s. Sikorsky S-42A flying boat	40	50

1987.

767*	80s. Boeing 737	1·10	1·25

1988.

769*	45s. Boeing 727 of Polynesian Airlines in flight and on runway	80	90
770*	45s. Nose of Boeing 727	80	90
771*	45s. Boeing 727 landing	80	90

1988. Opening of Faleolo Airport.

773	40s. Douglas DC-9 over Faleolo International Airport	60	40
774	45s. Boeing 727	65	40
775	60s. de Havilland DHC-6 Twin Otter	80	70
776	70s. Boeing 737	90	1·40
777	80s. Boeing 727 and control tower	1·00	1·50
778	$1 Douglas DC-9	1·10	1·75
773/778 *Set of 6*		4·50	5·50

1990.

842*	60s. de Havilland Canada DHC-6 Twin Otter of Polynesian Airlines	1·75	1·40

1995.

961*	70s. Vought Sikorsky OS2U Kingfisher	65	55
962*	90s. Vought F4U Corsair	80	70

1995.

972*	90s. Bell Sioux Scout	1·40	85
973*	$1 Bell Model 212	1·60	1·00
974*	$4 Hawker Siddeley HS 780 Andover	3·50	5·00

1998. 80th Anniv of Royal Air Force.

1029	70s. Westland Wallace	60	35
1030	80s. Hawker Fury Mk 1	60	40
1031	$2 Vickers Type 684 Varsity	1·50	1·75
1032	$5 BAC (Hunting Percival) P84 Jet Provost	3·00	4·50
1029/1032 *Set of 4*		5·25	6·25
MS1033	$2 Norman Thompson N.T.2b; $2 Nieuport 27 Scout; $2 Miles M.16 Magister; $2 Bristol Type 130 Bombay (catalogued 'Bomber')	5·00	5·50

2000.

1086	95s. Boeing 737	1·00	55

SAN MARINO

Southern Europe

1933. 100 centesimi = 1 lira

2002. 100 cents = 1 euro

1933. Nos. 164/9 in new colours surcharged with airship LZ-127 *Graf Zeppelin*, **ZEPPELIN 1933** and value.

191	3l. on 50c. Mt. Titano	1·30	48·00
192	5l. on 80c. Mt. Titano	24·00	48·00
193	10l. on 1l. Mt. Titano	24·00	60·00
194	12l. on 2l. Mt. Titano	24·00	90·00
195	15l. on 2l.60 Mt. Titano	24·00	95·00
196	20l. on 3l. Mt. Titano	24·00	£110
191/196 *Set of 6*		£110	£400

1942.

247*	25c. Airplane	25	10
248*	50c. Airplane	25	10
249*	75c. Airplane	25	10
250*	1l. Airplane	60	45
251*	5l. Airplane	7·50	3·25

1946.

326*	75c. Airplane	15	15
328*	2l. Airplane	15	15
329*	3l. Airplane	15	15
330*	5l. Four aircraft	15	20
334*	20l. Four aircraft	65	1·60
332*	35l. Four aircraft	3·50	3·25
335*	50l. Four aircraft	7·50	5·25
333*	100l. Airplane	1·10	1·20

1946. Nos. 329/30 surcharged **CONVEGNO FILATELICO 30 NOVEMBRE 1946** and premium.

336a*	3l. +25l. Airplane	55	80
336b*	5l. +25l. Four aircraft	55	80

1947. No. 333 overprinted **Giornata Filatelica Rimini-San Marino 18 Luglio 1947.**

347	100l. Airplane	1·10	85

1950.

423	1000l. Douglas DC-6	£375	£325

1952.

447*	2l. Douglas DC-6	10	20
449*	5l. Douglas DC-6	10	20
450*	25l. Douglas DC-6	35	80
451*	200l. Douglas DC-6	60·00	26·00

1952. Aerial Survey of San Marino.

452	25l. Airplane	1·70	1·60
453	75l. Airplane	5·25	3·25

1953.

459*	10l. Model glider	25	20

1954.

473	1000l. Douglas DC-6	75·00	70·00

1956. No. 504 overprinted with Douglas DC-3 airplane and **POSTA AEREA.**

522	100l. Ice hockey	1·40	1·40

1958.
547*   125l. Bristol 173 Rotocoach helicopter and airplane .... 2·40 2·50

1959. Alitalia Inaugural Flight, Rimini-London.
576   120l. Vickers Viscount 700 of Alitalia .... 1·10 1·20

1961.
636   1000l. Bell 47J Ranger helicopter .... 30·00 29·00

1962. Vintage Aircraft.
659   1l. Wright Type A 10 15
660   2l. Archdeacon-Voisin "Boxkite" float glider, 1905 (shown with propeller).. 10 15
661   3l. Bonnet-Labranche biplane 10 15
662   4l. Curtiss June Bug, 1908 .... 10 15
663   5l. Farman H.F.III biplane 10 15
664   10l. Bleriot XI 10 15
665   30l. Hubert Latham's Antoinette IV, 1909 ... 10 20
666   60l. Santos-Dumont's biplane 14 bis........ 10 25
667   70l. A.V. Roe Triplane II 20 30
668   115l. Faccioli's airplane, 19........................ 50 60
659/668 Set of 10 .... 1·30 2·00

1963. Contemporary Aircraft.
732   5l. Tupolev Tu-104A 10 10
733   10l. Boeing 707 .... 10 15
734   15l. Douglas DC-8 .... 10 10
735   25l. Boeing 707 .... 10 10
736   50l. Vickers Viscount 837 .... 10 10
737   75l. Sud Aviation SE 210 Caravelle.......... 10 10
738   120l. Vickers VC-10 .... 10 20
739   200l. Hawker Siddeley Comet 4C 10 10
740   300l. Boeing 727-100 .... 10 20
741   500l. Rolls Royce Dart 527 turboprop engine. .... 3·00 3·00
742   1000l. Boeing 707 .... 1·50 1·50
732/742 Set of 11 .... 4·75 5·00

1973.
976   25l. Couzinet 70 F-AMBV Arc en Ciel.......... 10 15
977   55l. Macchi Castoldi MC-72-181 seaplane. 10 10
978   60l. Tupolev ANT-9 .... 10 10
979   90l. Ryan NYP Special Spirit of St. Louis..... 10 10
980   220l. Handley Page H.P.42 .... 10 15
976/980 Set of 5 .... 45 55

1974. 50th Anniv of Gliding in Italy.
1012   40l. Glider 15 10
1013   120l. Glider 15 15
1014   500l. Glider 25 40
1012/1014 Set of 3 .... 50 60

1977. Centenary of Enrico Forlanini's First Vertical Flight Experiment.
1074   120l. Leonardo da Vinci's drawing of a "helicopter"........................ 15 20

1978. 75th Anniv of First Powered Flight.
1097   10l. Wright Flyer I 15 10
1098   50l. Wright Flyer I 15 10
1099   200l. Wright Flyer I 15 10
1097/1099 Set of 3 .... 40 25

1983.
1210*   400l. Auguste Piccard and his stratosphere balloon F.N.R.S., 1931 .... 1·50 1·00

1983. Bicentenary of Powered Flight.
1214   500l. Montgolfier balloon (first manned free flight, 1783).................. 1·70 1·30

1987.
1302   600l. Baroudeur microlight of the San Marino Flying Club.................... 45 65

1988.
1312*   15l. Airship LZ-127 Graf Zeppelin overprint (on stamp No. 191) and airship at mooring mast (on printed envelope)............................ 10 15

1995.
1517*   600l. Airplane... 30 50
1519*   850l. Airplane... 50 75

2000.
1749   650l. Wright Flyer, Boeing 777 airship........ 40 55

2003. Centenary of Powered Flight.
1950   36c. Wright Flyer I 45 45
1951   41c. Bleriot XI 55 55
1952   62c. Aermacchi MB339 .... 80 80
1953   77c. Aermacchi MB339s of Frecce Tricolori (Italian Air Force aerobatic flight) ... 1·00 1·00
1950/1953 Set of 4.. 2·50 2·50

SARAWAK

South-east Asia

100 cents = 1 dollar

1949. As Nos. 114/15 of Antigua.
167*   8c. Airplane.. 1·25 60
168*   15c. Jet-powered Vickers Viking .... 3·50 2·50

SAUDI ARABIA

Arabia

1949. 110 guerche = 10 riyals

1960. 5 halalahs = 1 guerche (piastre)

20 guerche = 1 riyal

1976. 100 halalahs = 1 riyal

1949.
357   1g. Airliner... 3·50 10
358   3g. Airliner... 4·50 15
359   4g. Airliner... 4·50 15
360   10g. Airliner... 12·00 40
361   20g. Airliner... 11·50 1·60
362   100g. Airliner... £110 11·50
357/362 Set of 6 .... £130 12·50

1960. Size 27½×22 mm.
428*   1p. Vickers Viscount 800 .... 55 15
429*   2p. Vickers Viscount 800 .... 55 15
430*   3p. Vickers Viscount 800 .... 55 15
431*   4p. Vickers Viscount 800 .... 55 15
432*   5p. Vickers Viscount 800 .... 55 15
433*   6p. Vickers Viscount 800 .... 95 25
434*   8p. Vickers Viscount 800 .... 1·10 25
435*   9p. Vickers Viscount 800 .... 1·80 25
436*   10p. Vickers Viscount 800 .... 4·75 50
437*   15p. Vickers Viscount 800 .... 4·75 30
438*   20p. Vickers Viscount 800 .... 4·75 40
439*   30p. Vickers Viscount 800 .... 11·50 1·20
440*   50p. Vickers Viscount 800 .... 24·00 80
441*   100p. Vickers Viscount 800 .... 49·00 2·40
442*   200p. Vickers Viscount 800 .... 75·00 4·00

1963. Opening of Dhahran Airport and Inauguration of Jet Service.
462   1p. Boeing 707 over Dhahran Airport 95 15
463   3½p. Boeing 707 over Dhahran Airport ..... 2·00 30
464   6p. Boeing 707 over Dhahran Airport ..... 4·75 50
465   7½p. Boeing 707 over Dhahran Airport ..... 4·75 55
466   9½p. Boeing 707 over Dhahran Airport ..... 6·50 65
462/466 Set of 5 .... 17·00 1·90

1963. As Nos. 430, 436 and 438 but larger, 29×23 mm.
490*   3p. Vickers Viscount 800 .... 4·75 50

491*	10p. Vickers Viscount 800	9·75	75
492*	20p. Vickers Viscount 800	18·00	1·80

1964. Design includes cartouche of King Saud as illustrated.

585*	1p. Boeing 720B of S.A.A	80·00	2·75
586*	2p. Boeing 720B of S.A.A	£2750	95·00
587*	3p. Boeing 720B of S.A.A	9·75	25
588*	4p. Boeing 720B of S.A.A	5·75	25
589*	5p. Boeing 720B of S.A.A	£1800	£400
590*	6p. Boeing 720B of S.A.A	£110	1·80
591*	7p. Boeing 720B of S.A.A	6·25	40
592*	8p. Boeing 720B of S.A.A	80·00	1·80
593*	9p. Boeing 720B of S.A.A	5·75	30
594*	10p. Boeing 720B of S.A.A	80·00	5·75
595*	11p. Boeing 720B of S.A.A	80·00	19·00
596*	12p. Boeing 720B of S.A.A	5·75	30
597*	13p. Boeing 720B of S.A.A	4·50	30
598*	14p. Boeing 720B of S.A.A	4·50	40
599*	15p. Boeing 720B of S.A.A	80·00	5·75
600*	16p. Boeing 720B of S.A.A	6·50	50
601*	17p. Boeing 720B of S.A.A	5·25	40
602*	18p. Boeing 720B of S.A.A	5·25	40
603*	19p. Boeing 720B of S.A.A	5·75	50
604*	20p. Boeing 720B of S.A.A	£150	6·50
605*	23p. Boeing 720B of S.A.A	£150	11·50
606*	24p. Boeing 720B of S.A.A	5·25	50
607*	26p. Boeing 720B of S.A.A	5·25	50
608*	27p. Boeing 720B of S.A.A	6·00	50
609*	31p. Boeing 720B of S.A.A	7·75	55
610*	33p. Boeing 720B of S.A.A	9·75	55
610a*	50p. Boeing 720B of S.A.A		
610b*	100p. Boeing 720B of S.A.A		
610c*	200p. Boeing 720B of S.A.A		

1966. As Nos. 585/606 and 610/c, but with cartouche of King Faisal as illustrated.

716*	1p. Boeing 720B of S.A.A	21·00	95
717*	2p. Boeing 720B of S.A.A	21·00	1·50
718*	3p. Boeing 720B of S.A.A	21·00	50
719*	4p. Boeing 720B of S.A.A	10·50	25
720*	5p. Boeing 720B of S.A.A	£1800	£450
721*	6p. Boeing 720B of S.A.A	£130	9·75
812*	7p. Boeing 720B of S.A.A	9·75	1·60
813*	8p. Boeing 720B of S.A.A	41·00	6·50
724*	9p. Boeing 720B of S.A.A	5·25	55
725*	10p. Boeing 720B of S.A.A	16·00	95
726*	11p. Boeing 720B of S.A.A	13·00	50
727*	12p. Boeing 720B of S.A.A	49·00	3·75
728*	13p. Boeing 720B of S.A.A	14·50	95
729*	14p. Boeing 720B of S.A.A	14·00	1·60
730*	15p. Boeing 720B of S.A.A	11·50	75
731*	16p. Boeing 720B of S.A.A	16·00	3·00
732*	17p. Boeing 720B of S.A.A	14·50	1·50
733*	18p. Boeing 720B of S.A.A	14·00	2·40
734*	19p. Boeing 720B of S.A.A	19·00	95
735*	20p. Boeing 720B of S.A.A	£180	13·00
736*	23p. Boeing 720B of S.A.A	24·00	3·00
737*	24p. Boeing 720B of S.A.A	29·00	3·00
741*	33p. Boeing 720B of S.A.A	11·50	50
742*	50p. Boeing 720B of S.A.A		
743*	100p. Boeing 720B of S.A.A	£800	£300
744*	200p. Boeing 720B of S.A.A		

1974.

1087	3p. Northrop F.5	2·10	15
1088	4p. Northrop F.5	4·00	30
1089	10p. Northrop F.5	10·50	1·60
1087/1089 Set of 3		15·00	1·80

1975. 30th Anniv of Saudia (national airline).

1108	4p. Douglas DC-3 (on ground) and Lockheed L-1011 TriStar of S.A.A	8·00	30
1109	10p. Douglas DC-3 (on ground) and Lockheed L-1011 TriStar of S.A.A	13·00	50

1981. Inauguration of King Abdul-Aziz International Airport, Jeddah.

1259	20h. Douglas DC-9-80 Super Eighty over King Abdul-Aziz International Airport, Jeddah	55	25
1260	80h. Boeing 747 over King Abdul-Aziz International Airport, Jeddah	2·30	40

1983. Opening of King Khaled International Airport, Riyadh.

1361	20h. Airliners at King Khaled International Airport, Riyadh	30	25
1362	65h. King Khaled International Airport, Riyadh	1·30	30

1986.

1461*	20h. Pilgrims disembarking from jet airliner	1·60	1·20

1987.

1527	50h. King Khaled International Airport, Riyadh	55	30
1528	75h. King Khaled International Airport, Riyadh	1·10	50

1990. 45th Anniv of Saudi Airlines.

1680	75h. Boeing 747-300/400 of S.A.A. and map of international routes	65	40
1681	75h. Douglas DC-10 of S.A.A. and map of domestic routes	65	40
1682	150h. Boeing 747-300/400 of S.A.A. and map of international routes	1·30	80
1683	150h. Douglas DC-10 of S.A.A. and map of domestic routes	1·30	80
1680/1683 Set of 4		3·50	2·20

1995. 50th Anniv of Saudia (national airline).

1892	75h. Anniversary emblem	75	40
1893	150h. Tailfins	1·50	75

1999.

1944*	1r. Boeing 747	1·60	1·10

1999. Inauguration of King Fahd International Airport.

1948	1r. Boeing 747 over airport	90	50
1949	2r. Air traffic control tower and airplane	1·80	90

2003.

2055	1r. Boeing Chinook	80	80

2003.

2088	1r. Pilgrims at airport	80	75

2004.

2105	1r. McDonnell Douglas MD-11F	80	75
2106	1r. Boeing 747-400	80	75
2107	1r. Boeing 777-268	80	75
2108	1r. McDonnell Douglas MD-90-30	80	75
2105/2108 Set of 4		3·00	2·75

SELANGOR

South-east Asia

100 cents = 1 dollar

1949. As Nos. 114/15 of Antigua.

111*	10c. Airplane	30	10
112*	15c. Jet-powered Vickers Viking	2·25	2·50

SENEGAL

West Africa

100 centimes = 1 franc

1935.

178	25c. Airplane over African village	1·70	4·00
179	50c. Airplane over African village	1·40	3·50
180	1f. Airplane over African village	1·00	55
181	1f.25 Airplane over African village	1·10	2·30
182	1f.90 Airplane over African village	1·50	3·25
183	2f. Airplane over African village	1·80	40
184	2f.90 Airplane over African village	1·20	3·75
185	3f. Airplane over African village	1·50	1·40
186	3f.50 Airplane over camels	1·90	1·50
187	4f.50 Airplane over camels	1·10	2·75
188	4f.75 Airplane over camels	1·40	2·75
189	4f.90 Airplane over camels	2·30	2·75
190	6f.50 Airplane over camels	80	2·30
191	6f.90 Airplane over African village	2·00	3·50
192	8f. Airplane over camels	2·50	2·50
193	15f. Airplane over camels	2·30	2·75
178/193 Set of 16		21·00	36·00

1942. As design of Nos. 186, 188, 190 and 192/3 but with twin-engined monoplane.

217	50f. Twin-engine airliner over camels	1·50	3·25
218	100f. Twin-engine airliner over camels	1·70	3·00

1962. Air Afrique. As No. 307 of Cameroun.
249   25f. Boeing 707 airliners of Air Afrique   95   50

1966. Inauguration of Douglas DC-8F Air Services. As No. 438 of Cameroun.
334   30f. Douglas DC-8F Jet Trader of Air Afrique.......   95   45

1966.
339*   20f. Couzinet 70 F-AMBV *Arc en Ciel*.........   95   30
340*   35f. Latecoere 300 flying boat F-AKGF *Croix du Sud* ....   1·20   50

1967.
352   200f. Terminal building at Dakar-Yoff Airport ....   4·25   1·70

1969. 10th Anniv of ASECNA (air safety organization). As No. 552 of Cameroun.
414   100f. Airliner over airport ....   1·90   80

1970. 40th Anniv of Disappearance of Emile Lecrivain (aviator).
419   50f. Emile Lecrivain and Latecoere 25 ......   1·50   70

1976.
559   100f. Fokker F.28 Fellowship 4000..............   3·25   1·50

1976. Concorde's First Flight.
581   300f. Concorde of Air France.........   6·00   3·25

1976. Embossed on silver or gold foil.
615   500f. Concorde of Air France.........   9·25   9·00
616   1500f. Concorde of Air France.........   32·00   31·00

1977. No. 581 overprinted **22.11.77 PARIS NEW-YORK**.
646   300f. Concorde of Air France..............   5·25   3·25

1978.
675*   75f. Wilbur and Orville Wright and Wright Type A.......   1·10   45
MS678* 150f. Wilbur and Orville Wright and Wright Type A (sheet contains two other designs).............   7·75   7·50

1980. 50th Anniv of First South Atlantic Airmail Flight.
728   300f. J. Dabry, L. Gimie, Jean Mermoz and Latecoere 28-3 seaplane F-AJNQ *Comte de la Vaulx* ....   4·25   1·60

1985. 55th Anniv of First South Atlantic Airmail Flight.
821   250f. Latecoere 28-3 seaplane F-AJNQ *Comte de la Vaulx* ....   4·25   1·70

1987.
878*   125f. Helicopter.......   1·50   90

1989. 45th Anniv of Disappearance of Antoine de Saint-Exupery (aviator and writer).
985   180f. Antoine de Saint-Exupery and Potez 25A2 biplane F-AECS.............   2·40   95
986   220f. Antoine de Saint-Exupery and Morane Saulnier Type AI F-AIUL.........   3·00   1·40
987   410f. Antoine de Saint-Exupery and Bloch 174 ....   5·50   2·40
985/987 *Set of 3*..............   9·75   4·25

1989. 79th Anniv of First Flight of Henri Fabre's Seaplane.
1034   125f. Fabre's seaplane *Hydravion*, 1910......   1·50   55
1035   130f. Henri Fabre working on engine of seaplane *Hydravion*..........   1·60   70
1036   475f. Henri Fabre and technical drawings of seaplane *Hydravion* ....   5·50   2·20
1034/1036 *Set of 3*.........   7·75   3·00
MS1037 700f. Henri Fabre and technical drawings of seaplane *Hydravion*.......   7·75   7·50

1991. Centenary (1990) of First Heavier than Air Powered Flight.
1108*   180f. Clement Ader and his monoplane *Eole*, 1890..........   2·50   1·10
1109*   615f. Clement Ader and his monoplane *Eole*, 1890..........   8·25   3·50
MS1110* 940f. Clement Ader and his monoplane *Eole*, 1890..........   10·50   8·00

1993.
1233*   200f. Sikorsky S-65 CH-53 Sea Stallion helicopter, Sud Aviation SO 1221 Djinn helicopter and crashed airliner   2·20   1·40

1994. 10th (1993) Toulouse-Saint Louis Aerial Rally .
1278   100f. Breguet Bre.14 over route map   65   30
1279   145f. Henri Guillaumet and route map.......   90   55
1280   180f. Jean Mermoz and route map.............   1·00   65
1281   220f. Antoine de Saint-Exupery and route map ....   1·30   75
1278/1281 *Set of 4*..............   3·50   2·00

1996.
1422*   500f. Balloon *'Drop of Hope'*.............   2·75   1·50

1999.
1579   500f. Concorde ....   2·00   1·90

SERBIA

South-east Europe

100 paras = 1 dinar

German Occupation

1941. As Nos. 360/7 and 443/4 of Yugoslavia, with coloured network background, overprinted **SERBIEN**.
G16   50p. Fokker F.VIIa/3m   5·75   65·00
G17   1d. Junkers G.31   5·75   65·00
G18   2d. Fokker F.VIIa/3m   5·75   65·00
G19   2d.50 Fokker F.VIIa/3m   5·75   65·00
G20   5d. Fokker F.VIIa/3m   5·75   65·00
G21   10d. Junkers G.31   5·75   65·00
G22   20d. Fokker F.VIIa/3m   5·75   65·00
G23   30d. Fokker F.VIIa/3m   7·50   65·00
G24   40d. Junkers Ju 86   13·00   £300
G25   50d. Fokker F.VIII/3m   16·00   £450
G16/25 *Set of 10*   70·00   £1100

1941. Nos. 365/7 and 443/4 of Yugoslavia surcharged **SERBIEN** and value.
G26   1d. on 10d. Junkers G.31   1·75   50·00
G27   3d. on 20d. Fokker F.VIIa/3m   1·75   50·00
G28   6d. on 30d. Fokker F.VIIa/3m   1·75   50·00
G29   8d. on 40d. Junkers Ju 86   3·50   £110
G30   12d. on 50d. Fokker F.VIIa/3m   5·00   £450
G26/30 *Set of 5*   12·50   £450

1942. Nos. 418, 420, 423 and 425/6 of Yugoslavia surcharged with airplane, "SERBIA" in Cyrillic characters and value.
G69   2 on 2d. King Peter II   15   1·50
G70   4 on 4d. King Peter II   15   1·50
G71   10 on 12d. King Peter II   15   2·75
G72   14 on 20d. King Peter II   15   2·75
G73   20 on 30d. King Peter II   50   13·00
G69/73 *Set of 5*   1·00   19·00

1943.
G86* 50d. Junkers Ju 52/3m .... 30 1·50

SERBIA AND MONTENEGRO

South-east Europe
100 para = 1 dinar

2003. Centenary of Powered Flight.
54 16d. Wilbur and Orville Wright and Wright *Flyer I* 25 25
55 28d.70 Wright *Flyer I* and horse-drawn carriages 45 45

2004.
81* 16d. Paragliding 25 25

2005. Centenary of International Airline Federation.
164 49d.50 Santos-Dumont's *No. 14 bis* and balloon 80 80
165 58d. Glider, parachute and hang-glider.... 90 90

2005.
167 16d.50 Boeing 737 .... 25 25

2007. 75th Anniv of Amelia Earhart's Trans-Atlantic Flight.
301 50d. Amelia Earhart and Lockheed Vega 5B .... 2·50 2·50

SEYCHELLES

Indian Ocean
100 cents = 1 rupee

1949. As Nos. 114/15 of Antigua.
154* 18c. Airplane.. 20 25
155* 50c. Jet-powered Vickers Viking .... 1·75 1·50

1969.
272* 85c. Impression of proposed airport .... 3·50 1·75
273a* 95c. Impression of proposed airport .... 5·50 3·25

1971. Airport Completion.
294 5c. Piper PA-31 Navajo...................... 30 50
295 20c. Westland Wessex HAS-1 helicopter .. 65 10
296 50c. Consolidated PBY-5A Catalina amphibian 70 10
297 60c. Grumman SA-16 Albatross flying boat 75 10
298 85c. Short S.26 "G" Class flying boat G-AFCI *Golden Hind*.................... 80 10
299 3r.50 Supermarine Walrus Mk I amphibian 2·25 3·50
294/299 *Set of 6* .... 5·00 3·50

1971. No. 272 surcharged **95c.**
305* 95c. on 85c. Impression of proposed airport .... 45 1·00

1971. No. 273a overprinted **VISIT OF Q.E. 11.**
336* 95c. Impression of proposed airport 25 40

1976.
389* 3r.50 Wright *Flyer I*................................ 35 70

1980.
478* 40c. Boeing 747-200 of British Airways 10 10

1981. 10th Anniv of Opening of Seychelles International Airport.
514 40c. Britten-Norman BN-2 Islander S7-AAA of Air Seychelles at Seychelles International Airport 15 10
515 2r.25 Britten-Norman BN-2A Mk III "long nose" Trislander of Air Seychelles at Seychelles International Airport 40 45
516 3r.50 Vickers Super VC-10 .... 60 70
517 5r. Boeing 747-100 .... 75 1·00
514/517 *Set of 4* .... 1·70 2·00

1983. Bicentenary of Manned Flight.
563 40c. Charles Green's balloon *Royal Vauxhall*, 1836........................... 15 10
564 1r.75 Sir Alan Cobham's de Havilland DH.50J G-EBFO............................ 30 30
565 2r.75 Grumman SA-16 Albatross flying boat 35 55
566 7r. Swearingen Merlin IIIA .... 55 1·75
563/566 *Set of 4* .... 1·20 2·40

1983.
567 2r. Douglas DC-10-30 of Air Seychelles (leased from British Caledonian)........ 2·00 2·00

1984.
598* 2r. Paraskiing 90 45

The Life and Times of
Her Majesty Queen Elizabeth The Queen Mother

1985.
MS618* 10r. Westland Wessex helicopter of the Queen's Flight .... 3·25 2·25

1986.
647* 7r. Britten-Norman BN-2A Mk III "short nose" Trislander S7-AAG of Air Seychelles................................... 4·00 3·50

1986.
654* 50c. Seychelles Airport 75 30

1988.
704* 10r. Airship LZ-129 *Hindenburg* on fire at Lakehurst, New Jersey, 1937............... 6·00 5·00

1988.
706* 2r. Hindustan Aircraft Chetak helicopter SY-DD4 of the Seychelles Defence Force.. 4·00 2·25

1990. Air Seychelles Boeing 767-200ER World Record Breaking Flight (1989).
781* 3r. Boeing 767-200ER of Air Seychelles . 4·25 3·75

1993.
835* 10r. Boeing 747-400 of Air France and Boeing 737-200 of Air Seychelles ...... 6·00 8·50

SHARJAH

Arabia 1964

100 naye paise = 1 rupee

1966. 100 dirhams = 1 riyal

1964.

81* 20np. Helicopter on oil rig platform 60 20

1965.

121* 50np. Lilienthal biplane glider 50 30
122* 50np. Sud Aviation SE 210 Caravelle............ 50 30

1970.

286* 5d. Airport 20 20
297* 40d. Airport 40 30
302* 60d. Airport 60 40

APPENDIX

The following stamps have either been issued in excess of postal needs or have not been made available to the public in reasonable quantities at face value. Miniature sheets, imperforate stamps, etc are excluded from this section.

1970

Events of 1970. 5d. (Douglas DC-9).

1971

De Gaulle Memorial. 5d. (Concorde).

1972

Famous People. 5d. (North American F-100 Super Sabre), 10d. (Dassault Mirage F.1), 35d. (Northrop F-5A Freedom Fighter), 75d. (Concorde), 1r. (Boeing Vertol H-46 Sea Knight helicopter), 3r. (Dassault Breguet Mirage III).

SIERRA LEONE

West Africa

1949. 12 pence = 1 shilling

20 shillings = 1 pound

1964. 100 cents = 1 leone

1949. As Nos. 114/15 of Antigua.

205* 1½d. Airplane.. 20 50
206* 3d. Jet-powered Vickers Viking .... 2·00 5·50

1956.

218* 1s.3d. Bristol 170 Freighter Mk 31 .... 11·00 30

1980.

650* 6c. Boeing 707 at Freetown Airport and in flight 10 10

1983.

743* 1l. Beech 80 Queen Air at Freetown Airport .... 1·50 1·25

1983. Bicentenary of Manned Flight.

755 6c. Montgolfier balloon (first manned free flight, 1783) 35 10
756 20c. Wolfert's airship *Deutschland*.............. 1·00 30
757 50c. Amundsen's airship N.1 *Norge* over the North Pole, 1926 .... 2·75 2·25
758 1l. Hot-air balloon *Cap Sierra*.................... 2·25 3·00
755/758 *Set of 4*.. 5·75 5·00
MS759 2l. "Airship of the 21st Century"........................ 1·00 1·75

1984.

797 4l. Concorde of British Airways .... 3·00 1·75

1985. 40th Anniv of ICAO.

862 70c. Edward Rickenbacker, SPAD XIII and German biplane trailing smoke.......... 1·50 75
863 1l.25 Samuel Pierpont Langley's *Aerodrome A*, 1903 (wrongly inscribed "Aerodrome No. 5")................ 2·00 1·75
864 1l.30 Orville and Wilbur Wright and Wright *Flyer I* .... 2·00 1·75
865 2l. Charles Lindbergh and Ryan NYP Special *Spirit of St. Louis*...................... 2·25 2·75
862/865 *Set of 4*.. 7·00 6·25
MS866 5l. Boeing 707-384C of Sierra Leone Airlines 2·00 1·75

1986.

933* 50c. Northrop T-38A Talon jet trainers of NASA escorting Space Shuttle at Edwards Air Force Base, California 40 10

1986. No. 933 overprinted with Halley's Comet emblem.

988* 50c. Northrop T-38A Talon jet trainers of NASA escorting Space Shuttle at Edwards Air Force Base, California 30 10

1987.

1058* 5l. Blanchard's balloon, 1793 .... 40 30
1059* 10l. Amelia Earhart's Lockheed Vega 5B NR-7952, 1932 .... 1·25 60
1060* 15l. Alcock and Brown's Vickers FB-27 Vimy, 1919... 1·50 80
1062* 25l. Vought-Sikorsky VS-300 helicopter prototype .... 2·00 1·60
1063* 30l. Wright *Flyer I* .... 2·00 1·60
1064* 35l. Bleriot XI, 1909 .... 2·00 2·00
1065* 40l. Paraplane, 1983..................................... 2·00 2·25

1988.

1165* 3l. Sikorsky S-58 helicopters and flight deck of aircraft carrier .... 1·25 30

1988.

1173* 40l. First World War German biplanes ...... 3·75 3·25

1990. American Aircraft.

1417 1l. James Doolittle's North American B-25 Mitchell *Ruptured Duck* taking off from aircraft carrier U.S.S. Hornet 30 30
1418 2l. Consolidated B-24 Liberator of the U.S.A.F.. 40 30
1419 3l. Douglas A-20J Boston of the U.S.A.F 40 30
1420 9l. Captain Thomas G. Lanphier's Lockheed P-38 Lightning of the U.S.A.F.. 60 35
1421 12l. Martin B-26 Marauder of the U.S.A.F 75 40
1422 16l. Boeing B-17F Flying Fortress bombers of the U.S.A.F...................... 85 55
1423 50l. North American B-25D Mitchell of the U.S.A.F .... 2·50 1·75
1424 80l. Boeing B-29 Superfortress of the U. S. A. F .... 2·75 2·75
1425 90l. Boeing B-17G Flying Fortress of the U.S.A.F.. 2·75 3·00
1426 100l. Boeing B-29 Superfortress *Enola Gay* of the U.S.A.F .... 3·00 3·00
1417/1426 *Set of 10* .... 13·00 11·50
MS1427 Two sheets. (a) 150l. James Doolittle's North American B-25 Mitchell *Ruptured Duck* taking off from aircraft carrier U.S.S. *Hornet*; (b) 150l. Boeing B-17G Flying Fortress of the 447th Bomber Group, U.S.A.F. *Set of 2 sheets* .... 7·50 8·00

1990.

1430* 10l. Lungi Airport.. 40 20

1991.

1677* 10l. Supermarine Spitfire 20 20
1685* 300l. North American B-25 Mitchell .... 3·00 3·25
MS1687* Three sheets. (b) 450l. Boeing B-17 Flying Fortress; (c) 450l. Mitsubishi A6M Zero-Sen fighter-bombers over Pearl Harbour, 1942 (other sheet does not show aircraft) *Set of 3 sheets* .... 11·00 11·00

1991. 50th Anniv of Japanese Attack on Pearl Harbour.

1752* 75l. Aichi D3A "Val" dive bomber 75 75
1753* 75l. Aichi D3A "Val" dive bomber and smoke 75 75
1754* 75l. Aircraft over burning ships in "Battleship Row" 75 75
1755* 75l. Aircraft and burning dockyard 75 75
1757* 75l. Two Aichi D3A "Val" dive bombers...... 75 75
1758* 75l. Aircraft over burning ships and hangars 75 75

1759*	75l. Aircraft attacking airfield	75	75
1760*	75l. Curtiss P-40C of the U.S. Army Air Corps	75	75
1761*	75l. Two Mitsubishi A6M Zero-Sen fighter-bombers	75	75
1762*	75l. Two Mitsubishi A6M Zero-Sen fighter-bombers over suburbs	75	75
1763*	75l. Two Nakajima B5N "Kate" bombers attacking ships	75	75
1764*	75l. Nakajima B5N "Kate" on fire	75	75
1765*	75l. Two Nakajima B5N "Kate" bombers over jungle	75	75
1766*	75l. Mitsubishi A6M Zero-Sen fighters	75	75

SIERRA LEONE
The Graf Zeppelin
Le 170

1993.

1945*	170l. Airship LZ-127 *Graf Zeppelin*	1·50	90
1953*	700l. Construction drawings of airship LZ-127 *Graf Zeppelin*	3·75	4·00
MS1954*	Three sheets. (a) 900l. Count Ferdinand von Zeppelin (airship pioneer) (75th death anniversary) (other miniature sheets do not show aircraft) Price for 3 sheets	10·50	11·50

SIERRA LEONE   Le500

1994.

2115	500l. Parachute drops	1·50	1·50
2116	750l. Parachute drops	2·00	2·00
MS2117	1000l. Douglas C-47 Skytrain	3·00	3·50

Sierra Leone   Le250
Minnie's Christmas Flight

1995.

2183*	250l. Minnie Mouse in airplane (cartoon)	1·10	85

SIERRA LEONE   Le250
HMS ARK ROYAL

1995.

2317	250l. Aircraft carriers	75	75
MS2324*	1500l. Aircraft carriers	4·00	4·50

Sierra Leone   LE300
B-17G

1995.

2340*	300l. Boeing B-17 Flying Fortress*	80	80
2341*	300l. North American B-25 Mitchell	80	80
2342*	300l. Consolidated B-24 Liberator	80	80
2344*	300l. Douglas B-29 Boston	80	80
MS2346*	1500l. Boeing B-29 Superfortress	3·00	3·50

1996.

MS2573*	1500l. Space Shuttle landing	3·75	4·00

SIERRA LEONE   Le 300
USS ENTERPRISE - CURRENT

1996.

2640*	300l. Aircraft carrier	90	90

Sierra Leone   Le600
BENOIST TYPE XIV

1997. Development of the Civil Airliner.

2828	600l. Benoist Type XIV	1·50	1·50
2829	600l. Douglas DC-3	1·50	1·50

2830	600l. Junkers Ju52/3m	1·50	1·50
2831	600l. Sikorsky S-42	1·50	1·50
2832	600l. Aerospatiale (Sud-Aviation) SE 210 Caravelle VI	1·50	1·50
2833	600l. Boeing 707	1·50	1·50
2834	600l. de Havilland DH.106 Comet	1·50	1·50
2835	600l. Airbus Industries A300	1·50	1·50
2828/2835	Set of 8	11·00	11·00
MS2836	Two sheets. (a) 2000l. Lockheed L.1649A Starliner; (b) 2000l. Concorde Set of 2 sheets	8·00	8·50

SIERRA LEONE   Le800
The Royal Air Force 80th Anniversary

1998. 80th Anniv of Royal Air Force.

2956	800l. McDonnell Douglas F-4M Phantom II FRG Mk 2	2·00	2·00
2957	800l. Panavia Tornado GR Mk 1s	2·00	2·00
2958	800l. SEPECAT Jaguar GR Mk 1A	2·00	2·00
2959	800l. Lockheed C-130 Hercules	2·00	2·00
2956/2959	Set of 4	7·00	7·00
MS2960	Two sheets. (a) 2000l. Westland Lysander and Eurofighter EF-2000 Typhoon; (b) 2000l. Bristol F2B Set of 2 sheets	8·50	9·00

SIERRA LEONE   Le200
THE GRUMMAN X-29

1999.

3011	200l. Grumman X-29A	40	20
3012	300l. Bell X-1	50	20
3013	400l. Mikoyan-Gurevich MiG-21 'Fishbed'	60	30
3014	600l. Bleriot XI	80	85
3015	600l. Niueport 11 Bébé	80	85
3016	600l. de Havilland DH.100 Vampire	80	85
3017	600l. Avions de Transport Regional ATR 72	80	85
3018	600l. Fiat CR-32	80	85
3019	600l. Curtiss P-6E Hawk	80	85
3020	600l. Saab JA37 Viggen	80	85
3021	600l. Piper PA-46 Malibu	80	85
3022	600l. Grumman F-14 Tomcat	80	85
3023	600l. Grumman F3F-1	80	85
3024	600l. North American F-86A Sabre	80	85
3025	600l. Cessna Model 337 Super Skymaster	80	85
3026	600l. Lockheed Martin (General Dynamics) F-16 Fighting Falcon	80	85
3027	600l. Rutan *Voyager*	80	85
3028	600l. Fairchild Republic A-10 Thunderbolt II (Warthog)	80	85
3029	600l. Wiley Post's Lockheed Vega 5B *Winnie Mae*, 1933	80	85
3030	600l. Amelia Earhart's Lockheed Vega 5C, 1930	80	85
3031	600l. Sopwith Tabloid	80	85
3032	600l. Vickers F.B.5 Gunbus	80	85
3033	600l. Savoia-Marchetti S.M. 79-II	80	85
3034	600l. Mitsubishi A6M3 Zero-Sen	80	85
3035	600l. Morane-Saulnier 1	80	85
3036	600l. Shorts 360	80	85
3037	600l. Tupolev Tu-160 'Blackjack'	80	85
3038	600l. Mikoyan-Gurevich MiG-15 'Fagot'	80	85
3039	800l. Fokker F.VIIa/3m *Southern Cross*	1·25	1·40
3040	1500l. Supermarine S6B	2·00	2·50
3011/3040	Set of 30	21·00	22·00
MS3041	Two sheets. (a) 3000l. Ryan NYP Special *Spirit of St. Louis*; (b) 3000l. Canadair CL-215 Set of 2 sheets	8·50	9·00

No. 3023 is inscribed Gumman F3F-1, No. 3027 'NICK' (instead of Dick) and No. 3030 "Amella Earhart", all in error.

(LZ-129) Hindenburg 1936   Le2000
SIERRA LEONE

2000. Centenary of First Zeppelin Flight.

3400	2000l. LZ-129 *Hindenburg*, 1936	2·00	2·25
3401	2000l. LZ-4, 1908	2·00	2·25
3402	2000l. LZ-6 *Delag*, 1909	2·00	2·25
3400/3402	Set of 3	5·50	6·00
MS3403	4000l. LZ-127 *Graf Zeppelin*, 1928	6·00	6·50

No. 3400 is inscribed *Hindenberg* in error.

Sierra Leone   Le1000

2001.

3706*	1000l. Rescuing British pilot	1·25	1·25
3716*	1000l. Hawker Hurricanes	1·25	1·25
3717*	1000l. Brendan Finucane–fighter pilot	1·25	1·25
3718*	1000l. Hawk 75 (probably Curtiss)	1·25	1·25
3730*	1000l. Dornier Do17	1·25	1·25
MS3735*	Four sheets. (c) 6000l. Supermarine Spitfire; (d) 6000l. British bomber crew Price for 4 sheets	32·00	35·00

SIERRA LEONE
The Spirit of St.Cloud Powered from the Ryan Airplane Factory
Le2500

2002. 75th Anniv of First Solo Trans-Atlantic Flight.

4031	2500l. Ryan NYP Special *Spirit of St. Louis*	3·00	3·25
4032	2500l. Ryan NYP Special *Spirit of St. Louis* at Curtis Field, 1927	3·00	3·25
4033	2500l. Ryan NYP Special *Spirit of St. Louis* taking off from Roosevelt Field, 1927	3·00	3·25
4031/4033	Set of 3	8·00	8·75
MS4034	2500l. Charles Lindbergh	3·00	3·25

SIERRA LEONE
Le1500
Wright Brothers First Plane (U.S.A.) 1903

2003. Centenary of Powered Flight.

MS4149	1500l. Wright *Flyer I* (USA), 1903; 1500l. Voisin-Farman (France), 1907 (blue background) (inscribed Farmin' in error); 1500l. Levavasseur Antoinette (France), 1909 (No. 29 on fuselage); 1500l. Nieuport (France), 1910	7·50	8·50
MS4150	1500l. Curtiss Triad (USA), 1911 (inscribed Wright Brothers first plane (USA) 1903); 1500l. Avro Biplane (Britain), 1911 (inscribed Voisin-Farmin (France), 1907 (blue/grey background); 1500l. Curtiss America (USA), 1913 (inscribed Levavasseur Antoinette (France), 1909; 1500l. Farnborough Be-2 (Britain) 1913 (inscribed Nieuport (France), 1910)	7·50	8·50
MS4150a	1500l. Curtiss Triad (USA) 1911; 1500l. Avro Biplane (Britain) 1911; 1500l. Curtiss America (USA) 1913; 1500l. Farnborough Be-2 (Britain) 1913	7·50	8·50
MS4151	Two sheets. (a) 5000l. Voisin-Farman plane crossing finishing line, Aero Club, 1908; (b) 5000l. Roland Garros and Morane-Saulnier monoplane after first non-stop Mediterranean crossing, 1913 Set of 2 sheets	7·50	8·50

No. MS4150 was issued with incorrect aircraft inscriptions and No. MS4150a was issued subsequently with the correct inscriptions.

Sierra Leone   Le 3,000
Concorde 206 G-BOAA

2004. Last Flight of Concorde.

MS4184	3000l. Concorde over river, Rio de Janeiro; 3000l. Concorde over Brazil flag (top left of blue circle); 3000l. Concorde over Brazil flag (bottom left of blue circle)	12·00	12·00
MS4185	3000l. Concorde (pink background); 3000l. Concorde and pyramid (red background); 3000l. Concorde and pyramid (dark brown background)	12·00	12·00
MS4186	3000l. Concorde and Nairobi skyline; 3000l. Concorde over Kenyan bush (black and red background); 3000l. Concorde over Kenyan bush (red and green background)	12·00	12·00

No. MS4184 shows Concorde 206 G-BOAA over Rio de Janeiro, No. MS4185 Concord 101 G-AXDN and Egyptian pyramid and No. MS4186 Concorde 101 G-AXDN over Kenya.

Sierra Leone   Spitfire
Le 1000

2004.

MS4267*	Six sheets. (b) 1000l. North American P-51 Mustang; 1000l. Paratroops; 1000l. Lockheed P-38 Lightning (other stamps in the miniature sheet do not show aircraft). (c) 1000l. Supermarine Spitfire; 1000l. Hawker Typhoon; 1000l. Tail of Hawker Typhoon; 1000l. North American P-51 Mustang; 1000l. Douglas C-47 Skytrain; 1000l. Warplane and wing of Hawker Typhoon; 1000l. Lockheed P-38 Lightning; 1000l. US Air Force patch. (d) 1000l. Republic P-47 Thunderbolt; 1000l. Paratroops, map and planes (other miniature sheets do not show aircraft) Price for 6 sheets	45·00	50·00

"LITTLE BOY"- ATOMIC BOMB DROPPED ON HIROSHIMA AUGUST 6th, 1945
LE 2000   SIERRA LEONE

2005.

MS4330*	2000l. Little Boy (Hiroshima bomb); 2000l. Fat Man (Nagasaki bomb) (other stamps in the miniature sheet do not show aircraft)	8·00	9·00

2005.
4342*	2000l. Messerschmitt Bf 109s		2·50	2·50
4344*	2000l. Pilots running to planes		2·50	2·50
4345*	2000l. Planes fighting		2·50	2·50
MS4346*	5000l. Pilot and plane		7·00	7·50

2006. 50th Death Anniv of Ludwig Durr (Zeppelin engineer).
4453	4000l. Zeppelin L-30		4·00	4·50
4454	4000l. Zeppelin LZ-129 *Hindenburg*		4·00	4·50
4455	4000l. Zeppelin LZ-129 *Graf Zeppelin*		4·00	4·50
4453/4455 *Set of 3*			11·00	12·00

2007. Concorde.
4513	2000l. Speedometer (Mach 2.23, speed record, 26 March 1974)		2·25	2·25
4514	2000l. Concorde silhouette and 'MACH 2.23'		2·25	2·25
4515	2000l. Concorde with BAe Hawks of the Red Arrows (Golden Jubilee Flypast over London, 4 June 2002)		2·25	2·25
4516	2000l. Golden Jubilee Flypast over London, 4 June 2002)		2·25	2·25
4513/4516 *Set of 4*			8·00	8·00

SINGAPORE

South-east Asia

100 cents = 1 dollar

1949. As Nos. 114/15 of Antigua.
33*	10c. Airplane		75	70
34*	15c. Jet-powered Vickers Viking		6·00	4·25

1955.
47*	25c. Douglas DC-4M2 "Argonaut" of B.O.A.C.		7·00	1·50

1969.
121*	15c. Airliner		2·50	70
125*	$5 Tail of Japanese bomber		18·00	45·00

1977.
288*	75c. Pilot and Douglas A-4 Skyhawk		3·50	4·50

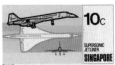

1978. Aviation.
339	10c. Concorde		1·00	30
340	35c. Boeing 747-200		1·00	1·25
341	50c. Ross and Keith Smith's Vickers Vimy G-EAOU, 1919		1·25	2·50
342	75c. Wilbur and Orville Wright and Wright *Flyer I*		1·50	4·00
339/342 *Set of 4*			4·25	7·25

1981. Opening of Changi Airport.
411	10c. Control tower and terminal building at Changi Airport		10	10
412	35c. Control tower and terminal building at Changi Airport		20	30
413	50c. Control tower and terminal building at Changi Airport		30	75
414	75c. Control tower and terminal building at Changi Airport		40	1·50
415	$1 Control tower and terminal building at Changi Airport		45	1·60
411/415 *Set of 5*			1·30	3·75

1984.
479*	$1 Control tower and terminal building at Changi Airport (on stamp No. 415)		80	1·75

1987.
555*	10c. Pilot, Northrop F-5 and Douglas A-4 Skyhawk		55	70

1990.
637*	15c. Pilot and Douglas A-4 Skyhawks of the Republic of Singapore Air Force		1·00	20
639*	75c. Airliners over airport		2·25	2·50

1991. Singapore Civil Aviation.
656	20c. Boeing 747-400 and Terminal II, Changi Airport		1·25	25
657	75c. Boeing 747-200 and Terminal I, Changi Airport		2·50	2·00
658	$1 Concorde of British Airways at Paya Libar Airport		2·50	2·25
659	$2 Douglas DC-2 at Kallang Airport		3·75	6·00
656/659 *Set of 4*			9·00	9·50

1992.
693*	35c. Lockheed Martin (General Dynamics) F-16 Fighting Falcon		85	75
694*	$1 Lockheed Martin (General Dynamics) F-16 Fighting Falcon		2·50	4·00

1994. 50th Anniv of ICAO.
780	20c. ICAO logo and globe		20	20
781	35c. Boeing 747 and Changi Airport control tower		60	60
782	75c. Hypersonic aircraft project		85	1·25
783	$2 Boeing 747 and control tower		2·00	3·25
780/783 *Set of 4*			3·25	4·75

1995.
800*	75c. Boeing 747 (on stamp)		90	1·50

1999.
1019*	60c. Lockheed C-130 Hercules		60	70

2003. Centenary of Powered Flight.
1309	22c. Aerospatiale (Eurocopter) SA 316 Alouette III		30	30
1310	22c. Grumman E-2C Hawkeye		30	30
1311	22c. Hawker Hunter		30	30
1312	22c. Eurocopter AS-332M Super Puma		30	30
1313	22c. Lockheed Hercules C-130H		30	30
1314	22c. Lockheed Martin (General Dynamics) F-16 C/D Fighting Falcon		30	30
1315	22c. Boeing (Hughes/McDonnell Douglas) AH-64D Apache		30	30
1316	22c. Boeing KC-135R Stratotanker		30	30
1317	22c. Cessna 172		30	30
1318	22c. Northrop F-5E Tiger II		30	30
1319	22c. Airbus A340-500		30	30
1320	22c. Boeing 747-400		30	30
1321	22c. Boeing 777-200		30	30
1322	22c. Boeing 747-400 Freighter		30	30
1323	22c. Airbus A320		30	30
1324	22c. Concorde		30	30
1325	22c. Boeing 737-100		30	30
1326	22c. de Havilland DH.106 Comet IV		30	30
1327	22c. Vickers Viscount		30	30
1328	22c. Airspeed AS.65 Consul		30	30
1309/1328 *Set of 20*			5·50	5·50

SINKIANG

See under CHINA.

SLOVAKIA

Central Europe

100 haleru = 1 koruna

1939.

55	30h. Heinkel He 111C	20	30
56	50h. Heinkel He 111C	20	30
57	1k. Heinkel He 111C	25	30
58	2k. Heinkel He 116A	40	45
59	3k. Heinkel He 116A	75	85
60	4k. Heinkel He 116A	1·40	1·75
62	5k. Aero A-204	1·10	1·25
63	10k. Aero A-204	1·40	1·50
64	20k. Aero A-204	1·40	1·90
55/64 Set of 9		6·50	7·75

1943.

107*	1k.30 +2k. Pilot and Messerschmitt Bf 109 fighters	45	85

1994.

197	10k. Stefan Banic (inventor of parachute)	75	40

1995.

210	6k. Jan Bahyl and helicopter design	45	30

1996.

250	6k. Andrej Kvasz and his aeroplane	50	30

2003. Centenary of Powered Flight.

426	18k. Wright *Flyer I*	1·75	1·00

SLOVENIA

South-east Europe

Italian Occupation

100 paras = 1 dinar

1941. Nos. 446/9 of Yugoslavia overprinted **R. Commissariato Civile Territori Sloveni occupati LUBIANA.**

45	50p. +50p. on 5d. Fokker F.VIIa/3m	4·00	5·00
46	1d. +1d. on 10d. Junkers G.31	4·00	5·00
47	1d.50 +1d.50 on 20d. Fokker F.VIIa/3m	4·00	5·00
48	2d. +2d. on 30d. Fokker F.VIIa/3m	4·00	5·00
45/48 Set of 4		1·40	18·00

1941. Nos. 360/7 and 443/4 of Yugoslavia overprinted **R. Commissariato Civile Territori Sioveni occupati LUBIANA.**

49	50p. Fokker F.VIIa/3m	1·10	2·00
50	1d. Junkers G.31	1·10	2·00
51	2d. Fokker F.VIIa/3m	1·25	2·00
52	2d.50 Fokker F.VIIa/3m	1·25	2·00
53	5d. Fokker F.VIIa/3m	3·00	3·00
54	10d. Junkers G.31	3·00	3·00
55	20d. Fokker F.VIIa/3m	14·00	15·00
56	30d. Fokker F.VIIa/3m	30·00	30·00
57	40d. Junkers Ju 86	70·00	80·00
58	50d. Fokker F.VIIa/3m	70·00	70·00
49/58 Set of 10		£170	£190

1998.

371	90t. Airbus A320	65	65

2004.

639a	23t. Cartoon airplane dropping supplies	15	15

2006. Slovenia Air Traffic Control and Air Navigation Services.

MS712 95t. Radar screen	55	55

German Occupation

100 centesimi = 1 lira

AIR EXPRESS STAMP

1944. No. E370 of Italy overprinted with eagle and **LJUBJANIKA POKRAJINA PROVINZ LAIBACH.**

E91	2l. Savoia Marchetti S-55A flying boat	13·00	95·00

SOLOMON ISLANDS

West Pacific

1949. 12 pence = 1 shilling

20 shillings = 1 pound

1966. 100 cents = 1 dollar

1949. As Nos. 114/15 of Antigua.

77*	2d. Airplane	50	1·00
78*	3d. Jet-powered Vickers Viking	2·25	1·50

1956.

90*	8d. Douglas DC-3 over Henderson Airfield	25	15
108*	9d. Douglas DC-3 over Henderson Airfield	40	35

1967.

160*	8c. Boeing B-17 Flying Fortress over Henderson Airfield	15	15

1968.

175*	20c. Piper PA-23 Aztec on geological survey	4·50	3·00
180*	$2 Beech 100 King Air	6·50	3·50

1976.

323*	35c. Boeing B-17 Flying Fortress at Henderson Airfield	60	60
324*	45c. Boeing B-17 Flying Fortress	60	80

1976. 50th Anniv of First Flight to Solomon Islands.

330	6c. B.A.C. One Eleven 200/400 DQ-FBO of Air Pacific	35	15
331	20c. Britten-Norman BN-2 Islander of Solair	65	20
332	35c. Douglas DC-3 VH-EBU of Qantas Empire Airways	90	30
333	45c. de Havilland DH.50A seaplane A8-1 of the Royal Australian Air Force	95	75
330/333 Set of 4		2·50	1·30

1980.

418*	45c. Douglas C-47 Skytrain	30	45
419*	45c. B.A.C. One Eleven of Air Pacific	30	45

1983. Bicentenary of Manned Flight.

493*	30c. Montgolfier balloon (first manned free flight, 1783)	25	40
494*	35c. Lockheed C-130 Hercules of the Royal Australian Air Force	30	45
495*	40c. Wright Type A	35	55
497*	50c. Beech C55 Baron H4-AAB of Solair	40	65

1987.

607*	30c. de Havilland Canada DHC-6 Twin Otter 300 of Solair	45	20
609*	$2 Beech 80 Queen Air of Solair and control tower at Henderson Airfield	2·00	2·75

1992.

729*	80c. Boeing 737-400 *Guadalcanal* of Solomon Airlines	1·40	1·25

1992.

737*	30c. Consolidated PBY-5 Catalina flying boat of the Royal New Zealand Air Force	80	80
738*	80c. Grumman F4F Wildcats of the U.S. Marine Corps	1·00	1·00
739*	80c. Grumman F4F Wildcat at Henderson Airfield	1·00	1·00
742*	80c. Grumman F4F Wildcat over landing craft	1·00	1·00
743*	80c. Aircraft taking off from Japanese aircraft carrier *Ryujo*	1·00	1·00
744*	80c. Mitsubishi A6M Zero-Sen fighters	1·00	1·00
745*	80c. Mitsubishi G4M "Betty" bombers	1·00	1·00

1993.

770*	$4 Curtiss SB2C Helldiver, Grumman F6F Hellcat and Mitsubishi A6M Zero-Sen	4·25	5·50

SOLOMON ISLANDS

1994.

807*	$1.10 Boeing 737-400	80	1·25
808*	$1.10 Boeing 737-400 and de Havilland Canada DHC-6 Twin Otter	80	1·25
809*	$1.10 de Havilland Canada DHC-6 Twin Otter at Fera Airfield	80	1·25

1995.

832*	95c. Mitsubishi A6M Zero-Sen	1·00	1·00
835*	$3 Grumman F6F Hellcat	2·50	3·50

1996.

848*	$1.35 Wireless transmitter, Croydon Aerodrome, 1920	90	1·50

2003. Centenary of Powered Flight.

MS1054	$4 Boeing 747; $4 Boeing 707; $4 Lockheed L-649 Constellation; $4 Boeing Model 247D; $4 Fokker F.VII; $4 Orville and Wilbur Wright	6·00	6·50
MS1055	$15 Concorde Set of 2 sheets	4·50	4·75

2005.

1119*	$5 Grumman F4F Wildcat attacking a Mitsubishi A6M Zero-Sen	1·00	1·00
1121*	$5 Lockheed P-38 Lightning shoots down Admiral Yamamoto's Mitsubishi G4MI Betty	1·00	1·00

SOMALIA

East Africa

1934. 100 centesimi = 1 lira

1950. 100 centesimi = 1 somalo

1961. 100 cents = 1 Somali shilling

1934.

193	25c. Caproni Ca 101	3·50	10·00
194	50c. Caproni Ca 101	3·50	8·25
195	75c. Caproni Ca 101	3·50	8·25
196	80c. Caproni Ca 101	3·50	10·00
197	1l. Caproni Ca 101	3·50	11·00
198	2l. Caproni Ca 101	3·50	19·00
193/198	Set of 6	19·00	60·00

1936.

223	25c. Macchi Castoldi MC-94 flying boat	1·25	3·00
224	50c. Caproni Ca 101	25	25
225	60c. Caproni Ca 101	1·90	5·50
226	75c. Caproni Ca 101	1·20	1·50

227	1l. Macchi Castoldi MC-94 flying boat	25	25
228	1l.50 Macchi Castoldi MC-94 flying boat	1·20	75
229	2l. Caproni Ca 101	4·25	1·20
230	3l. Macchi Castoldi MC-94 flying boat	13·00	5·00
231	5l. Caproni Ca 101	15·00	9·25
232	10l. Caproni Ca 101	19·00	15·00
223/232	Set of 10	50·00	37·00

1950.

244	30c. Savoia Marchetti S.M.75	30	30
245	45c. Savoia Marchetti S.M.75	30	30
246	65c. Savoia Marchetti S.M.75	30	30
247	70c. Savoia Marchetti S.M.75	30	30
248	90c. Savoia Marchetti S.M.75	30	30
249	1l. Savoia Marchetti S.M.75	45	30
250	1s.35 Savoia Marchetti S.M.75	70	70
251	1s.50 Savoia Marchetti S.M.75	85	50
252	3s. Savoia Marchetti S.M.75	7·00	2·25
253	5s. Savoia Marchetti S.M.75	8·00	3·00
254	10s. Savoia Marchetti S.M.75	9·50	2·25
244/254	Set of 11	25·00	9·50

1951.

257*	1s. Savoia Marchetti S.M.95C	2·25	70
258*	1s.50 Savoia Marchetti S.M.95C	3·75	2·75

1952.

261*	1s.20 Douglas DC-4	2·00	2·00

1953.

268*	1s.20 Airplane	40	40
269*	1s.50 Airplane	40	40

1959.

342*	1s.20 Airplane	25	25
343*	2s. Airplane	40	40

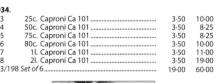

1961.

376	60c. Boeing 707	25	15
377	90c. Boeing 707	30	20
378	1s. Boeing 707	3·25	25
379	1s.80 Boeing 707	75	45
380	3s. Boeing 707	90	60
381	5s. Boeing 707	3·25	90
382	10s. Boeing 707	6·75	2·40
376/382	Set of 7	14·00	4·50

1964. Inauguration of Somali Airlines.

416	5c. Douglas DC-3	20	35
417	20c. Passengers disembarking from Douglas DC-3	65	35

418	1s. Douglas DC-3 (air)	1·10	55
419	1s.80 Douglas DC-3	2·25	1·60
416/419	Set of 4	3·75	2·50

1977. 30th Anniv of ICAO.

612	1s. Leonardo da Vinci's drawing of a "helicopter"	35	25
613	1s.50 Montgolfier balloon (first manned free flight, 1783)	45	35
614	2s. Wright Flyer I	65	45
615	2s.90 Boeing 720B of Somali Airlines	1·40	65
612/615	Set of 4	2·50	1·50

1981.

668	2s. +50c. Aircraft	70	45
669	6s.80 +50c. Aircraft	2·50	1·25

1983.

700*	3s.20 Pilot and fighter aircraft	1·00	55

1985. 40th Anniv of ICAO.

727	3s. Emblem with winged horse	65	35
728	6s.40 Emblem with winged horse	1·10	80

SOMALILAND PROTECTORATE

East Africa

12 pies = 1 anna

16 annas = 1 rupee

1949. As Nos. 114/15 of Antigua, surcharged.

121*	1a. on 10c. Airplane	20	40
122*	3a. on 30c. Jet-powered Vickers Viking	1·25	2·75

SOUTH AFRICA

Southern Africa

1925. 12 pence = 1 shilling

20 shillings = 1 pound

1961. 100 cents = 1 rand

1925.

26	1d. Airco (de Havilland) D.H.9 biplane	4·25	10·00
27	3d. Airco (de Havilland) D.H.9 biplane	7·00	10·00
28	6d. Airco (de Havilland) D.H.9 biplane	9·00	11·00

29	9d. Airco (de Havilland) D.H.9 biplane	23·00	55·00
26/29	Set of 4	39·00	80·00

1929.

40	4d. de Havilland DH.60 Cirrus Moth........	5·50	2·50
41	1s. de Havilland DH.60 Cirrus Moth........	16·00	13·00

1961. 50th Anniv of First South African Aerial Post.

220	3c. Bleriot XI and Boeing 707	50	10

1979.

456	15c. de Havilland DH.60 Cirrus Moth (on stamp No. 40)................................	30	20

1993. Aviation in South Africa.

779	45c. Bristol "Boxkite", 1907	65	60
780	45c. Voisin "Boxkite", 1909	65	60
781	45c. Jan Olieslagers' Bleriot XI, 1911..............	65	60
782	45c. Paterson No. 2 biplane, 1913..................	65	60
783	45c. Farman H.F.27, 1915...............................	65	60
784	45c. Royal Aircraft Factory B.E.2E, 1918	65	60
785	45c. Van Ryneveld and Brand's Vickers Vimy *Silver Queen II*, 1920............	65	60
786	45c. Royal Aircraft Factory S.E.5A, 1921	65	60
787	45c. Avro 504K biplane, 1921	65	60
788	45c. Armstrong Whitworth A.W.15 Atalanta G-ABPI (incorrectly inscribed "1930").............................	65	60
789	45c. de Havilland DH.66 Hercules G-ABMT, 1931..............................	65	60
790	45c. Westland Wapiti, 1931	65	60
791	45c. Junkers F-13 ZS-AEA, 1932..................	65	60
792	45c. Handley Page H.P.42 G-AAGX, 1933..	65	60
793	45c. Junkers Ju 52/3m, 1934........................	65	60
794	45c. Junkers Ju 86, 1936..............................	65	60
795	45c. Hawker Hartbees, 1936	65	60
796	45c. Short S.23 Empire "C" Class flying boat G-ADHL *Canopus*, 1937............	65	60
797	45c. Airspeed A.S.10 Oxford and Miles Master II, 1940..............................	65	60
798	45c. North American AT-6 Harvard Mk IIa, 1942..	65	60
799	45c. Short S.25 Sunderland flying boat, 1945..	65	60
800	45c. Avro Type 685 York G-AGNR of B.O.A.C., 1946...........................	65	60
801	45c. Douglas DC-7B of South African Airways, 1955...........................	65	60
802	45c. Sikorsky S-55C helicopter, 1956........	65	60
803	45c. Boeing 707-344 ZS-SAG of South African Airways, 1959..................	65	60
779/803	Set of 25	15·00	13·50

1995. Aviation Anniversaries.

873	50c. Airco (de Havilland) D.H.9 and Atlas Cheetah D (75th anniv of South African Air Force)........................	55	30
874	95c. Vickers F.B. 27 Vimy *Silver Queen II* (75th anniv First Trans-African flight)	80	75

2003. Centenary of Powered Flight.

1455*	1r.65 Paterson biplane..............................	50	50
1456*	1r.65 Vickers F.B. 27 Vimy *Silver Queen II* ...	50	50
1457*	1r.65 Westland Wapiti..............................	50	50
1458*	1r.65 Airco (de Havilland) D.H.9.............	50	50
1459*	1r.65 Junkers Ju52/3m.............................	50	50
1460*	1r.65 Sikorsky S-55.................................	50	50
1461*	1r.65 Boeing 707.....................................	50	50
1462*	1r.65 Denel (Atlas) AH-2A Rooivalk............	50	50

2004.

1516*	1r.70 Police helicopter	55	55
1518*	1r.70 Police parachutists	55	55

2006.

1583*	1r.85 Eurocopter (MBB) BO 105....................	90	90
1585*	1r.85 Pilatus PC-12	90	90

SOUTH GEORGIA AND THE SOUTH SANDWICH ISLANDS

South Atlantic

100 pence = 1 pound

1986.

160*	29p. Westland WG-13 Lynx helicopter of the Royal Navy...........................	1·75	1·75

1992.

221*	68p. +32p. Westland AS.1 Wasp helicopter	3·50	3·00

2004.

370	40p. First powered flight over South Georgia, 1938 by Supermarine Walrus..	1·40	1·00

2006.

427	25p. Lockheed C-130 J	1·25	1·25

2007.

435*	25p. Westland Wasp	1·10	1·10
436*	50p. Westland Wessex	1·90	1·90

SOUTH KOREA

See under KOREA

SOUTH VIETNAM

See under VIETNAM

SOUTH WEST AFRICA

Southern Africa

1930. 12 pence = 1 shilling

20 shillings = 1 pound

1961. 100 cents = 1 rand

1930. Nos. 40/1 of South Africa overprinted **S.W.A.**

72	4d. de Havilland DH.60 Cirrus Moth........	1·25	6·00
73	1s. de Havilland DH.60 Cirrus Moth........	3·25	15·00

1931.

86	3d. Fokker monoplane.............................	27·00	2·50
87	10d. Handley Page H.P.25 Hendon biplane	42·00	7·00

Nos. 86/7 exist inscribed in either English or Afrikaans. The prices quoted are for one of each language in horizontal pairs.

1937.

96	1½d. Junkers Ju 52/3m..............................	26·00	35

No. 96 exists inscribed in either English or Afrikaans. The prices quoted are for one of each in horizontal pair.

1977. J. G. Strijdom Airport, Windhoek.

305	20c. Tail of Boeing 747 at J.G. Strijdom Airport, Windhoek..........................	40	30

1989. 75th Anniv of Aviation in South West Africa.

507	18c. Beech Commuter 1900 ZS-LTC of Namib Air	55	20
508	30c. Ryan Navion 205 ZS-BAI..................	90	60
509	40c. Junkers F-13 ZS-ABU	1·00	65
510	50c. Pfalz Otto biplane..........................	1·25	85
507/510	Set of 4	3·25	2·10

OFFICIAL STAMPS

1938. No. 96 overprinted **OFFICIAL** or **OFFISIEEL** alternately.

O25*	1½d. Junkers Ju 52/3m.............................	24·00	5·00

The prices quoted are for a horizontal pair containing one of each overprint.

SOUTHERN RHODESIA

Central Africa

12 pence = 1 shilling

20 shillings = 1 pound

1949. As No. 115 of Antigua.

68*	2d. Jet-powered Vickers Viking................	70	25

1953.

75*	1s. Airliner.......................................	3·00	1·50

SOUTHERN YEMEN

Arabia

1000 fils = 1 dinar

1970.

48*	35f. Airliner being attacked by terrorists........	50	45

SPAIN

South-west Europe

100 centimos = 1 peseta

1926. Trans-Atlantic and Madrid-Manila Flights.

407	5c. CASA-built Dornier Do-J Wal flying boat M-MWAL *Plus Ultra*.....................	1·70	1·70
408	10c. CASA-built Dornier Do-J Wal flyingboat M-MWAL *Plus Ultra*............	2·10	2·10
409	15c. Gallarza and Loriga's Breguet 19A2 biplane.....................................	30	30
410	20c. Gallarza and Loriga's Breguet 19A2 biplane.....................................	30	30
411	25c. CASA-built Dornier Do-J Wal flying boat M-MWAL *Plus Ultra*..................	30	30
412	30c. Gallarza and Loriga's Breguet 19A2 biplane.....................................	30	30
413	40c. Gallarza and Loriga's Breguet 19A2 biplane.....................................	30	30
414	50c. CASA-built Dornier Do-J Wal flying boat M-MWAL *Plus Ultra*..................	30	30
415	1p. CASA-built Dornier Do-J Wal flying boat M-MWAL *Plus Ultra*..................	2·50	2·50
416	4p. Gallarza and Loriga's Breguet 19A2 biplane.....................................	95·00	95·00
407/416 *Set of 10*......................................		90·00	90·00

1927. Nos. 407/16 overprinted **17-V-1902 17-V-1927 A XIII** (5c., 10c., 25c., 50c., 1p.) or **17 MAYO 17 1902 1927 ALFONSO XIII** (others).

445	5c. CASA-built Dornier Do-J Wal flying boat M-MWAL *Plus Ultra*..................	1·50	1·50
446	10c. CASA-built Dornier Do-J Wal flying boat M-MWAL *Plus Ultra*..................	3·25	3·25
447	15c. Gallarza and Loriga's Breguet 19A2 biplane.....................................	30	30
448	20c. Gallarza and Loriga's Breguet 19A2 biplane.....................................	30	30
449	25c. CASA-built Dornier Do-J Wal flying boat M-MWAL *Plus Ultra*..................	30	30
450	30c. Gallarza and Loriga's Breguet 19A2 biplane.....................................	30	30
451	40c. Gallarza and Loriga's Breguet 19A2 biplane.....................................	30	30
452	50c. CASA-built Dornier Do-J Wal flying boat M-MWAL *Plus Ultra*..................	30	30
453	1p. CASA-built Dornier Do-J Wal flying boat M-MWAL *Plus Ultra*..................	2·75	2·75
454	4p. Gallarza and Loriga's Breguet 19A2 biplane.....................................	£120	£120
445/454 *Set of 10*......................................		£120	£120

1927. Nos. 445/6, 449 and 452 further surcharged **75 cts. 75**.

455	75c. on 5c. CASA-built Dornier Do-J Wal flying boat M-MWAL *Plus Ultra*	5·00	5·00
456	75c. on 10c. CASA-built Dornier Do-J Wal flying boat M-MWAL *Plus Ultra*	23·00	23·00
457	75c. on 25c. CASA-built Dornier Do-J Wal flying boat M-MWAL *Plus Ultra*	44·00	44·00
458	75c. on 50c. CASA-built Dornier Do-J Wal flying boat M-MWAL *Plus Ultra*	18·00	18·00
455/458 *Set of 4*.......................................		80·00	80·00

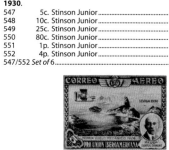

1929.

515	5c. Ryan NYP Special *Spirit of St. Louis*.....	5·50	5·50
516	10c. Ryan NYP Special *Spirit of St. Louis*.....	5·75	5·75
517	25c. Ryan NYP Special *Spirit of St. Louis*.....	6·25	6·25
518	50c. Ryan NYP Special *Spirit of St. Louis*.....	7·50	7·50
519	1p. Ryan NYP Special *Spirit of St. Louis*.....	35·00	35·00
520	4p. Ryan NYP Special *Spirit of St. Louis*.....	25·00	25·00
515/520 *Set of 6*.......................................		75·00	75·00

1930.

547	5c. Stinson Junior	5·50	5·50
548	10c. Stinson Junior	5·50	5·50
549	25c. Stinson Junior	5·50	5·50
550	80c. Stinson Junior	13·50	13·50
551	1p. Stinson Junior	27·00	27·00
552	4p. Stinson Junior	27·00	27·00
547/552 *Set of 6*.......................................		75·00	75·00

1930.

643	5c. Alberto Santos-Dumont and Wright Flyer I over Rio de Janeiro.....................	90	90
644	10c. Teodoro Fels and Douglas 0-2-M biplane	90	90
645	25c. Dagoberto Godoy and Nieuport 17 biplane	90	90
646	50c. Admiral Gago Coutinho, Sacadura Cabral and Fairey IIID seaplane (blue)	1·80	1·80
647	50c. Sidar and Douglas 0-2-M biplane (black)	1·80	1·80
648	1p. Jimenez, Iglesias and Breguet Bre. 19GR *Jesus del Gran Poder* (red)	4·50	4·50
649	1p. Jimenez, Iglesias and Breguet Bre. 19GR *Jesus del Gran Poder* (purple)....	80·00	80·00
650	1p. Charles Lindbergh and Ryan NYP Special *Spirit of St. Louis* (green)	4·50	4·50
651	4p. Breguet Bre. 19GR *Jesus del Gran Poder*	8·25	8·25
643/651 *Set of 9*.......................................		95·00	95·00

1931.

707	5c. Monoplane	15	15
708	10c. Monoplane	15	15
709	25c. Monoplane	15	15
710	50c. Biplane	50	50
711	1p. Biplane	75	75
712	4p. Monoplane	10·50	10·50
707/712 *Set of 6*.......................................		11·00	11·00

1931.

726	5c. Airplane...	55	55
727	10c. Airplane...	2·75	2·75

728	25c. Airplane...	10·50	10·50
729	50c. Airplane...	38·00	38·00
730	1p. Airplane...	25·00	25·00
726/730 *Set of 5*.......................................		70·00	70·00

1935.

780	2p. Cierva C.30A autogyro................	15	15

1936.

802*	2c. Airplane...	15	15
804*	10c. Airplane...	15	15
805*	15c. Cierva C.30A autogyro..................	15	15
807*	25c. Airplane...	15	15
808*	30c. Cierva C.30A autogyro..................	15	15
810*	50c. Cierva C.30A autogyro..................	40	30
811*	60c. Airplane...	80	30
812*	1p. Cierva C.30A autogyro..................	80	30

1938. No. 719 surcharged with two aircraft, **CORREO AEREO** (twice) and value.

851	50c. on 25c. "Black Virgin" (profile)...........	34·00	34·00
852	1p. on 25c. "Black Virgin" (profile)...........	1·30	1·30
853	1p.25 on 25c. "Black Virgin" (profile)...........	1·30	1·30
854	1p.50 on 25c. "Black Virgin" (profile)...........	1·30	1·30
855	2p. on 25c. "Black Virgin" (profile)...........	34·00	34·00
851/855 *Set of 5*.......................................		65·00	65·00

1939.

1010	20c. Juan de la Cierva and Cierva C.30A autogyro	25	15
1011	25c. Juan de la Cierva and Cierva C.30A autogyro	25	15
943	35c. Juan de la Cierva and Cierva C.30A autogyro	65	30
1013	50c. Juan de la Cierva and Cierva C.30A autogyro	40	10
945	1p. Juan de la Cierva and Cierva C.30A autogyro	65	20
1015	2p. Juan de la Cierva and Cierva C.30A autogyro	1·70	10
947	4p. Juan de la Cierva and Cierva C.30A autogyro	5·00	3·25
1017	10p. Juan de la Cierva and Cierva C.30A autogyro	3·75	65

1940.

996*	25c. +5c. Bombers..................................	25	25
997*	70c. +15c. Bombers..................................	25	25
1005*	10p. +4p. Bomber....................................	£250	£250

1944.

1055	5p. Douglas DC-2................................	18·00	17·00

1945.

1062	10p. Airplane...	21·00	18·00

1945. Civil War Air Aces.
1063	4p. Carlos de Haya Gonzalez and airplane	11·50	6·75
1064	10p. J. Garcia Morato and Fiat CR-32 biplane	26·00	7·75

1948.
1108*	2p. Lockheed Constellation	2·10	2·00

1948.
1112*	25c. Lockheed Constellation	30	25

1955.
1234	20c. Lockheed L.1049 Super Constellation	20	15
1235	25c. Lockheed L.1049 Super Constellation	20	15
1236	50c. Lockheed L.1049 Super Constellation	20	15
1237	1p. Lockheed L.1049 Super Constellation	20	15
1238	1p.10 Lockheed L.1049 Super Constellation	20	15
1239	1p.40 Lockheed L.1049 Super Constellation	20	15
1240	3p. Lockheed L.1049 Super Constellation	20	15
1241	4p.80 Lockheed L.1049 Super Constellation	20	15
1242	5p. Lockheed L.1049 Super Constellation	1·70	15
1243	7p. Lockheed L.1049 Super Constellation	80	15
1244	10p. Lockheed L.1049 Super Constellation	60	20
1234/1244	Set of 11	4·25	1·50

1961. 50th Anniv of Spanish Aviation.
1462	1p. Cierva C.30A autogyro	15	15
1463	2p. CASA-built Dornier Do-J Wal flying boat M-MWAL *Plus Ultra*	30	15
1464	3p. Breguet Bre. 19GR *Jesus del Gran Poder*	1·40	75
1465	5p. Avro 504K biplane	3·25	1·30
1466	10p. North American F-86F Sabre jet fighters	1·50	50
1462/1466	Set of 5	6·00	2·50

1964.
1645*	2p. Douglas DC-8	15	15

1966.
1773*	80c. Hot-air balloons	15	15

1971. 50th Anniv of Spanish Airmail Service.
2117	2p. Airco (de Havilland) D.H.9B of Compania Espanola del Trafico Aereo	25	15
2118	15p. Boeing 747-100 of Iberia	25	15

1976.
2374*	1p. Jet airliner	15	15

1977. 50th Anniv of Iberia (state airline).
2496	12p. Rohrbach RO.VII Roland M-CBBB (top) and Douglas DC-10 EC-CPN of Iberia	15	15

1978.
2528	5p. Jet airliner	15	15

1979.
2573	5p. Hawker Siddeley Matador	15	15

1980.
2618	8p. McDonnell Douglas F-4 Phantom II.	15	15

1980. Aviation Pioneers.
2631	5p. Pedro Vives and Farman M.F.7 biplane	15	15
2632	10p. Benito Loygorri and Farman H.F.20 type biplane	15	15
2633	15p. Alfonso de Orleans Bourbon and Caudron G-3	15	15
2634	22p. Alfredo Kindelan Duany and biplane	20	15
2631/2634	Set of 4	60	55

1981.
2655*	30p. CASA C-212 Aviocar	30	15

1981.
2661	13p. Jet airliner	15	15
2662	20p. Jet airliner	20	15

1994.
3293	65p. Douglas DC-8	85	15

1994.
3295*	29p. Bolkow (MBB/Eurocopter) BO 105	40	15

1996.
MS3382*	100p. Cover flown by Zeppelin LZ-127 *Graf Zeppelin* 1930; 100p. Hispano HA200 Saeta (other stamps and miniature sheet do not show aircraft)	5·25	2·50

1999.
3558	35p. Bolkow (MBB/Eurocopter) BO 105	40	20

1999.
3599*	20p. Boeing 747	25	15

2001. 75th Anniv of Spanish Aviation.
3724	40p. Dornier Do-J Wal *Plus Ultra*	40	20
3725	75p. Breguet 19A2	75	25
3726	155p. Dornier	1·50	40
3727	260p. C-295	2·75	60
3724/3727	Set of 4	5·00	1·30

2001.
3811*	155p. Map of Spain showing airports	1·50	25

2002. 75th Anniv of IBERIA Airlines.
3877	25c. Rohrbach R.VIII	40	15
3878	50c. Boeing 747	85	20

2003. 75th Anniv of Aircraft Engineering Technical College.
3996   51c. College building 60 10

2003. Centenary of Powered Flight.
4010   76c. Wright *Flyer* ...... 1·00 40

2005.
MS4139 28c. Ballooning (other stamps in the miniature sheet do not show aircraft) ...... 2·40 2·40

SPANISH GUINEA

West Africa

100 centimos = 1 peseta

1942. No. 945 of Spain overprinted **Golfo de Guinea**.
324   1p. Cierva C.30A autogyro ...... 1·60 15

1951.
351 25c. Lockheed L.1049 Super Constellation 15 15
352 50c. Lockheed L.1049 Super Constellation 15 15
353 1p. de Havilland DH.84 Dragon 15 15
354 2p. Lockheed L.1049 Super Constellation 25 15
355 3p.25 Lockheed L.1049 Super Constellation 75 15
356 5p. de Havilland DH.84 Dragon 6·25 2·40
357 10p. Lockheed L.1049 Super Constellation 24·00 8·25
351/357 *Set of 7* 29·00 10·00

1957. 30th Anniv of Spain-Fernando Poo Flight by Atlantida Seaplane Squadron.
421   25p. Stylised seaplanes ...... 7·25 1·60

SPANISH MOROCCO

North Africa

100 centimos = 1 peseta

1938.
203* 5c. Airplane 10 10
205* 25c. Fokker F.XXII of KLM 10 10
206* 40c. Savoia Marchetti S-74 ...... 2·00 60

207* 50c. Airplane 10 10
208* 75c. Airplane 10 10
209* 1p. Savoia Marchetti S-74 ...... 1·00 10
211* 2p. Junkers Ju 52/3m 45 10

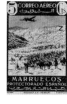

1942. Overprinted **Z**.
258 5c. Junkers Ju 52/3m 10 10
259 10c. Junkers Ju 52/3m 10 10
260 15c. Junkers Ju 52/3m 10 10
261 90c. Junkers JU 52/3m EC-AAX 10 10
262 5p. Junkers Ju 52/3m 80 40
258/262 *Set of 5* ...... 1·10 70

1948.
319* 25c. Airplane ...... 1·50 70
323* 5p. +1p. Airplane ...... 9·50 5·75

1949.
324 5c. Airplane 10 10
325 10c. Airplane 10 10
326 30c. Airplane 10 10
327 1p.75 Airplane 10 10
328 3p. Airplane 15 10
329 4p. Airplane 40 15
330 6p.50 Airplane ...... 1·20 20
331 8p. Airplane ...... 1·90 50
324/331 *Set of 8* ...... 3·50 1·20

1949.
333* 1p. +10c. Airplane 80 20

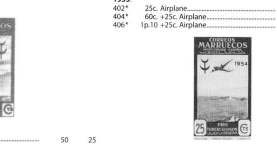

1949.
336* 25c. Airplane 50 25

1950.
353* 25c. Airplane 50 30

1951.
364* 25c. Airplane 55 35
368* 1p.10 +25c. Airplane ...... 2·75 1·60

1952.
382 2p. Airplane 10 10
383 4p. Airplane 30 10
384 8p. Airplane 40 20
385 16p. Shadow of airplane ...... 2·10 1·00
382/385 *Set of 4* ...... 2·50 1·30

1952.
388* 25c. Airplane 30 20
390* 60c. +25c. Airplane 55 30
392* 1p.10 +25c. Airplane ...... 1·60 75

1953.
394 35c. Airplane 10 10
395 60c. Airplane 10 10
396 1p.10 Airplane 20 10
397 4p.50 Airplane 70 15
394/397 *Set of 4* ...... 1·00 40

1953. No. 208 surcharged **50**.
398 50c. on 75c. Airplane 25 10

1953.
402* 25c. Airplane 70 40
404* 60c. +25c. Airplane ...... 1·50 80
406* 1p.10 +25c. Airplane ...... 2·50 1·30

1954.
422* 25c. Airplane 15 10

EXPRESS LETTER STAMPS

1950.
E351   25c. Airplane.................................. 27·00   19·00

SPANISH POST OFFICES IN TANGIER

North Africa

100 centimos = 1 peseta

1938. No. 780 of Spain overprinted **Correo Espanol Tanger**.
81*   2p. Cierva C.30A autogyro............................ 14·50   5·75

1938. No. 780 of Spain overprinted **CORREO AEREO TANGER**.
85*   2p. Cierva C.30A autogyro............................ 70   35

1939. No. 780 of Spain overprinted **Tanger**.
100*   2p. Cierva C.30A autogyro............................ 16·00   11·00

1949.
140   20c. Lockheed Constellation 30   35
141   25c. Douglas DC-3 30   10
142   35c. Boeing 377 Stratocruiser 30   10
143   1p. Lockheed Constellation 90   10
144   2p. Douglas DC-3 .... 1·60   30
145   10p. Boeing 377 Stratocruiser .... 3·00   1·10
140/145 Set of 6.. 5·75   1·80

SPANISH SAHARA

West Africa

100 centimos = 1 peseta

1943.
72   5c. Airplane........................ 20   15
73   25c. Airplane........................ 20   15
74   50c. Airplane........................ 20   15
75   1p. Airplane........................ 20   15
76   1p.40 Airplane........................ 20   15
77   2p. Airplane........................ 1·10   85
78   5p. Airplane........................ 1·60   1·20
79   6p. Airplane........................ 23·00   17·00
72/79 Set of 8.. 24·00   18·00

1950.
83   5p. Airplane................................. 2·00   2·00

1961.
186   25p. Airplane.. 2·10   1·10

SPANISH WEST AFRICA

West Africa

100 centimos = 1 peseta

1951.
19   25c. Airplane........................ 15   15
20   50c. Airplane........................ 15   15
21   1p. Airplane........................ 20   15
22   2p. Airplane........................ 60   15
23   3p.25 Airplane........................ 1·30   1·00
24   5p. Airplane........................ 13·00   3·25
25   10p. Airplane........................ 27·00   19·00
19/25 Set of 7.. 38·00   21·00

SRI LANKA

Indian Ocean

100 cents = 1 rupee

1979. Inauguration of Airlanka Airline.
678   3r. Boeing 707 80   1·75

1988.
1041   75c. Airliner 75   10
1042   5r.75 Airliner .... 2·75   1·60

1992.
1180*   1r. Boeing 747-300/400 .... 1·50   80

1994. 50th Anniv of ICAO.
1280   10r. Boeing 747 .... 4·00   3·50

1997.
1365   20r. Boeing 747 .... 2·75   3·25

1998.
1414   2r.50 Airliner .... 1·00   55

2000.
1478*   100r. Airliner .... 3·00   4·00

2000.
1508   3r.50 Airliner .... 1·25   80

2001. 50th Anniv of Sri Lanka Air Force.
1524*   3r.50 Aircraft............................ 1·00   55

SUDAN

North-east Africa

1000 milliemes = 100 piastres = 1 pound

1931.
49b   3m. Fokker F.VIIb/3m .... 2·50   6·50
50   5m. Fokker F.VIIb/3m .... 1·00   10
51   10m. Fokker F.VIIb/3m .... 1·00   20
52   15m. Fokker F.VIIb/3m 40   10
53   2p. Fokker F.VIIb/3m 30   10
53c   2½p. Fokker F.VIIb/3m .... 3·00   10
54   3p. Fokker F.VIIb/3m 60   15
55   3½p. Fokker F.VIIb/3m .... 1·50   80
56   4½p. Fokker F.VIIb/3m .... 10·00   15·00
57   5p. Fokker F.VIIb/3m .... 1·00   30
57b   7½p. Fokker F.VIIb/3m .... 4·00   10·00
57d   10p. Fokker F.VIIb/3m .... 9·00   1·75
49b/57d Set of 12.. 31·00   32·00

1935. Nos. 49b/51, 53c, 55/6, 57b and 57d surcharged with new value.
74   5m. on 2½p. Fokker F.VIIb/3m .... 3·50   10
68   15m. on 10m. Fokker F.VIIb/3m 40   10
69   2½p. on 3m. Fokker F.VIIb/3m 85   4·00
70   2½p. on 5m. Fokker F.VIIb/3m 50   1·50
75   3p. on 3½p. Fokker F.VIIb/3m .... 38·00   50·00
71   3p. on 4½p. Fokker F.VIIb/3m .... 1·75   18·00
76   3p. on 7½p. Fokker F.VIIb/3m .... 7·00   6·50
77   5p. on 10p. Fokker F.VIIb/3m .... 1·75   4·75
72   7½p. on 4½p. Fokker F.VIIb/3m .... 6·50   48·00
73   10p. on 4½p. Fokker F.VIIb/3m .... 6·50   48·00
68/77 Set of 10.. 60·00   £160

1968. 20th Anniv of Sudan Airways.
284   15m. Douglas DC-3 of Sudan Airways 15   15
285   2p. de Havilland DH.104 Dove SN-AAA of Sudan Airways.................................. 30   15
286   3p. Fokker F.27 Friendship of Sudan Airways.. 40   25
287   55m. Hawker Siddeley Comet 4C of Sudan Airways.. 85   50
284/287 Set of 4.. 1·50   95

SURINAM

South America

100 cents = 1 gulden

1949. First Flight on Paramaribo-Amsterdam Service.
376   27½c. Airplane.............................. 6·00   2·75

1960. Opening of Zanderij Airport Building.

462	8c. Seaplane	1·10	1·10
463	10c. Fokker F.XVIII PH-AIS *De Snip*, 1934...	1·60	1·60
464	15c. Cessna 170A, 1954	1·60	1·60
465	20c. Lockheed L.1049 Super Constellation	2·00	2·00
466	40c. Boeing 707	2·75	2·75
462/466 *Set of 5*		8·00	8·00

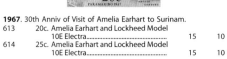

1964. Aeronautical and Astronomical Foundation, Surinam.

529*	3c. +2c. North American X-15 of the U.S.A.F	40	20
532*	15c. +7c. North American X-15 of the U.S.A.F	40	20

1965. Size 25×18 mm.

551	10c. Fokker F.27 Friendship	20	20
552	15c. Douglas DC-8-60 Super Sixty	20	20
553	20c. Douglas DC-8	20	20
554	25c. Douglas DC-8-60 Super Sixty	25	20
555	30c. Douglas DC-8-60 Super Sixty	25	20
556	35c. Boeing 707	30	20
557	40c. Douglas DC-8-60 Super Sixty	30	20
558	45c. Boeing 707	30	20
559	50c. Boeing 707	30	20
560	55c. Fokker F.27 Friendship	30	20
561	65c. Douglas DC-8-60 Super Sixty	35	30
562	75c. Douglas DC-8-60 Super Sixty	35	30
551/562 *Set of 12*		3·00	2·30

1967. 30th Anniv of Visit of Amelia Earhart to Surinam.

613	20c. Amelia Earhart and Lockheed Model 10E Electra	15	10
614	25c. Amelia Earhart and Lockheed Model 10E Electra	15	10

1970. 40 Years of Inland Airmail Flights.

676	10c. Aircraft	40	30
677	20c. Aircraft	40	30
678	25c. Aircraft	40	30
676/678 *Set of 3*		1·10	80

1971.

700	25c. Fokker F.27 Friendship and jet airliner	30	30

1974.

772*	15c. Biplane spraying crops	30	30

1976. As Nos. 551/7 and new values, but size 22×18 mm.

843a	5c. Douglas DC-8-60 Super Sixty	10	10
843b	10c. Fokker F.27 Friendship	15	10
843c	20c. Douglas DC-8	25	15
843d	25c. Douglas DC-8-60 Super Sixty	25	15
843e	30c. Douglas DC-8-60 Super Sixty	30	15
843f	35c. Boeing 707	35	20
843g	40c. Douglas DC-8-60 Super Sixty	50	25
843h	60c. Boeing 707	75	35
843a/843h *Set of 8*		2·40	1·30

1978. 75th Anniv of First Powered Flight.

943*	60c. Wright *Flyer I*	60	50
944*	95c. Douglas DC-8-63 of Surinam Airways	85	70
945*	125c. Concorde of Air France	1·25	1·25

1983. Bicentenary of Manned Flight.

1149	5c. Montgolfier balloon *Le Martial*, 1783	10	10
1150	10c. Montgolfier balloon (first manned free flight, 1783)	10	10
1151	40c. Charles' hydrogen balloon, 1783	40	40
1152	65c. Balloon *Armand Barbes*, Paris, 1870	65	65
1153	70c. Balloon *Double Eagle II*, 1978	70	70
1154	80c. Hot-air balloons at Albuquerque, United States	75	75
1149/1154 *Set of 6*		2·40	2·40

1984. 40th Anniv of ICAO.

1178	35c. Sikorsky S-40 flying boat of Pan Am.	40	40
1179	65c. de Havilland Canada DHC-6 Twin Otter 200/300 PZ-TCE of Surinam Airways	85	85

1987.

1339	25c. Jacob Degen's balloon-assisted "ornithopter", 1808	20	20
1340	25c. Microlight airplane	20	20
1341	35c. Ellehammer II, 1906	30	30
1342	35c. Concorde	30	30
1343	60c. Fokker F.VII H-NACC, 1924 (inscribed "F.7")	50	50
1344	60c. Fokker F.28 Fellowship	50	50
1345	90c. Fokker monoplane *Haarlem Spin*	75	75
1346	90c. Douglas DC-10	75	75
1347	110c. Lockheed 9 Orion, 1932	80	80
1348	110c. Boeing 747	80	80
1349	120c. Amelia Earhart and Lockheed 10E Electra (on stamp No. 614)	95	95
1350	120c. Douglas DC-8-63 of Surinam Airways (on stamp No. 944)	95	95
1339/1350 *Set of 12*		6·25	6·00

1994.

1610*	50g. de Havilland Canada DHC-6 Twin Otter	15	15

1997. Linda Finch's Reconstruction of Amelia Earhart's Last Flight.

1719	275g. Lockheed 18 Lodestar	85	85

2003. Centenary of Powered Flight.

2007	1700g. Santos-Dumont's *14 bis*	1·50	1·50
2008	5300g. Replica of Richard Pearse's aircraft (first flight, 31 March 1903)	4·50	4·50

2006.

2174*	80c. AeroVironment Helios unmanned solar-powered aircraft	45	45
MS2176*	3srd.50 Glider (other stamp in miniature sheet does not show an aircraft)	1·90	1·90

SWAZILAND

Southern Africa

1949. 12 pence = 1 shilling
20 shillings = 1 pound
1975. 100 cents = 1 lilangeni

1949. As Nos. 114/15 of Antigua.

48*	1½d. Airplane	15	20
49*	3d. Jet-powered Vickers Viking	2·00	3·50

1975. 10th Anniv of Internal Air Service.

225	4c. Hawker Siddeley H.S.748 over Matsapa Airport	30	10
226	5c. Cessna 310L Skynight	70	20
227	15c. Douglas DC-3 3D-ABI of Swazi Air (inscribed "C 47 DAKOTA")	1·25	1·40
228	25c. Hawker Siddeley H.S.748 3D-ABJ of Swazi Air	2·00	2·00
225/228 *Set of 4*		3·75	3·25

1981.

369*	25c. Fokker F.28 Fellowship of Royal Swazi National Airways	25	15

1983.

424*	1e. Cessna 188 Ag Wagon spraying sugar crop	70	1·00

1983. Bicentenary of Manned Flight.

431	5c. Montgolfier balloon (first manned free flight, 1783)	10	10
432	10c. Wright Flyer I	15	10
433	25c. Fokker F.28 Fellowship of Royal Swazi National Airlines	35	35
434	50c. Bell X-1	85	65
431/434 *Set of 4*		1·30	1·10

1994. 50th Anniv of ICAO.

642	30c. Fokker 100	40	10
643	40c. Control tower	45	20
644	1e. Crash tender	1·00	1·00
645	2e. Air traffic controllers	1·50	2·50
642/645 *Set of 4*		3·00	3·50

SWEDEN

Northern Europe
100 ore = 1 krona

1924.
161*	5ore Friedrichshafen FF-49 seaplane		2·75	2·75
162*	10ore Friedrichshafen FF-49 seaplane		2·75	3·50
163*	15ore Friedrichshafen FF-49 seaplane		2·50	2·10
164*	20ore Friedrichshafen FF-49 seaplane		18·00	17·00
165*	25ore Friedrichshafen FF-49 seaplane		25·00	19·00
166*	30ore Friedrichshafen FF-49 seaplane		22·00	19·00
167*	35ore Friedrichshafen FF-49 seaplane		28·00	33·00
168*	40ore Friedrichshafen FF-49 seaplane		27·00	21·00
169*	45ore Friedrichshafen FF-49 seaplane		36·00	23·00
170*	50ore Friedrichshafen FF-49 seaplane		42·00	35·00
171*	60ore Friedrichshafen FF-49 seaplane		47·00	47·00
172*	80ore Friedrichshafen FF-49 seaplane		36·00	22·00

1930.
175f	10ore Junkers F-13 fitted with skis		20	35
175g	50ore Junkers F-13 fitted with skis		90	1·00

1936.
199*	1k. Junkers Ju 52/3m seaplane		8·50	6·50

1936. Inauguration of Bromma Aerodrome.
200	50ore Junkers W.34		4·25	6·25

1958.
396*	30ore Bell 47G Trooper helicopter with floats		20	20
398*	1k.40 Bell 47G Trooper helicopter with floats		3·50	70

1960. 10th Anniv of Scandinavian Airlines System (SAS). As No. 431 of Denmark.
428	40ore Douglas DC-8 of Scandinavian Airlines System		35	20

1972. Swedish Mailplanes.
695	5ore Junkers F-13 SA-GAA		20	20
696	15ore Junkers Ju 52/3m		30	20
697	25ore Friedrichshafen FF-49 seaplane		30	20
698	75ore Douglas DC-3 SE-BAB Hoken of Swedish Airlines		30	20
695/698 Set of 4			1·00	70

1973.
748*	1k. Salomon Andree and wreckage of his balloon *Ornen*, 1897		75	80

1975.
860*	90ore Boeing-Vertol 107-II helicopter		30	25

1978.
965*	1k.15 Glider		30	30

1984.
MS1213 1k.90 Thulin Type D biplane; 1k.90 SAAB 90 Scandia; 1k.90 C.G. Cedarstrom and Bleriot XI; 1k.90 A. Ahrenberg and Junkers F-13 S-AAAB *The Gnome*; 2k.70 C.R. Nyberg and *The Tiny Fly* .... 3·25 3·00

1987. Swedish Aircraft.
1335	25k. SAAB-Fairchild SF-340 SE-ISS		5·75	60

1988.
1383*	3k.60 Charles Lindbergh and Ryan NYP Special *Spirit of St. Louis*		95	80

1989.
1463*	3k.30 Lockheed C-130 Hercules		80	70
1467*	3k.30 Hughes 500 helicopter		80	70

1993. World Gliding Championships, Borlange.
1674*	6k. "Big Bird" glider		1·40	1·20

1999.
2030*	5k. Douglas DC-4		95	75

2001.
2178	5k. Otto Lilienthal's biplane glider, 1895		1·10	1·00
2179	5k. DFS Weihl glider and emblem of Royal Swedish Flying Club		1·10	1·00
2180	5k. SAAB J29, 1962		1·10	1·00
2181	5k. Friedrichshafen FF-49, 1920		1·10	1·00
2182	5k. Nyberg Flugan, 1999		1·10	1·00
2183	5k. Douglas DC-3, 1938		1·10	1·00
2178/2183 Set of 6			6·00	5·50

2005.
2398*	5k.50 Airplane		1·50	1·20

2007.
2493*	(5k.) Agusta-Bell AB206 JetRanger		1·30	1·10

2007.
2499*	(5k.50) Stylised airliner		1·50	1·20

SWITZERLAND

Central Europe
100 centimes = 1 franc

1925.
316*	15c. Monoplane		2·50	4·50
317a*	20c. Monoplane		40	30
318*	25c. Monoplane		7·50	12·00
323*	45c. Biplane		1·40	4·25
324a*	50c. Biplane		1·70	75

1935. No. 316 surcharged 10.
358*	10 on 15c. Monoplane		5·75	32·00

1938. No. 324a surcharged 1938 "PRO AERO". 75 75.
386	75c. on 50c. Biplane			4·75

1941.
415	30c. Douglas DC-2 (blue on orange)		85	15
415a	30c. Douglas DC-2 (grey on orange)		7·25	9·00
416	40c. Douglas DC-2 (grey on orange)		85	15
416a	40c. Douglas DC-2 (blue on orange)		36·00	1·50
417	50c. Koolhoven FK		1·10	15
418	60c. Koolhoven FK		1·50	15
419	70c. Douglas DC-2		1·20	30
420	1f. Koolhoven FK		2·30	35
421	2f. Koolhoven FK		7·25	1·70
422	5f. Douglas DC-2		24·00	9·25
415/422 Set of 10			75·00	20·00

1941. As No. 420, additionally inscribed "PRO AERO 28.V.1941".
423	1f. Koolhoven FK 50		35	45

1944. 25th Anniv of National Air Post.
441	10c. Haefeli DH-3 biplane		10	20
442	20c. Fokker F.VIIb/3m CH-157		25	20
443	30c. Lockheed 9B Orion of Swissair		50	65
444	1f.50 Douglas DC-3 HB-IRI of Swissair		7·25	14·50
441/444 Set of 4			7·25	14·00

1946. Special (Lausanne, Lucerne, Locarno) Flights.
466   1f.50 Zoglig glider .... 23·00   22·00

1947. First Geneva-New York Swissair Flight.
472   2f.50 Douglas DC-4 of Swissair .... 11·50   15·00

1953. Inauguration of Zurich Airport.
546   40c. Tail of Swissair airliner at Zurich-Kloten Airport .... 3·50   4·75

1956.
570*   40c. Fokker F.VIIb/3m and Douglas DC-6.   3·00   1·00

1959.
597*   5c. Douglas DC-7C "Seven Seas" of Swissair 35   15

1960.
613*   75c. Douglas DC-8 .... 4·00   4·75

1963. 25th Anniv of Swiss Pro Aero Foundation, Berne-Locarno or Langenbruck-Berne (helicopter feeder) Special Flights.
681   2f. Glider and jet aircraft .... 3·00   3·25

1969.
771*   2f. Haefeli DH-3 biplane and Douglas DC-8 of Swissair .... 2·00   1·40

1972. Pro Aero Foundation and 50th Anniv of North Atlantic and International Airmail Service.
828   2f. +1f. Boeing 747.100 of Swissair .... 2·50   1·90

1972. Swiss Air Rescue Service.
837*   30c. Sud Aviation SE 3160 Alouette III helicopter 40   10

1975.
897*   90c. Astra airship *Ville de Lucerne* .... 1·00   70

1977. Swiss Aviation Pioneers.
923   40c. Oskar Bider and Bleriot XI 45   15
924   80c. Eduard Spelterini and balloon basket 80   60
925   100c. Armand Dufaux and Dufaux IV biplane .... 1·00   80
926   150c. Walter Mittelhalzer and Dornier Do-B Merkur seaplane *Switzerland* ... 1·50   1·40
923/926 *Set of 4* .... 3·25   2·50

1979.
973*   70c. Hot-air balloon *Esperanto* 75   60
974*   80c. Tail fins of airliners at Basle-Mulhouse Airport 85   55

1986.
1110*   60c. Fokker 100 of Swissair being loaded with mail 65   30

1987.
1122*   90c. Boeing 747-300/400 of Swissair .... 1·20   75

1988. 50th Anniv of Pro Aero Foundation.
1144   140c. +60c. Junkers Ju 52/3m HB-HOT A-702 of Swissair .... 2·50   2·50

1994.
1283*   180c. Airliner .... 2·10   1·80

1997. 50th Anniv of Swissair's North Atlantic Service.
1349   180c. Douglas DC-4 *'Grand Old Lady'* .... 2·00   1·70

1999. First World Circumnavigation by Balloon.
1414   90c. Breitling *Orbiter 3* .... 1·00   70

2000.
1459*   400c. Airplane fin .... 4·50   3·25

2001.
1473*   90c. Airplane (Centenary of Aero-Club of Switzerland) .... 1·00   80

2002. 50th Anniv of Swiss Air Rescue.
1502   180c. Augusta A-109-K2 helicopter and Hawker 800B Air Ambulance .... 1·70   1·50

2004.
1612   1f.80 Zeppelin NT Type Z No. 7 .... 1·60   1·40

International Organizations in Switzerland
INTERNATIONAL TELECOMMUNICATION UNION

1976.
LT12*   90c. Boeing 747 75   65

SYRIA

Middle East

100 centimes = 1 piastre

1926. Nos. 182 and 184/6 overprinted with Bleriot XI airplane.
192   2p. Palmyra .... 3·00   4·50
193   3p. Bridge of Daphne .... 1·10   2·75
194   5p. Aleppo .... 2·30   3·50
195   10p. Aleppo .... 2·50   6·00
192/195 *Set of 4* .... 8·00   15·00

1926. Nos. 192/5 further surcharged in French and Arabic, **Secours aux Refugies Afft** and value.
208*   1p. on 2p. Palmyra (Bleriot XI overprint)   2·00   7·50
209*   2p. on 3p. Bridge of Daphne (Bleriot XI overprint) .... 1·50   7·50
210*   3p. on 5p. Aleppo (Bleriot XI overprint)..   1·50   4·00
211*   5p. on 10p. Aleppo (Bleriot XI overprint)   1·50   6·50

1929. Nos. 177, 179/80 and 187 overprinted with Bleriot XI airplane or surcharged also.
225   0p.50 Alexandretta 60   1·30
226   1p. Damascus .... 1·90   2·30
227   2p. on 1p.25 Latakia .... 3·75   4·00
228   15p. on 25p. Palmyra .... 3·50   6·50
229   25p. Palmyra .... 6·00   6·75
225/229 *Set of 5* .... 14·00   19·00

1929. Nos. 192/5, 225/6 and 229 overprinted **EXPOSITION INDUSTRIELLE DAMAS 1929** in French and Arabic.
237   0p.50 Alexandretta (Bleriot XI overprint) .... 3·25   6·50
238   1p. Damascus (Bleriot XI overprint) .... 2·75   6·75

239	2p. Palmyra (Bleriot XI overprint)...............	3·25	3·75
240	3p. Bridge of Daphne (Bleriot XI overprint)		
		2·50	3·50
241	5p. Aleppo (Bleriot XI overprint)	2·30	6·75
242	10p. Aleppo (Bleriot XI overprint)	2·50	4·75
243	25p. Palmyra (Bleriot XI overprint)	2·50	4·75
237/243 Set of 7		17·00	33·00

1931.

261	0p.50 Potez 29-4 biplane F-AIVD (yellow)...	1·30	1·30
261a	0p.50 Potez 29-4 biplane F-AIVD (brown) ..	3·00	3·00
262	1p. Potez 29-4 biplane F-AIVD	2·75	1·90
263	2p. Potez 29-4 biplane F-AIVD	3·25	3·00
264	3p. Potez 29-4 biplane F-AIVD	2·00	1·30
265	5p. Potez 29-4 biplane F-AIVD	1·50	1·20
266	10p. Potez 29-4 biplane F-AIVD	1·90	85
267	15p. Potez 29-4 biplane F-AIVD	2·30	2·50
268	25p. Potez 29-4 biplane F-AIVD	4·25	3·00
269	50p. Potez 29-4 biplane F-AIVD	5·25	5·25
270	100p. Potez 29-4 biplane F-AIVD	6·25	4·25
261/270 Set of 11		30·00	24·00

1934.

290	0p.50 Farman F.190	3·00	3·50
291	1p. Farman F.190	2·75	2·30
292	2p. Farman F.190	3·00	3·00
293	3p. Farman F.190	3·25	6·00
294	5p. Farman F.190	6·00	6·25
295	10p. Farman F.190	42·00	42·00
296	15p. Farman F.190	40·00	32·00
297	25p. Farman F.190	50·00	48·00
298	50p. Farman F.190	55·00	60·00
299	100p. Farman F.190	80·00	80·00
290/299 Set of 10		£250	£250

1936. Nos. 261a/5 overprinted **FOIRE DE DAMAS 1936** in French and Arabic.

309	0p.50 Potez 29-4 biplane	3·75	7·75
310	1p. Potez 29-4 biplane	2·75	2·75
311	2p. Potez 29-4 biplane	3·25	5·25
312	3p. Potez 29-4 biplane	3·25	5·25
313	5p. Potez 29-4 biplane	3·50	6·00
309/313 Set of 5		15·00	24·00

1937.

322	½p. Savoia Marchetti S-73	10	45
323	1p. Potez 62 F-ANDO	1·10	1·10
324	2p. Savoia Marchetti S-73	1·70	1·50
325	3p. Potez 62 F-ANDO	1·50	1·70
326	5p. Savoia Marchetti S-73	2·30	90
327	10p. Potez 62 F-ANDO	1·60	1·10
328	15p. Savoia Marchetti S-73	2·75	1·90
329	25p. Potez 62 F-ANDO	5·00	6·25
322/329 Set of 8		14·50	13·50

1938. 10th Anniv of First Air Service Flight between Syria and France.

337	10p. Maurice Nogues and CAMS 53H flying boat...............................	2·50	7·75

1940.

351	0p.25 Potez 62	10	1·50
352	0p.50 Potez 62	10	1·30
353	1p. Potez 62	35	1·70
354	2p. Potez 62	50	1·70
355	5p. Potez 62	95	1·80
356	10p. Potez 62	1·10	90
357	50p. Potez 62	5·00	6·00
351/357 Set of 7		7·25	13·50

1942.

362*	10p. Airplane...........................	2·50	2·50
363*	50p. Airplane...........................	2·50	2·50

1944. Nos. 327, 267/8 and 270 overprinted with circle containing scales and Arabic text.

387*	10p. Savoia Marchetti S-73	2·20	2·20
388*	15p. Potez 29-4 FAIVD	2·20	2·20
389*	25p. Potez 29-4 FAIVD	2·20	2·20
390*	100p. Potez 29-4 FAIVD	6·50	6·50

1945. Nos. 267/8 overprinted with oval containing Arabic text.

394*	15p. Potez 29-4 F-AIVD......................	2·20	2·20
395*	25p. Potez 29-4 F-AIVD......................	2·20	2·20

1945.

403*	5p. Airplane...........................	35	35
404*	10p. Airplane...........................	35	35
405*	15p. Airplane...........................	35	35
406*	25p. Airplane...........................	60	35
407*	50p. Airplane...........................	1·00	35
408*	100p. Airplane...........................	2·50	95
409*	200p. Airplane...........................	8·75	3·75

1946.

433*	3p. Airplane...........................	60	15
434*	5p. Airplane...........................	60	15
435*	6p. Airplane...........................	60	15
436*	10p. Airplane...........................	45	15
437*	15p. Airplane...........................	45	15
438*	25p. Airplane...........................	50	25
439*	50p. Airplane...........................	85	25
440*	100p. Airplane...........................	2·00	45
441*	200p. Airplane...........................	4·25	1·30
442*	300p. Airplane...........................	16·00	2·50
443*	500p. Airplane...........................	17·00	4·00

1946. No. 438 overprinted with oval containing Arabic text.

447*	25p. Airplane...........................	2·20	1·30

1946. Nos. 438/40 overprinted with two horizontal and two vertical lines of Arabic text.

449*	25p. Airplane...........................	2·20	1·30
450*	50p. Airplane...........................	2·75	1·70
451*	100p. Airplane...........................	5·25	3·00

1947. No. 447 further overprinted with two vertical lines of Arabic characters.

455*	25p. Airplane...........................	2·20	1·30

1948. Nos. 433, 435 and 440/3 surcharged.

474*	2p.50 on 3p. Airplane	10	10
475*	2p.50 on 6p. Airplane	10	10
475*	2p.50 on 100p. Airplane	10	10
476*	25p. on 200p. Airplane	50	15
477*	50p. on 300p. Airplane	13·00	65
478*	50p. on 500p. Airplane	13·00	65

1949.

482*	50p. Lockheed L.1049 Super Constellation	23·00	16·00

1952. No. 439 overprinted with curved line of Arabic text and **U.N.S.W.S. Damascus 8-20 Dec. 1952.**

521*	50p. Airplane..................................	9·50	2·75

1955.

559*	60p. Jet fighters	1·00	70

1955.

563	5p. Lockheed L.1049 Super Constellation	60	25
564	15p. Lockheed L.1049 Super Constellation	80	45

1957. Gliding Festival.

641	25p. Glider	1·30	25
642	35p. Glider	1·70	45
643	40p. Glider	2·50	85
641/643 Set of 3		5·00	1·40

1958. Gliding Festival.

674	7½p. Light airplane and model airplane......	1·00	60
675	12½p. Light airplane and model airplane.....	3·50	2·00

1969. Construction of Damascus International Airport.

1023	12½p. Airliners at Damascus International Airport.......................	15	10
1024	17½p. Airliners at Damascus International Airport.......................	45	15
1025	60p. Airliners at Damascus International Airport.......................	1·10	35
1023/1025 Set of 3...		1·50	55

1977. Civil Aviation Day.

1343	35p. Boeing 747SP of Syrian Air..................	25	15

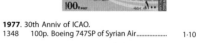

1977. 30th Anniv of ICAO.

1348	100p. Boeing 747SP of Syrian Air..................	1·10	85

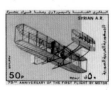

1979. 75th Anniv of Powered Flight.

1423	50p. Wright Type A	1·00	25
1424	75p. Bleriot XI	1·50	45
1425	100p. Ryan NYP Special *Spirit of St. Louis*	1·90	50
1423/1425 *Set of* 3		4·00	1·10

1980.

1484	50p. Mikoyan Gurevich MiG-21	1·10	35

1983.

1550	60p. Airliner at Damascus International Airport	1·40	60

1984. 40th Anniv of ICAO.

1586	45p. Emblem and stylised aircraft	60	25
1587	245p. Emblem and stylised aircraft	2·50	1·50

1987.

1676	100p. Stylised Mikoyan Gurevich MiG-21D	1·10	45

1990. Arab Civil Aviation Day.

1796	175p. Douglas DC-9-80 Super Eighty	50	25

1994. 50th Anniv of ICAO.

1905	£S17 Airport	1·30	70

1999.

2033	£S17 Douglas DC-8	1·00	70

TAIWAN

See under China.

TAJIKISTAN

Central Asia

2002. 100 dirams (d) = 1 somoni (s)

2001.
MS181* 1s. Tupolev Tu-154M 'Careless' of Air Tajic (inscribed Ty-154M, the Russian language designation) .... 6·75   5·50

2003.
MS248 1s. Aero L-29 Delfin Akrobat; 1s. Yakovlev Yak-55; 1s. Cessna 172; 1s. SIAI-Marchetti SF.260; 1s. Europa XS; 1s. Bölkow BO-209 Monsun; 1s. Mundry CAP-10; 1s. Soko 2 .... 11·00   11·00

2004.
273*   1s. Mil Mi-8 .... 1·70   1·30

2005. Maiden Flight of Airbus A380.
278   1r.50 Left wing and tailplane .... 1·90   1·70
278b   1r.50 Nose .... 1·90   1·70
279   1r.80 Tail section .... 2·30   2·00
280   1r.80 Right wing .... 2·30   2·00
278/280 Set of 4... 7·50   6·75·

2005.
286   5d. Ilyushin Il-62 'Classic' 20   10
287   7d. Ilyushin Il-62 'Classic' 30   15
288   11d. Ilyushin Il-62 'Classic' 40   20
289   20d. Ilyushin Il-62 'Classic' 55   30
290   55d. Ilyushin Il-62 'Classic' 85   45
291   75d. Ilyushin Il-62 'Classic' .... 1·00   80
286/291 Set of 6... 3·00   1·80

TANGIER

See SPANISH POST OFFICES IN TANGIER

TANZANIA

East Africa

100 cents = 1 shilling

1978. 75th Anniv of Powered Flight.
255   50c. Fokker F.27 Friendship of Air Tanzania over airport 20   10
256   1s. de Havilland DH.84 Dragon Mk 1 VP-KBA of Wilson Airways at airfield in Zanzibar 25   10
257   2s. Concorde of British Airways .... 1·00   75
258   5s. Wright Flyer I.................................. 1·25   1·25
255/258 Set of 4.. 2·40   2·00

1980.
280*   5s. Cessna 206 Stationair 6 of the Flying Doctor service.............................. 35   50

1980. No. 280 overprinted **District 920 - 55th Annual Conference, Arusha, Tanzania.**
295*   5s. Cessna 206 Stationair 6 of the Flying Doctor service.............................. 30   50

1984. 40th Anniv of ICAO.
406*   1s.50 Douglas DC-10 and Boeing 737 of Air Tanzania 15   20
407*   5s. Boeing 737 of Air Tanzania................. 55   1·25

1985.
417*   5s. Douglas DC-10 .... 2·00   1·50

1987.
MS534* 20s. Boeing 737 .... 2·50   1·75

1990.
714*   100s. Boeing 737 .... 3·00   2·50

1990.
716*   9s. Bell X-1...................................... 75   50

1991.
825*   75s. Sir Alan Cobham's Short S.5 Singapore I flying boat G-EBUP, 1928.................................. 1·10   1·10
826*   100s. Fokker F.27 Friendship of Air Tanzania .... 1·10   1·10
830*   200s. Handley Page H.P.42 at Croydon Airport .... 2·00   2·00

1991.
MS895*Two sheets. (b) 400s Curtiss R3C-2 seaplane, 1925 (other sheet does not show aircraft) Price for 2 sheets .... 9·50   11·00

1992. 50th Anniv of Japanese Attack on Pearl Harbour.
1316*   75s. Mitsubishi G3M "Nell" bombers attacking battle cruiser H.M.S. Repulse.. 1·90   1·40
1317*   75s. Mitsubishi G3M "Nell" bombers attacking battleship H.M.S. Prince of Wales.. 1·90   1·40
1320*   75s. Mitsubishi A6M Zero-Sen attacking Bristol Type 142 Blenheim Mk IV bombers at Malayan airfield............... 1·90   1·40

1992.
1326*   150s. Concorde at Charles de Gaulle Airport, Paris................................... 8·00   6·50

1992.
1471*   300s. Airship LZ-127 Graf Zeppelin............... 1·75   1·75
MS1475* Five sheets. (a) 500s. Airship LZ-5 damaged after crash (other sheets do not show aircraft) Set of 5 sheets............... 15·00   16·00

1993. Military Aircraft.
1673   20s. Dassault/ Dornier Alpha Jet................ 20   20
1674   30s. Northrop F-5E Tiger II...................... 20   25
1675   50s. Dassault Mirage III......................... 25   30
1676   70s. Aermacchi MB 339C 35   45
1677   100s. Mikoyan MiG-31........................... 35   50
1678   150s. CASA C-101 Aviojet........................ 40   70
1679   200s. Lockheed Martin (General Dynamics) F-16 Fighting Falcon...................... 45   80
1673/1679 Set of 7... 2·00   3·00
MS1680 500s. British Aerospace EAP.................... 1·40   2·00

1994. Aviation Anniversaries.
1786   200s. Sopwith Pup............................... 1·75   1·75
1787   200s. Hot air balloons.......................... 1·75   1·75
1788   400s. BAe Harrier............................... 2·75   2·75
1789   400s. Jean-Pierre Blanchard and his balloon...................................... 2·75   2·75
1786/1789 Set of 4... 8·00   8·00
MS1790 Two sheets. (a) 500s. Supermarine Spitfire; (b) 500s. Hot air balloons Set of 2 sheets.......... 7·50   7·50
  Nos. 1786 and 1788 commemorate the 75th anniv of the Royal Air Force; Nos. 1787 and 1789 commemorate the bicentenary of first balloon flight in U.S.

1994.
1822* 100s. Boeing 737 .... 1·75 1·00

1994.
1980* 150s. Capsule in sea ....
1981* 150s. Recovery crew opening hatch ....
1982* 150s. Transferring astronauts by Sikorsky
S-61 helicopter

1994.
1998* 200s. Supermarine Spitfire 85 85
2011* 200s. North American P-51 Mustang 85 85

1999.
2168* 150s. Boeing 747 .... 45 20

2005.
MS2459* 600s. de Havilland DH.98 Mosquitos
(other stamps in the miniature sheet do not show
aircraft) .... 6·00 7·00

THAILAND

South-east Asia
100 satangs = 1 baht

1969. 50th Anniv of Thai Airmail Services.
635 1b. Breguet Bre. 14 biplane 85 20

1973.
768* 75s. Concorde 20 10

1977.
924 5b. Silhouette of helicopter 85 15

1981.
1057 75s. Boeing 747 .... 30 10

1983.
1144* 8b.50 Boeing 747 of Thai Airways and
Breguet Bre. 14T biplane 55 30

1984.
1165 1b.25 Northrop F-5 Tiger II 30 10

1984.
1170* 1b.25 Agricultural aircraft 25 10

1985. 25th Anniv of Thai Airways.
1198 2b. Douglas DC-6 and Douglas DC-8 of
Thai Airways 10 10
1199 7b.50 Douglas DC-10-30 of Thai Airways 55 30
1200 8b.50 Airbus Industrie A300 of Thai
Airways 65 35
1201 9b.50 Boeing 747-200 of Thai Airways 65 40
1198/1201 Set of 4 .... 1·80 1·00

1987. 72nd Anniv of Royal Thai Air Force.
1276 2b. Pilot, Northrop F-5 Tiger II and
Lockheed Martin (General Dynamics)
F-16 Fighting Falcon 30 10

1987.
1278 2b. Balloon, Airbus Industrie A300 of
Thai Airways at airport and Boeing
747-200 of Thai Airways in flight 15 10

1989.
1420 2b. Jet airliner 15 10

1989.
1431 2b. Boeing 747-200 .... 15 10

1992.
1591* 5b. Boeing 747-200 .... 15 15

1992.
1628* 5b. Boeing 747-100 .... 20 10

1994. 50th Anniv of ICAO.
1755 2b. Boeing 707 .... 10 10

1995. 80th Anniv of Royal Thai Air Force.
1769 2b. Breguet Bre.16 and Lockheed Martin
(General Dynamics) F-16 Fighting
Falcon.. 10 10

1996.
1822 2b. Breguet AG4 and airliner 10 10

1996.
1863* 3b. Harbin (NAMC) Y-11 .... 10 10

1997.
1994* 2b. Model airplane 10 10

227

1998. 50th Anniv of Aerothai (air traffic control).
2032   2b. Boeing 747   10   10

2002.
2327   3b. Suvarnabhumi Airport Passenger
            Terminal   20   15

2004. Kites.
2588   3b. Chula kite   10   10
2589   3b. Pakpao kite   10   10
2590   3b. Snake kite   10   10
2591   15b. Buffalo kite   10   10
2588/2591 Set of 4   35   35

2006.
2761   3b. Suvarnabhumi Airport   20   20

TOGO

West Africa
100 centimes = 1 franc

1940. As Nos. 117/21 of Dahomey.
120   1f.90 Twin-engine airliner   40   3·75
121   2f.90 Twin-engine airliner   30   4·50
122   4f.50 Twin-engine airliner   75   3·00
123   4f.90 Twin-engine airliner   50   4·75
124   6f.90 Twin-engine airliner   70   5·75
120/124 Set of 5 ....   2·50   20·00

1942. As No. 143k of Dahomey.
154a   50f. Twin-engine airliner ....   2·00   5·50

1947.
181*   40f. Sud Ouest SO.95 Corse II ....   12·00   6·00
182*   50f. Airplane ....   3·75   1·50
183*   100f. Lockheed Constellation ....   3·50   2·75
184*   200f. Lockheed Constellation ....   8·75   11·50

1949. As No. 254 of Cameroun.
185   25f. Lockheed Constellation ....   3·25   15·00

1954. As No. 264 of Cameroun.
188   15f. Bomber ....   6·50   3·50

1961.
287*   20f. Outline of jet airliner   60   10

1963.
324*   30f. Douglas DC-3 ....   1·70   50
325*   100f. Boeing 707 (air) ....   3·50   1·40

1964. Inauguration of Air Togo.
392   5f. Charles' hydrogen balloon, 1783,
            Henri Giffard's steam-powered
            dirigible airship, 1852, and airship
            LZ-5   10   10
393   10f. Charles' hydrogen balloon, 1783,
            Henri Giffard's steam-powered
            dirigible airship, 1852, and airship
            LZ-5   50   30
394   25f. Farman H.F.III biplane, Lilienthal
            biplane glider and Boeing 707   90   30
395   45f. Farman H.F.III biplane, Lilienthal
            biplane glider and Boeing 707 ....   2·40   65
396   100f. Boeing 707 (air) ....   3·50   1·20
392/396 Set of 5 ....   6·75   2·30

1966.
445*   5f. Boeing 707   15   10
450*   90f. Boeing 707 (air) ....   2·75   1·10

1966. Inauguration of Douglas DC-8F Services by Air Afrique. As
No. 438 of Cameroun.
475   30f. Douglas DC-8F Jet Trader of Air
            Afrique ....   1·10   40

1971. 10th Anniv of ASECNA.
817   30f. Sud Aviation SE 210 Caravelle ....   2·10   55
818   100f. Sud Aviation SE 210 Caravelle (air) ....   2·40   1·10

1973.
964*   100f. Jet airliner and early aircraft ....   3·75   1·10

1974.
1048*   40f. Supermarine Spitfires ....   1·20   50
1050*   200f. Supermarine Spitfires (air) ....   3·75   1·40

1975.
1117   50f. Wreckage of airplane ....   16·00   13·00
1118   60f. Wreckage of airplane ....   16·00   13·00

1977. 50th Anniv of Lindbergh's Trans-Atlantic Flight.
1207*   25f. Charles Lindbergh and Ryan NYP
            Special *Spirit of St. Louis* being
            refuelled   60   30
1208*   50f. Charles Lindbergh and Ryan NYP
            Special *Spirit of St. Louis* ....   1·20   50
1211*   90f. Ryan NYP Special *Spirit of St. Louis*
            (air) ....   1·50   50
1212*   100f. Concorde ....   1·80   50

1978. 75th Anniv of First Flight by Wright Brothers.
1259*   50f. Wilbur Wright in Wright Glider
            No. 111, 1902 ....   1·10   30
1260*   60f. Orville Wright in Wright Type A (air) .   1·60   60
1261*   70f. Wreckage of Wright Type A, 1908 ......   1·80   65
1263*   300f. Wright Flyer I, 1903 ....   3·25   1·40

1980. 20th Anniv of ASECNA.
1458   50f. Concorde   90   30
1459   60f. Concorde (air)   90   50

1984.
1645*   70f. Wreckage of airplane   90   30
1646*   90f. Wreckage of airplane ....   1·20   45

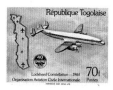

1984. 40th Anniv of ICAO.
1729   70f. Lockheed Constellation ....   1·10   50
1730   105f. Boeing 707 (air) ....   1·10   65
1731   200f. Douglas DC-8-61 ....   2·40   2·50
1732   500f. Concorde ....   6·00   1·40
1729/1732 Set of 4 ....   9·50   4·50

1985.
1819*   500f. Airbus Industrie A300 of Alitalia ....   7·00   2·50

1986. 25th Anniv of Air Afrique.
1927   90f. Douglas DC-10 of Air Afrique ....   1·10   65

1988.
1995*   180f. Boeing 707 Air Force One at Orly
            Airport, Paris ....   2·50   85

1989.
2024	10f. Wreckage of airplane	25	15
2025	80f. Wreckage of airplane	1·10	40
2026	125f. Wreckage of airplane	1·60	85
2024/2026 *Set of 3*		2·75	1·30

1990. New Lome Airport.
2103	90f. Boeing 737 of Air Afrique, Concorde of Air France and other airliners at Lome Airport	1·10	50

La Luftwaffe lance une attaque finale désespérée

1995.
2162*	200f. Focke Wulf F.W. 190	1·20	70

TOKELAU

South Pacific
100 sene = 1 dollar

1983.
96*	75s. Grumman Mackinnon G-21C Goose flying boat	30	50

TONGA

South Pacific
1949. 12 pence = 1 shilling
20 shillings = 1 pound
1967. 100 seniti = 1 pa'anga

1949. As Nos. 114/15 of Antigua.
88*	2½d. Airplane	20	1·00
89*	3d. Jet-powered Vickers Viking	2·00	3·50

1953.
108*	6d. Douglas DC-3 at Fua'amotu Airport	1·00	30

1961.
119*	1s. Douglas DC-4	1·25	45

1962. No. 108 overprinted 1862 TAU'ATAINA EMANCIPATION 1962.
123*	6d. Douglas DC-3 at Fua'amotu Airport	20	1·25

1967. No. 108 surcharged SENITI and value.
233*	6s. on 6d. Douglas DC-3 at Fua'amotu Airport	10	20
192*	8s. on 6d. Douglas DC-3 at Fua'amotu Airport	30	10
200*	50s. on 6d. Douglas DC-3 at Fua'amotu Airport	1·25	1·75

1967. No. 108 surcharged S AIRMAIL Friendly Islands Field & Track Trials South Pacific Games Port Moresby 1969.
263*	6s. on 6d. Douglas DC-3 at Fua'amotun Airport	10	15

1969. As No. 108, imperf and with colour changed, surcharged 1s.
273*	1s. on 6d. Douglas DC-3 at Fua'amotu Airport	60	70

1979. Self-adhesive.
720	5s. Boeing 737	40	70
721	11s. Boeing 737	50	70
722	14s. Boeing 737	50	70
723	15s. Boeing 737	55	70
724	17s. Boeing 737	55	70
725	18s. Boeing 737	55	50
726	22s. Boeing 737	65	50
726a	29s. Boeing 737	12·00	5·00
727	31s. Boeing 737	85	1·50
727a	32s. Boeing 737	13·00	5·50
728	39s. Boeing 737	1·00	1·00
728a	47s. Boeing 737	13·00	6·50
729	75s. Boeing 737	1·50	3·50
730	1p. Boeing 737	2·00	4·50
720/730 *Set of 14*		42·00	29·00

1982. Self-adhesive.
815*	47s. de Havilland Canada DHC-6 Twin Otter 300 of South Pacific Island Airways	1·50	1·00
816*	1p. de Havilland Canada DHC-6 Twin Otter 300 of South Pacific Island Airways	2·40	3·00

1983. Self-adhesive.
836*	47s. Montgolfier balloon (first manned free flight, 1783) and Concorde	4·25	3·00
837*	1p.50 Montgolfier balloon and Concorde	6·50	10·00
MS838*	2p.50 Concorde	4·00	7·00

1983. Inauguration of Niuafo'ou Airport. Self-adhesive.
843	32s. de Havilland Canada DHC-6 Twin Otter 300 of South Pacific Island Airways	1·00	30
844	47s. de Havilland Canada DHC-6 Twin Otter 300 of South Pacific Island Airways	1·10	35
845	1p. Boeing 707 of South Pacific Island Airways	1·75	1·25
846	1p.50 Boeing 707 of South Pacific Island Airways	2·75	1·75
843/846 *Set of 4*		6·00	3·25

1985. Self-adhesive.
902*	47s. Airplane on oil survey	1·50	1·50

1988.
988*	2p.50 de Havilland Canada DHC-6 Twin Otter 200/300 of Friendly Islands Airways	7·50	8·50

1988.
MS989 42s. Ross and Keith Smith's Vickers Vimy G-EAOU, 1919 (on Great Britain stamp No. 795); 42s. Piper PA-31 Navajo (on Australia stamp No. 663) (sheet contains 10 other designs) ...... 29·00 30·00

1989. Aviation in Tonga.
1055	42s. Short S.30 modified "G" Class flying boat ZK-AMA *Aotearoa* of Tasman Empire Airways	2·50	1·10
1056	57s. Chance Vought F4U Corsair of the U.S.A.F.	3·00	1·50
1057	90s. Boeing 737 at Fua'amotu Airport	5·00	4·50
1058	3p. Montgolfier balloon (first manned free flight, 1783), Wright *Flyer I* and Concorde	13·00	13·00
1055/1058 *Set of 4*		21·00	18·00

1989.
1059	32s. CASA C-212 Aviocar	1·75	80
1060	42s. CASA C-212 Aviocar	2·00	80
1061	57s. CASA C-212 Aviocar	2·25	90
1062	3p. CASA C-212 Aviocar	7·50	9·00
1059/1062 *Set of 4*		12·00	10·50

1989.
MS1063 57s. Mail balloon, Paris, 1870; 57s. Airco (de Havilland) DH.4M biplane of the U.S. Mail; 57s. Airship LZ-127 *Graf Zeppelin* (on United States of America stamp No. A732, illustrated cover and postmark); 57s. Westland Dragonfly helicopter G-AKCU (sheet contains 8 other designs) ...... 35·00 35·00

1990. As No. 988, but inscribed "Silver Jubilee of His Majesty King Taufa'ahau Tupou IV 1965–1990".
1085*	2p.50 de Havilland Canada DHC-6 Twin Otter of Friendly Islands Airways	7·00	8·00

1992.
1165	42s. Mitsubishi A6M Zero-Sen	1·90	1·75
1168*	42s. Boeing B-29 Superfortress *Enola Gay*	1·90	1·75
1173*	42s. Mitsubishi A6M Zero-Sen	1·90	1·75
1174*	42s. Douglas SBD Dauntless	1·90	1·75
1175*	42s. Grumman FM-2 Wildcat	1·90	1·75
1176*	42s. Supermarine Seafire Mk III	1·90	1·75

OFFICIAL STAMPS

1983. No. 836 overprinted OFFICIAL.
O219*	47s. Montgolfier balloon and Concorde	10·00	7·50

TRANSKEI

Southern Africa

100 cents = 1 rand

TRANSKEI AIRWAYS   A H Barrett 1977

1977.

22	4c. Beech 100 King Air ZS-XGB of Transkei Airways......................		25	15
23	15c. Beech 100 King Air of Transkei Airways landing at airport and on ground..............................		75	85

1987. 10th Anniv of Transkei Airways Corporation.

197	14c. Hawker Siddeley (BAe/Avro) HS748 *Ulundi*............................		20	15
198	20c. Hawker Siddeley (BAe/Avro) HS748 *Ulundi*............................		30	30
199	25c. Beech 100 King Air of Transkei Airways..............................		40	40
200	30c. K.D. Matanzima Airport..................		55	60
197/200 *Set of 4*..........................			1·30	1·30

TRENGGANU

South-east Asia

100 cents = 1 dollar

1949. As Nos. 114/15 of Antigua.

63*	10c. Airplane..............................		30	75
64*	15c. Jet-powered Vickers Viking..............		1·90	3·75

TRIESTE

Southern Europe

Zone A - Allied Military Government

100 centesimi = 1 lira

1947. Nos. 670, 674, 678 and 911/14 of Italy overprinted **A.M.G. F.T.T.** in two lines.

18*	1l. Caproni Campini N-1....................		25	20
21*	10l. Caproni Campini N-1...................		1·25	40
23*	50l. Caproni Campini N-1...................		21·00	2·00
24*	100l. Douglas DC-2........................		80·00	3·50
25*	300l. Douglas DC-2........................		9·00	11·00
26*	500l. Douglas DC-2........................		12·00	10·00
27*	1000l. Douglas DC-2.......................		£110	85·00

1947. Nos. 690 and 693 of Italy overprinted **A.M.G. F.T.T.**

61*	20l. Heinkel He 70 Blitz...................		5·25	1·40
64*	50l. Heinkel He 70 Blitz...................		4·50	5·25

1948. Nos. 674 and 678 of Italy overprinted **A.M.G. F.T.T. 1948 TRIESTE** and posthorn.

80*	10l. Caproni Campini N-1..................		30	20
82*	50l. Caproni Campini N-1..................		40	55

1949. No. 725 of Italy overprinted **A.M.G. F.T.T.**

91*	50l. Douglas DC-4........................		2·00	1·75

1949. Nos. 674, 678 and 911/14 of Italy overprinted **A.M.G. F.T.T.** in one line.

115*	10l. Caproni Campini N-1.................		15	10
117*	50l. Caproni Campini N-1.................		20	10
118*	100l. Douglas DC-2.......................		80	10
119*	300l. Douglas DC-2.......................		9·75	3·50
120*	500l. Douglas DC-2.......................		11·00	7·25
121*	1000l. Douglas DC-2......................		16·00	12·00

1951. No. 783 of Italy overprinted **A.M.G. F.T.T.**

199*	20l. Westland W.81 helicopter.............		1·40	65

1952. No. 823 of Italy overprinted **A.M.G. F.T.T.**

242	60l. Savoia Marchetti S.M.95C..............		90	1·00

1952. No. 827 of Italy overprinted **A.M.G. F.T.T.**

246*	60l. Airplane.............................		50	20

Zone B - Yugoslav Military Government

1949. 100 centesimi = 1 lira

1949. 100 paras = 1 dinar

S.O.TRST-A VUJA-ZRAČNA P.

1949.

B7*	1l. Flying boat..........................		20	10
B8*	2l. Junkers Ju 86........................		20	10
B9*	5l. Flying boat..........................		20	10
B10*	10l. Junkers Ju 86.......................		1·25	40
B11*	25l. Flying boat.........................		1·40	2·00
B12*	50l. Junkers Ju 86.......................		1·60	1·60

1949. Nos. 612/13 of Yugoslavia overprinted **VUJA-STT.**

B24	5d. Airplane............................		5·75	6·00
B25	12d. Airplane...........................		5·75	6·00

1949. Nos. B7/12 overprinted **DIN** or surcharged also.

B26*	1d. Flying boat.........................		15	10
B27*	2d. Junkers Ju 86.......................		15	10
B28*	5d. Flying boat.........................		20	10
B29*	10d. Junkers Ju 86......................		40	10
B30*	15d. on 25l. Flying boat................		6·25	7·00
B31*	20d. on 50l. Junkers Ju 86..............		1·40	3·00

1952.

B54a	5d. Airliner............................		4·00	4·00
B54b	15d. Airliner...........................		7·25	4·00
B54c	25d. Airliner...........................		6·25	3·50
B54a/54c *Set of 3*.....................			16·00	10·50

1954. As Nos. 675/83c of Yugoslavia, in new colours, overprinted **STT VUJNA.**

B108	1d. Airplane...........................		20	10
B109	2d. Airplane...........................		20	10
B110	3d. Airplane...........................		20	10
B111	5d. Airplane...........................		20	10
B112	10d. Airplane..........................		20	10
B113	20d. Airplane..........................		30	10
B114	30d. Airplane..........................		30	40
B115	50d. Airplane..........................		50	40
B116	100d. Airplane.........................		1·60	65
B117	200d. Airplane.........................		2·50	80
B118	500d. Airplane.........................		12·00	6·00
B108/118 *Set of 11*...................			16·00	8·00

TRINIDAD AND TOBAGO

West Indies

100 cents = 1 dollar

1949. As Nos. 114/15 o1 Antigua.

261*	5c. Airplane............................		35	1·00
262*	6c. Jet-powered Vickers Viking...........		2·00	2·25

1962.

301*	8c. Piarco Airport, Trinidad..............		40	1·00

1966.

316*	35c. B.A.C. One Eleven...................		1·50	70

1969.

360*	40c. Boeing 727-100 "Sunjet" of B.W.I.A....		40	90

1970.

378*	5c. Boeing 727-100......................		10	10

1974.

451*	40c. Boeing 727-100.....................		30	15

1975. 35th Anniv of British West Indies Airways.

461	20c. Boeing 707 of B.W.I.A...............		40	80
462	30c. Boeing 707 of B.W.I.A...............		60	90
463	40c. Boeing 707 of B.W.I.A...............		70	1·00
461/463 *Set of 3*.....................			1·50	2·40

1977. 50th Anniv of Airmail Service.

503*	20c. Sikorsky S-38 flying boat of Pan Am.		40	20
505*	45c. Boeing 707 of B.W.I.A..............		60	60
506*	50c. Boeing 747-200 of British Airways....		1·00	3·75

1983.

626	35c. Lockheed L-1011 TriStar 500 9Y-TGY *Flamingo* of B.W.I.A................		2·00	2·25

1987.

724*	10c. Boeing 707 of B.W.I.A..............		1·50	20

1988.

750*	$1.10 Lockheed L-1011 TriStar 500 of B.W.I.A............................		2·75	1·40

1990. 50th Anniv of British West Indies Airways (BWIA).

782	40c. Lockheed L.18 Lodestar of B.W.I.A....		1·75	30
783	80c. Vickers Viking 1A VP-TAB of B.W.I.A...		2·25	1·25
784	$1 Vickers Viscount 702 VP-TBH of B.W.I.A. over airport and two aircraft on ground........................		2·50	1·25
785	$2.25 Boeing 707 of B.W.I.A.............		3·50	6·50
782/785 *Set of 4*.....................			9·00	8·25
MS786 $5 Lockheed L-1011 TriStar 500 of B.W.I.A....			4·75	7·00

1991.

804*	80c. Fairey Barracuda Mk III.............		2·50	1·25
805*	$1 Avro Type 683 Lancaster.............		2·75	1·25
806*	$2.25 Consolidated PBY-5 Catalina flying boat.............................		4·50	6·50
MS807 Two sheets. (a) $2.50 Supermarine Spitfire, (b) $2.50 Vickers-Armstrong Wellington *Set of 2 sheets*............................			10·00	11·00

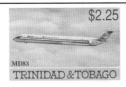

1992.
816	$2.25 McDonnell Douglas MD-83 of B.W.I.A.	2·50	3·00
817	$2.25 Lockheed L-1011 TriStar of B.W.I.A ...	2·50	3·00

1996.
870*	$3 Fairey Fulmar 1	1·60	2·25
MS871*	$3 Grumman Mackinnon G-21C Goose; $3 US Navy airship	3·50	4·50

TRIPOLITANIA

North Africa

100 Centesimi = 1 lira

1931.
116	50c. Marina Fiat MF.5 flying boat	50	15
117	60c. Marina Fiat MF.5 flying boat	1·90	6·00
117a	75c. Marina Fiat MF.5 flying boat	1·90	4·75
118	80c. Marina Fiat MF.5 flying boat	5·25	9·50
119	1l. Marina Fiat MF.5 flying boat	45	10
120	1l.20 Marina Fiat MF.5 flying boat	16·00	10·50
121	1l.50 Marina Fiat MF.5 flying boat	5·25	10·50
122	5l. Marina Fiat MF.5 flying boat	17·00	16·00
116/122 Set of 8		43·00	50·00

1931.
131*	50c. Airplane	5·25	14·00

1931.
139	50c. Savoia Marchetti S-55A flying boat...	2·75	9·50
140	80c. Savoia Marchetti S-55A flying boat...	2·75	9·50
141	1l. Savoia Marchetti S-55A flying boat...	2·75	14·00
142	2l. Savoia Marchetti S-55A flying boat...	4·25	21·00
143	5l. +2l. Savoia Marchetti S-55A flying boat	5·25	30·00
139/143 Set of 5		16·00	75·00

1932.
150*	1l.25 Mogadishu Aerodrome	5·25	10·50
154*	50c. Marina Fiat MF.5 flying boat (air)	7·00	19·00
155*	1l. Marina Fiat MF.5 flying boat	7·00	19·00
156*	2l. +1l. Marina Fiat MF.5 flying boat	19·00	48·00
157*	5l. +2l. Marina Fiat MF.5 flying boat	60·00	£100

1933.
165*	50c. Seaplane	6·00	11·00
166*	75c. Caproni Ca 101	6·00	11·00
167*	1l. Seaplane	6·00	11·00
168*	2l. +50c. Seaplane	11·00	23·00
169*	5l. +1l. Seaplane	20·00	38·00
170*	10l. +2l.50 Caproni Ca 101	20·00	80·00

1933. Airship *Graf Zeppelin.*
171	3l. Airship LZ-127 *Graf Zeppelin*	6·00	60·00
172	5l. Airship LZ-127 *Graf Zeppelin*	6·00	60·00
173	10l. Airship LZ-127 *Graf Zeppelin*	6·00	£110
174	12l. Airship LZ-127 *Graf Zeppelin*	6·00	£120
175	15l. Airship LZ-127 *Graf Zeppelin*	6·00	£120
176	20l. Airship LZ-127 *Graf Zeppelin*	6·00	£150
171/176 Set of 6		32·00	£550

1933. Balbo Trans-Atlantic Mass Formation Flight.
177	19l.75 Savoia Marchetti S-55X flying boat...	12·00	£300
178	44l.75 Savoia Marchetti S-55X flying boat...	12·00	£300

1934. As No. 122 with colour changed overprinted with Savoia Marchetti S-71 airplane and **1934-XII PRIMO VOLO DIRETTO ROMA=BUENOS-AYRES TRIMOTORE LOMBARDI-MAZZOTTI** or surcharged also.
179	2l. on 5l. Marina Fiat MF.5 flying boat	2·10	33·00
180	3l. on 5l. Marina Fiat MF.5 flying boat	2·10	33·00
181	5l. Marina Fiat MF.5 flying boat	2·10	36·00
182	10l. on 5l. Marina Fiat MF.5 flying boat	2·10	36·00
179/182 Set of 4		7·50	£120

1934.
190*	50c. Marina Fiat MF.5 flying boat	5·25	14·00
191*	75c. Airplane	5·25	14·00
192*	5l. +1l. Marina Fiat MF.5 flying boat	80·00	£100
193*	10l. +2l. Airplane	80·00	£100
194*	25l. +3l. Caproni Ca 101	85·00	£120

1934. Nos. 190/4 overprinted **CIRCUITO DELLE OASI TRIPOLI MAGGIO 1934-XII.**
197	50c. Marina Fiat MF.5 flying boat	8·50	55·00
198	75c. Airplane	8·50	55·00
199	5l. +1l. Marina Fiat MF.5 flying boat	8·50	55·00
200	10l. +2l. Airplane	£170	£350
201	25l. +3l. Caproni Ca 101	£170	£350
197/201 Set of 5		£325	£800

1934.
213*	80c. Caproni Ca 101	3·00	9·50
214*	1l. Caproni Ca 101	3·00	10·50
215*	2l. Caproni Ca 101	3·00	17·00

1934. Rome-Mogadiscio Flight.
216	25c. +10c. Caproni Ca 101	3·50	5·25
217	50c. +10c. Caproni Ca 101	3·50	5·25
218	75c. +15c. Caproni Ca 101	3·50	5·25
219	80c. +15c. Caproni Ca 101	3·50	5·25
220	1l. +20c. Caproni Ca 101	3·50	5·25
221	2l. +20c. Caproni Ca 101	3·50	5·25
222	3l. +25c. Caproni Ca 101	16·00	44·00
223	5l. +25c. Caproni Ca 101	16·00	44·00
224	10l. +30c. Caproni Ca 101	16·00	44·00
225	25l. +2l. Caproni Ca 101	16·00	44·00
216/225 Set of 10		75·00	£190

1935.
232*	25c. +10c. Caproni Ca 101	70	3·75
233*	50c. +10c. Caproni Ca 101	70	3·75
234*	1l. +25c. Caproni Ca 101	70	3·75
235*	2l. +30c. Caproni Ca 101	70	3·75
236*	3l. +1l.50 Caproni Ca 101	70	3·75
237*	10l. +5l. Caproni Ca 101	7·00	21·00

EXPRESS LETTER STAMPS

1934.
E195	2l.25 Caproni Ca 101	21·00	34·00
E196	4l.50 +1l. Caproni Ca 101	21·00	34·00

1934. Nos. E195/6 overprinted **CIRCUITO DELLE OASI TRIPOLI MAGGIO 1934.XII.**
E202	2l.25 Caproni Ca 101	8·50	55·00
E203	4l.50 +1l. Caproni Ca 101	8·50	55·00

OFFICIAL AIR STAMP

1934. As No. 225, overprinted with crown and SERVIZIO DI STATO.
O226	25l. +2l. Caproni Ca 101	£1700	£2500

TRISTAN DA CUNHA

South Atlantic Ocean

1996. 100 pence = 1 pound

1996.
592*	45p. Mil Mi26	3·00	3·25

2000. Helicopters.
689*	10p. Sud Aviation SA-330J Puma, 1999	85	95
691*	15p. Westland Wessex HAS 1,1964	95	1·25
693*	20p. Westland Lynx HAS 3, 1996	1·10	1·40
695*	50p. Sikorsky UH-19F 2001.	1·50	1·75

2001. Nos. 689, 691, 693 and 695 overprinted **HURRICANE RELIEF.**
717*	10p. Sud Aviation SA-330J Puma, 1999	1·00	1·25
719*	15p. Westland Wessex HAS 1, 1964	1·40	1·60
721*	20p. Westland Lynx HAS 3, 1996	1·50	1·75
723*	50p. Sikorsky UH-19F	2·25	2·50

2008. 90th Anniv of Royal Air Force.
907	30p. Hawker Hart	90	90
908	30p. Hawker Typhoon	90	90
909	30p. Royal Aircraft Factory SE 5a	90	90
910	30p. Avro Type 698 Vulcan	90	90
911	30p. SEPECAT Jaguar	90	90
907/911 Set of 5		4·00	4·00
MS912	£1.50 Sir Hugh Trenchard	5·00	5·00

TUNISIA

North Africa

1927. 100 centimes = 1 franc

1959. 1000 milliemes = 1 dinar

1927. Various stamps showing views overprinted with Bleriot XI airplane or surcharged also.
148	1f. Carthaginian galley	75	1·40
152	1f.30 Amphitheatre, El Djem	1·30	2·00
169	1f.50 on 1f.30 Amphitheatre, El Djem	1·60	30
170	1f.50 on 1f.80 Amphitheatre, El Djem	1·70	30
171	1f.50 on 2f.55 Amphitheatre, El Djem	3·50	75
149	1f.75 on 75c. Ruins of Hadrian's aqueduct	1·00	1·80
150	1f.75 on 5f. Carthaginian galley	2·30	6·75
153	1f.80 Amphitheatre, El Djem	1·50	4·50
151	2f. Carthaginian galley	2·30	2·75
154	2f.55 Amphitheatre, El Djem	1·10	2·50

1949.

323	5f. Sud Est SE 161 Languedoc	95	5·25
324	15f. Sud Est SE 161 Languedoc	1·30	5·50
325	25f. Sud Est SE 161 Languedoc (air)	70	3·00
323/325 *Set of 3*		2·75	12·50

1955.

392	12f. +3f. Balloon *Armand Barbes*, Paris, 1870	2·30	2·00

1978. 20th Anniv of Tunisian Civil Aeronautics and Meteorology.

922	50m. Boeing 747	55	30

1988. 40th Anniv of Tunis Air.

1160	500m. Boeing 747 of Tunis Air	1·80	85

1994. 50th Anniv of ICAO.

1286	450m. Tailfins	1·60	55

1996.

1330*	200m. Hot air balloon	95	55

2007.

1655*	250m. Balloons	60	30

TURKEY

South-east Europe and Asia Minor

1934. 40 paras = 1 piastre or grush

1942. 40 paras = 1 kuru

1947. 100 kurus = 1 lira

1934. Nos. 1086, 1089, 1092 and 1094 overprinted with airplane and 1934 or surcharged also.

1157	7½k. Gorge and River Sakarya	30	20
1158	12½k. on 15k. Fortress of Ankara	45	30
1159	20k. on 25k. Gorge and River Sakarya	45	40
1160	25k. Gorge and River Sakarya	70	50
1161	40k. Gorge and River Sakarya	1·40	1·30
1157/1161 *Set of 5*		3·00	2·40

1935.

1175*	4k. +4k. Pilot and de Havilland DH.60G Gipsy Moth	1·40	1·00

1938. Nos. 1086, 1089 and 1094 surcharged with airplane, **1937** and value.

1198	4½k. on 7½k. Gorge and River Sakarya	6·00	1·40
1199	9k. on 15k. Fortress of Ankara	37·00	13·50
1200	35k. on 40k. Forge and River Sakarya	10·00	11·00
1198/1200 *Set of 3*		48·00	23·00

1941. Nos. 1092 and 1097/8 surcharged with airplane and value.

1286	4½k. on 25k. Gorge and River Sakarya	1·90	1·60
1287	9k. on 200k. Kemal Ataturk	9·00	9·00
1288	35k. on 500k. Kemal Ataturk	5·75	5·75
1286/1288 *Set of 3*		15·00	15·00

1949.

1399*	5k. Douglas DC-6	25	10
1400	20k. Vickers Viking 1B	30	10
1401	30k. Light monoplane	55	10
1402	40k. Douglas DC-6	1·00	25
1403	50k. Vickers Viking 1B	1·00	25
1404	1l. Light monoplane	3·00	1·10
1399/1404 *Set of 6*		5·50	1·70

1950.

1422	2l.50 Sud Est SE 161 Languedoc	22·00	21·00

1950. International Civil Aviation Congress, Istanbul.

1435	20k. Hezarfen Celebi's "bird flight"	40	25
1436	40k. Biplane	70	75
1437	60k. Douglas DC-3	1·20	1·30
1435/1437 *Set of 3*		2·10	2·10

1951. Nos. 1399, 1401 and 1403 overprinted **SANAYI KONGRESI 9-NISAN-1951.**

1454	5k. Douglas DC-6	90	1·00
1455	30k. Light monoplane	2·40	1·50
1456	50k. Vickers Viking 1B	2·75	2·50
1454/1456 *Set of 3*		5·50	4·50

1953.

1528*	35k. Yesilkoy Airport	40	40

1954.

1539	20k. Glider	25	15
1540	35k. Baron Delagrange and glider	45	35
1541	45k. de Havilland DH.82 Tiger Moth biplanes	1·10	50
1539/1541 *Set of 3*		1·60	90

1954.

1545	5k. Douglas DC-3 of Devlet Hava Yollari at Yesilkoy Airport	15	15
1546	20k. Douglas DC-3 at Yesilkoy Airport	25	15
1547	35k. Douglas DC-3 TC-TUG at Ankara Airport	45	15
1548	40k. Douglas DC-3 of Devlet Hava Yollari at Yesilkoy Airport	70	15
1549	45k. Douglas DC-3 at Yesilkoy Airport	1·10	25
1550	55k. Douglas DC-3 TC-TUG at Ankara Airport	1·90	50
1545/1550 *Set of 6*		4·00	1·20

1956.

1637*	25k. Douglas DC-3	4·00	3·75

1958.

1838*	25k. +5k. Republic F-84G Thunderjets	25	25

1959.

1853*	1k. Vickers Viscount 700 of Turk Hava Yollari	10	10

1961. 50th Anniv of Turkish Air Force.

1941*	40k. North American F-100 Super Sabre	35	15
1942*	75k. North American F-100 Super Sabre	50	25

1965. 40th Anniv of Turkish Civil Aviation League.

2081	60k. Airplane (in emblem)	25	25
2082	90k. Airplane (in emblem) and glider	40	30
2083	130k. Airplane (in emblem) and squadron of aircraft	80	45
2081/2083 *Set of 3*		1·30	90

1965.

2123*	10k. Airliner	10	10

1967. Aircraft.

2176	10k. de Havilland DH.89 Dragon Rapide..	25	10
2177	60k. Fokker F.27 Friendship TC-TOY of Turk Hava Yollari	35	10
2178	130k. Douglas DC-9-30 of Turk Hava Yollari	1·10	25
2179	220k. Douglas DC-3 TC-EGE of Turk Hava Yollari	1·60	40
2180	270k. Vickers Viscount 700	2·50	55
2176/2180 Set of 5		5·25	1·30

1969. 55th Anniv of First Turkish Airmail Service.

2300*	60k. Bleriot XI Prince Celaladdin, 1914	35	25

1970.

2324*	60k. Dornier Do-28 on aerial survey	35	25

1971. 60 Years of Turkish Aviation.

2372	110k. Lockheed F-104S Super Starfighter..	1·00	15
2373	200k. Four aircraft	2·10	25
2374	250k. Jet fighters of the Turkish Air Force...	2·10	25
2375	325k. Pilot and Lockheed F-104S Super Starfighter of the Turkish Air Force .	3·00	30
2376	400k. Bleriot XI	3·50	45
2377	475k. Hezarfen Celebi's "bird flight"	4·00	55
2372/2377 Set of 6		14·00	1·80

1973.

2479	110k. Fokker F.28 Fellowship TC-JAD of Turk Hava Yollari	50	15
2480	250k. Douglas DC-10 of Turk Hava Yollari...	1·00	40

1979.

2652*	2½l. Jet airliner	5·00	60

1981. No. 2177 surcharged **10 LIRA**.

2739*	10l. on 60k. Fokker F.27 Friendship TC-TOY of Turk Hava Yollari	80	15

1983. 50th Anniv of Turkish State Airline.

2812	50l. Boeing 727 and Junkers Ju 52/3m (wrongly inscribed "F-13")	1·10	40
2813	70l. Airport at night	1·40	75

1985. 60th Anniv of Turkish Aviation League.

2887	10l. Glider	40	15
2888	20l. Cameron Viva 77 hot-air balloon	60	25

1988.

2989*	200l. Stylised airplane	1·60	75

1988. Turkish Aerospace Industries.

3012	50l. Lockheed Martin (General Dynamics) F-16 Fighting Falcons	15	15
3013	200l. Stylised jet fighter	80	25

1990.

3099*	200l. Airliner	35	25

1996.

MS3298	25000l. Dassault Falcon/Mystére 50; 50000l. Helicopter (other stamps in the miniature sheet do not show aircraft)	9·75	9·00

1997. First International Aerial Sports Meeting.

3326	40000l. Glider	1·00	90
3327	40000l. Hang-glider	1·00	90
3328	100000l. Hot air balloon	2·30	2·10
3329	100000l. Aerobatics display	2·30	2·10
3326/3329 Set of 4		6·00	5·50

2001. 87th Anniv of First Istanbul-Cairo Flight by Turkish Crews.

3461	250000l. Capt. Mehmet Fethi Bey and Bleriot X1	40	40
3462	300000l. First Lt. Sadik Bey and Bleriot X1	50	45
3463	450000l. First Lt. Nuri Bey and Bleriot X1	75	70
3464	500000l. Capt. Ismail Hakki Bey and Bleriot X1	80	75
3461/3464 Set of 4		2·20	2·10

2004. Turkish Stars Air Display Team.

MS3609	600000l. Two Northrop NF-5A Freedom Fighters; 700000l. Five Northrop NF-5A Freedom Fighters with coloured smoke; 800000l. Northrop NF-5A Freedom Fighters in vertical flight; 900000l. Northrop NF-5A Freedom Fighters in level flight .	2·75	2·50

2006. Early Aircraft of Turkish Air Force, 1912–14.

3717	60ykr. Deperdussin monoplane	75	70
3718	70ykr. REP parasol monoplane	90	90
3719	70ykr. Bleriot monoplane	90	90
3717/3719 Set of 4		2·30	2·30

COMPULSORY TAX STAMPS

1926. Aviation Fund.

T1039	20pa. Biplane (brown and green)	95	1·00
T1040	1g. Biplane (green and stone)	95	1·00
T1041	5g. Biplane (violet and green)	1·90	2·10
T1042	5g. Biplane (red and green)	70·00	9·25
T1039/1042 Set of 4		65·00	12·00

1927. Aviation Fund. As Nos. T1039/40 but smaller, 25×15 mm.

T1043	20pa. Biplane (red and green)	25	50
T1044	1g. Biplane (green and ochre)	25	50
T1045	2g. Biplane	25	1·00
T1046	2½g. Biplane	2·40	1·80
T1047	5g. Biplane	50	50
T1048	10g. Biplane	2·40	2·10
T1049	15g. Biplane	2·40	1·60
T1050	20g. Biplane	4·75	2·50
T1051	50g. Biplane	4·75	10·50
T1052	100g. Biplane	£110	70·00
T1043/1052 Set of 10		£110	80·00

1930. Aviation Fund. Nos. T1039, T1043, T1045 and T1049 surcharged.

T1099	Bir on 20pa. Biplane (No. T1039)	£225	75·00
T1100	Bir (1)k. on 20pa. Biplane (No. T1043)	50	1·00
T1101	Yuz (100)pa. on 2g. Biplane	50	1·00
T1102	5k. on 20pa. Biplane (No. T1043)	50	1·00
T1103	Bes (5)k. on 20pa. Biplane (No. T1043)	4·75	2·50
T1104	On (10)k. on 2g. Biplane	95	1·00
T1105	Elli (50)k. on 2g. Biplane	19·00	21·00
T1106	Bir l. on 2g. Biplane	55·00	60·00
T1107	Bes (5)l. on 15g. Biplane	£2500	£1400
T1099/1107 Set of 9		£2500	£1400

1931. Aviation Fund.

T1141	20pa. Biplane	1·40	5·25

1932. Aviation Fund. As No. T1141, but larger, 22×30 mm, and with sky shaded.

T1154	1k. Biplane	95	1·60
T1155	5k. Biplane	1·40	3·75
T1156	10k. Biplane	2·40	7·75
T1154/1156 Set of 3		4·25	12·00

1933. Aviation Fund.

T1162	On (10)pa. Biplane	95	1·80
T1163	Bir (1)k. Biplane	2·40	4·00
T1164	Bes (5)k. Biplane	7·25	9·25
T1162/1164 Set of 3		9·50	13·50

TURKMENISTAN

Central Asia

1996. 100 tenge = 1 manat

1996.

55*	300m. Boeing 737 at Saparmyrat International Airport Ashgabat	80	70

TURKS AND CAICOS ISLANDS

West Indies

1949. 12 pence = 1 shilling

20 shillings = 1 pound

1969. 100 cents = 1 dollar

1949. As Nos. 114/15 of Antigua.
217*	2½d. Airplane	20	1·60
218*	3d. Jet-powered Vickers Viking	2·25	50

1972.
363*	15c. Sikorsky S-61B Sea King helicopter	15	10

1978. 75th Anniv of Powered Flight.
502	1c. Wilbur Wright and Wright Type A (inscribed "FLYER III")	10	10
503	6c. Orville and Wilbur Wright and Cessna 337 Super Skymaster N-389	10	10
504	10c. Wilbur Wright and Lockheed L.188 Electra	10	10
505	15c. Wilbur Wright and Douglas C-47 Skytrain	15	15
506	35c. Wilbur Wright and Britten-Norman BN-2 Islander at Grand Turk Airport	35	35
507	$2 Wilbur Wright and Wright Type A	1·00	2·00
502/507	Set of 6	1·60	2·50
MS508	$1 Orville Wright and Wright Glider No. III	60	1·60

1979. Self-adhesive.
561*	40c. Mail balloon, Paris, 1870	45	45
562*	40c. Aeronautical Syndicate Valkyrie A biplane, 1911	45	45
563*	40c. Concorde	45	45

1982.
716	8c. Cessna 337 Super Skymaster	15	15
717	15c. Lockheed JetStar II N-9118	20	25
718	65c. Sikorsky S-58 helicopter	65	80
719	$1.10 Cessna 182 Skylane seaplane N318T	1·10	1·25
716/719	Set of 4	1·90	2·20
MS720	$2 Boeing 727-200	2·00	2·50

1983. Bicentenary of Manned Flight.
754*	25c. Charles' hydrogen balloon *The Globe*, 1783	20	25
756*	70c. Montgolfier balloon *Le Martial*, 1783	40	70
MS758*	$2 Montgolfier balloon (first manned free flight, 1783)	1·25	2·00

1985. 40th (1984) Anniv of ICAO.
834*	8c. Leonardo da Vinci's drawing of a wing	65	40

835*	25c. Sir Alliott Verdon Roe and Avro (Canada) CF-102 Jetliner	1·75	55
837*	$1 Igor Sikorsky and Vought-Sikorsky VS-300 helicopter prototype	6·00	4·25
MS838*	$2 Amelia Earhart's Lockheed 10E Electra	2·75	3·25

1985
855*	50c. Westland Wessex helicopter of the Queen's Flight	2·25	1·00

1988.
930*	8c. Boeing 747	55	30

1991.
1073*	10c. Amundsen's airship N.1 *Norge*, 1926	85	55
1077*	$1 Fokker F.VIIa/3m *Josephine Ford* over North Pole, 1926	3·25	2·00
1078*	$1.25 Northrop Gamma *Polar Star* over Antarctic, 1935	3·50	3·50

1998. 80th Anniv of Royal Air Force.
1500	20c. Royal Aircraft Factory S.E.5.A	1·00	40
1501	50c. Sopwith Camel	1·50	85
1502	60c. Supermarine Spitfire	1·60	1·25
1503	80c. Avro Type 683 Lancaster	2·00	2·00
1504	$1 Panavia Tornado	2·25	2·25
1505	$1.25 Hawker Hurricane	2·50	3·00
1500/1505	Set of 6	9·75	8·75
MS1506	Two sheets. (a) $2 BAe Harrier; (b) $2 Avro Type 698 Vulcan *Set of 2 sheets*	9·00	9·00

2000. 60th Anniv of Battle of Britain.
1610*	50c. Barrage balloon	1·25	1·25
1611*	50c. Heinkel HeIII/CASA 2 IIIE	1·25	1·25
1613*	50c. Hawker Hurricane	1·25	1·25
1615*	50c. RAF squadron scramble	1·25	1·25
1617*	50c. James 'Ginger' Lacey	1·25	1·25
1618*	50c. Douglas Bader	1·25	1·25
1619*	50c. Edgar 'Cobber' Kain	1·25	1·25
1620*	50c. Air Vice-Marshall Keith Park	1·25	1·25
1621*	50c. James 'Johnny' Johnson	1·25	1·25
1622*	50c. Adolph 'Sailor' Malan	1·25	1·25
1623*	50c. Alan 'Al' Deere	1·25	1·25
1624*	50c. Air Vice-Marshall Trafford Leigh-Mallory	1·25	1·25
MS1625*	Two sheets. (b) $2 Churchill, Union Jack, and pilots *Price for 2 sheets*	8·50	8·50

2002. 75th Anniv of First Solo Trans-Atlantic Flight.
1763	60c. Charles Lindbergh as a young man	1·50	1·50
1764	60c. Lindbergh with Ryan NYP Special *Spirit of St. Louis*	1·50	1·50
1765	60c. Ryan NYP Special *Spirit of St. Louis*	1·50	1·50
1766	60c. Ryan NYP Special *Spirit of St. Louis* taking off from Roosevelt Field	1·50	1·50
1767	60c. Ryan NYP Special *Spirit of St. Louis* above Atlantic	1·50	1·50
1768	60c. Lindbergh in Paris	1·50	1·50
1763/1768	Set of 6	8·00	8·00

2003. Centenary of Powered Flight.
MS1807	60c. Vought F4U Corsair; 60c. Messerschmitt Me 262; 60c. Mitsubishi A6M Zero-Sen; 60c. Hawker Hurricane	5·00	5·50
MS1808	$2 Supermarine Spitfire Mk IX *Set of 2 sheets*	3·50	3·75

TUVA

Central Asia

1934. 100 kopeks = 1 tugrik

1936. 100 kopeks = 1 aksha

1934.
51	1k. Kalinin K-5	1·30	90
52	5k. Tupolev ANT-25	1·30	90
53	10k. Junkers F-13 fitted with skis	5·25	2·75
54	15k. Tupolev ANT-25	2·50	90
55	25k. Junkers F-13 fitted with skis	2·50	90
56	50k. Kalinin K-5	2·50	90
57	75k. Junkers F-13	2·50	90
58	1t. Kalinin K-5	3·50	1·80
59a	2t. Tupolev ANT-9	19·00	23·00
51/59a	Set of 9	32·00	33·00

1936.
100	5k. Airplane	2·50	1·30
101	10k. Airplane	4·00	1·30
102	15k. Airplane	4·00	1·30
103	25k. Airship	5·25	1·70
104	50k. Biplane	5·25	1·70
105	75k. Airship	5·25	1·70
106	1a. Seaplane	7·00	3·25
107	2a. Seaplane	6·50	2·50
108	3a. Seaplane	7·00	2·75
100/108	Set of 9	42·00	16·00

1938. Nos. 58 and 107/8 surcharged with large numerals and old value obliterated.
110*	5k. on 2a. Seaplane		£300
111*	10k. on 1t. Kalinin K-5		£250
113*	30k. on 2a. Seaplane		£250
114*	30k. on 3a. Seaplane		£250

1938. As No. 102, but without dates and "AIR MAIL".
117*	15k. Airplane		£170

1939. No. 58 surcharged with small numerals and old value obliterated.
120*	10k. on 1t. Kalinin K-5		£300

1940. Nos. 58 and 104/5 surcharged with small numerals only.
122*	10k. on 11k. Kalinin K-5		£130
126*	20k. on 50k. Airplane		85·00
127*	20k. on 75k. Airship		90·00

TUVALU

Pacific Ocean

100 cents = 1 dollar

1979. Internal Air Service.
127	8c. Grumman Mackinnon G-21C Goose flying boat	15	15
128	20c. Grumman Mackinnon G-21C Goose flying boat	15	15
129	30c. Grumman Mackinnon G-21C Goose flying boat	20	20
130	40c. Grumman Mackinnon G-21C Goose flying boat	25	30
127/130 Set of 4		70	70

1980.
145*	30c. Airplane (on United States of America stamp No. A901 on cover)	15	20

1980. Aviation Commemorations.
153	8c. de Havilland DH.114 Heron 2 DD-FAE of Air Pacific	10	10
154	20c. Hawker Siddeley H.S.748 DQ-FBH of Air Pacific	15	10
155	30c. Short S.25 Sunderland flying boat of the Royal New Zealand Air Force	15	15
156	40c. Orville Wright and Wright Flyer III	20	15
153/156 Set of 4		55	45

1983. Bicentenary of Manned Flight.
225	25c. Montgolfier balloon (first manned free flight, 1783)	20	20
226	35c. Grumman Mackinnon G-21E Turbo Goose ZX-ERX of Sea Bee Air (inscribed "McKINNON")	20	25
227	45c. Beech 200 Super King Air DQ-FDS of Fiji Airways	25	30
228	50c. Balloon Double Eagle II	25	35
225/228 Set of 4		80	1·00

1985. World War II Aircraft.
329	15c. Curtiss P-40N Warhawk of the U.S. Army Air Corps	2·00	1·00
330	40c. Consolidated B-24 Liberator of the U.S.A.F	2·50	1·75
331	50c. Lockheed PV-1 Ventura of the U.S.A.F	2·50	2·00
332	60c. Douglas C-54 of the U.S.A.F	2·50	2·25
329/332 Set of 4		8·50	6·25

1991.
615*	60c. Fairey Sea Fox seaplane	3·50	2·50

1993.
668*	40c. Nakajima B5N "Kate" bombers	1·50	1·10

1995.
747*	40c. Aerial view of airfield	50	50

1998. 80th Anniv of Royal Air Force.
804	40c. Hawker Woodcock	60	50
805	50c. Vickers Victoria	65	60
806	60c. Bristol Type 164 Brigand	75	70
807	$1.50 de Havilland Canada DHC-1 Chipmunk	2·00	2·25
804/807 Set of 4		3·50	3·75
MS808	$1 Sopwith Pup; $1 Armstrong Whitworth FK8; $1 North American Harvard; $1 Vultee A-31 Vengeance	3·75	5·00

2003. Centenary of Powered Flight.
MS1095*	$1.75 Orville Wright, Dayton, Ohio, 1903; $1.75 Wilbur Wright with King Alphonso of Spain, Pau, France, 1909; $1.75 Wright Type A biplane, Le Mans, France, 1908; $1.75 Voisin Boxkite France, 1907	9·00	9·50
MS1096	$1.75 Voisin's motor-boat powered glider, France, 1905; $1.75 Trajan Vuia in Vuia No 1, France, 1906; $1.75 Santos-Dumont's biplane 14 bis, France, 1906; $1.75 Wright Type A biplane, Virginia, 1908	9·00	9·50
MS1097*	Two sheets. (a) $4 Wright Type A biplane, Virginia, 1908; (b) $4 Curtiss June Bug, 1908 Set of 4 sheets	9·00	9·50

2005.
MS1170*	$3 Boeing B-29 Superfortress Enola Gay	8·00	8·50

2007. Centenary of First Helicopter Flight.
1249	20c. Bolkow (MBB/Eurocopter) BO-105	30	30
1250	75c. NH Industries NH	1·20	1·20
1251	$1 Sikorsky S-65/RH-53D Sea Stallion	1·50	1·50
1252	$1.30 Bolkow (MBB/ Eurocopter) BO 105 (different)	1·80	1·80
1253	$1.30 Sikorsky S-65/RH-53D Sea Stallion (different)	1·80	1·80
1254	$1.30 Boeing (Hughes/McDonnell Douglas) AH-64 Apache (different)	1·80	1·80
1255	$1.30 NH Industries NH 90 (different)	1·80	1·80
1256	$2 Boeing (Hughes/McDonnell Douglas) AH-64 Apache (different)	3·00	3·00
1249/1256 Set of 8		12·00	12·00
MS1257	$3 Piasecki HUP Retriever	4·25	4·25

UGANDA

East Africa

100 cents = 1 shilling

1978. 75th Anniv of Powered Flight.
229	1s. Wright *Flyer III* and cattle being unloaded from Boeing 737.200 5X-UAL of Uganda Airlines	15	10
230	1s.50 Wright *Flyer III* and passengers boarding Britten-Norman BN-2 Islander of Uganda Airlines	25	15
231	2s.70 Wright *Flyer III* and sacks of coffee being loaded onto Boeing 737 of Uganda Airlines	25	35
232	10s. Concorde airliners and Wright *Flyer III*	75	1·50
229/232 *Set of 4*		1·30	1·90

1979. Nos. 229/32 overprinted **UGANDA LIBERATED 1979**.
275*	1s. Wright *Flyer III* and cattle being unloaded from Boeing 737.200 5X-UAL of Uganda Airlines	35	20
276*	1s.50 Wright *Flyer III* and passengers boarding Britten-Norman BN-2 Islander of Uganda Airlines	45	25
277*	2s.70 Wright *Flyer III* and sacks of coffee being loaded onto Boeing 737 of Uganda Airlines	55	55
278*	10s. Concorde airliners and Wright *Flyer III*	2·00	2·50

1981.
338*	2s.70 Handley Page H.P.45 G-AAXD *Horatius*	40	20

1984. 40th Anniv of ICAO.
447	5s. Airliner at Entebbe Airport and Boeing 707 of Uganda Airlines overhead	15	10
448	115s. Airplane being loaded with cargo	1·50	1·75
449	155s. Police helicopter	2·50	2·75
450	175s. Twin Piper trainer over Soroti Flying School	2·75	3·25
447/450 *Set of 4*		6·25	7·00
MS451 250s. Hot-air balloons		2·00	1·75

1987. Milestones of Transportation.
568*	2s. Glen Tremml's man-powered microlight *Eagle*, 1987	20	50
569*	3s. Junkers W.33 Bremen, 1928	20	50
570*	5s. Wiley Post's Lockheed Vega 5 NR-105-W *Winnie Mae*	30	60
571*	10s. Dick Rutan and Jeana Yeager's *Voyager*, 1986	40	60
572*	15s. Chanute's glider over Chicago, 1896	70	80
573*	25s. Amundsen's airship N.1 *Norge*, 1926	1·00	1·00
574*	35s. Curtiss *Golden Flyer* taking off from battleship U.S.S. *Pennsylvania*, 1911.	1·40	1·25
576*	100s. Concorde	6·50	6·50

1989.
772*	90s. Boeing 314A flying boat *Dixie Clipper* of Pan Am	2·25	1·50
774*	150s. Flight deck of Concorde	3·75	3·25
776*	300s. Concorde	4·25	4·25

1990.
810*	150s. Aircraft and paratroops	1·75	1·40
812*	300s. Douglas SBD Dauntless of the U.S. Navy attacking Japanese aircraft carrier	2·00	2·00
813*	350s. Curtiss P-40B Tomahawk II of the R. A. F.	2·25	2·25
MS815* 1000s. Hawker Hurricane Mk I of the R.A.F..		3·75	4·50

1990.
835*	200s. Curtiss JN-4 "Jenny" (on United States of America stamp No. A548 with centre inverted)	1·75	1·25

1991. No. 573 surcharged **20/-**.
1034*	20s. on 25s. Amundsen's airship N.1 *Norge*, 1926		

1992.
1047*	400s. Lilienthal glider No. 8	1·50	1·75

1992.
1051	200s. Aichi D3A "Val" bomber attacking U.S.S. Vestal	1·25	1·10
1052	200s. Mitsubishi A6M Zero-Sen	1·25	1·10
1053	200s. Mitsubishi A6M Zero-Sen over U.S.S. Arizona	1·25	1·10
1054	200s. Mitsubishi A6M Zero-Sen over U.S.S. Nevada	1·25	1·10
1055	200s. Aichi D3A "Val" bomber attacking ship	1·25	1·10
1056	200s. Douglas SBD Dauntless attacking Japanese aircraft carrier *Hiryu*	1·25	1·10
1057	200s. Mitsubishi A6M Zero-Sen and torpedo bombers attacking Midway Island	1·25	1·10
1058	200s. Brewster F2A Buffalo of the U.S. Marine Corps	1·25	1·10
1059	200s. Grumman F6F Hellcat and aircraft carrier	1·25	1·10
1060	200s. Grumman F6F Hellcat over aircraft carrier U.S.S. *Yorktown*	1·25	1·10
1051/1060 *Set of 10*		11·50	10·00

1992. 120th Anniv of Paris Balloon Post.
1061	200s. Three hot-air balloons	1·25	1·10
1062	200s. Three hot-air balloons and top of balloon *Double Eagle II*	1·25	1·10
1063	200s. Top of Richard Branson's balloon *Virgin Otsuka Pacific Flyer* and hot-air balloon *Pro Juventute*	1·25	1·10
1064	200s. Blanchard and Jeffries' balloon, 1785, and modern hot-air balloons	1·25	1·10
1065	200s. Nadar's balloon *Le Geant*, 1863, hot-air balloon and centre of balloon *Double Eagle II*	1·25	1·10
1066	200s. Lower part of Richard Branson's balloon *Virgin Otsuka Pacific Flyer* and two hot-air balloons	1·25	1·10
1067	200s. Montgolfier balloon (first manned free flight, 1783) and modern hot-air balloon	1·25	1·10
1068	200s. Basket of balloon *Double Eagle II* and balloon *Le Neptune*, Paris, 1870	1·25	1·10
1069	200s. Henri Giffard's balloon *Le Grand Ballon Captif*, 1878	1·25	1·10
1061/1069 *Set of 9*		10·00	9·00

1992.
1188*	1000s. Count Ferdinand von Zeppelin and Zeppelin airship	3·25	3·50
1190*	3000s. Count Ferdinand von Zeppelin and Clement-Bayard airship *Fleurus*	8·00	9·00
MS1191* Four sheets. (c) 2500s. Count Ferdinand von Zeppelin and Robert Brothers and Colin Hullin's balloon, 1784 (other miniature sheets do not show aircraft) *Price for 4 sheets*		22·00	23·00

1995.
1468*	500s. Boeing B-17 Flying Fortress	1·10	1·10

1996.
1721*	500s. Douglas DC-10	1·75	1·75

1998.
1974*	500s. Grumman F4F Wildcat	80	80
1975*	500s. Mitsubishi A6M Zero-Sen	80	80
1976*	500s. Supermarine Seafire (inscr. Spitfire)..	80	80
1977*	500s. BAe Harrier	80	80
1978*	500s. Lockheed S-3A Viking	80	80
1979*	500s. Vought F4U Corsair	80	80
1980*	600s. Dornier Do-X	80	80
1982*	600s. North American X-15	80	80
1984*	600s. Wright *Flyer I*	80	80
1985*	600s. Sikorsky VX-300 (inscribed 160R in error)	80	80
MS1986* Two sheets. (a) 2500s. Curtiss P-40 tomahawk; (b) 2500s. Sikorsky S-58 Seabat *Set of 2 sheets*		7·50	7·50

2001.
2348*	1000s. Aircraft carrier	1·75	1·75
2350*	1000s. Aircraft carrier	1·75	1·75

UKRAINE

South-east Europe

100 kopeks = 1 rouble

1993. 75th Anniv of First Vienna-Cracow-Lviv-Kyiv Flight.
69	35k. Hansa Brandenburg C-I	1·80	1·50
70	50k. Airbus Industrie A300 of Air Ukraine International	1·90	1·60

1994.
94*   500k. Ilyushin Il-2 Shturmovik   35   30

1996. 90th Birth Anniv of Oleg Antonov (aircraft designer).
150   20000k. Oleg Antonov and glider.....................   45   40
151   20000k. Antonov An-2 'Colt'................................   45   40
152   40000k. Antonov An-124 Ruslan   85   75
153   40000k. Antonov An-225 Mriya   85   75
150/153 Set of 4...   2·30   2·10

1997.
188   20k. Antonov An-74 TK-200   50   40
189   40k. Antonov An-70.......................................   1·00   85

2004.
576   80k. Antonov An-140.....................................   50   40
577   80k. Iran 140   50   40

2006. Birth Centenary of Oleg Konstantinovich Antonov (aircraft designer).
646   70k. Oleg Antonov and Antonov An-2......   55   50

UMM AL QIWAIN

Arabian Peninsula
100 dirhams = 1 riyal

APPENDIX

The following stamps have either been issued in excess of postal needs or have not been made available to the public in reasonable quantities at face value. Miniature sheets, imperforate stamps, etc are excluded from this section.

1968

Aviation History. Postage 25d., 50d., 1r., 1r.50, 2r.
Air 1r.25, 2r.50, 3r., 5r.

1968

Aviation History Appendix issue overprinted with capsule and text.
Postage 25d., 50d., 1r.,.1r.50, 2r. Air 1r.25, 2r.50, 3r., 5r.

1969

Apollo 8 Moon Orbit.

1972

International Airlines. Postage 5d., 10d., 15d., 20d., 25d.
Air 50d. Apollo 15 Moon Mission. 5r. (helicopters).

UNITED ARAB EMIRATES

Arabian Peninsula
1000 fils = 1 dirham

1975.
34*   125f. Helicopter on oil rig platform ....   8·75   2·20

1980.
104   15f. Dassault Mirage III jet fighters and Sud Aviation SE 3160 Alouette III helicopter   45   25
105   50f. Dassault Mirage III jet fighters and Sud Aviation SE 3160 Alouette III helicopter ....   1·30   45
106   80f. Dassault Mirage III jet fighters and Sud Aviation SE 3160 Alouette III helicopter ....   1·70   1·00
107   150f. Dassault Mirage III jet fighters and Sud Aviation SE 3160 Alouette III helicopter ....   2·50   1·70
104/107 Set of 4 ....   5·25   3·00

1986. First Anniv of Emirates Airlines.
205   50f. Boeing 737 of Emirates Airline   95   70
206   175f. Boeing 737 of Emirates Airline ....   3·25   3·00

1987. First Anniv of United Arab Emirates Flight Information Region.
222   200f. Boeing 737 ....   2·50   2·50
223   250f. Boeing 737 ....   3·25   3·25

1988. Sixth Anniv of Abu Dhabi International Airport.
242   50f. Lockheed L-1011 TriStar 500 at Abu Dhabi International Airport   60   60
243   50f. Interior of terminal building at Abu Dhabi International Airport   60   60
244   100f. Lockheed L-1011 TriStar 500 over control tower at Abu Dhabi International Airport ....   1·70   1·70
245   100f. Lockheed L-1011 TriStar 500 and Boeing 737 at boarding gangways at Abu Dhabi International Airport........   1·70   1·70
242/245 Set of 4 ....   4·25   4·25

1989. 10th Anniv of Sharjah International Airport.
268   50f. Sharjah International Airport   60   60
269   100f. Sharjah International Airport ....   1·30   1·30

1989.
270*   50f. Short S.23 flying boat.....................   85   85

1991.
351*   50f. Airbus A300/A310 at Abu Dhabi International Airport   45   35

1991. International Aerospace Exhibition, Dubai.
357   175f. Panavia Tornado F Mk 3 over Dubai Airport ....   1·30   1·30
358   2d. Panavia Tornado F Mk 3 over Dubai Airport ....   1·50   1·50

1995.
479*   50f. Helicopters.......................................   35   35

1997.
552*   50f. Helicopters.......................................   25   25

1997. International Aerospace Exhibition.
576   250f. Lockheed Martin (General Dynamics) F-16 Fighting Falcon.....................   75   75
577   3d. Bell Agusta BA609   85   85

2000. Expansion of Dubai International Airport.
659   50f. Airplanes...   45   45
660   350f. Airplanes (?).......................................   3·00   3·00

2001.
685   1d. Lockheed Martin (General Dynamics)
F-16 Fighting Falcon .... 1·10   1·10

UNITED NATIONS

New York Headquarters

100 cents = 1 dollar

1951.
A53*   7c. Douglas DC-8-60 Super Sixty 15   15

1963.
A126*   25c. Douglas DC-8 40   30

1967.
177*   5c. Stylised airliner (on luggage label) ... 10   10

1968.
A190* 20c. Airplane 25   20

1974.
A256* 13c. Airplane 15   15

1977.
A295* 31c. Airplane 40   30

1978. International Civil Aviation Organisation.
307   13c. Safety in the air – abstract design 15   15
308   25c. Safety in the air – abstract design 30   25

2003. Centenary of Powered Flight.
902   23c. Propeller 40   25
903   70c. Propeller .... 1·20   70

Geneva Headquarters

100 centimes = 1 franc

1978. International Civil Aviation Organisation.
G77   70c. Airliners and flight paths .... 1·00   1·00
G78   80c. Airliners and flight paths .... 1·20   1·20

1990.
G188* 90c. Jet airliner .... 1·50   1·50

1997.
G317 70f. Fokker F.IX and Zeppelin .... 1·50   1·50
G318 70f. Lockheed Constellation and Boeing
        314 Clipper .... 1·50   1·50
G319 70f. de Havilland DH.106 Comet and
        Boeing 747 .... 1·50   1·50
G320 70f. Ilyushin Il-62 and Boeing 747 .... 1·50   1·50
G321 70f. Concorde .... 1·50   1·50
G317/321 *Set of 5* .... 6·75   6·75

2005.
G516* 1f. Lockheed C-130 Hercules .... 1·20   70

Vienna Headquarters

100 groschen = 1 schilling

1991.
V119* 10s. Airplane dropping chemicals on
        trees .... 1·60   1·60

1998.
V267* 4s. Airplane 65   70

2000.
MSV313 3s.50 Helicopters (other stamps in the
miniature sheet do not show aircraft) .... 2·30   2·30

2001.
V343* 7s. Airship .... 1·10   1·10
V344* 7s. Balloon .... 1·10   1·10

UNITED STATES OF AMERICA

North America

100 cents = 1 dollar

1918.
A546   6c. Curtiss JN-4 "Jenny" .... 60·00   28·00
A547   16c. Curtiss JN-4 "Jenny" .... 95·00   30·00
A548   24c. Curtiss JN-4 "Jenny" .... 95·00   34·00
A546/548 *Set of 3* .... £225   85·00

1923.
A616* 24c. Airco (de Havilland) DH-4 Liberty ...... 90·00   27·00

1926. Lindbergh's Trans-Atlantic Flight.
A628   10c. Boeing Model 16/OH-4M .... 2·75   40
A629   15c. Boeing Model 16/OH-4M .... 4·25   2·50
A630   20c. Boeing Model 16/OH-4M .... 7·25   1·70
A628/630 *Set of 3* .... 13·00   4·25

1927.
A646   10c. Lindbergh's Ryan NYP Special *Spirit
of St. Louis* .... 7·00   2·50

1928.
A649   5c. Airplane .... 4·50   60

1928. Civil Aeronautics Conference and 25th Anniv of Wright
Brothers' First Flight.
652   2c. Wright *Flyer I* .... 1·20   80
653   5c. Ryan B-5 Brougham .... 5·50   3·25

1930. Airship *Graf Zeppelin* European Pan-American Flight.
A687	65c. Airship LZ-127 *Graf Zeppelin*	£225	£180
A688	$1.30 Airship LZ-127 *Graf Zeppelin*	£475	£375
A689	$2.60 Airship LZ-127 *Graf Zeppelin*	£800	£650
A687/689 *Set of 3*		£1400	£1100

1933. *Graf Zeppelin* Chicago Flight.
A732	50c. Airship LZ-127 *Graf Zeppelin*	80·00	60·00

1935. Trans-Pacific Air Mail.
A775	20c. Martin M-130 flying boat	7·25	1·30
A776	25c. Martin M-130 flying boat	1·10	95
A777	50c. Martin M-130 flying boat	7·25	4·25
A775/777 *Set of 3*		14·00	5·75

1941.
A901	6c. Airplane	25	15
A902	8c. Airplane	25	15
A903	10c. Airplane	85	15
A904	15c. Airplane	1·90	30
A905	20c. Airplane	1·60	35
A906	30c. Airplane	2·10	40
A907	50c. Airplane	8·25	3·00
A901/907 *Set of 7*		13·50	4·00

1945.
931	3c. Aircraft over Paris	25	15

1946.
A941	5c. Douglas DC-4	25	15

1947.
A943	5c. Douglas DC-4	25	15
A944	6c. Douglas DC-4	25	15

1947.
944	3c. Douglas DC-4	25	15

1947.
A948	10c. Martin 2-0-2	30	15
A949	15c. Lockheed Constellation	35	15
A950	25c. Boeing 377 Stratocruiser	80	15
A948/950 *Set of 3*		1·30	25

1949.
A984*	10c. Boeing 377 Stratocruiser	25	30
A986*	25c. Boeing 377 Stratocruiser	60	55

1949. 46th Anniv of Wright Brothers First Flight.
A987	6c. Wilbur and Orville Wright and Wright *Flyer I*	25	15

1952.
A1005	80c. Boeing 377 Stratocruiser	5·00	1·10

1953.
1014	3c. North American F-86 Sabre	25	15

1953. 50th Anniv of Aviation.
A1018	6c. Wright *Flyer I* and stylised Boeing	30	15

1957. 50th Anniv of United States Air Force.
A1097	6c. Boeing B-52 Stratofortress and Lockheed F-104 Starfighters of the U.S.A.F	25	15

1959. Centenary of Balloon Jupiter's Mail-carrying Flight.
A1132	7c. John Wise's Balloon *Jupiter*, 1859	40	15

1961. 50th Anniv of US Naval Aviation.
1184	4c. Curtiss A-1 seaplane, 1911	25	15

1962.
A1210*	8c. Douglas DC-8	20	15

1963. Amelia Earhart Commemoration.
A1216	8c. Amelia Earhart and Lockheed 10E Electra	30	20

1968.
A1327	10c. Curtiss JN-4 "Jenny"	25	20

1975.
1573	10c. Curtiss JN-4 "Jenny" and Boeing 747-100	25	20

1976.
A1610	25c. Stylised Boeing 737	45	15
A1611	31c. Stylised Boeing 737	50	15

1976. Commercial Aviation.
1664	13c. Stout Air Pullman and Laird Swallow biplane of the U.S. Mail	30	15

1977. 50th Anniv of Lindbergh's Trans-Atlantic Flight.
1686	13c. Ryan NYP Special *Spirit of St. Louis*	40	15

1978. 75th Anniv of First Powered Flight.
A1735	31c. Wilbur and Orville Wright and Wright *Flyer I* (at lower right)	55	15
A1736	31c. Wilbur and Orville Wright and Wright *Flyer I* (overhead)	55	15

1979. Aviation Pioneers. Octave Chanute.
A1748	21c. Octave Chanute and glider (at lower right)	50	35
A1749	21c. Octave Chanute and glider (overhead)	50	35

1979. Aviation Pioneers. Wiley Post.
A1775	25c. Wiley Post and nose of Lockheed Vega 5 NR-105-W *Winnie Mae*	1·00	40
A1776	25c. Wiley Post (lower right) and Lockheed Vega 5 NR-105-W *Winnie Mae*	1·00	40

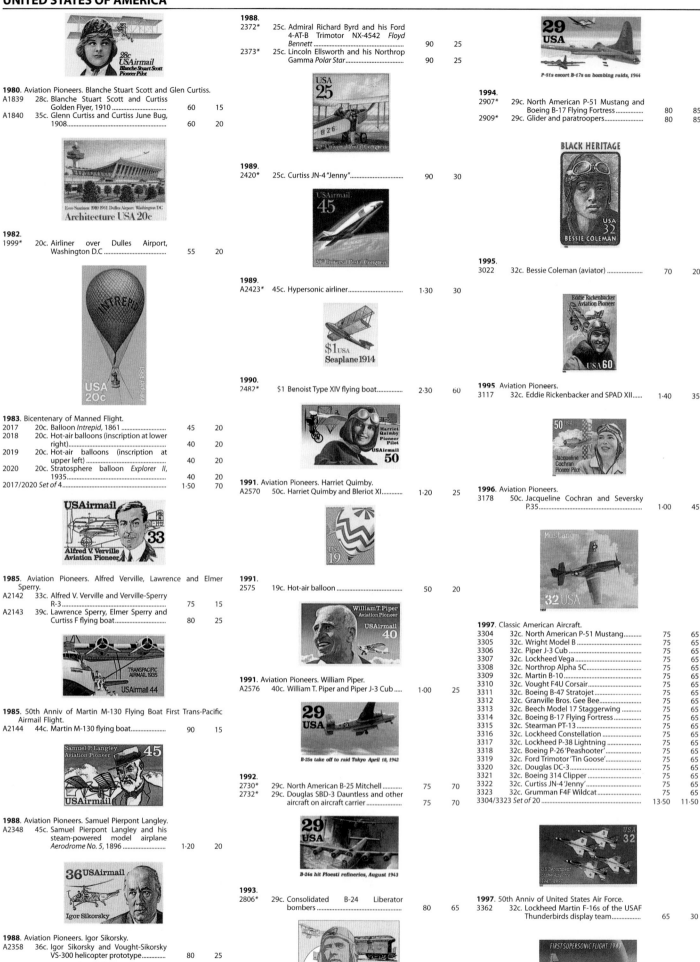

1980. Aviation Pioneers. Blanche Stuart Scott and Glen Curtiss.
A1839	28c. Blanche Stuart Scott and Curtiss Golden Flyer, 1910	60	15
A1840	35c. Glenn Curtiss and Curtiss June Bug, 1908	60	20

1982.
1999*	20c. Airliner over Dulles Airport, Washington D.C	55	20

1983. Bicentenary of Manned Flight.
2017	20c. Balloon *Intrepid*, 1861	45	20
2018	20c. Hot-air balloons (inscription at lower right)	40	20
2019	20c. Hot-air balloons (inscription at upper left)	40	20
2020	20c. Stratosphere balloon *Explorer II*, 1935	40	20
2017/2020	*Set of 4*	1·50	70

1985. Aviation Pioneers. Alfred Verville, Lawrence and Elmer Sperry.
A2142	33c. Alfred V. Verville and Verville-Sperry R-3	75	15
A2143	39c. Lawrence Sperry, Elmer Sperry and Curtiss F flying boat	80	25

1985. 50th Anniv of Martin M-130 Flying Boat First Trans-Pacific Airmail Flight.
A2144	44c. Martin M-130 flying boat	90	15

1988. Aviation Pioneers. Samuel Pierpont Langley.
A2348	45c. Samuel Pierpont Langley and his steam-powered model airplane *Aerodrome No. 5*, 1896	1·20	20

1988. Aviation Pioneers. Igor Sikorsky.
A2358	36c. Igor Sikorsky and Vought-Sikorsky VS-300 helicopter prototype	80	25

1988.
2372*	25c. Admiral Richard Byrd and his Ford 4-AT-B Trimotor NX-4542 *Floyd Bennett*	90	25
2373*	25c. Lincoln Ellsworth and his Northrop Gamma *Polar Star*	90	25

1989.
2420*	25c. Curtiss JN-4 "Jenny"	90	30

1989.
A2423*	45c. Hypersonic airliner	1·30	30

1990.
2482*	$1 Benoist Type XIV flying boat	2·30	60

1991. Aviation Pioneers. Harriet Quimby.
A2570	50c. Harriet Quimby and Bleriot XI	1·20	25

1991.
2575	19c. Hot-air balloon	50	20

1991. Aviation Pioneers. William Piper.
A2576	40c. William T. Piper and Piper J-3 Cub	1·00	25

1992.
2730*	29c. North American B-25 Mitchell	75	70
2732*	29c. Douglas SBD-3 Dauntless and other aircraft on aircraft carrier	75	70

1993.
2806*	29c. Consolidated B-24 Liberator bombers	80	65

1993.
2841*	29c. Pilot and Curtiss JN-4 "Jenny" biplane	80	20

1994.
2907*	29c. North American P-51 Mustang and Boeing B-17 Flying Fortress	80	85
2909*	29c. Glider and paratroopers	80	85

1995.
3022	32c. Bessie Coleman (aviator)	70	20

1995 Aviation Pioneers.
3117	32c. Eddie Rickenbacker and SPAD XII	1·40	35

1996. Aviation Pioneers.
3178	50c. Jacqueline Cochran and Seversky P.35	1·00	45

1997. Classic American Aircraft.
3304	32c. North American P-51 Mustang	75	65
3305	32c. Wright Model B	75	65
3306	32c. Piper J-3 Cub	75	65
3307	32c. Lockheed Vega	75	65
3308	32c. Northrop Alpha 5C	75	65
3309	32c. Martin B-10	75	65
3310	32c. Vought F4U Corsair	75	65
3311	32c. Boeing B-47 Stratojet	75	65
3312	32c. Granville Bros. Gee Bee	75	65
3313	32c. Beech Model 17 Staggerwing	75	65
3314	32c. Boeing B-17 Flying Fortress	75	65
3315	32c. Stearman PT-13	75	65
3316	32c. Lockheed Constellation	75	65
3317	32c. Lockheed P-38 Lightning	75	65
3318	32c. Boeing P-26 'Peashooter'	75	65
3319	32c. Ford Trimotor 'Tin Goose'	75	65
3320	32c. Douglas DC-3	75	65
3321	32c. Boeing 314 Clipper	75	65
3322	32c. Curtiss JN-4 'Jenny'	75	65
3323	32c. Grumman F4F Wildcat	75	65
3304/3323	*Set of 20*	13·50	11·50

1997. 50th Anniv of United States Air Force.
3362	32c. Lockheed Martin F-16s of the USAF Thunderbirds display team	65	30

1997. 50th Anniv of First Supersonic Flight.
3368	32c. Bell X-1 *Glamorous Glennis* (pilot Captain Charles 'Chuck' Yeager, USAF)	70	30

1998.
3383*   32c. Wright Brothers *Flyer I* 65   65

1998.
3433*   32c. Charles Lindbergh and Ryan NYP
          Special *Spirit of St. Louis* 65   70

1998. 50th Anniv of Berlin Airlift.
3443   32c. Douglas C-54 Skymaster 70   25

1998.
3539* $11.75 Boeing 747-123 Space Shuttle
          Carrier with Space Shuttle on board   23·00   12·00

1999. 120th Birth Anniv of Billy Mitchell (aviation pioneer).
3636   55c. Mitchell and SPAD XVI .... 1·00   70

1999.
3658*   33c. Bell UH-1 Iroquois 70   70

1999.
3718*   33c. Boeing 747 70   70

2000.
3764*   33c. Boeing CH-47 Chinooks 70   65

2003. Centenary of Powered Flight.
4285   37c. Wright *Flyer I* 55   35

2004. 50th Anniv of Air Force Academy.
4346   37c. Cadets' Chapel 40   10

2005.
4430*   37c. TWA Terminal, New York 40   10

2005.
4444   37c. Boeing 247 40   10
4445   37c. Consolidated PBY-5 Catalina 40   10
4446   37c. Grumman F6F Hellcat 40   10
4447   37c. Republic P-47 Thunderbolt 40   10
4448   37c. Erco Ercoupe 415 40   10
4449   37c. Lockheed P-80 Shooting Star...... 40   10
4450   37c. Consolidated B-24 Liberator....... 40   10
4451   37c. Boeing B-29 Superfortress 40   10
4452   37c. Beechcraft 35 Bonanza 40   10
4453   37c. Northrop YB-49 40   10
4444/4453 *Set of* 10 .... 3·50   90

2006. X-planes.
4560 $4.05 North American X-15 .... 6·00   3·75
4561 $14.40 North American X-15 (different) .... 21·00   14·00

2007. Presidential Aircraft.
4715 $4.60 Boeing VC-25A (Air Force One).......... 2·50   2·50
4716 $16.25 Sikorsky VH-3D (Marine One) .... 4·75   4·75

PARCEL POST STAMPS

1912.
P430*   20c. Wright Type A .... £100   16·00

UPPER VOLTA

West Africa

100 centimes = 1 franc

1962.
90   100f. Holste MH 1521 Broussard .... 2·20   1·00

91   200f. Lockheed Constellation and Holste
          MH 1521 Broussard at Ouagadougou
          Airport .... 6·00   1·90
92   500f. Lockheed Constellation .... 14·50   6·00
90/92 *Set of* 3 .... 20·00   8·00

1962. Inauguration of Air Afrique. As No. 307 of Cameroun.
95   25f. Boeing 707 airliners of Air Afrique 80   45

1963. First Jet Flight, Ouagadougou-Paris.
133   200f. Douglas DC-8 .... 5·25   2·75

1963. First Anniv of Air Afrique. No. 133 surcharged **AIR AFRIQUE 19-11-63 50F.**
136   50f. on 200f. Douglas DC-8 .... 1·50   85

1964.
144*   60f. Jet airliner .... 1·20   80

1966. Inauguration of Douglas DC-8F Air Services. As No. 438 of Cameroun.
200   25f. Douglas DC-8F Jet Trader of Air
          Afrique 80   50

1968.
233   500f. Sud Aviation SE 210 Caravelle
          Ouagadougou over airport .... 11·50   5·75

1969. 10th Anniv of ASECNA. As No. 552 of Cameroun.
279   100f. Airliner over airport .... 1·70   1·00

1978. Aviation History.
475   65f. Jean Mermoz and Latecoere 28-3
          seaplane F-AJNQ *Comte de la Vaulx*.. 75   25
476   75f. Anthony Fokker and his monoplane
          Spin III, Haarlem Spin 75   25
477   85f. Wiley Post and Lockheed Vega 5
          NR-105-W *Winnie Mae* 95   35
478   90f. Otto Lilienthal and Lilienthal
          monoplane glider .... 1·20   30
479   100f. Concorde .... 1·40   80
475/479 *Set of* 5 .... 4·50   1·80
MS480 500f. Charles Lindbergh and Ryan NYP
          Special *Spirit of St. Louis* .... 6·00   2·10

1978.
493*   100f. Montgolfier balloon (first manned
          free flight, 1783), Bleriot XI and
          Concorde .... 1·30   55

1979.
515*   65f. Beech A100 King Air of Air Volta
          being loaded with mail 75   45

1979.
519* 100f. Concorde .... 3·25 2·50

1979. 20th Anniv of ASECNA.
544 65f. Boeing 747 over airport 95 60

1980.
573* 65f. Jet airliner 55 30

1983. Bicentenary of Manned Flight.
652 15f. Joseph Montgolfier and Montgolfier balloon (unmanned flight, 1783) 10 10
653 25f. Jean-Francois Pilatre de Rozier and Montgolfier balloon (tethered flight, 1783) 30 10
654 70f. Professor Jacques Charles, the first ascent of his hydrogen balloon *The Globe*, 1783, and the destruction of *The Globe* 75 25
655 90f. John Jeffries and Blanchard and Jeffries' balloon, 1785 .... 95 35
656 100f. Wilhelmine Reichardt, Pierre Testu-Brissy's balloon ascent on horseback, 1798, and balloon *L'Entreprenant*, 1794 (air) .... 1·30 45
657 250f. Salomon Andree and his balloon *Ornen*,1897 .... 2·50 75
652/657 *Set of 6* .... 5·25 1·80
MS658 300f. Auguste Piccard and his stratosphere balloon *F.N.R.S.*, 1931 .... 4·00 1·40

1983.
663* 45f. Boeing 727 .... 75 25

1984.
707* 250f. Louis Bleriot and Bleriot XI .... 2·50 75

APPENDIX
The following stamps have either been issued in excess of postal needs or have not been made available to the public in reasonable quantities at face value. Miniature sheets, imperforate stamps, etc are excluded from this section.

1976
Zeppelin Airships. Postage 10f., 40f., 50f. Air 100f., 200f., 300f.

1983
Bicentenary of Manned Flight. 1500f.

URUGUAY

South America

1000 milesimos = 100 centesimos = 1 peso

1921. No. 121 overprinted with airplane and **CORREO AEREO**.
377 25c. Figure of Justice .... 5·75 4·25

1924.
436 6c. Biplane .... 1·70 1·60
437 10c. Biplane .... 2·30 2·30
438 20c. Biplane .... 3·75 3·50
436/438 *Set of 3* .... 7·00 6·50

1925.
475* 45c. Biplane .... 9·25

1939.
817 20c. Airplane (blue) 40 30
818 20c. Airplane (violet) 50 50
820 35c. Airplane 60 45
821 50c. Airplane 60 25
822 75c. Airplane 65 15
823 1p. Airplane .... 1·90 35
824 1p.38 Airplane (violet) .... 3·25 1·30
825 1p.38 Airplane (orange) .... 3·00 2·30
826a 2p. Airplane .... 2·25 45
827 5p. Airplane (lilac) .... 6·25 1·60
828 5p. Airplane (green) .... 8·75 3·75
829 10p. Airplane .... 60·00 37·00
817/829 *Set of 12* .... 80·00 44·00

1945. Nos. 821 and 825 surcharged with winged emblem, **1945** and value.
914 14c. on 50c. Airplane 80 35
915 23c. on 50c. Airplane 80 35
916 23c. on 1p.38 Airplane 85 35
917 1p. on 1p.38 Airplane .... 2·20 1·10
914/917 *Set of 4* .... 4·25 1·90

1946. New values as Nos. 874/5 overprinted with airplane and **SERVICIO AEREO**.
928 8c. Arms 15 10
929 50c. Arms 40 15
930 1p. Arms 80 30
931 2p. Arms .... 2·75 1·60
932 3p. Arms .... 4·00 1·90
933 5p. Arms .... 7·50 4·75
928/933 *Set of 6* .... 14·00 8·00

1947.
941 1p. Sud Est SE 161 Languedoc over Montevideo Airport .... 1·50 50
942 3p. Sud Est SE 161 Languedoc over Montevideo Airport (brown and blue) .... 3·75 1·90
943 5p. Sud Est SE 161 Languedoc over Montevideo Airport (brown and green) .... 7·75 3·75
944 10p. Sud Est SE 161 Languedoc over Montevideo Airport (brown and purple) .... 8·75 5·25
941/944 *Set of 4* .... 20·00 10·00

1947.
947 3c. Douglas DC-4 .... 15 10
948 8c. Douglas DC-4 .... 20 15
949 10c. Douglas DC-4 (black) 15 10
950 10c. Douglas DC-4 (red) 15 10

---

951 14c. Douglas DC-4 .... 30 20
952 15c. Douglas DC-4 .... 20 15
953 20c. Douglas DC-4 .... 25 20
954 21c. Douglas DC-4 .... 30 25
955 23c. Douglas DC-4 .... 30 25
956 27c. Douglas DC-4 .... 30 15
957 31c. Douglas DC-4 .... 45 20
958 36c. Douglas DC-4 (blue) 30 15
959 36c. Douglas DC-4 (black) 30 30
960 50c. Douglas DC-4 (turquoise) 50 35
961 50c. Douglas DC-4 (blue) 35 15
962 62c. Douglas DC-4 .... 55 35
963 65c. Douglas DC-4 .... 55 35
964 84c. Douglas DC-4 .... 70 45
965 1p.08 Douglas DC-4 .... 1·10 50
966 2p. Douglas DC-4 .... 1·80 85
967 3p. Douglas DC-4 (orange) .... 2·10 1·10
968 5p. Douglas DC-4 (green) .... 4·50 2·40
969 5p. Douglas DC-4 (grey) .... 2·50 1·60
970 10p. Douglas DC-4 (green) .... 11·50 7·75
947/970 *Set of 24* .... 27·00 16·00

1948. New values as Nos. 874/5 overprinted with airplane and **AVIACION**.
986 12c. Arms 15 15
987 24c. Arms 35 20
988 36c. Arms 50 30
986/988 *Set of 3* 90 60

1952.
1021 3c. Wing and engines over shadow of Boeing 377 Stratocruiser 15 10
1022 7c. Wing and engines over shadow of Boeing 377 Stratocruiser 15 15
1023 12c. Wing and engines over shadow of Boeing 377 Stratocruiser 20 20
1021/1023 *Set of 3* 45 40

1956.
1052* 20c. Airliners 35 30
1053* 31c. Airliners 45 25
1054* 36c. Airliners 65 40

1959. Santos-Dumont Commemoration.
1101 31c. Alberto Santos-Dumont and his biplane *14 bis* 20 15
1102 36c. Alberto Santos-Dumont and his biplane *14 bis* 20 15

1960. No. 956 surcharged with caduceus and **20c.**
1128 20c. on 27c. Douglas DC-4 .... 20 15

1961. Carrasco National Airport.
1165 1p. Airliner over Carrasco National Airport 25 15
1166 2p. Airliner over Carrasco National Airport 45 10
1167 3p. Airliner over Carrasco National Airport 75 35
1168 4p. Airliner over Carrasco National Airport 90 40
1169 5p. Airliner over Carrasco National Airport .... 1·20 60
1170 10p. Airliner over Carrasco National Airport .... 2·40 95
1171 20p. Airliner over Carrasco National Airport .... 3·75 2·00
1165/1171 *Set of 7* .... 8·75 4·00

1966. Honouring Capt. Boiso Lanza (pioneer military aviator).
1305 25c. Captain Boiso Lanza and early monoplane .... 1·00 55

1967. 30th Anniv of PLUNA Airline.
1335   10p. Douglas DC-4 of PLUNA...................... 35   25

1974. History of Aviation.
1583*	100p. Balloon	35	20
1584*	100p. Farman H.F.III biplanes........................	35	20
1585*	100p. Castaibert's Morane Saulnier Type I..	35	20
1586*	100p. Bleriot XI	35	20
1588*	150p. Nieuport 17 biplane	35	20
1589*	150p. Breguet Bidon biplane........................	35	20
1590*	150p. Caproni Ca 5 biplane	35	20

1976. 50th Anniv of *Plus Ultra*, Spain-South America Flight.
1633   63c. CASA-built Dornier Do-J Wal flying
           boat M-MWAL *Plus Ultra*....................... 55   30

1976. 50th Anniv of Lufthansa Airline.
1634   83c. Dornier Do-J II 10-t Wal flying boat
           of Lufthansa and stylised modern
           airliner.. 55   40

1978. PLUNA Airline Inaugural Boeing 727 Flight.
1698   50c. Boeing 727 of PLUNA............................ 45   15

1980. Inauguration of Lufthansa Cargo Container Service.
1742   2p. Boeing 747-200C of Lufthansa 45   25

1981. Inaugural Flight to Madrid of PLUNA.
1778	2p. Boeing 707 of PLUNA.........................	50	25
1779	5p. Boeing 707 of PLUNA.........................	95	45
1780	10p. Boeing 707 of PLUNA........................	2·10	90
1778/1780 *Set of 3*		3·25	1·40

Nos. 1778/80 are inscribed "BOEING 737".

1982. 25th Anniv of First Germany-Uruguay Lufthansa Flight.
1798	3p. Lockheed L.1049G Super Constellation of Lufthansa...................	75	70
1799	7p. Boeing 747-200 of Lufthansa.............	1·80	80

1983. Zeppelin Flight over Montevideo (1934).
1826   7p. Airship LZ-127 *Graf Zeppelin*............... 1·30   55

1986. 40th Anniv of First Scheduled Spain-Uruguay Flight.
1900   20p. Douglas DC-10 (top) and Douglas
            DC-3 of Iberia 40   15

1986. 50th Anniv (1986) of PLUNA.
1908	10p. de Havilland DH.90 Dragonfly	15	10
1909	20p. Douglas DC-3 of PLUNA.....................	20	15
1910	25p. Vickers Viscount 810 of PLUNA...........	30	20
1911	30p. Boeing 707 of PLUNA........................	40	20
1908/1911 *Set of 4*		95	60

1988. 75th Anniv of Air Force.
1922   17p. Farman M.F.11 Type 14 "Shorthorn".. 20   15

1991.
2030   1510p. CASA-built Dornier Do-J Wal flying
             boat M-MWAL *Plus Ultra*...................... 3·25   3·25

1993.
MS2133 Two sheets. (a) 1p. Zeppelin stamps of
    Germany and Uruguay (125th birth anniversary
    of Hugo Eckener, Zeppelin engineer) (other
    stamps and other miniature sheet do not show
    aircraft) *Price for 2 sheets* .... 14·50   14·00

1995. 70th Anniv of Naval Aviation.
2198   2p. CANT 18 .... 1·00   1·00

1995. 50th Anniv of ICAO.
2205   5p. Boeing 737 and emblem .... 2·40   2·30

1995.
MS2236 4p. Fairchild Hiller FH-227 (other stamps in
    the miniature sheet do not show aircraft)............. 5·75   5·50

1997. Third International Aeronautics and Space History Congress.
2389   6p. Arme 2 biplane *Montevideo*............... 1·40   1·30

1998.
2466	6p. Junkers Ju52/3m...............................	1·40	1·30
2467	6p. SPAD VII	1·40	1·30
2468	6p. Ansaldo SVA-10.................................	1·40	1·30
2469	6p. Piper PA 18 Super Cub (Neybar?).......	1·40	1·30
2466/2469 *Set of 4*		5·00	4·75

No. 2466 incorrectly inscribed "J52".

1998.
2477   25p. Stylised airliner................................. 5·50   5·25

1998.
MS2486 3p.50 Zeppelin NT airship; 4p. Transport
    aircraft (other stamps in the miniature sheet do
    not show aircraft).. 4·25   4·00

1999.
MS2553 4p. Zeppelin LZ-1 (first) and NT (last)
    airships (other stamps in the miniature sheet do
    not show aircraft)... 4·00   4·00

1999.
2555	7p. Piper J-3 Cub	1·30	1·30
2556	7p. Short S-25 Sunderland	1·30	1·30

2000.
2583*   3p.50 Airport (and other buildings)............. 65   65

2000. 75th Anniv of Uruguay Naval Aviation.
2624   9p. Vought Sikorsky OS 2U Kingfisher.....   1·90   1·80

2001. 25th Anniv of First Flight of Concorde.
2689   22p. Concorde.........................   4·00   4·00

2003. 50th Anniv of Uruguayan Air Force.
2871   14p. Lockheed F-80C Shooting Star...........   1·10   1·10

2003. Centenary of Powered Flight.
2875   14p. Wright Brothers and *Flyer I* ....   1·10   1·10

2004.
2917   16p. Robinson R22............................   1·40   1·40

PARCEL POST STAMPS

1964. No. 964 surcharged **$5.00 ENCOMIENDAS**.
P1268   5p. on 84c. Douglas DC-4   35   15

1969.
P1397   10p. Sud Aviation SE 210 Caravelle............   15   15
P1398   20p. Sud Aviation SE 210 Caravelle............   40   15

1974.
P1559*   500p. Monoplane ....   1·50   80

UZBEKISTAN

Central Asia 1995
100 tyin = 1 sum

1995.
86   6s. Lisunov Li-2..   85   50
87   10s. Kamov Ka-22...   1·30   90
88   10s. Antonov An-8..   1·30   90
89   10s. Antonov An-12......................................   1·30   90
90   10s. Antonov An-22......................................   1·30   90
91   10s. Ilyushin Il-76...   1·30   90
92   15s. Ilyushin Il-114.......................................   1·90   1·40
86/92 *Set of 7*...   8·25   5·75
MS93 20s. Ilyushin Il-114..   3·00   3·00

2001.
MS315* 70s. Sukhoi Su-25; 80s. Helicopter (other stamps in the miniature sheet do not show aircraft) ....   9·00   9·00

2001.
319*   90s. Ilyushin Il-76 facing right......................   1·10   85
320*   115s. Ilyushin Il-76 facing left........................   1·50   1·20

2005.
MS480 125s. Lisunov Li-2 (other stamps in the miniature sheet do not show aircraft)......................   9·00   8·75

VANUATU

South Pacific

Vatus

1983. Bicentenary of Manned Flight.
366	15v. Montgolfier balloon (first manned free flight, 1783)		15	15
367	20v. Charles' hydrogen balloon, 1783		20	25
368	25v. Blanchard and Jeffries' balloon, 1785		20	30
369	35v. Henri Giffard's steam-powered dirigible airship, 1852		30	40
370	40v. Renard and Krebs' airship *La France*, 1884		35	45
371	45v. Airship LZ-127 *Graf Zeppelin*		40	55
366/371 *Set of 6*			1·40	1·90

1983.
372*	15v. Boeing 737 at Bauerfield Airport		20	25

1984.
383*	25v. Boeing 737 of Air Vanuatu		35	40

1984. As No. 371, but inscribed "UPU CONGRESS" and logo.
385	45v. Airship LZ-127 *Graf Zeppelin*		80	80

1987.
450*	20v. Cessna 172 Skyhawk		30	30

1989.
523	20v. Consolidated PBY-5 Catalina flying boat of Qantas Empire Airways		85	30
524	45v. Douglas DC-3 VH-EAW		1·25	65
525	55v. Embraer EMB-110 Bandeirante YJ-RVB of Air Melanesia		1·50	80
526	200v. Boeing 737-300 of Air Vanuatu		4·25	3·00
523/526 *Set of 4*			7·00	4·25

1989.
536	65v. Concorde of Air France (on New Hebrides stamp No. F274)		3·75	2·50
MS537	65v. Concorde of British Airways (on New Hebrides stamp No. 258) (sheet contains one other design)		8·50	8·50

1990.
544*	100v. Embraer EMB-110 Bandeirante		1·90	2·00

1990.
556*	45v. Supermarine Spitfire of the Free French Squadron, R.A.F. over Biggin Hill Airfield		95	1·10

1992.
592	50v. Grumman F 4F Wildcat		2·25	1·25
593	55v. Douglas SBD-3 Dauntless		2·25	1·25
594	65v. Consolidated PBY-5A Catalina amphibian		2·50	1·50
595	80v. Douglas SBD Dauntless dive bombers on aircraft carrier U.S.S. *Hornet*		3·25	3·25
592/595 *Set of 4*			9·25	6·50
MS596	200v. Vought Sikorsky OS-2-3 Kingfisher seaplane		8·50	8·50

1993. 50th Anniv of Outbreak of Pacific War.
623	20v. Grumman F6F Hellcat		1·75	80
624	55v. Lockheed P-38F Lightning		2·75	1·75
625	65v. Grumman TBF Avenger		2·75	1·75
626	80v. Grumman F6F Hellcat taking off from aircraft carrier U.S.S. *Essex*		3·00	3·00
623/626 *Set of 4*			9·25	6·50
MS627	200v. Douglas C-47 Skytrain		8·50	8·50

1994.
657*	60v. de Havilland Canada DHC-6 Twin Otter 200/300		80	75

1994.
671*	90v. Boeing 737		1·90	2·00
672*	200v. Eurocopter (MBB) BO-105		3·25	3·50

1994. 50th Anniv of ICAO.
679	25v. Consolidated PBY-5 Catalina		65	45
680	60v. Douglas DC-3		1·10	90
681	75v. de Havilland Australia DHA.3 Drover		1·25	1·40
682	90v. Boeing 737		1·50	2·00
679/682 *Set of 4*			4·00	4·25

1995.
703	60v. Curtiss SB 2C Helldiver		2·75	1·75
704	70v. Supermarine Spitfire Mk VIII		2·75	1·90
705	75v. Chance Vought F4U-1A Corsair		2·75	2·00
706	80v. Lockheed PV-1 Ventura		2·75	2·00
703/706 *Set of 4*			10·00	7·00

1996.
724*	60v. Boeing 737		90	1·25

1997. 10th Anniv of Air Vanuatu.
746	25v. View from cockpit		55	40
747	60v. Boeing 737 being serviced at Bauerfield International Airport, Port Vila		1·00	75
748	90v. Air Stewardess serving drinks		1·50	1·40
749	200v. Passengers disembarking		2·50	4·00
746/749 *Set of 4*			5·00	6·00

2007. 20th Anniv of Air Vanuatu.
1018	40v. de Havilland Canada DHC-6 Twin Otter (foreground), Avions de Transport Régional ATR 42 (centre) and Boeing 737-300 (background) of Air Vanuatu		75	80
1019	130v. Boeing 737-300		2·50	2·75
1020	180v. de Havilland Canada DHC-6 Twin Otter		3·00	3·25
1021	250v. Avions de Transport Régional ATR 42		3·75	4·00
1018/1021 *Set of 4*			9·00	9·75

2008. Arrival of New Air Vanuatu Boeing 737-800.
1022	90v. Boeing 737 in flight over Vanuatu		1·60	1·75

VATICAN CITY

Southern Europe

100 centesimi = 1 lira

1967.
492*	20l. Jet airliner		10	10
495*	100l. Jet airliner		10	10

VENEZIA GIULIA AND ISTRIA

Southern Europe

100 centesimi = 1 lira

Allied Military Government

1945. Nos. 670, 674 and 677 of Italy overprinted **A.M.G.V.G.**

48*	1l. Caproni Campini N-1	40	3·25
51*	10l. Caproni Campini N-1	2·00	1·60
54*	50l. Caproni Campini N-1	4·25	5·50

VENEZUELA

South America

100 centimos = 1 bolivar

1930.

395	5c. Biplane (brown)	15	10
575	5c. Biplane (green)	30	10
396	10c. Biplane (yellow)	15	10
576	10c. Biplane (orange)	60	15
577	12½c. Biplane	80	50
397	15c. Biplane (grey)	15	10
578	15c. Biplane (blue)	70	15
398	25c. Biplane (violet)	15	10
579	25c. Biplane (brown)	1·40	20
399	40c. Biplane	15	10
581	70c. Biplane	21·00	7·00
400	75c. Biplane	45	15
401	1b. Biplane	55	15
402	1b.20 Biplane	75	35
403	1b.70 Biplane	95	40
404	1b.90 Biplane	1·00	50
405	2b.10 Biplane	1·50	40
406	2b.30 Biplane	1·50	50
407	2b.50 Biplane	1·75	50
408	3b.70 Biplane	1·75	75
409	10b. Biplane	3·50	1·50
410	20b. Biplane	7·50	4·00

1932. As Nos. 395/410, but on paper printed with pattern of arcs and "WINCHESTER SECURITY PAPER".

426	5c. Biplane	40	10
427	10c. Biplane	40	10
428	15c. Biplane	40	10
429	25c. Biplane	55	10
430	40c. Biplane	50	10
431	70c. Biplane	65	10
432	75c. Biplane	70	25
433	1b. Biplane	85	10
434	1b.20 Biplane	1·50	60
435	1b.70 Biplane	3·25	40
436	1b.80 Biplane	1·90	30
437	1b.90 Biplane	4·00	2·50
438	1b.95 Biplane	4·25	2·10
439	2b. Biplane	3·50	1·75
440	2b.10 Biplane	6·50	4·25
441	2b.30 Biplane	3·00	1·60
442	2b.50 Biplane	4·50	1·00
443	3b. Biplane	4·50	75
444	3b.70 Biplane	5·00	4·25
445	4b. Biplane	4·50	1·00
446	5b. Biplane	7·00	2·25
447	8b. Biplane	12·50	3·50
448	10b. Biplane	24·00	7·00
449	20b. Biplane	50·00	19·00
426/449	Set of 24	£130	48·00

1937. Nos. 435, 440 and 444/7 surcharged **1937 VALE POR** and value.

455	5c. on 1b.70 Biplane	12·00	6·00
456	10c. on 3b.70 Biplane	12·00	6·00
457	15c. on 4b. Biplane	5·75	3·00
458	25c. on 5b. Biplane	5·75	3·00
459	1b. on 8b. Biplane	4·75	4·00
460	2b. on 2b.10 Biplane	32·00	22·00
455/460	Set of 6	65·00	40·00

1937.

472*	15c. Airplane	40	35
473*	25c. Northrop Alpha	50	35
476*	75c. Airplane	1·90	65
480*	1b.95 Airplane	7·50	4·00
481*	2b. Northrop Alpha	2·75	1·75
482*	2b.50 Northrop Alpha	10·00	6·50
484*	3b.70 Northrop Alpha	10·00	8·00
485*	10b. Airplane	17·00	10·00

1937. Nos. 473, 480/2 and 485 overprinted **RESELLADO 1937–1938**.

496*	25c. Northrop Alpha	22·00	14·00
502*	1b.95 Airplane	7·50	3·75
503*	2b. Northrop Alpha	60·00	23·00
504*	2b.50 Northrop Alpha	65·00	21·00
506*	10b. Airplane	80·00	42·00

1938.

550*	5c. Douglas DC-2	20	10
551*	10c. Douglas DC-2	20	10
552*	12½c. Douglas DC-2	35	30
520*	15c. Douglas DC-2 (violet)	4·50	1·70
553*	15c. Douglas DC-2 (blue)	1·20	20
521*	25c. Douglas DC-2 (blue)	4·50	1·70
554*	25c. Douglas DC-2 (brown)	35	20
555*	30c. Douglas DC-2	2·75	20
522*	40c. Douglas DC-2 (violet)	5·00	1·60
556*	40c. Douglas DC-2 (brown)	3·50	20
557*	45c. Douglas DC-2	1·40	20
558*	50c. Douglas DC-2	1·80	20
523*	70c. Douglas DC-2	1·20	30
524*	75c. Douglas DC-2 (brown)	10·00	3·75
559*	75c. Douglas DC-2 (green)	2·00	30
560*	90c. Douglas DC-2	1·40	20
525*	1b. Douglas DC-2 (green)	10·00	3·75
561*	1b. Douglas DC-2 (violet)	1·80	20
526*	1b.20 Douglas DC-2 (orange)	29·00	8·00
562*	1b.20 Douglas DC-2 (brown)	2·75	75
527*	1b.80 Douglas DC-2	2·75	75
528*	1b.90 Douglas DC-2	7·75	3·75
529*	1b.95 Douglas DC-2	6·00	3·50
530*	2b. Douglas DC-2 (green)	65·00	21·00
563*	2b. Douglas DC-2 (red)	2·40	95
531*	2b.50 Douglas DC-2 (brown)	65·00	27·00
564*	2b.50 Douglas DC-2 (orange)	14·50	3·50
565*	3b. Douglas DC-2	7·75	2·75
533*	3b.70 Douglas DC-2	11·00	7·50
566*	3b.70 Douglas DC-2 (red)	11·00	2·75
771*	5b. Douglas DC-2 (green)	13·00	4·50
534*	10b. Douglas DC-2 (purple)	29·00	3·25
773*	10b. Douglas DC-2 (yellow)	17·00	6·50
535*	20b. Douglas DC-2	85·00	34·00

1938. Nos. 481/2 and 484 surcharged **1938 VALE** and value in words.

538*	10c. on 2b.50 Northrop Alpha	4·00	1·90
539*	15c. on 2b. Northrop Alpha	2·00	1·60
541*	40c. on 3b.70 Northrop Alpha	5·00	4·50

1938.

583*	20c. Airplane	50	35
585*	45c. Airplane	85	25
586*	50c. Airplane	70	25
587*	70c. Airplane	15·00	8·00
589*	1b.35 Airplane	1·60	75
590*	1b.40 Airplane	6·25	1·75

1940.

609	15c. Lockheed 10 Electra	50	15
610	20c. Lockheed 10 Electra	45	10
611	25c. Lockheed 10 Electra	1·90	35
612	40c. Lockheed 10 Electra	1·50	15
613	1b. Lockheed 10 Electra	3·50	25
614	2b. Lockheed 10 Electra	6·50	60
609/614	Set of 6	13·00	1·40

1940.

626*	5c. Airplane (green)	10	10
752*	5c. Airplane (orange)	10	10
627*	10c. Airplane (red)	10	10
753*	10c. Airplane (green)	10	10
628*	12½c. Airplane (violet)	45	35
754*	12½c. Airplane (green)	25	45
629*	15c. Airplane (blue)	25	10
755*	15c. Airplane (grey)	15	10
630*	20c. Airplane (brown)	35	10
756*	20c. Airplane (violet)	20	10
631*	25c. Airplane (brown)	25	10
757*	25c. Airplane (green)	15	10
632*	30c. Airplane (violet)	25	10
758*	30c. Airplane (blue)	20	10
633*	40c. Airplane (brown)	35	10
759*	40c. Airplane (green)	35	10
634*	45c. Airplane (green)	50	10
760*	45c. Airplane (red)	30	15
635*	50c. Airplane (blue)	50	10
761*	50c. Airplane (claret)	30	15
636*	70c. Airplane (pink)	1·40	35
762*	70c. Airplane (red)	50	30
637*	75c. Airplane (olive)	4·25	1·00
763*	75c. Airplane (orange)	3·50	2·00
764*	75c. Airplane (violet)	30	15
638*	90c. Airplane (orange)	65	35
765*	90c. Airplane (black)	45	40
639*	1b. Airplane (mauve)	35	10
766*	1b. Airplane (blue)	35	20
640*	1b.20 Airplane (green)	1·75	60
767*	1b.20 Airplane (brown)	65	45
641*	1b.35 Airplane	7·00	3·00
642*	2b. Airplane	1·40	20
643*	3b. Airplane (black)	2·50	60
768*	3b. Airplane (brown)	11·50	2·75
769*	3b. Airplane (blue)	1·40	35
644*	4b. Airplane	2·00	35
645*	5b. Airplane	12·00	5·25

1943. Nos. 473, 476, 480/2 and 484/5 overprinted **Resellado 1943**.

663*	25c. Northrop Alpha	1·25	1·00
667*	75c. Northrop Alpha	1·75	1·10
672*	1b.95 Airplane	3·75	2·00
673*	2b. Northrop Alpha	3·75	2·75
674*	2b.50 Northrop Alpha	4·00	2·75
676*	3b.70 Northrop Alpha	55·00	45·00
677*	10b. Airplane	21·00	14·50

1944. No. 590 surcharged **Habilitado 1944 VALE Bs. 0.30**.

697	30c. on 1b.40 Airplane	35	35

1945.

708*	5c. Douglas DC-4	20	15
709*	10c. Douglas DC-4	25	20
710*	20c. Douglas DC-4	35	25
711*	30c. Douglas DC-4	55	40
712*	40c. Douglas DC-4	55	35
713*	45c. Douglas DC-4	70	35
714*	90c. Douglas DC-4	1·25	45
715*	1b. Douglas DC-4	90	35
716*	1b.20 Douglas DC-4	2·50	2·25
717*	1b. Douglas DC-4	3·75	1·50

1947. Nos. 535 and 635 surcharged.

735*	20c. on 50c. Airplane	40	25
737*	20b. on 20b. Douglas DC-2	23·00	12·00

1949.

814*	5c. Silhouette of Douglas DC-3	40	15
815*	10c. Silhouette of Douglas DC-3	50	15
816*	15c. Silhouette of Douglas DC-3	60	15
817*	25c. Silhouette of Douglas DC-3	1·10	30
818*	30c. Silhouette of Douglas DC-3	1·10	30
819*	1b. Silhouette of Douglas DC-3	6·25	1·25

1950.

864	5c. Airplane	15	10
865	10c. Airplane	10	10
866	15c. Airplane	30	15
867	25c. Airplane	50	25
868	30c. Airplane	60	20
869	50c. Airplane	50	25
870	60c. Airplane	50	35
871	90c. Airplane	1·50	60
872	1b. Airplane	2·50	1·75
864/872	Set of 9	6·00	3·25

1954.

1359	15c. Lockheed Constellation	15	10
1360	45c. Lockheed Constellation	45	15
1361	40c. Lockheed Constellation	35	15
1362	65c. Lockheed Constellation	1·25	45
1363	80c. Lockheed Constellation	1·00	35
1364	1b. Lockheed Constellation	2·00	30
1359/1364	Set of 6	4·50	1·40

1959.
1572*	1b. Douglas DC-6	1·90	70
1575*	1b. Douglas DC-6 (air) (inscribed "AEREO")	1·50	70

1966.
1984	45c. Sud Aviation SE 210 Caravelle	65	20

1970. 50th Anniv of Venezuelan Air Force.
2172	5c. Caudron G-3 biplane and Lockheed Martin (General Dynamics) F-16 Fighting Falcon	20	10

1973.
2231	5c. Jet airliner	15	10

1973.
2243*	10c. Lockheed Martin C-130 Hercules	25	15

1974.
2278*	50c. Jet airliner	40	20

1976.
2308	1b. Survey airplane	50	20

1979. 59th Anniv of Air Force.
2418	75c. Caudron G-3 biplane	35	20
2419	75c. Stearman PT-17 Kaydett biplane	35	20
2420	75c. Bell Model 204 UH-1B Iroquois helicopter	35	20
2421	75c. Dassault Mirage IIIC jet fighter	35	20
2418/2421 Set of 4		1·30	70

1986. 25th Anniv of VIASA (airline).
2590*	3b. Douglas DC-8 in flight	35	20
2591*	3b. Douglas DC-8 on ground	35	20
2592*	3b. Boeing 747 over sea	35	20
2593*	3b. Tail fins of Douglas DC-10 airliners	35	20
2595*	3b.25 Douglas DC-10 flying through cloud	35	20
2596*	3b.25 Douglas DC-8 and tail of Douglas DC-10	35	20
2597*	3b.25 Douglas DC-9 over mountains	35	20
2598*	3b.25 Flight deck of airliner	35	20

1987.
2696*	2b.25 Boeing 737	35	20

1987.
2710*	2b. Agusta A.109A helicopters	50	20
2719*	4b. Agusta A.109A helicopters	80	30

1995.
3112*	80b. Shorts SC 7 Skyvan	1·10	55

1996. 25th Anniv of Liberator Simon Bolivar International Airport, Maiquetia.
3248	80b. Emblem	60	30
3249	80b. Flight paths into airport	60	30
3250	80b. La Guaira Aerodrome, 1929	60	30
3251	80b. Maiquetia Airport, 1944	60	30
3252	80b. Liberator Simon Bolivar Airport, 1972	60	30
3253	80b. Airport interior by Carlos Cruz Diez	60	30
3254	80b. Control Tower and airport police	60	30
3255	80b. Fire tender	60	30
3256	80b. Airplanes at terminal buildings	60	30
3257	80b. Boeing 747 and terminal buildings	60	30
3248/3257 Set of 10		5·50	2·75

VIETNAM

South-east Asia

South Vietnam

100 cents = 1 piastre

1971.
S383	3p. Lockheed C-130 Hercules, Boeing-Vertol CH-47 Chinook helicopter and other aircraft	1·10	1·10
S384	40p. Lockheed C-130 Hercules, Boeing-Vertol CH-47 Chinook helicopter and other aircraft	1·90	75

1972. 20th Anniv of Vietnam Airlines.
S407	10p. Yakolev Yak-40 over Dalat	1·10	75
S408	10p. Yakolev Yak-40 over Ha Tien	1·10	75
S409	10p. Yakolev Yak-40 over Hue	1·10	75
S410	10p. Yakolev Yak-40 over Saigon	1·10	75
S411	25p. Yakolev Yak-40 over Dalat	2·30	2·30
S412	25p. Yakolev Yak-40 over Ha Tien	2·30	2·30
S413	25p. Yakolev Yak-40 over Hue	2·30	2·30
S414	25p. Yakolev Yak-40 over Saigon	2·30	2·30
S407/414 Set of 8		12·00	11·00

1975.
S494*	10p. Airliner	75	75

National Front for the Liberation of South Vietnam

100 xu = 1 dong

1963.
NLF5*	10x. Boeing-Vertol H-47 Chinook	7·50	7·50

1964.
NLF8*	30x. Douglas A-3 Skywarrior sinking in the sea	3·75	3·75

1965.
NLF9*	10x. Lockheed Martin C-130 Hercules, Bien Hoa airfield	3·75	3·75

1967.
NLF12*	20x. Helicopter of the American Army	3·75	3·75

1968.
NLF20*	20x. Burning airplane	3·75	3·75

North Vietnam

100 xu = 1 dong

1959.
N120   20x. Convair CV 340 ....   7·50   1·90

1964.
N329*   12x. Glider ....   1·50   60

1964.
N338*   12x. Boeing B-52 Stratofortress crashing.   1·10   40

1965. 500th US Aircraft brought down over North Vietnam.
N390   12x. Republic F-105D Thunderchief..........   4·25   2·75

1966. 1000th US Aircraft brought down over North Vietnam.
N439   12x. Republic F-105D Thunderchief on
        fire ....   5·25   3·75

1966. 1500th US Aircraft brought down over North Vietnam.
N447   12x. Convair F-106 Delta Dart on fire ....   7·50   2·75
N448   12x. Convair F-106 Delta Dart on fire ....   11·50   2·75
        No. N447 overprinted **NGAY 14.10.1966.**

1967. 2000th US Aircraft brought down over North Vietnam.
N478   6x. Captured American pilot and
        wreckage of airplane............................   2·75   1·50
N479   12x. Captured American pilot and
        wreckage of airplane............................   2·75   1·50

1967.
N492   12x. Republic F-105D Thunderchief on
        fire and Mikoyan Gurevich MiG-15 ...   3·25   95
N493   12x. Boeing B-52 Stratofortress on fire ......   3·25   95

1967. Anti-Aircraft Defences.
N496   12x. Machine gun crew and airplane on
        fire   45   40
N497   12x. Soldiers firing rifles at airplane..........   45   40
N498   12x. Naval anti-aircraft gun and crew and
        airplane crashing into the sea............   45   40
N499   12x. Captured American pilot and
        wreckage of McDonnell Douglas
        F-4F Phantom II   45   40
N500   20x. Jet fighters in air battle....................   90   40
N501   30x. Aircraft over anti-aircraft guns..........   1·80   40
N496/501 Set of 6..   4·00   2·20

1967.
N512*   12x. Mortars and wreckage of airplane   60   60

1968. 3000th US Aircraft brought down over North Vietnam.
N532*   12x. Airplane and women with anti
        aircraft gun ....   1·50   1·10
N533*   40x. Republic F-105D Thunderchief and
        Mikoyan Gurevich MiG-15....................   3·75   1·10
N534*   40x. Surface-to-air missile and airplane ...   3·75   1·10

1969.
N560*   40x. Painting showing wreckage of
        American airplane.................................   1·40   1·10

1969.
N561*   12x. Wreckage of Boeing-Vertol CH-47
        Chinook helicopter, Bell Model 204
        UH-1B helicopter and Lockheed C-5
        Galaxy...   40   40

1969.
N592   12x. Republic F-105 Thunderchief..............   1·90   40

1970.
N604*   50x. Model airplane ....   1·10   40

1972. 3500th US Aircraft brought down over North Vietnam.
N702   12x. American pilot and falling airplane
        (green and red).................................   1·90   1·10
N703   12x. American pilot and falling airplane
        (black and red)..................................   1·90   1·10

1972. 4000th US Aircraft brought down over North Vietnam.
N712   12x. Anti-aircraft gunner and falling
        airplane ....   2·30   75
N713   12x. Surface-to-air missile and falling
        airplane ....   2·30   75

1973.
N752   12x. Mikoyan Gurevich MiG-23 shooting
        down Boeing B-52 Stratofortress   75   45
N753   12x. Boeing B-52 Stratofortress
        exploding   75   45
N754   12x. General Dynamics F-111 on fire.........   75   45
N755   1d. Wreckage of aircraft in sea..............   3·00   45
N752/755 Set of 4..   4·75   1·60

Socialist Republic of Vietnam

100 xu = 1 dong

1979.
278*   50x. Model glider................................   90   40

1983. Bicentenary of Manned Flight.
544   30x. Montgolfier balloon (first manned
        free flight, 1783)................................   25   10
545   50x. Charles' hydrogen balloon, 1783   40   10
546   1d. Parseval Sigsfeld kite-type
        observation balloon, 1898.....................   45   15
547   2d. Eugene Godard's balloon L'Aigle,
        1864..   90   25
548   3d. Blanchard and Jeffries' balloon, 17....   1·10   25
549   5d. Nadar's balloon Le Geant, 1863 ....   1·50   40
550   8d. Balloon ....   2·30   60
544/550 Set of 7...   6·25   1·70
MS551 10d. Montgolfier balloon (tethered flight,
        1783) ....   4·50   1·50

1984.
695*	3d. Fairchild C-119 Flying Boxcar and three aircraft overhead	75	30
696*	5d. Airplane at Dien Bien Phu	1·20	45

1984. 50th Anniv of First South Atlantic Air Service.
MS699 10d. Junkers Ju 52/3m		4·25	1·50

1984.
789*	1d. Boeing B-52 Stratofortress on fire	40	15

1985.
856*	2d. Jet airliner	55	25

1985.
872	1d. Helicopter	85	40
873	1d. Airplane	85	40

1986. Historic Aircraft.
939	1d. Hawker Hart	25	10
940	1d. Curtiss JN-4 "Jenny"	25	10
941	2d. PZL P-23 Karas	45	15
942	3d. Yakovlev Yak-11	75	30
943	3d. Fokker Dr-1 triplane	75	30
944	5d. Boeing P12, 1920	1·10	55
945	5d. Nieuport-Delage 29C1, 1929	1·10	55
939/945 Set of 7		4·25	1·80

1987.
1109*	5d. Ilyushin Il-62M	60	40

1987. Flying Boats.
1136	5d. Consolidated PBY-5 Catalina flying boat	15	15
1137	10d. Liore et Olivier Leo 246 flying boat	30	15
1138	15d. Dornier Do-18 flying boat	45	15
1139	20d. Short S.25 Sunderland flying boat	60	25
1140	25d. Flying boat, 1923	75	30
1141	30d. Chetverikov ARK-3 flying boat	85	40
1142	40d. Cant Z.509 flying boat	1·10	55
1136/1142 Set of 7		3·75	1·80
MS1143 50d. Flying boat		2·75	1·20

1987. 15th Anniv of US Air Bombardment of Vietnam.
1165*	10d. Wreckage of Boeing B-52 Stratofortress	40	40

1988. Helicopters.
1208	10d. Kamov Ka-26 helicopter	30	15
1209	10d. Boeing-Vertol 234 Commercial Chinook helicopter	30	15
1210	20d. MBB-Bolkow Bo 105 helicopter	55	25
1211	20d. Mil Mi-10K helicopter	55	25
1212	30d. Kawasaki-Hughes 369HS helicopter	60	30
1213	30d. Bell 206 JetRanger helicopter	60	30
1214	50d. Mil Mi-8 helicopter	75	45
1208/1214 Set of 7		3·25	1·70
MS1215 80d. Sud Aviation SA 330 Puma helicopter.		2·75	1·30

1990. Airships.
1430	100d. Henri Giffard's steam-powered dirigible airship, 1852	10	10
1431	200d. Lebaudy-Juillot airship No. 1 *La Jaune* (inscribed "Lebandy")	10	10
1432	300d. Airship LZ-127 *Graf Zeppelin*	15	15
1433	500d. Airship R-101	30	30
1434	1000d. Airship *Osoaviakhim*,1936	60	60
1435	2000d. Tissandier Brothers' airship, 1883	1·20	1·20
1436	3000d. U .S. Navy "N" Class airship ZPN-1	1·80	1·80
1430/1436 Set of 7		3·75	3·75
MS1437 3500d. Airship *Zodiac*, 1931		2·10	2·10

1992.
1670	400d. Tupolev Tu-154M of C.S.A.	15	15
1671	500d. Concorde of Air France	15	15
1672	1000d. Airbus Industrie A320 of Cyprus Airways	25	15
1673	3000d. Airbus Industrie A340.300	30	25
1674	4000d. de Havilland Canada DHC-8 Dash Eight-400	90	25
1675	5000d. Boeing 747-200 of Lufthansa	1·30	55
1676	6000d. McDonnell Douglas MD-11CF of Martinair	1·50	55
1670/1676 Set of 7		4·00	4·00

1993.
1811*	400d. Aircraft	10	10

1994.
1914	400d. Boeing 737	15	10
1915	3000d. Boeing 737 on ground	75	30

1995. Balloons.
1958	500d. Montgolfier's hot air balloon, 1783	10	10
1959	1000d. Jacques Charles and Marie-Noel Robert's balloon (first untethered flight by manned hydrogen balloon)	15	15
1960	2000d. Jean-Pierre Blanchard's oared balloon	40	15
1961	3000d. Jean-Francois Pilatre de Rozier and Jules Romain's balloon over English Channel, 1785	55	15
1962	4000d. Free balloon	60	25
1963	5000d. Captive balloon over Red Square, Moscow, 1890	75	25
1964	7000d. Auguste Piccard's balloon *'FNRS'*, 1931	1·30	55
1958/1964 Set of 7		3·50	1·40

1995. Parachuting.
1965	400d. Parachutist	15	10
1966	2000d. Two parachutists	40	15
1967	3000d. Landing	60	25
1968	4000d. Gathering in the parachute	1·50	70
1965/1968 Set of 4		2·40	1·10

1996.
2057	400d. Airbus Industrie Airbus A320	10	10
2058	1000d. Antonov An-72	15	15
2059	2000d. McDonnell Douglas MD-11F	30	30
2060	6000d. Avro RJ-85	1·00	1·00
2061	10000d. Boeing 747-400F	1·50	1·50
2057/2061 Set of 5		2·75	2·75
MS2062 13000d. Boeing 747-123 Space Shuttle Carrier with shuttle on board (shows incorrect tailplane layout)		2·00	2·00

1999. Kites.
2230	400d. Eagle kite	10	10
2231	5000d. Kite with bamboo flute	75	75
2232	7000d. Peacock kite	1·10	1·10
2230/2232 Set of 3		1·80	1·80

2002. Civilian Aircraft.
2513	800d. Beech 200 Super King Air	15	15
2514	2000d. Fokker 70	30	30
2515	3000d. Avions de Transport Regionale ATR 72-202	45	45
2516	8000d. Boeing 767-300	1·10	1·10
2513/2516 Set of 4		1·80	1·80
MS2517 14000d. Beech 200 Super King Air (different)		2·10	2·10

VIETNAM

1979. No value indicated.
MF304*   (–) Pilot and airplane ....   1·10   1·10

1979. No value indicated.
MF310*   (–) Pilot and MiG-21s ....   1·10   40

1983.
MF581   (–) MiG-21s...   75   75

WALLIS AND FUTUNA ISLANDS

South Pacific
100 centimes = 1 franc

1949. As No. 254 of Cameroun.
156   10f. Lockheed Constellation .... 3·25   19·00

1949. Nos. 325/6 of New Caledonia overprinted **WALLIS ET FUTUNA**.
157   50f. Sud Est SE 161 Languedoc.................... 7·25   21·00
158   100f. Sud Est SE 161 Languedoc................. 7·50   29·00

1954. As No. 264 of Cameroun.
160   3f. Bomber.. 4·75   19·00

1969. First Flight of Concorde. As No. 83 of Comoro Islands.
198   20f. Concorde of Air France......................... 8·75   20·00

1975. First Regular Air Service to New Caledonia.
243   100f. Boeing 707..................................... 12·00   12·00

1976. First Commercial Flight of Concorde.
253   250f. Concorde of Air France.......................... 34·00   34·00

1977. No. 253 overprinted **PARIS NEW YORK 22.11.77 1er VOL COMMERCIAL**.
270   250f. Concorde of Air France.......................... 28·00   30·00

1979.
307*   46f. Britten-Norman BN-2 Islander F-ORCA of U.T.A..................... 1·90   4·50
309*   80f. Boeing 737 at Hihifo Airport .... 2·75   5·75

1980.
348   86f. Concorde of Air France.......................... 5·75   7·75

1980. As Nos. 307 and 309.
349*   1f. Britten-Norman BN-2 Islander F-ORCA of U.T.A..................... 60   2·50
351*   5f. Boeing 737 at Hihifo Airport 65   2·50

1980. 50th Anniv of First South Atlantic Airmail Flight.
361   122f. Jean Mermoz and Couzinet 70 F-AMBV *Arc en Ciel*................. 9·25   7·75

1982. 50th Death Anniv of Alberto Santos-Dumont (aviation pioneer).
407   95f. Alberto Santos-Dumont with his airship *Ballon No. 14* and biplane *14 bis*................... 6·25   4·75

1983. Bicentenary of Manned Flight.
421   205f. Vincenzo Lunardi's balloon (flight from London to Ware, 1784)............... 12·00   8·50

1987.
516   135f. Auguste Piccard and his stratosphere balloon *F.N.R.S.*, 1931.................. 6·25   5·25

1988. 70th Death Anniv of Roland Garros (aviator).
529   600f. Roland Garros and Morane Saulnier Type I................... 20·00   21·00

1990. Centenary of First Heavier-than-Air Flight and First Anniv of Wallis-Tahiti Air Link.
560   56f. Boeing 737 of Air Caledonie, Clement Ader and his *Avion III* .... 1·80   3·25

1991. Microlight Aircraft Flying in Wallis and Futuna.
581   85f. Microlight.............................. 4·75   4·50

1992.
594   48f. Dassault 200 Falcon Mystere.............. 1·70   3·00

1993.
617   130f. Dassault HU-25B Gardian .... 4·50   4·50

1994. 50th Death Anniv of Antoine de Saint-Exupery (aviation pioneer).
650   800f. Saint-Exupery and Breguet Bre. 14 (top) Potez 630 (middle) and Potez 63 (bottom)..................... 18·00   14·00

1997. Inauguration of Hihifo Airport.
702   130f. de Havilland Canada DHC-6 Twin Otter................... 2·30   2·75

2000. 30th Anniv of Air Transport on Futuna Island.
761   350f. Boeing 737 (in flight) and de Havilland Canada DHC-6 Twin Otter   5·50   3·75

2003. 40th Anniv of Last Escadrille 9S Lancaster WU21 Flight (26 January 1963).
817   135f. Avro Type 683 Lancaster WU21 and Insignia of Escadrille 9S................... 1·90   1·40

2004. First Flight over Wallis and Futuna.
855*   380f. Gourdou-Leseurre GL 832.................... 5·25   3·50

2005. 58th Anniv of First Flight between Noumea and Hihifo.
881   380f. Consolidated PBY-5A Catalina............ 6·25   3·25

2006. 20th Anniv of de Havilland Canada DHC-6 Twin Otter *Ville de Paris*.
898   30f. de Havilland Canada DHC-6 Twin Otter *'Ville de Paris'*................... 45   25

2007. 50th Anniv of Regular Noumea-Hihifo Air Flight.
912   290f. Douglas DC-3 Dakota F-BGXN............ 9·25   9·25

WEST BERLIN

See under Germany

WEST GERMANY

See under Germany (Federal Republic)

WURTTEMBERG

See under Germany (Allied Occupation)

YEMEN

Arabia

1947. 40 bogaches = 1 imadl

1964. 40 bogaches = 1 rial

1975. 100 fils = 1 riyal

1947.

63*	10b. Douglas DC-4	7·75	3·75
64*	20b. Douglas DC-4	11·50	7·75

1951.

81	6b. Airplane	1·50	1·20
82	8b. Airplane	1·90	1·50
83	10b. Airplane	2·30	1·90
84	12b. Airplane	2·75	2·30
85	16b. Airplane	3·50	2·75
86	20b. Airplane	4·25	3·00
87	1i. Airplane	11·00	6·25
81/87 Set of 7		25·00	17·00

1960. Nos. 16 and 18 overprinted with Douglas DC-4 airliner and **AIR MAIL 1959** in English and Arabic.

121	6b. Arabic pattern	1·90	1·50
122	10b. Arabic pattern	3·00	2·30

1961.

150*	16b. Douglas DC-6	2·75	1·40

1961.

155*	16b. Hawker Siddeley Comet 4	90	90

1963. Nos. 22/6 overprinted with airplane, Arabic inscription and **AIR MAIL**.

226	6b. Flags of Saudi Arabia, Yemen and Iraq	1·70	1·70
227	10b. Flags of Saudi Arabia, Yemen and Iraq	2·20	2·20
228	14b. Flags of Saudi Arabia, Yemen and Iraq	2·50	2·50
229	20b. Flags of Saudi Arabia, Yemen and Iraq	3·50	3·50
230	1i. Flags of Saudi Arabia, Yemen and Iraq	7·50	7·50
226/230 Set of 5		15·00	15·00

1964.

258*	16b. Vickers Viscount 800	1·90	1·70

1964. Inauguration of Hodeida Airport.

262	4b. Boeing 707	50	45
263	6b. Boeing 707 at Hodeida Airport	70	60
264	10b. Boeing 707 at Hodeida Airport	95	70
262/264 Set of 3		1·90	1·60

1964.

265*	¼b. Boeing 707	35	15
268*	1b. Boeing 707	85	45
271*	20b. Boeing 707 (air)	4·25	3·00

1964. Inauguration of Sana'a International Airport.

306	1b. Boeing 707 and Hawker Siddeley Comet 4.	45	45
307	2b. Boeing 707 and Vickers Viscount 800s at Sana'a International Airport.	45	45
308	4b. Boeing 707 and Vickers Viscount 800s at Sana'a International Airport.	45	45
309	8b. Boeing 707 and Hawker Siddeley Comet 4.	85	85
310	6b. Hawker Siddeley Comet 4 airliners (air)	85	85
306/310 Set of 5		2·75	2·75

1966. Nos. 265, 268 and 271 overprinted **SANA'A** in English and Arabic.

425*	¼b. Boeing 707	25	15
428*	1b. Boeing 707	45	25
431*	20b. Boeing 707 (air)	4·75	4·00

1966.

444*	½b. Sikorsky S-61B SH-3 Sea King helicopter and aircraft carrier	25	15
446*	8b. Sikorsky S-61B SH-3 Sea King helicopter and aircraft carrier (air)	1·50	1·20

1966. Nos. 444 and 446 overprinted **GEMINI IX CERNAN-STAFFORD JUNE 3** 1966.

453*	½b. Sikorsky S-61B SH-3 Sea King helicopter and aircraft carrier	25	15
455*	8b. Sikorsky S-61B SH-3 Sea King helicopter and aircraft carrier (air)	1·90	1·40

1980.

611*	35f. Concorde	1·60	60

1981.

651*	75f. Jet airliner	3·50	2·20
653*	150f. Jet airliner	8·75	4·00

1982.

662*	400f. Jet fighters over airport	6·00	3·75

1982. Progress in Air Transport.

681	25f. Otto Lilienthal and his monoplane glider	1·50	50
682	50f. Alberto Santos-Dumont and his biplane *14 bis*	2·20	80
683	60f. Biplane	2·75	85
684	75f. Early airplane	3·25	85
685	100f. de Havilland DH.60G Gipsy Moth	3·75	1·60
686	125f. Fokker F.VIIa/3m	5·25	2·20
681/686 Set of 6		17·00	6·25

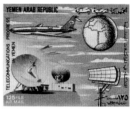

1982.

700*	125f. Boeing 727	2·50	1·90
MS701*	Two sheets. (b) 125f. Jet airliner (sheet contains 3 other designs) (other sheet does not include aircraft) Price for 2 sheets	19·00	19·00

1983. 20th Anniv of Yemen Airways.

724	75f. Douglas DC-3, Douglas DC-4, Boeing 727 and Boeing 737	1·50	85
725	125f. Douglas DC-3, Douglas DC-4, Boeing 727 and Boeing 737	2·50	1·40
725	325f. Douglas DC-3, Douglas DC-4, Boeing 727 and Boeing 737	5·75	3·00
724/726 Set of 3		8·75	4·75

1983.

736*	100f. Airliner	1·90	1·00

1985. 40th Anniv of ICAO.

754	25f. Emblem	45	15
755	50f. Emblem	85	35
756	150f. Emblem	2·20	90
757	325f. Emblem	5·25	2·30
754/757 Set of 4		8·00	3·50

APPENDIX

The following stamps have either been issued in excess of postal needs or have not been made available to the public in reasonable quantities at face value. Miniature sheets, imperforate stamps, etc are excluded from this section.

1970

Inauguration of New U.P.U. Headquarters Building, Berne. Postage 2b. (biplane). Air 3½b. (airship LZ-127 *Graf Zeppelin*), 4½b. (airliner).

Royalist Issues

1964.

R39	½b. Jet fighter	1·00	85
R40	1b. Jet fighter	1·00	85
R41	2b. Jet fighter	1·10	1·00
R42	4b. Jet fighter	1·10	1·00
R43	6b. Jet fighter	2·30	1·40
R39/43 *Set of 5*		5·75	4·50

1964. Nos. R39 and R42 surcharged with red cross, Arabic characters, **AIR MAIL 1963–64 HONOURING BRITISH RED CROSS SURGICAL TEAM** and value.

R44	10b. on 4b. Jet fighter	7·00	6·00
R45	18b. on ½b. Jet fighter	10·50	9·50

1964. Nos. R33/5 surcharged with airplane, **AIRMAIL** and Arabic text.

R46	10b. on18b. Red Cross field post	4·25	3·50
R47	18b. on ¼b. Red Cross field post	7·00	6·00
R48	28b. on ½b. Red Cross field post	11·50	10·50
R46/48 *Set of 3*		20·00	18·00

1964. Nos. R39/41 surcharged **4 REVALUED** and Arabic text.

R49	4b. on ½b. Jet fighter	10·50	8·75
R50	4b. on 1b. Jet fighter	10·50	8·75
R51	4b. on 2b. Jet fighter	10·50	8·75
R49/51 *Set of 3*		28·00	24·00

1965. Nos. R46/8 additionally overprinted with Arabic text and **HONOURING BRITISH YEMEN RELIEF COMMITTEE 1963–1965.**

R59	10b. on18b. Airplane	4·25	4·25
R60	18b. on ¼b. Airplane	8·75	8·75
R61	28b. on ½b. Airplane	10·50	10·50
R59/61 *Set of 3*		21·00	21·00

APPENDIX

The following stamps have either been issued in excess of postal needs or have not been made available to the public in reasonable quantities at face value. Miniature sheets, imperforate stamps, etc are excluded from this section.

1969

Moon Flight of "Apollo 10". 8b. (helicopters).

YEMEN PEOPLE'S DEMOCRATIC REPUBLIC

Arabia

1000 fils = 1 dinar

1981. Democratic Yemen Airlines.

253	60f. Douglas DC-3 ZQ-ACB of Alyemda	70	45
254	90f. Boeing 707 YO-ABY of Alyemda	1·40	75
255	250f. de Havilland Canada DHC-7 Dash Seven D-ACK of Alyemda	3·00	1·80
253/255 *Set of 3*		4·50	2·75

1983. Bicentenary of Manned Flight.

310	50f. Pierre Testu-Brissy's balloon ascent on horseback, 1798	75	40
311	100f. Montgolfier balloon (unmanned flight, 1783)	1·50	75
MS312	Two sheets. (a) 20f. Vincenzo Lunardi's balloon (over London, 1785); 40f. Charles's hydrogen balloon, 1783; 60f. John Wise's balloon *Atlantic*, 1859; 80f. Blanchard and Jeffries' balloon, 1785; (b) 200f. Eugene Godard's quintuple "acrobatic" balloon, 1850 *Set of 2 sheets*	25·00	21·00

YEMEN REPUBLIC (COMBINED)

Arabia

100 fils = 1 rial

1993. Nos. 684, 686 and 700 of Yemen surcharged **AIR MAIL** and value.

90*	3r. on 125f. Fokker F.VIIa/3m	1·80	1·80
91*	3r. on 125f. Jet airliner	1·80	1·80
95*	5r. on 75f. Early airplane	75	30

YUGOSLAVIA

South-east Europe

100 paras = 1 dinar

1934.

300	50p. Airplane	10	15
301	1d. Rohrbach Ro.VII Roland	20	15
302	2d. Airplane	35	35
303	3d. Rohrbach Ro.VII Roland	1·10	40
304	10d. Biplane	2·50	3·00
300/304 *Set of 5*		3·75	3·75

1934. As No. 303, but with black borders.

319*	3d. Rohrbach Ro.VII Roland	3·75	3·50

1937.

360	50p. Fokker F.VIIa/3m	10	10
361	1d. Junkers G.31	15	10
362	2d. Fokker F.VIIa/3m	20	15
363	2d.50 Fokker F.VIIa/3m	30	15
364	5d. Fokker F.VIIa/3m	30	25
365	10d. Junkers G.31	55	25
366	20d. Fokker F.VIIa/3m	85	85
367	30d. Fokker F.VIIa/3m	1·10	1·50
360/367 *Set of 8*		3·25	3·00

1939.

395*	4d. +4d. Lockheed 10 Electra	2·25	4·50

1940.

443	40d. Junkers Ju 86	1·75	1·75
444	50d. Fokker F.VIIa/3m	2·00	3·00

1940. Nos. 364/7 surcharged.

446	50p. +50p. on 5d. Fokker F.VIIa/3m	15	15
447	1d. +1d. on 10d. Junkers G.31	20	40
448	1d.50 +1d.50 on 20d. Fokker F.VIIa/3m	90	1·25
449	2d. +2d. on 30d. Fokker F.VIIa/3m	1·25	2·00
446/449 *Set of 4*		2·30	3·50

1947. Country name in Cyrillic characters at top.

546	50p. Ilyushin Il-4 DB-3	15	15
547	1d. Ilyushin Il-4 DB-3	25	20
548	2d. Ilyushin Il-4 DB-3	40	25
549	5d. Ilyushin Il-4 DB-3	45	30
550	10d. Ilyushin Il-4 DB-3	55	40
551	20d. Ilyushin Il-4 DB-3	1·00	65
546/551 *Set of 6*		2·50	1·70

1947. As Nos. 546/551, but country name in Cyrillic characters at foot.

546b	50p. Ilyushin Il-4 DB-3	15	15
547b	1d. Ilyushin Il-4 DB-3	25	20
548b	2d. Ilyushin Il-4 DB-3	40	25
549b	5d. Ilyushin Il-4 DB-3	45	30
550b	10d. Ilyushin Il-4 DB-3	55	40
551b	20d. Ilyushin Il-4 DB-3	1·00	65
546b/551b *Set of 6*		2·50	1·70

1948.

590*	15d. Lisunov Li-2	90	45

1949. Nos. 607/8a overprinted with Lisunov Li-2 airplane and **AVIONSKA POSTA.**

609*	3d. Soldiers	2·50	2·50
610*	5d. Industrial and agricultural workers	2·50	2·50
610a*	12d. Arms and flags of Yugoslavia and Macedonia	2·50	2·50

1949.

611	3d. Airplane	2·75	2·75
612	5d. Airplane	40	40
613	12d. Airplane	45	45
611/613 *Set of 3*		3·25	3·25

1950. Third Aeronautical Meeting.

642*	2d. Model glider	80	90
643*	3d. Glider	85	90
646*	20d. Glider on water	15·00	15·00

1951.

675	1d. Airplane	15	10
676	2d. Airplane	20	10
677	3d. Airplane	25	10
677a	5d. Airplane	30	10
678	6d. Airplane	4·50	4·00
679	10d. Airplane	50	10
680	20d. Airplane	75	10
681	30d. Airplane	2·50	10
682	50d. Airplane	3·75	10
683	100d. Airplane (grey)	60·00	5·00
683a	100d. Airplane (green)	1·40	15
683b	200d. Airplane	1·75	25
683c	500d. Airplane	7·00	1·25
675/683c *Set of 13*		75·00	10·00

1951. As Nos. 678 and 683 in new colours.

684	6d. Airplane (overprinted **ZEFIZ 1951**)	90	50
MS684a	100d. Airplane (brown, imperf)	£140	£110

1951.

687	3d. Airplane	3·50	3·25
688	5d. Airplane	3·50	3·25
689	20d. Airplane	90·00	60·00
687/689 *Set of 3*		90·00	60·00

1951. First World Parachuting Jumping Championship, Bled.

696	6d. Airplane	5·00	2·00

1951. As No. 682 in new colours overprinted **I SVETSKO TAKMICENJE PADOBRANACA 1951.**

697	50d. Airplane	80·00	45·00

1957.
843   2d. Airplane..   25   15

1960.
972*   40d. Edvard Rusijan and Bleriot XI, 1910 ..   10   10

1972. 13th World Gliding Championship, Vrsac.
1528   2d. Glider   20   15

1974.
1594*   8d. Boeing 707..   40   45

1978. Aeronautical Day.
1807   1d.50 S-49A trainer, 1949................................   10   10
1808   3d.40 SOKO Galeb 3 jet trainer   15   10
1809   4d.90 UTVA 75 elementary trainer   25   10
1810   10d. Jurom Orao jet fighter   60   50
1807/1810 Set of 4..   1·00   70

1982. 40th Anniv of Air Force.
2033*   4d. Breguet 19 and Potez 25 biplane   20   10
2034*   6d.10 SOKO G-4 Super Galeb jet trainer of
            the Yugoslav Air Force   30   10

1985.
2197   500d. Douglas DC-10 ....   1·75   65
2199   1000d. Airplane ....   2·50   1·25

1985. Air Force Day.
2216   10d. Franjo Kluz, Rudi Cajavec and Potez
            25 biplane   30   10

1985. World Free Flight Aeromodels Championship.
2229   70d. Model airplane   80   35

1986.
2261*   70d. Mil Mi-14 helicopter of Red Cross......   1·25   75

1987. 60th Anniv of Civil Aviation in Yugoslavia.
2362   150d. Potez 29-4 biplane UN-EHI................   75   40
2363   400d. Douglas DC-10 of Jugoslavenski
            Aerotransport ....   1·75   1·00

1987.
2396*   60d. Canadair   CL-215   Fire-fighting
            amphibian................................   25   25

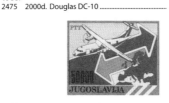

1988.
2475   2000d. Douglas DC-10   90   30

1989.
2576 50000d. Avions de Transport Régional ATR
            4a..   1·60   80

1990.
2596*   5d. Avions de Transport Régional ATR
            4a..   70   40

1991. Centenary of First Heavier-than-Air Flight by Lilienthal.
2694   7d.50 Edvard Rusijan and Bleriot XI   75   35
2695   15d. Otto Lilienthal and Lilienthal biplane
            glider..   1·50   75

1992. 80th Anniv of Aviation in Yugoslavia.
2842   500d. Bleriot XI ....   1·00   1·00

1994. 71st Anniv of First Regular Paris-Belgrade-Bucharest-Istanbul
        Night Flight.
2913   60p. Caudron C-61 and route map............   1·50   1·10
2914   1d.80 Caudron C-61, Belgrade and route
            map..   2·50   1·75

1994.
2951   50p. Avions de Transport Regional ATR
            42..   1·10   80

1995.
3007   1d.10 Saric No. 1   60   45
3008   1d.10 Douglas DC-3   60   45
3009   2d.20 Fizir FN biplane................................   1·10   80
3010   2d.20 Sud Aviation Caravelle................   1·10   80
3007/3010 Set of 4..   3·00   2·25

1997.
3082   2d.50 Convair 580 (?)................................   50   30

1998. 50th Anniv of Aviation in Yugoslavia.
3121   2d.50 Glider and emblems................   25   15

2000. Air Force and Air Defence Command.
3241*   20d. Building, Zemun................   2·25   1·40

2000. Centenary of First Zeppelin Flight.
3254   10d. Zeppelin LZ-127 *Graf Zeppelin*............   30   15

2002. 75th Anniv of Civil Aviation.
3349   7d. Potez 29................................   20   10
3350   28d. Boeing 737................................   85   55

CHARITY TAX POSTAGE DUE STAMPS

1957. As No. 843, but inscribed "PORTO".
D844   2d. Airplane................................   40   15

ZAIRE

Central Africa

100 sengi = 1 kuta

100 kuta = 1 zaire

1978. History of Aviation.
927	30s. Leonardo da Vinci's drawing of a "helicopter", Francesco de Lana-Terzi's "Aerial Ship", 1670, and Lilienthal glider	15	10
928	70s. Wright Type A and Santos-Dumont's biplane *14 bis*	15	10
929	1k. Bleriot XI and Farman F.60 Goliath	15	10
930	5k. Ryan NYP Special *Spirit of St. Louis* and Junkers G.38ce D-2000 *Deutschland*	15	10
931	8k. Macchi Castoldi MC-72 seaplane and Sikorsky S-42B flying boat of Pan Am	25	15
932	10k. Fokker F.VIIb/3m OO-AIX and Boeing 707 of SABENA	45	20
933	50k. Concorde	1·75	55
934	75k. Sikorsky S-61N helicopter G-BCED of British Airways and Douglas DC-10 of Air Zaire	2·10	90
927/934 *Set of 8*		4·75	2·00
MS935 5k. Henri Giffard's steam-powered dirigible airship, 1852		1·50	85

1978. Nos. 932 and 934 overprinted **20e Anniversaire Independance 1960–1980**.
1036*	10k. Fokker F.VIIb/3m OO-AIX and Boeing 707 of Sabena	50	50
1038*	75k. Sikorsky S-61N helicopter G-BCED of British Airways and Douglas DC-10 of Air Zaire	70	70

1982.
1091*	1k. Helicopters of the Red Cross	10	10

1984. Bicentenary of Manned Flight.
1201	10k. Montgolfier balloon (first manned free flight, 1783)	10	10
1202	15k. Charles' hydrogen balloon, 1783	10	10
1203	3z. Montgolfier balloon *Le Gustave*, 1784	15	10
1204	5z. Santos-Dumont's airship *Ballon No. 3*, 1899	30	15
1205	10z. Piccard's stratosphere balloon *F.N.R.S.*, 1931	70	40
1206	15z. Airship LZ-129 *Hindenburg*	1·10	60
1207	37z.50 Balloon *Double Eagle II*	2·50	1·40
1208	80z. Hot-air balloons, 1983	6·00	3·00
1201/1208 *Set of 8*		9·75	5·25

1985. 50th Anniv of SABENA, Brussels-Kinshasa Air Service. Nos. 927/31 and 933/4 surcharged **SABENA 1935–1985**.
1214	2z.50 on 30s. Leonardo da Vinci's drawing of a "helicopter", Francesco de Lana-Terzi's "Aerial Ship", 1670, and Lilienthal glider	15	10
1215	5z. on 5k. Ryan NYP Special *Spirit of St. Louis* and Junkers G.38ce D-2000 *Deutschland*	40	20
1216	6z. on 70s. Wright Type A and Santos-Dumont's biplane *14 bis*	45	30
1217	7z.50 on 1k. Bleriot XI and Farman F.60 Goliath	55	35
1218	8z.50 on 1k. Bleriot XI and Farman F.60 Goliath	65	40
1219	10z. on 8k. Macchi Castoldi MC-72 seaplane and Sikorsky S-42B flying boat of Pan Am	80	45
1220	12z.50 on 75k. Sikorsky S-61N helicopter G-BCED of British Airways and Douglas DC-10 of Air Zaire	90	60
1221	30z. on 50k. Concorde	2·25	1·25
1214/1221 *Set of 8*		5·50	3·25

1990. Nos. 930/1, 1036 and 1038 surcharged.
1315*	100z. on 5k. Ryan NYP Special *Spirit of St. Louis* and Junkers G.38ce D-2000 *Deutschland*	70	80
1319*	100z. on 8k. Macchi Castoldi MC-72 seaplane and Sikorsky S-42B flying boat of Pan Am	70	65
1324*	100z. on 10k. Fokker F.VIIb/3m OO-AIX and Boeing 707 of SABENA	65	70
1340*	100z. on 75k. Sikorsky S-61N helicopter G-BCED of British Airways and Douglas DC-10 of Air Zaire	70	80

ZAMBIA

Central Africa

1967. 12 pence = 1 shilling

20 shillings = 1 pound

1968. 100 ngwee = 1 kwacha

1967. Opening of Lusaka International Airport.
122	6d. Undercarriage of airliner at Lusaka Airport and B.A.C. One Eleven	15	10
123	2s.6d. Undercarriage of airliner at Lusaka Airport and B.A.C. One Eleven	60	1·00

1968.
131*	3n. BAC One-Eleven of Zambia Airways.	10	10

1974.
219*	9n. Hawker Siddeley H.S.748	30	30

1975.
237*	50n. Britten Norman long nose Islander 9J-ACB of the Flying Doctor Service.	3·25	2·50

1978.
277*	28n. Bell 206 JetRanger helicopter	75	1·10

1984. Air Transport.
400	12n. Boeing 737 9J-AEG of Zambia Airways	25	10
401	28n. de Havilland Canada DHC-2 Beaver VP-YHH of Central African Airways	45	40
402	35n. Short S.45A Solent 3 flying boat G-AHIT *Severn* of B.O.A.C.	55	70
403	1k. de Havilland DH.66 Hercules G-AAJH *City of Basra* of Imperial Airways	1·00	3·00
400/403 *Set of 4*		2·00	3·75

1985. No. 237 surcharged **5K**.
424	5k. on 50n. Britten-Norman BN-2 long nose Islander 9J-ACB of the Flying Doctor Service	1·75	3·25

1987. 20th Anniv of Zambia Airways.
524	35n. de Havilland Canada DHC-2 Beaver 9J-RFZ of Zambia Airways	85	10
525	1k.70 Douglas DC-10 of Zambia Airways	2·00	80
526	5k. Douglas DC-3 9J-RDR of Zambia Airways	4·25	3·75
527	10k. Boeing 707 of Zambia Airways	6·50	8·00
524/527 *Set of 4*		12·00	11·50

1991. No. 401 surcharged **K2**.
660*	2k. on 28n. de Havilland Canada DHC-2 Beaver VP-YHH of Central African Airways		5·00

1992. 60th Anniv of Airmail Service.
704	4k. de Havilland DH.66 Hercules G-AAJH *City of Basra* of Imperial Airways	50	40
705	40k. Vickers Super VC-10 of B.O.A.C.	2·00	85
706	45k. Short S.45A Solent 3 flying boat G-AHIT *Severn* of B.O.A.C.	2·00	85
707	100k. Douglas DC-10	3·50	5·50
704/707 *Set of 4*		7·25	6·75

2001. Airships.
MS865 2000k. Zeppelin LZ-1, 1900; 2000k. Parseval PL-25, 1915; 2000k. Zeppelin LZ-3, 1906; 2000k. Baldwin, 1908; 2000k. Zeppelin LZ-129 *Hindenburg*, 1936; 2000k. *Norge*, 1926	4·50	5·00

2003. Centenary of Powered Flight. Planes of A. V. Roe.
923	4000k. Avro 547A Triplane	1·50	1·50
924	4000k. Avro 504O with floats	1·50	1·50
925	4000k. Avro 584 Avocet	1·50	1·50
926	4000k. Avro 504M	1·50	1·50
923/926 *Set of 4*		5·50	5·50
MS927 9000k. Avro 621 Tutor Replica		4·25	4·50
No. 925 is inscribed "Avrocet" in error.			

ZANZIBAR

Indian Ocean

100 cents = 1 shilling

1949. As Nos. 114/15 of Antigua.
335*	20c. Airplane	30	3·00
336*	30c. Jet-powered Vickers Viking	1·75	1·50

ZIMBABWE

Central Africa

100 cents = 1 dollar

1983.
631*	11c. Airport controller directing airliner	20	10

1986.
692* 26c. Boeing 737 of Air Zimbabwe.............. 2·50 2·00

1990.
784* $1 Boeing 737 of Air Zimbabwe.............. 2·25 90

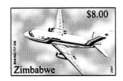

2001.
1044	$8 Boeing 737-200	40	25
1045	$12 BAe Hawk Mk	55	40
1046	$14 Hawker Hunter FGA-9	60	60
1047	$16 Cessna/Reims F337	70	75
1048	$21 Aerospatiale Alouette III	85	95
1049	$28 Boeing 767-200 ER	1·10	1·40
1044/1049 *Set of 6*		3·75	4·00

Chronology of Aviation Events and Anniversaries

Most of the events listed are represented by stamps in the catalogue which may be found by reference to the index.

1670

Francesco de Lana-Terzi: "Aerial Ship" design.

1709

8 August. Bartolomeu de Gusmao: Aerostat model balloon experiment and *La Passarola*.

1731

Kryakutni: reputed balloon flight over Moscow.

1764

Melchior Bauer: man-powered airplane design.

1783

4 June. Montgolfier Brothers: unmanned hot-air balloon experiment.
27 August. Jacques Charles: *The Globe* - unmanned hydrogen balloon experiment.
19 September. Montgolfier Brothers: *Le Martial* - hot-air balloon flight with animals,
15 October. Montgolfier Brothers: tethered flight by Jean-Francois Pilatre de Rozier and the Marquis d'Arlandes at Chateau Reveillon.
21 November. Montgolfier Brothers. first manned free flight by hot-air balloon made by Pilatre de Rozier and D'Arlandes from the Chateau la Muette, Paris.
1 December. Jacques Charles and Marie-Noel Robert: first free flight by manned hydrogen balloon, Paris.

1784

First balloon flight in Mauritius.
First balloon flight over Warsaw.
Galiffet's balloon flight, Haiti.
Masse's oar-powered balloon design.
Jean-Baptiste Meusnier's dirigible balloon design.
Utopic Balloon Post: engraving by Balthasar Antoine Dunker.
19 January. Joseph Montgolfier and Pilatre de Rozier: *Le Flesselles* - flight at Annonay - the only ascent by either of the Montgolfier brothers.
March. Adorne's hot-air balloon *Aerostat* flight at Strasbourg.
2 March. Jean-Pierre Blanchard: attempt to control flight by oars.
25 April. Guyton de Morveau: attempt at controlling flight with oars.
4 June. Montgolfier Brothers: *Le Gustave* flight by M. Fleurant and Mme. Thible at Lyons. The first flight by a woman.
23 June. Pilatre de Rozier and Proust: *Marie Antoinette* - 36-mile flight from Versailles.
6 July. Johann Stuwer: first balloon flight in Austria, at Vienna.
15 September. Vicenzo Lunardi's first flight in England from London to Ware.
19 September. Robert Brothers and Colin-Hullin: balloon flight from Paris to Bethune.
16 October. Blanchard: flight at Chelsea with attempt at propulsion by hand-cranked propeller.

1785

Richard Crosbie: first balloon ascent in Ireland at Dublin.
7 January. Jean-Pierre Blanchard and Dr. John Jeffries: first crossing of the English Channel by balloon.
13 May. Lunardi: second ascent at Moorfields, London.
15 June. Pilatre de Rozier and Jules Romain attempt to cross the English Channel in a combined hydrogen and hot-air balloon. Both killed when it catches fire and crashes.

1788

27 September. Blanchard's ascent at Berlin.

1789

Engraving of a "sail steered balloon".

1793

9 January. Blanchard makes the first balloon flight in the U.S.A. at Philadelphia.

1794

26 June. Jean Marie Coutelle: *L'Entreprenant* - the first military use of a balloon at the Siege of Mauberg and later at the Battle of Fleurus.

1797

22 October. Andre Jacques Garnerin makes the first parachute descent from a balloon at Paris.

1798

Pierre Testu-Brissy makes an ascent on horseback using a platform supported by a cylindrical hydrogen balloon.

1804

Joseph Gay-Lussac makes a 4,000 metre ascent at Paris.

1808

Johan Colding: experiments with unmanned mail-carrying balloons between the Danish islands.

1809

Jacob Degen tests his balloon-assisted "ornithopter".

1811

Albrecht Berblinger ("The Tailor of Ulm") makes an unsuccessful test of a man-powered machine, similar to Degen's but without balloon support.
Dr. Menner: first balloon ascent in Hungary.

1816

The Dolphin: unfinished dirigible balloon designed by Pauley and Egg.

1820

October. Wilhelmine Reichart: ascent at Munich Oktoberfest.

1830

Adolfo Teodore: first balloon ascent in Cuba.

1831

Jose Domingo Blino: first Cuban balloonist.

1834

17 August. Comte de Lennox, balloon *Eagle's* abortive flight at Paris.

1836

7/8 November. Charles Green: *Royal Vauxhall* balloon - 480 mile flight from London to Weilburg in the Duchy of Nassau. Balloon subsequently re-named *Royal Nassau Balloon*.

1837

Sir George Cayley: airship propulsion design.

1843

Sir George Cayley: "convertiplane" design.
April. William S. Henson publishes the design of his *Aerial Steam Carriage*.

1848

John Stringfellow tests his steam-powered model airplane.

1850

Eugene Godard: quintuple "acrobatic" balloon demonstrated in Paris.

1852

24 September. Henri Giffard flies his steam-powered dirigible airship 15½ miles from Paris to Trappes.

1859

Camille Vert: *Poisson Volant* airship.
1/2 July. John Wise: balloon *Atlantic*- 890 mile flight from St. Louis to Henderson, New York,
17 August. Wise: balloon *Jupiter* - abortive postal flight from Lafayette to New York. The balloon came down after 30 miles at Crawfordsville, Virginia.

1862

Joaquin de la Cantolla y Rico: first Mexican balloon flight at Mexico City.
31 May. Thaddeus Lowe: balloon *Washington* - Battle of Fair Oaks.
1 June. Lowe: balloon *Intrepid*: Battle of Fair Oaks.

1863

4 October. Gaspard Felix Tournachon ("Nadar"), the photographer: flight in balloon *Le Geant*.

1864

Godard makes two ascents in England in his balloon. *L'Aigle*.

1870

23 September. Paris Balloon Post: Jules Durouf - balloon *Le Neptune*. First balloon to leave Paris.
7 October. Paris Balloon Post: Alexandre Trichot and Leon Gambetta - balloon *Armand Barbes*.
24 November. Paris Balloon Post: Paul Rolier and Leonard Bezier - balloon *Ville d'Orleans*. Overnight flight to Telemark, Norway.
30 December. Paris Balloon Post: balloon *L'Armee de la Loire*.

1872

2 February. Dupuy de Lome: hand-powered dirigible airship.
13 December. Paul Hanlein tests his dirigible airship powered by a gas engine.

1875

Thomas Moy tests his *Aerial Steamer* airplane model.
15 April. Gaston Tissandier: balloon *Zenith*. Ascent to 26,250 feet during which Tissandier's two companions are killed by oxygen starvation.

1878

Giffard: *Le Grand Ballon Captif* - tethered ascents at the Paris Universal Exhibition.

1883

8 October. Gaston and Albert Tissandier: 4-mile powered flight in an electrically-powered airship.

1884

Aleksandr Mozhaisky makes a 20 to 30 yard "hop" in his steam-powered monoplane, launched from a sloping ramp at St. Petersburg.
9 August. Renard and Krebs: airship *La France* - first "out and back" flight around Paris, lasting 23 minutes.

1890

9 October. Clement Ader: *Eole* - Ader makes the first powered take-off, but does not achieve any sustained flight.

1891

Otto Lilienthal's first successful flight in his monoplane Glider No. 3.
3 January. Baldwin Brothers' balloon demonstration in Hong Kong.

1892

Pioneer balloon flight over Plovdiv, Bulgaria.

1893

May. Horatio F. Phillips tests his "multiplane" model airplane at Harrow.

1894

31 July. Sir Hiram Maxim successfully tests his "Flying Test Rig" at Baldwyns Park, Kent.

1895

Lilienthal tests his first biplane glider.

1896

Menner demonstrates a military observation balloon at the Budapest Exhibition, dropping a dog on a parachute.
Octave Chanute's glider experiments at Chicago, piloted by Augustus Herring.
6 May. Samuel Pierpont Langley successfully tests his steam-powered model *Aerodrome No. 5* from his houseboat on the Potomac River.
9 August. Fatal crash of Otto Lilienthal in his Glider No. 11.
28 August. Karl Wolfert makes his first flight in petrol-engined dirigible airship *Deutschland* at Tempelhof, Berlin.

1897

12 June. Wolfert is killed when the *Deutschland* catches fire and crashes at Tempelhof.
11 July. Salomon Andree leaves Spitzbergen in his balloon *Ornen* on his fatal Polar flight.
12/14 October. Ader makes unsuccessful tests of his *Avion III*.
11 November. Abortive test of the late David Schwartz's metal-skinned airship at Tempelhof. It is destroyed in a crash.

1898

Successful test of the Parseval Sigsfeld kite-type observation balloon.
3 October. Eduard Spelterini makes the first crossing of the Alps by balloon, flying from Scion in the Valois to Dijon.

1899

13 November. Alberto Santos-Dumont reaches a speed of 15½ m.p.h. in his airship *Ballon No. 3*, Paris.

1900

2 July. First flight of Zeppelin airship LZ-1 over Lake Constance at Friedrichshafen.
September. Wilbur and Orville Wright test their unmanned Glider No. I at the Kill Devil Hills, Kitty Hawk, North Carolina.
17 October. Zeppelin airship LZ-1 is given a second test over Lake Constance after a partial rebuild.

1901

13 July. Santos-Dumont makes an unsuccessful attempt at a round trip flight via the Eiffel Tower from St. Cloud in his airship *Ballon No. 5*.
27 July. Wright Brothers make a manned test of their Glider No. II.
19 October. Santos-Dumont makes a successful flight around the Eiffel Tower in his airship *Ballon No. 6* and wins the Merthe Prize.

1902

Lawrence Hargrave builds his "multiplane" seaplane at Sydney Harbour, but is unable to test it for lack of a suitable engine.
12 May. Auguste Severo is killed when his airship *Pax* explodes over Paris.
June. Successful flight of Captain Ferdinand Ferber's Glider No. 5.
20 September. Wright Brothers test their Glider No. III.
13 November. Successful first flight of the Lebaudy-Juillot airship No. 1 *La Jaune*.

1903

Santos-Dumont makes first flight in his airship *Ballon No. 9 La Badaleuse*.
7 October. Langley makes an unsuccessful test of his full-size *Aerodrome A* from his houseboat on the Potomac River.
17 December. Orville Wright makes the first manned, controlled, powered flight, landing at the same elevation as on take-off, in *Flyer I* at Kitty Hawk, covering 120 feet in 12 seconds. Wilbur Wright makes a 59-second flight later the same day.

1904

Alleged pursuit race between a balloon and a car (probably based on a race between a car and Thomas Baldwin in his dirigible airship, 1905).

1905

8 June. Archdeacon-Voisin "Boxkite" float glider tested on the Seine. Towed behind a motor boat, it makes a "hop" of 150 yards.
30 November. First flight of Zeppelin airship LZ-2 at Lake Constance.

1906

17 January. Destruction of Zeppelin airship LZ-2 after a forced landing in a storm.
18 March. First flight by Traian Vuia at Montesson in his airplane No. 1, achieving a distance of 79 feet.
May. First flight of Parseval non-rigid Airship No. 1.
July. First test of Santos-Dumont's biplane, suspended from his airship *Ballon No. 14* - hence the name *14 bis* for the biplane.
12 September. Jacob Ellehammer makes a "tethered hop" of 138 feet in his *Ellehammer II* at Lindholm, Denmark.
30 September. First Gordon Bennett balloon race starts from Paris.
9 October. First flight of Zeppelin airship LZ-3, covering 60 miles.
23 October. First sustained, controlled, powered flight in Europe, made by Santos-Dumont in his biplane *14 bis*, covering 60 metres in 7 seconds.
11 November. First flight of the Astra airship *Ville de Paris*.
16 November. First flight of the Lebaudy-Juillot airship *Patrie*.

1907

25 April. Aaron de Anchorena and Jorge Newbery make the first aerial crossing of the River Plate from Buenos Aires to Conchillas, in the balloon *Pampero*.
3 October. First flight of the British airship *Nulli Secundus*.
13 November. Paul Cornu's helicopter achieves first vertical take-off by a manned heavier-than-air machine.

1908

20 June. First flight of Zeppelin airship LZ-4.

4 July. First officially-recorded flight in the U.S.A. of over one kilometre, made by Glenn Curtiss in *June Bug*. This distance had long been exceeded by the Wright Brothers.

24 July. First flight of British airship *Nulli Secundus II*.

August. First flight of Thomas Baldwin's airship *U.S. Military No. 1*.

5 August. Zeppelin airship LZ-4 completes a 21-hour, 370-mile endurance flight. After landing at Echterdingen the airship escapes from the ground crew, crashes and bursts into flames.

12 September. First flight of German semi-rigid airship *Gross Basenach II* lasting 13 hours.

15 September. First flight of German military non-rigid Parseval airship PL-II covering 180 miles.

17 September. Orville Wright and Lieutenant Thomas Selfridge crash in a Wright Type A. Selfridge is killed and becomes the first aircraft fatality.

7 November. Demonstration flight by the LZ-3, after a complete rebuild, before being handed over to the German Army as Z.1.

1909

Hans Grade makes the first flight in Germany.

23 February. John McCurdy makes the first powered flight in Canada in his *Silver Dart* biplane.

6 March. First flight of Santos-Dumont's monoplane No. 20 Demoiselle, the first commercially produced light airplane.

6 April. First flight of Henri Farman's H.F.III.

May. First flight of Lebaudy-Juillot airship *Lebedj*, built for the Russian Government.

26 May. First flight of Zeppelin airship LZ-5. After flying 603 miles in 38 hours it is forced by shortage of fuel to land in a field near Schweinfurt where it is damaged by hitting a tree. It is later repaired and flown back to Friedrichshafen.

19 July. Unsuccessful cross-Channel attempt by Hubert Latham in an Antoinette IV. He is forced to ditch 7½ miles out and is rescued by the destroyer *Harpon*, which also recovers his airplane.

25 July. First powered crossing of the English Channel when Louis Bleriot flies from Sangatte to Dover in his Bleriot XI.

August. First flight over Prague made by Jan Kaspar in a Bleriot XI.

11 November. Count Ferdinand von Zeppelin forms the world's first airline: Deutsche Luftschiffahrts Aktien Gesellschaft (DELAG).

20 November. German airships *Gross Basenach II* and *Parseval I* fly in formation from Cologne to Metz.

24 December. Alliott Verdon Roe makes a flight of half a mile in the A.V. Roe Triplane II (Avro Mercury). The first flight in Great Britain of a British designed, built and piloted airplane.

1910

Astra passenger-carrying airship *Ville de Lucerne* makes its first flight.

Edvard Rusijan makes the first flight in Yugoslavia (then a part of Austria-Hungary) in a Bleriot XI.

8 March. Baroness De la Roche becomes the first woman to gain a pilot's licence, flying a Voisin "Boxkite".

28 March. Henri Fabre makes the first successful seaplane flight in his *Hydravion* at Monaco.

29 April. Zeppelin airship LZ-5 is destroyed in a forced landing at Weilburg.

22 June. First commercial flight by Zeppelin airship LZ-7 *Deutschland*.

28 June. Zeppelin airship LZ-7 crashes in the Teutonberg Forest as a result of engine failure. There are no casualties, but the airship is destroyed.

10 August. Armand Dufaux flies the length of Lake Geneva (41 miles) in a biplane of his own design.

September. Geoffrey de Havilland's first flight in his FE-1 at Beacon Hill.

2 September. First solo flight by an American woman when Blanche Stuart Scott takes off during taxiing practice in a Curtiss Golden Flyer at Hammondsport, New York.

14 September. First flight of Lebaudy-Juillot semi-rigid airship *Morning Post*, bought by public subscription for the British Government.

23 September. Jorge Chavez in Bleriot XI makes first crossing of the Alps by airplane. He flies from Brig to Domodossola over the Simplon Pass, but crashes on landing and dies from his injuries.

October. Henri Coanda's turbine-powered model airplane is shown at the Paris Salon.

10 October. Walter Wellman attempts to cross the Atlantic in his non-rigid airship *America*, but is forced to come down in the sea.

14 November. Eugene Ely in Curtiss Golden Flyer makes first take-off from the deck of a ship, the U.S.S. *Birmingham*.

31 December. Samuel Cody wins the Michelin Cup in a biplane of his own design.

1911

First flight in Barbados by a Wright Type B.

18 February. Henri Pecquet in Humber Sommer biplane makes first official airmail flight, from the United Provinces Industrial and Agricultural Exhibition at Allahabad, India, to the railway at Naini Junction. Regular flights continued for the duration of the exhibition.

30 March. First flight of Zeppelin airship LZ-8 *Ersatz Deutschland*.

7 July. Jean Raoult in Bleriot XI makes first flight in Madagascar.

20 July. First flight of Zeppelin airship LZ-10 *Schwaben*.

August. First flight of Anthony Fokker's monoplane Haarlem Spin.

9 September. Gustav Hamel in Bleriot XI flies first U.K. aerial post, from London to Windsor. Further flights are made by a Farman H.F.III and an Aeronautical Syndicate Valkyrie A.

1 December. Jan Olieslaegers in Bleriot XI carries first airmail in South Africa.

1912

First flight by Clement-Bayard military airship *Fleurus*.

Airmail flight from Nancy to Luneville, France, made by Renaux in a Farman M.F.7.

14 February. First flight of Zeppelin airship LZ-11 *Viktoria Luise*.

1 June. Lieutenant Hans Dons in Etrich Taube *Start* makes first flight in Norway by a Norwegian, from Horten to Frederikstad across Oslo Fjord.

11 June. First airmail service in Germany inaugurated by Zeppelin airship LZ-10 *Schwaben*.

28 June. Zeppelin airship LZ-10 *Schwaben* is accidentally destroyed in a hangar fire.

1913

Agustin Parla Orduna in a Curtiss seaplane makes first flight from Florida to Cuba.

24 January. Oskar Bider in Bleriot XI makes first crossing of the Pyrenees by airplane.

15 April. Marcel Prevost wins the first Schneider Trophy seaplane race at Monte Carlo in a Deperdussin Monocoque.

8 August. Pyotr Nesterov makes the first "loop-the-loop" manoeuvre, in a Nieuport biplane.

23 September. Roland Garros in Morane Saulnier Type I makes first aerial crossing of the Mediterranean from Saint-Raphael to Bizerte.

15 October. First official airmail flight, by a Morane Saulnier MS-6 Type H, from Villacoublay to Pauillac, France.

29 November - 29 December. Jules Vedrines in Bleriot XI flies from Nancy to Cairo via Palestine.

1914

Bleriot XI *Prince Celaladdin* flies first airmail in Turkey.

1 January. Anthony Jannus in Benoist Type XIV flying boat inaugurates first daily scheduled air service, from St. Petersburg to Tampa, Florida (22 miles across Tampa Bay).

16/18 July. Maurice Guillaux in Bleriot XI makes first airmail flight in Australia from Melbourne to Sydney.

30 July. Tryggve Gran in Bleriot XI *Nordsjoen* makes first aerial crossing of the North Sea from Cruden Bay (near Aberdeen) to Stavanger, Norway.

1915

8 March. First flight of German military Zeppelin airship L-9 (LZ-36).

14 April. Zeppelin airship L-9 bombs Blyth.

7 June. Zeppelin airship LZ-37 is destroyed in flight near Ghent by Flight Sub-Lieutenant Warneford V.C.

12 August. Short Type 184 seaplane achieves the first sinking of a ship by air-launched torpedo.

8/9 September. Zeppelin airship L-13 (LZ-45), commanded by Heinrich Mathy, bombs London causing severe damage.

1916

Eduardo Bradley and Angel Zuloaga make the first aerial crossing of the Andes in the balloon *Eduardo Newbery*.

12 July. First flight of "Super Zeppelin" L-31 (LZ-72).

2 September. German military airship Schutte Lanz SL-11 is shot down over Cuffley by Lieutenant W. Leefe Robinson in a Royal Aircraft Factory B. E.2C.

16 September. Accidental destruction of Zeppelin L-9 (LZ-36).

1/2 October. Zeppelin airship L-31 (LZ-72) shot down near Potters Bar.

1917

Teodoro Fels in Bleriot XI Gnome makes first airmail flight from Buenos Aires to Montevideo across the River Plate.

May. First Italian airmail flight by Pomilio PC-1 from Turin to Rome.

6 July. Captain Horacio Ruiz Gavino in de Havilland D.H.6A makes first Mexican airmail flight from Pachuca to Mexico City.

19 September. First flight of Vickers rigid airship R-23.

1918

11 March. First scheduled international airmail service inaugurated from Vienna to Kiev by Hansa Brandenburg C.I.

1 April. Royal Air Force formed by combining the Royal Flying Corps and the Royal Naval Air Service.

13 April. Lieutenant Luis Candelaria in Morane Saulnier Type P makes first crossing of the Andes by airplane from Zapala in Argentina to Cunco in Chile.

4 July. First Hungarian airmail service, from Budapest to Vienna by Hansa Brandenburg C-I.

12 August. First regular airmail service in the U.S.A., from New York to Washington begun by Curtiss JN-4 "Jenny".

17 August. First regular airmail service in France from Paris to St. Nazaire by Letord 4 Lorraine.

12 December. First east–west crossing of the Andes by airplane, from Santiago de Chile to Mendoza made by Dagoberto Godoy in a Bristol M.1C monoplane.

1919

First airmail flight from Copenhagen to Stede in Sweden, by a Friedrichshafen FF-49 seaplane.

First flight over Bermuda by a Curtiss N-9 seaplane.

8 January. First Swiss airmail flight by Haefeli DH-3.

February. First airmail flight in Thailand, from Bangkok to Chanthaburi, by Breguet 14.

16/27 May. First aerial crossing of the North Atlantic, from Newfoundland to Lisbon via the Azores, by Lieutenant Commander Albert C. Read in a Curtiss NC-4 flying boat.

18 May. Unsuccessful attempt by Harry Hawker and K. Mackenzie-Grieve to cross the Atlantic in a Sopwith Atlantic.

28 May. Benjamin Matienzo in Nieuport 28 makes fatal attempt at east–west crossing of the Andes.

2/6 June, 9/13 June. First double crossing of the North Atlantic, by British Beardmore airship R-34.

14/15 June. First non-stop aerial crossing of the North Atlantic, from Newfoundland to Ireland, by John Alcock and Arthur Whitten Brown in a Vickers FB-27 Vimy.

18 June. First airmail flight in Colombia by Junkers F-13 seaplane *Tolima*.

20 August. First flight of Zeppelin airship LZ-120 *Bodensee*.

12 November. First flight from England to Australia by Ross and Keith Smith in their Vickers Vimy G-EAOU.

16 November–12 December. Captain H. Wrigley in Royal Aircraft Factory B.E.2E makes first flight across Australia from Melbourne to Darwin.

16 December. Captain Bolt in Boeing seaplane carries first official airmail in New Zealand from Auckland to Dargaville.

1920

First flight from Peru to Ecuador by a Curtiss JN-4 "Jenny".

4 February–20 March. First flight from London to Cape Town. Lieutenant-Colonel H. van Ryneveld and Flight Lieutenant Christopher Brand leave London in a Vickers F.B.27 Vimy *Silver Queen*, but crash at Wadi Halfa on the Nile. A replacement Vimy, *Silver Queen II* takes them as far as Bulawayo where they crash again. The flight is completed in a South African de Havilland D.H.9.

1921

22/23 February. First United States coast-to-coast airmail flight by de Havilland DH.4M.

11 November. First Russian airline founded in co-operation with Germany – Deutsche Russische Luftverkehrs Gesellschaft (Deruluft).

1922

April/July. Lisbon to Rio flight via Atlantic islands by Gago Coutinho and Sacadura Cabral. Begins in Fairey IIID seaplane *Lusitania* and is completed by *Santa Cruz*.

11 November. Etienne Oehmichen makes the first successful helicopter flight in his No. 2.

1923

E. Liut in Hanriot HD-1 *Telegrafo 1* makes first airmail flight in Ecuador.

9 January. First flight of Juan de la Cierva's C.4, the first practical autogyro.

2/3 May. First non-stop crossing of the U.S.A. by Lieutenants John Macready and Oakley Kelly in a Fokker F.IV.

1924

6 April–28 September. Douglas World Cruiser seaplanes make a round-the-world formation flight.

July. Major Pedro Zanni in Fokker C.IV *Provincia de Buenos Aires* makes unsuccessful round-the-world attempt.

27 August. First flight of Zeppelin airship LZ-126, built as war reparations to the U.S.A. and on delivery designated ZR-3 *Los Angeles*.

20 November–18 March 1925. Sir Alan Cobham in de Havilland DH.50 makes first "Empire Flight" from Croydon to Rangoon.

1925

Flight from Cordoba to Villa Dolores. Argentina, in a Junkers F-13L.

12 February–3 April. Edmond Thieffry in Handley Page H.P.26 W.8e Hamilton Princess Marie-Jose flies from Evere, Belgium to Leopoldville.

20 April–7 November. De Pinedo and Campanelli in Savoia S-16 ter flying boat *Gennariello* make round-the-world flight.

21 May–15 June. Roald Amundsen and Lincoln Ellsworth make an abortive attempt to fly to the North Pole in Dornier Do-J Wal flying boats N-24 and N-25. N-24 crashes en route.

31 August–10 September. Commander John Rogers attempts to fly a Philadelphia Navy Yard PN-9 flying boat non-stop from San Francisco to Hawaii. After 1,841 miles he runs out of fuel and lands in the sea. Constructing a sail and rudder, he sails the craft another 559 miles to Kauai Island.

26 October. Curtiss R3C-2 seaplane wins the Schneider Trophy race at Baltimore.

16 November–17 February 1926. Cobham in de Havilland DH.50J makes second "Empire Flight" from Croydon to Cape Town and back.

1926

First flight to the Solomon Islands by a de Havilland DH.50A seaplane of the Royal Australian Air Force.

Campanelli, Duggan and Olivera in Savoia S-16 ter flying boat fly from Buenos Aires to New York.

22 January–20 February. Major Ramon Franco in CASA-built Dornier Do-J Wal flying boat *Plus Ultra* flies from Palos de Mogues, Spain, via Atlantic islands to Buenos Aires.

16 March–23 June. Captain A. P. Botved in Fokker C.VE makes round-the-world flight.

April. Gallarza and Loriga in Breguet Bre. 19A2 fly from Madrid to Manila.

9 May. Richard Byrd and Floyd Bennett in Fokker F.VIIa/3m Josephine Ford make first flight over North Pole.

11 May. Roald Amundsen and General Umberto Nobile fly from Spitzbergen to Alaska via the North Pole in airship N.1 Norge.

30 June–1 October. Cobham in de Havilland DH.50J makes third "Empire Flight" from Croydon to Melbourne and back.

31 August–2 September. Tour of European capitals by Tupolev ANT-3.

12 October–14 January 1927. Jean Dagnaux flies from France to Madagascar in a Breguet Bre. 19A2.

13 November. Macchi M.39 seaplane wins the Schneider Trophy race at Norfolk. Virginia.

7 December–21 February 1927. Walter Mittelhalzer in Dornier Do-B Merkur seaplane *Switzerland* flies from Zurich to Cape Town.

1927

Sir Alan Cobham in Short S.5 Singapore I flying boat makes round Africa flight (continues in 1928).

8 January. Imperial Airways de Havilland DH.66 Hercules City of Delhi arrives at Karachi to take over the airmail route from the R.A.F.

13 February–16 June. De Pinedo and Del Prete fly from Sardinia to the U.S.A. and back to Rome in Savoia Marchetti S-55M flying boat *Santa Maria*.

8 May. Charles Nungesser and Francois Coli leave Paris on their fatal attempt to fly non-stop to New York in Levasseur PL-8 *L'Oiseau Blanc*.

20–21 May. Charles Lindbergh in Ryan NYP Special *Spirit of St. Louis* makes first solo non-stop crossing of the North Atlantic from New York to Paris.

5 July. Ribeiro de Barros in Savoia Marchetti S.55C flying boat *Jahu* flies from Genoa to Sao Paulo, Brazil.

14–15 October. Dieudonne Costes and Joseph Le Brix in Breguet Bre. 19 Super TR *Nungesser et Coli* make first non-stop crossing of the South Atlantic from Paris to Natal via St. Louis, Senegal.

27 October. First Pan American Airways airmail flight from Key West to Havana, by Fokker F.7 Trimotor *General New*.

1928

First flight to Barbados by a de Havilland DH.60 Cirrus Moth.

7/22 February. Bert Hinkler in Avro Type 581A Avian makes solo flight from England to Australia.

12/13 April. Gunther Hunefeld. James Fitzmaurice and Hermann Kohl in Junkers W.33 Bremen make first east–west crossing of the North Atlantic.

23 May. General Umberto Nobile leaves Spitzbergen in his airship N.4 *Italia* in attempt to fly to the North Pole. He crashes and in the rescue mission Roald Amundsen is lost.

31 May–9 June. Charles Kingsford Smith and Charles Ulm in Fokker F.VIIa/3m *Southern Cross* make first aerial crossing of the Pacific, from Oakland, California, via Hawaii and Fiji to Australia.

17/18 June. Amelia Earhart becomes the first woman to fly the Atlantic, as a passenger in Fokker F.VIIb/3m seaplane *Friendship* flown by Wilmer Schultz and Lou Gordon.

3/5 July. Arturo Ferranin and Carlos del Prete in Savoia Marchetti S-64 make non-stop "straight line" flight from Italy to Brazil.

8/9 September. Kingsford Smith in Fokker F.VIIa/3m *Southern Cross* makes first non-stop crossing of Australia from Perth to Sydney.

10/11 September. Kingsford Smith in Fokker F.VIIa/3m *Southern Cross* makes first aerial crossing of the Tasman Sea from Sydney to Christchurch.

18 September. First flight of Zeppelin airship LZ-127 *Graf Zeppelin*.

16 November. First exploratory flight over Antarctic by Hubert Wilkins and Carl Eielson in Lockheed Vega *San Francisco*.

1929

Antoine de Saint-Exupery makes the first flight from Bahia Blanca to Comodoro Rivadavia, Argentina, in a Latecoere 25.

March. Jimenez and Iglesias in Breguet 19GR *Jesus del Gran Poder* fly from Seville to Natal and round South America to Havana.

April. Squadron Leader A. G. Jones-Williams and Flight Lieutenant N. H. Jenkins in Fairey Long Range monoplane make 4,130-mile flight non-stop from Cranwell to Karachi.

8/29 August. First round-the-world flight by Zeppelin airship LZ-127 *Graf Zeppelin*.

23 August-1 November. Moscow to New York flight via Siberia by Shestuakov and Bolotev in Tupolev ANT-4.

28/29 November. Richard Byrd and Bernard Balchen in Ford 4-AT-B *Floyd Bennett* make first flight over South Pole.

1930

Antarctic exploration by Sir Douglas Mawson in a de Havilland DH.60G Gipsy Moth (also during 1931).

Maryse Hilsz in de Havilland DH.60G Gipsy Moth flies from Paris to Saigon.

First flight from United States to Bermuda made by Stinson Pilot Radio seaplane.

15/16 April. Gyorgy Endresz and Sandor Wilczec in Lockheed 8A Sirius *Justice for Hungary* fly from New York to Budapest via Newfoundland.

5/24 May. Amy Johnson in de Havilland DH.60G Gipsy Moth *Jason* makes solo flight fron England to Australia.

12 May. Jean Mermoz In Latecoere 28-3 seaplane *Comte de la Vaulx* makes first airmail flight from Dakar to Natal. On the return flight the plane is forced down into the sea and sinks.

18 May-6 June. First South American flight by Zeppelin airship LZ-127 *Graf Zeppelin*.

June. Captain C. G. Fenton in Simmonds Spartan seaplane inaugurates first commercial air service in Fiji.

13 June. Henri Guillaumet crashes in the Andes in his Potez 25A2.

1/3 September. Dieudonne Costes and Maurice Bellonte in Breguet Bre. 19 Super TR *Point d'Interrogation* make first non-stop flight from Paris to New York.

2 November-27 August 1931. Demonstration flight by Dornier Do-X flying boat from Friedrichshafen to New York via the South Atlantic, returning to Berlin.

17 December-15 January 1931. Mass formation flight from Ortebello to Rio de Janeiro by General Italo Balbo with 14 Savoia Marchetti S-55A flying boats.

1931

28 March-6 June. Sir Francis Chichester in de Havilland DH.60G Gipsy Moth *Madame Elijah* makes first solo crossing of the Tasman Sea from New Zealand to Australia via Norfolk Island and Lord Howe Island.

27 May. Stratosphere ascent to 51,775 feet by Professor Auguste Piccard in his balloon *F.N.R.S.*

22 June. Ruth Nichols In Lockheed Vega V *Akita* makes unsuccessful attempt to fly across the Atlantic.

23 June-1 July. Wiley Post and Harold Gatty in Lockheed Vega V *Winnie Mae* make round-the-world flight.

24/25 June. Hojriis Hillig in Bellanca J-300 Special *Liberty* flies from Newfoundland to Germany.

24/30 July. Zeppelin airship LZ-127 *Graf Zeppelin* makes Leningrad and Franz Josef Land flight.

13 September. Schneider Trophy won outright by Supermarine S6B seaplane.

1932

Round Europe race won by F. Zwirco and S. Wigura in a RWD-6.

Captain Hans Bertram in Junkers W.33 seaplane *Atlantis* flies from Germany to Australia.

April. De Verneilh, Deve and Munch in Couzinet 33 F-ALMV *Le Biarritz* fly from Paris to Noumea, New Caledonia.

20/21 May. Amelia Earhart In Lockheed Vega VB seaplane makes first solo Atlantic crossing by a woman, from Harbour Grace in Newfoundland to Londonderry.

29 June. First mid-air "hook-up". by Curtiss Sparrowhawk biplane on airship U.S.S. *Akron*.

21 July-9 November. Wolfgang von Gronau in Dornier Do-J Wal flying boat *Gronland Wal* makes round-the-world flight.

1933

Barberan and Collar in Breguet Bre. 19 Super Bidon *Cuatro Vientos* fly from Seville to Camaguey, Cuba.

Stanlislas Skarzynski in RWD-5 bis flies from Warsaw to Natal, Brazil.

Gordon Bennett Race won by Z. Burzynski of Poland in the balloon *Kosciuszko* covering 846 miles from Chicago to Quebec.

16 January. Jean Mermoz begins the first regular airmail service from France to South America in Couzinet 70 *Arc en Ciel*.

4 April. Destruction of airship U.S.S. *Akron*.

21 April. First flight of U.S. airship ZR-5 *Macon*.

July. Captain Steponas Darius and Captain Stasys Girenas in Bellanca monoplane *Lituanica* fly from New York to Lithuania. Both are killed when they crash near their destination.

1 July. First flight of Douglas DC-1, forerunner of the DC-3.

1/15 July. Mass formation flight from Ortebello to Chicago by General Balbo with 25 Savoia Marchetti S-55X flying boats.

9 July. Charles Lindbergh begins a 30,000 mile tour of the Atlantic in his Lockheed Model 8 Sirius seaplane *Tingmissartoq* to survey routes for Pan American Airways.

15/22 July. Wiley Post in Lockheed Vega V *Winnie Mae* makes first solo round-the-world flight.

September. Stratosphere flight to 58,700 feet by Prokofiev. Bernhaum and Gudunov in balloon *U.S.S.R.-1*.

September-December. Tour of French African territories by squadron of Potez 25 TOE biplanes.

9/31 December. Pander S.4 Postjager undertakes Amsterdam to Djakarta airmail flight.

1934

Lombardi and Mazzotti in Savoia Marchetti S-71 make Rome to Buenos Aires flight.

J. Bajon and J. Pokazywka win the Round Europe race in a RWD-9.

Antarctic expedition to Graham Land by John Rymill in a de Havilland DH.83 Fox Moth.

Antarctic exploration by Christensen in an Avro Type 581 Avian.

January. Stratosphere ascent to 72,178 feet by Russian balloon *Osoaviakhim* ends in a fatal crash.

3 January. Jean Mermoz makes the first regular scheduled South Atlantic crossing in the Latecoere 300 flying boat *Croix du Sud*.

February. Zeppelin airship LZ-127 *Graf Zeppelin* makes the first airmail flight from Argentina to Germany.

17 February. Charles Ulm in Avro Type 618 Ten *Faith in Australia* carries first official airmail across the Tasman Sea, Auckland to Sydney.

5 March. Rescue of Dr. Otto Schmidt and party from the icebreaker *Tchelyuskin*, trapped in Arctic ice, by Tupolev ANT-4 TB-1 and Polikarpov R-5 aircraft.

19 May. First flight of Tupolev ANT-20 *Maksim Gorky*.

24 July. Ulm in Avro Type 618 Ten *Faith in Australia* carries first official airmail from Australia to Papua (Melbourne to Port Moresby).

10 October. Macchi Castoldi MC-72 seaplane sets world seaplane record of 440.68 m.p.h.

22 October-4 November. Sir Charles Kingsford Smith in Lockheed Model 8D Altair *Lady Southern Cross* makes first flight from Australia to the U.S.A., via Fiji and Hawaii.

27 November. Bleriot 5190 Santos-Dumont flying boat makes first airmail flight from Dakar to Natal.

14/15 December. Fokker F.XVIII *De Snip* makes first airmail flight from Amsterdam to Curacao.

1935

Thor Solberg in Loening OA-2 amphibian *Lief Ericsson* flies from New York to Norway via Greenland.

Antarctic exploration by Lincoln Ellsworth In Northrop Gamma monoplane *Polar Star*.

Postal "glider train" experiment in Cuba: mail-carrying gliders towed by a single airplane and released at various destinations.

12 February Destruction of U.S. airship *Macon*.

18/21 June. Chalkov, Baidukov and Beliakov in Tupolev ANT-25 fly from Moscow to Portland, via the North Pole.

15 September. Gordon Bennett balloon race won by Z. Burzynski in the Polish balloon SP-AMY *Polonia II* covering 1,025 miles from Warsaw to Leningrad.

11 November. Stratosphere ascent to 74,185 feet by Stevens and Anderson in the U.S. balloon *Explorer II*.

22 November-6 December. Pan American Airways Martin M-130 flying boat *China Clipper* makes the first commercial crossing of the Pacific, from San Francisco to Manila via Hawaii, Midway, Guam and Wake Island.

17 December. First flight of Douglas DC-3.

1936

9 January-14 February. Lieutenant Antonio Menendez Pelaez in Lockheed Model 8A Sirius flies from Cuba to Seville and back.

23 March. First flight of Zeppelin airship LZ-129 *Hindenburg*.

28 June. Focke Achgelis Fa 61 makes the first flight by a practical helicopter.

September. Maryse Bastie in Caudron C-635 Simoun flies from Paris to Natal via Dakar.

5/6 October. Jean Batten in Percival P.3 Gull Six makes first flight from England to New Zealand by a woman.

21/26 October. First regular scheduled trans-Pacific flight by Martin M-130 flying boat *China Clipper*.

7 December. Disappearance over the South Atlantic of Jean Mermoz, flying the Latecoere 300 flying boat *Croix du Sud*.

1937

Gordon Bennett balloon race won by Ernst Demuyter for the sixth time in the balloon *Belgica* covering 889 miles from Brussels to Tukomo, Lithuania.

King's Cup won by Percival Mew Gull *Golden City*.

Imperial Airways inaugurates the first scheduled passenger service to Bermuda, using the Short S.23 Empire "C" Class flying boat *Cavalier*.

12 April-21 May. Moscow to North Pole flight led by Vodopyanov in Tupolev ANT-6 *Avia Arktika*.

6 May. Destruction of Zeppelin airship LZ-129 *Hindenburg* at Lakehurst, New Jersey.

21 May. Amelia Earhart begins round-the-world attempt in her Lockheed Model 10E Electra, during which she disappears.

12/14 July. Gromov, Yumashev and Danelin in Tupolev ANT-25 fly from Moscow to Los Angeles via the North Pole.

1938

Gordon Bennett balloon race won by Janusz in the Polish balloon *L.O.P.P.* covering 1,013 miles from Liege in Belgium to Trojan in Bulgaria.

Long-distance record for women set by Valentina Grizodubova, Marina Raskova and Paulina Osipenko with a flight from Moscow to Kerbi, Siberia, in the Tupolev ANT-37 *Rodina*.

3/21 June. Indian Ocean survey flight by Captain P. Taylor in the Consolidated PBY-5 Catalina flying boat *Guba*.

16 June. First regular air service between Bermuda and New York, operated jointly by Pan American Airways, using the Sikorsky S-42B flying boat *Bermuda Clipper*, and Imperial Airways with the Short S.23 Empire "C" Class flying boat *Cavalier*.

21 July. First commercial flight, with air launch over Foynes, Ireland. from Southampton to Montreal by the Short-Mayo composite.

14 September. First flight by Zeppelin airship LZ-130 *Graf Zeppelin II*.

1939

24 March. Martinet and Klein In Caudron C-600 *Aiglon* fly from Noumea, New Caledonia, to Paris.

28 June. Boeing 314A flying boat *Dixie Clipper* of Pan American Airways makes the first scheduled passenger crossing of the North Atlantic.

27 August. The Heinkel He-178, in the hands of Flugcapitain Erich Warsitz, became the first turbojet aircraft to fly.

14 September. Igor Sikorsky makes first flight by a commercially practicable helicopter in his Vought-Sikorsky VS-300.

1940

24 February. The Hawker Typhoon prototype made its first flight today. Production ran to 3330 examples.

12 May. The first Boulton Paul Defiant is delivered to RAF 264 Squadron. The Defiant is unusual in having a gun turret behind the pilot.

28 May. First flight of Italian Caproni Campini N-1, powered by a piston engine driving a high-speed compressor.

August-September. The Royal Air Force defeats the Luftwaffe in the Battle of Britain.

1941

9 January. The Avro Type 683 Lancaster makes its first flight in the hands of test pilot Bill Thorn. Avro managing director Roy Dobson, watching exclaims 'Boy oh boy, what a plane!' Subsequent events proved him right.

15 May. Gloster Whittle E28/39 makes first flight by a British jet-powered airplane.

2 October. Rocket-powered Messerschmitt Me 163B Komet flies at over 1,000 km./h. (624 m.p.h.).

30 October. First airmail by jet from Milan to Rome by Caproni Campini N-1.

7 December. Japanese carrier-borne aircraft attack Pearl Harbour.

1942

3 March. The Avro Lancaster makes its operational debut in a mine-laying mission off Heligoland with 44 Squadron, RAF.

21 April. Lt Col. James Doolittle led a formation of 16 North American B-25 Mitchell bombers in a daring attack on the Japanese mainland. The first of the war, the aircraft took off from the carrier USS *Hornet*.

4 July. Second Lt. Richard Bong flies his Lockheed P-38 Lightning up Market Street, San Francisco, at very low level, sending a local woman's washing flying. His C.O. sentences him to rewash the woman's laundry.

18 July. The prototype of the Messerschmitt Me-262, the world's first operational jet fighter, makes its first flight piloted by test pilot Fritz Wendel.

1 October. The Bell XP-59A Airacomet, flown by Bell test pilot Bob Stanley, made its first flight at Muroc Dry Lake (now Edwards) Base in California. It was America's first jet powered aircraft and used US built versions of the Whittle engine.

1943

9 January. The Lockheed Constellation, the world's heaviest, fastest and most powerful airliner made its maiden flight at Burbank today. Ordered by Howard Hughes for his airline, TWA, the production line was immediately taken over by the USAAF.

18 April. A USAAF Lockheed P-38 Lightning flown by Capt. T. G. Lanphier today shot down the Mitsubishi G4M1 'Betty' carrying Admiral Isoroku Yamamoto, the man who planned the attack on Pearl Harbour.

17 May. In what has become probably the most celebrated air attack in history, 19 Lancasters of RAF 617 (Dambusters) Squadron breached the Möhne and Eder dams, disrupting power supplies to German factories. Led by Wing Comm. Guy Gibson, flying from RAF Scampton, each aircraft carried one of Barnes Wallis's 'bouncing bombs'. Only 11 aircraft returned.

1 August. 178 American Consolidated B-24 Liberator bombers flew from Benghazi, Libya, to attack the Ploesti oilfields north of Bucharest, Romania. Intelligence had predicted light flak, but got it wrong. Fifty-three aircraft were destroyed.

1944

8 January. The prototype Lockheed XP-80 made its first successful test flight at Muroc Dry Lake today. Destined to be the USAAF's first production jet fighter, it climbed so fast in the test that it was decided to call it the Shooting Star.

6 March. A fleet of 658 B-17 and B-24 bombers of the USAAF, escorted by about 700 fighters, struck Berlin and the surrounding area. 69 of the bombers were shot down by over 400 German Messerschmitt Bf.109s and FockeWulf 190s.

13 June. Grove Road, Bethnal Green, in London's East End, had the dubious distinction of being on the receiving end of the first German 'doodlebug' – otherwise the Fieseler Fi-1003 V-1. The V-1 thus qualified as the first operational UAV.

3 October. Messerschmitt Me 262, the first German jet fighter, enters service.

1945

9 January. The new Boeing XC-97 today became the world's fastest transport aircraft, reaching speeds in excess of 380 mph on a flight from Seattle to Washington. Boeing is also marketing a civil equivalent, the 377 Stratocruiser.

12 April. Japanese kamikaze aircraft scored their first success off Okinawa today when they sank destroyer USS *Mannert L.Abele*. They had earlier damaged two allied warships.

8 May. The war in Europe ended today as Germany surrendered. During the conflict, the RAF, USAAF and Luftwaffe lost over 97,000 aircraft. Over 156,000 aircrew of the RAF and USAAF died together with more than 300,000 in Germany.

31 May. The last of over 18,000 Consolidated B-24 Liberator bombers rolled off the Detroit production line today, making it the most-produced Allied bomber of World War II.

31 May. Commercial service to Australia and New Zealand inaugurated by Avro Type 691 Lancastrian of B.O.A.C.

1946

31 May. Heathrow, London's new airport, received its first international passengers today. They were not impressed, having to queue on wooden slatted floors to protect them from the mud in a tent city housing customs and immigration.

8 August. Convair test pilots Beryl Erickson and Gus Green made the first flight of the prototype of the world's largest bomber, the Convair XB-36. Production ended with the 382nd example.

25 June. The prototype of the revolutionary Northrop XB-35 flying wing bomber made its maiden flight from Los Angeles to Muroc Dry Lake. 14 were ordered, of which some were converted to jet powered XB-49s. Production orders were cancelled but Jack Northrop's controversial design concepts were later validated in the Northrop B-2A Spirit.

1947

4 April. The International Civil Aviation Organisation (ICAO) was officially founded today in Montreal, Canada. An inter-governmental organisation, its role will be to regulate air transport worldwide.

17 June. The first round-the-world air service is introduced by Pan Am, using Lockheed Constellations.

24 June. Pilot Kenneth Arnold claims to see nine oddly shaped aircraft resembling 'saucers skipping over the water', thus giving rise to the term 'flying saucer'.

24 July. Test pilot brothers, V.K. and K.K. Kokinakki, make the first flight of Ilyushin's new four engined turbo prop bomber, the Il-22.

25 August. The world air speed record fell for the second time in 5 days when Major Marion Carl flew a Douglas D-558-1 Skystreak at an average speed over 4 runs of 650.8mph, beating the previous record, also by a Skystreak, by just over 10mph.

18 September. The United States Air Force today became an independent service. The former USAAF commander, General Carl Spaatz became Chief of Staff of the new service.

14 October. Captain Charles "Chuck" Yeager makes first manned supersonic flight, in Bell X-1 rocket airplane.

2 November. The Hughes H-4 Hercules flying boat, commonly referred to as the 'Spruce Goose', made its first (and last) flight at Long Beach California, today. Piloted by Howard Hughes, it reached an altitude of around 80 feet and landed about 1 mile after takeoff. It's next trip was by road to the building at Long Beach where it is now preserved.

17 December. Today, the 44th Anniversary of the Wright Brothers first flight, the Boeing XB-47 Stratojet bomber took to the air for the first time. With swept wings and six jet engines, its top speed of over 550 mph makes it faster then most fighter aircraft now in service. More than 1800 Stratojets were built.

1948

6 April. Vickers Viking tested with two Rolls Royce Nene turbojet engines, the first flight by a pure jet-powered transport.

28 April. A Lockheed Constellation of Air France made the first non-stop Paris-New York flight. It took 16 hours and 1 minute.

26 May. Charles 'Chuck' Yeager flies the Bell X-1 to a new altitude record of 64000ft.

20 July. Sixteen Lockheed P-80 Shooting Stars made the first west to east transatlantic flight by jet aircraft, landing at Stornoway after a flight of 9 hours 20 minutes from Selfridge Field, Michigan.

26 June. The Berlin Air Lift –Operation Vittles – began today on the orders of General Lucius Clay, commander of the US Zone of Berlin. For two days, two million people living in the Western sector had been under virtual siege after Soviet authorities cut all road, rail and canal links to West Germany.

1949

26 January. American Airlines equips its entire fleet with a loudspeaker system to allow the pilot to provide passengers with flight or emergency information.

4 March. The First Fighter Wing, USAF, begin to operate the North American F-86. After a competition to name the aircraft, Sabre is chosen from 78 suggestions.

13 May. Test pilot Roland Beamont makes the first flight of Britain's first jet bomber, the English Electric A.1 Canberra

27 July. The World's first jet airliner, the de Havilland DH.106 Comet makes its maiden flight from Hatfield, piloted by John (Cat's Eyes) Cunningham.

1950

27 January. USAF base Muroc Dry Lake, used for testing new and experimental types, is renamed Edwards Air Force Base in honour of Captain Glen Edwards who died on 5 June 1948, when the prototype Northrop YB-49 disintegrated.

1 March. The first production Boeing B-47 Stratojet rolled off the production line at Wichita, Kansas today. By the time production ended, over 2000 had been built.

17 December. On their first day in action, North American F-86 Sabres down four MiG-15s, 10 miles south of the Yalu River, Korea. It is the first encounter between swept-wing aircraft.

1951

18 April. An agreement was signed today to allow licensed production of the English Electric Canberra by Martin in the US. The US version will be designated B-57 and will be the first British designed aircraft to be built in the US since 1918.

31 May. Roosevelt Field, Long Island, New York from which Lindbergh's 1927 transatlantic flight took off, is closed after 40 years of use.

26 November. The prototype of the world's first twin-jet delta-winged aircraft, the Gloster G.A.5 Javelin, made a 34 minute first flight today, piloted by Squadron Leader W.A. Waterton.

1952

22 January. The de Havilland Comet 1 is awarded the first certificate of airworthiness to go to a jet powered airliner.

7 February. Consolidated PBY-5A Catalina amphibian makes first airmail flight to the Antarctic.

15 April. The Boeing YB-52 Stratofortress prototype flew for the first time. The US Air Force had already issued a letter of intent for production on 1 March 1951, well before the first flight.

1 May. TWA, BOAC and Air France launch the first scheduled tourist-class flight on their transatlantic routes.

3 May. The world's first scheduled service by a jet airliner was inaugurated today when a de Havilland Comet 1 of BOAC flew from London to Johannesburg.

30 August. The prototype of the Avro Type 698 Vulcan delta-winged bomber makes its first flight from Woodford.

1953

2 January. The first of some 430 North American F-86 Sabres ordered for the RAF arrived at RAF Abingdon. The Sabres will be the RAF's first supersonic aircraft.

3 April. BOAC inaugurates a weekly service from London to Tokyo using de Havilland Comet 1s. The flight takes over 33 hours.

8 July. New York Airways, America's first scheduled passenger helicopter service begins, linking Idlewild, La Guardia and Newark airports.

9 August. The Rolls Royce Thrust Measuring Rig, better known as the 'Flying Bedstead', today marked the beginning of British VTAOL research, flown at Hacknall by Rolls Royce, test pilot R.T. Shepherd.

1954

7 January. Lockheed's XF-104 Starfighter made its first flight today, piloted by Lockheed test pilot Tony Le Vier. Dubbed 'the missile with a man in it', it is capable of speeds in excess of Mach 2, more than twice that of the North American F-100 Super Sabre which it is intended to replace.

12 April. Prime Minister Winston Churchill ordered all de Havilland Comets grounded after a series of as yet unexplained disasters resulted in 3 crashes. It is a major blow to the UK aviation industry.

15 July. The prototype of the revolutionary Boeing 707 jetliner made its first flight today. Significantly faster then any airliner in service, it rapidly transformed air travel for business and holiday travellers alike. Before production ended 25 years later, over 765 had been built, in addition to hundreds of variations of the C-135 for the US Air Force.

23 August. The YC-130, prototype of Lockheed's C-130 Hercules tactical transport for the USAF, flew at Burbank, California for the first time today. Fifty-four years later, Lockheed are still building Hercules. Well over 2000 have been delivered to operators in over 60 countries.

1955

11 February. The inquiry into the Comet disasters of 1954 announced that the cause was structural failure caused by metal fatigue.

27 May. The first prototype of the French Sud-Est SE 210 Caravelle flew for the first time at Toulouse today. The airliner is the first short-haul jet airliner and also the first to have tail-mounted engines.

7 June. Douglas announce their intention to build a 4-jet airliner, the DC-8, to compete with Boeing's 707.

20 August. King's Cup won by Percival Mew Gull *Golden City*, the 1937 winner.

29 August. An English Electric Canberra B2., piloted by W.F. Gibb, reaches a world record altitude of 65,889 ft.

1956

10 March. The experimental Fairey Delta 2 became the first aircraft to set a world speed record of over 1000 mph., flown by Peter Twiss at an altitude of 38000ft.

29 July. The National Aeronautics and Space Agency (NASA) was created today, its stated mission to lead the exploration of space for peaceful purposes.

1 November. The first step toward creating a British supersonic airliner was taken today when the Supersonic Transport Aircraft Committee was set up at Farnborough to study its feasibility.

11 November. The Convair XB-58 Hustler, the first supersonic bomber, made a successful first flight today from Carswell Air Force Base, Fort Worth, Texas.

31 December. This year, for the first time, more passengers (1.2 million) have crossed the North Atlantic by air than by sea.

1957

11 July. The last Supermarine Spitfires in RAF service were ceremonially decommissioned today at Biggin Hill. Making its first flight in March 1936, over 20,000 Spitfires have been built during 20 years of continuous operational service.

13 July. President Eisenhower becomes the first US President to fly in a helicopter, a USAF Bell UH-13J.

28 August. A new world altitude record of 70,310 ft is set by an English Electric Canberra in a flight from Luton.

21 December. The first example of the Boeing 707 made its first flight today from Seattle. In May 1953 Boeing took a massive financial risk by spending $16 million (virtually the entire value of the company) on the Dash-80 prototype. The gamble paid off handsomely.

1958

14 January. Two Qantas Lockheed Super Constellations inaugurate the first regular round-the-world service.

27 April. The first de Havilland Comet 4 makes its first flight at Hatfield.

20 June. The prototype Westland Wessex helicopter makes its first flight at Yeovil.

24 September. The Beijing No.1 transport – the first aircraft to be designed and built entirely in China, makes its maiden flight.

1959

March. The Supersonic Transport Aircraft Committee proposes three designs for a supersonic transport. A variation of one eventually becomes Concorde.

14 July. Major V. Ilyushin takes the world absolute altitude record to 94,659 ft. flying a Sukhoi T-431.

26 August. French flyer Jacqueline Auriol, piloting a Mirage III becomes the first woman to attain Mach 2.

1960

1 May. BOAC opens its first London-New York service using Boeing 707s.

27 May. A Lockheed U-2 high altitude reconnaissance aircraft is shot down over Russia at an altitude of 65,000ft. It was hit by a ground-to-air missile, having previously been thought invulnerable to interception.

17 August. Gary Powers, the pilot of the Lockheed U-2 shot down over Russia in May is sentenced to 10 years in a labour camp for espionage.

20 August. Pan Am sells its last 14 Boeing Stratocruisers to a scrap merchant for $100,000.

1961

23 January. A double-deck French airliner, predating the A380 by some 45 years, the Breguet Universal, made its maiden flight at Toulouse today.

21 April. USAF Major Robert White pilots the North American X-15 research aircraft to a speed of 3074mph and an altitude of 105,100ft

10 May. A USAF Convair B-58 Hustler wins the Bleriot Trophy, created 30 years ago for the first aircraft to maintain a speed of more than 2000 kph for more than 30 minutes in a closed circuit.

26 May. Major Payne of the U.S.A.F. flies a Convair B-58A Hustler from New York to Paris in 3 hours, 19 minutes, 41 seconds.

17 June. The HAL HF-24 Marut, India's supersonic fighter made its maiden flight today. It was designed by German engineer Kurt Tank, the creator of the Focke Wulf Fw-190.

1962

12 January. The USAF begins Operation Ranch Hand, spraying defoliant Agent Orange over large areas of forest to expose roads and trails used by the Vietcong.

2 February. A Sikorsky HSS-2 Sea King helicopter sets a world speed record for helicopters at 210.6 mph.

10 February. U-2 pilot Gary Powers, shot down over Russia in May 1960, is exchanged for Soviet spy Col. Rudolf Abel.

26 April. The first Lockheed A-12, predecessor of the SR-71 Blackbird, made its first flight at Groom Dry Lake, Nevada today.

27 June. Pilot Joe Walker takes the North American X-15 to a speed of 4,159 mph, more than six times the speed of sound.

29 November. After a lengthy series of discussions the British and French governments at last decide to jointly develop a supersonic airliner.

1963

13 January. In a speech, French President General de Gaulle uses the word *'concorde'* with reference to the Anglo-French supersonic airliner project.

8 April. Douglas Aircraft announce they will not take up their option to build the French Caravelle deciding instead to build their own design, the DC-9.

23 August. J. A. Walker reaches a height of 354,200 feet (67 miles) in a North American X-15 rocket airplane.

28 October. The new BAC supersonic bomber, the TSR.2 was unveiled to the press today. It was subsequently cancelled.

1964

5 January. The first flight of the Short Belfast, a long-range heavy-lift transport for the RAF took place today. With no interest from civil carriers, only 10 were built. They were the largest aircraft to serve with the RAF.

7 March. The Kestrel, developed from the Hawker Siddeley P.1127, and forerunner of the Harrier V/STOL aircraft, made its first flight at Kingston today.

29 April. BOAC introduces the Vickers VC.10 on its London to Lagos service.

11 May. Jacqueline Cochrane set a new world speed record for women, flying a Lockheed F-104 Starfighter to a speed of 1,429 mph.

1965

6 April. After years of threats, the government finally cancelled the BAC TSR.2, Britain's most advanced military aircraft project.

26 May. British air pioneer Sir Geoffrey de Havilland died today. He built his first aircraft in 1908 with the help of a £500 loan from his grandfather.

16 June. The Antonov An-22 Antei arrived at the Paris Air Show and astonished onlookers with its immense size, undoubtedly the largest aircraft in the world.

1967

3 October. W. J. Knight flies a North American X-15 at Mach 6.72 (4,534 m.p.h.).

1968

31 December. Tupolev Tu-144 makes first flight by a supersonic jet airliner.

1969

2 March. First flight by Concorde supersonic jet airliner.

1974

20 January. The General Dynamics (now Lockheed Martin) YF-16A lightweight fighter made an unintended first flight in the hands of test pilot Phillip Oestricher. The official first flight took place 13 days later on 2 February. Christened Fighting Falcon, well over 4,000 have been built to date.

1 September. A USAF Lockheed SR-71A Blackbird shattered all previous records for transatlantic flights, covering the 3461 miles from New York to London in 1 hour 54 minutes 54.6 seconds, at an average speed of 1,807mph. On the return flight, it smashed the east to west record, making the 5447 mile London to Los Angeles trip in 3 hours 47 minutes and 39 seconds. Both records are unlikely to be broken in the foreseeable future.

1978

12/17 August. Ben Abruzzo. Max Anderson and Larry Newman make the first crossing of the North Atlantic by gas balloon in *Double Eagle II*.

1983

Gordon Bennett balloon race won by the Polish balloon *Polonez*.

Dick Smith, flying a Bell 206 Jet Ranger III makes the first solo circumnavigation of the globe in a helicopter.

1986

14/23 December. Dick Rutan and Jeana Yeager make the first non-stop circumnavigation of the wold without refuelling in *Voyager*, covering 25,012 miles at an average speed of 115.8 m.p.h.

1987

22 January. Glen Tremml makes a 37.2-mile flight of 2 hours 13 minutes 14 seconds in the man-powered microlight *Eagle* at Edwards Air Force Base, California.

1988

10 November. The US Department of Defence revealed the existence of the 'stealth fighter', Lockheed's F-117 Nighthawk. Until this time the aircraft which had been operational since 1985, had been restricted to night flying.

1989

19 March. The Bell Boeing V-22 Osprey, the first operational tilt-rotor aircraft, made its first flight. It made its first transition from helicopter to wing-borne flight on 14 September.

1990

29 September. Representing a massive leap forward in technology, the Lockheed Martin YF-22A Raptor made its first flight today. The Raptor won the USAF's Advanced Tactical Fighter contest (against the Northrop/McDonnell Douglas YF-23) and the first production example flew on 7 September 1997.

1991

15/17 January. Richard Branson and Per Lindstrand cross the Pacific from Japan to the Yukon (4,768 miles) in the hot-air balloon *Virgin Otsuka Pacific Flyer* at an average speed of 147 m.p.h.

17 January. Allied Coalition forces launched Operation Desert Storm with a massive air assault designed to drive Iraqi invaders out of Kuwait.

15 September. The Boeing (McDonnell Douglas) C-17 Globemaster III strategic transport makes its first flight.

1992

18 January. The USAF retire its McDonnell Douglas F-4 Phantom II force. The Royal Air Force follow suit on 6 July.

1993

Boeing produce their 1000th Boeing 747 since its launch in 1967.

1994

7 June. Vicki van Meter, 12 years old, became the youngest female to fly the Atlantic.

18 November – 5 December. NATO forces launch a series of air strikes against Serbian air bases and missile sites.

1995

26 April. A new world altitude record for Class C1h aircraft of 90,092 ft. is set by a Mikoyan-Gurevich MiG-29.

4 August. A new world altitude record for manned piston-engined aircraft is set by a Grob G820 at 60,867 ft.

16 August. Concord sets a new speed record for a round-the-world flight of 31 hours 27 minutes.

1 September. The first combat mission flown by the Luftwaffe since the end of World War II occurs when a Panavia Tornado ECR takes part in operation 'Deny Flight' over the former Yugoslavia.

1996

29 June. The original 'Air Force One', a Boeing VC137 used as the official aircraft of the United States Presidents since 1959, is retired.

15 December. A merger between United States aerospace giants, Boeing and McDonnell Douglas is agreed, the new company to be known as Boeing.

1997

October. The Boeing 777-300 made its first flight this month, currently the longest airliner ever, at over 240 ft.

1998

1 April. The Royal Air Force celebrated its 80th Anniversary. Many countries issued commemorative stamps to mark the occasion.

1999

17 April. The Northrop Grumman B-2A Spirit made its first operational sortie, a 30 hour round trip (with in-flight refuelling) between Missouri and Serbia.

2000

25 July. Air France Concorde F-BTSC crashes in flames after runway debris punctures a fuel tank. All on board perish in the first fatal accident in Concorde's 31 year history.

24 October. The X-35, prototype of the Lockheed Martin F-35, made its first flight today. One of two types under consideration for the USAF Joint Strike Fighter requirement, the other being the Boeing X-32.

2001

11 September. In the worst terrorist attack in history, two Boeing 767s on scheduled flights are hijacked and flown into the twin towers of the World Trade Centre in New York. The towers collapse with a death toll exceeding 2800.

25 October. The Lockheed Martin X-35 is announced as the winner of the Joint Strike Fighter competition. Production of up to 6000 is anticipated.

2002

The first modern operational unmanned air vehicles (UAVs), the General Atomics RQ-1 Predator and the Northrop Grumman/Ryan RQ-4 Global Hawk are deployed by the USAF on surveillance and strike missions.

2005

25 April. The Airbus A380, the world's largest passenger aircraft, made its maiden flight at Toulouse today. It has a capacity for 555 passengers in its initial version, but extended versions with capacity for up to 950 are proposed. Orders placed exceed 150.

2007

8 July. The rollout of Boeings new 787 Dreamliner took place today. The first flight has been rescheduled for mid-2009. The order book now tops 890, the highest number for any airliner before its first flight.

3 September. Aviation record breaker and adventurer Steve Fossett disappears on a routine solo flight in his Bellanca Super Decathlon.

26 October. Singapore Airlines, the first customer to receive the Airbus A380, today inaugurated services between Singapore and Sydney with 471 passengers on board. Regular services began on 29 October.

2008

23 February. The wreckage of an aircraft has been found in a remote location in the Sierra Nevada Mountains in California. DNA test of bones found nearby confirmed them to be those of Steve Fossett who disappeared in September 2007. He held over 100 records in aviation and sailing.

1 April. Today marks the 90th Anniversary of the formation of the Royal Air Force. Once again, many stamps are issued to commemorate the event.

31 October. Northrop Grumman B-2A Spirit, 'Spirit of Kansas' crashed on take-off at Anderson AFB, Guam. The two-man crew ejected safely but the aircraft was written off. The accident marked the first loss of a B-2A since the type's first flight in 1989.

Classification Index

This index provides a cross-referenced list of aircraft types and indicates under which part of the Sectional Index each is classified.

G

"G" Class flying boat	see Short S.26, Short S.30
GA-42 (airship)	A 2 (a)
Gabbiano (flying boat)	see Cant Z.501
Gakkel VII	B
Gakkel IX	B
Galaxy (jet transport)	see Lockheed C-5A
Galeb (jet trainer)	see SOKO Galeb 3
Galiffet (balloonist)	A 1 (a)
Gamecock	see Gloster Gamecock
Gamma (long distance)	see Northrop Gamma
Gardan GY-80 Horizon	C 2 (e)
Gardian (marine reconnaissance)	see Dassault Breguet Gardian
Garnerin, Andre Jacques (balloonist)	A 1 (a)
Garvan II	see DAR Garvan II
Gauntlet (fighter)	see Gloster Gauntlet II
Gay-Lussac, Joseph (balloonist)	A 1 (a)
Gazelle (helicopter)	see Sud Aviation SA 341
Gee Bee R-2	C 1 (b)
Gee Bee Super Sportster R-1	C 1 (b)
Gelberhund (early)	see Euler
General Aircraft G.A.L49 Hamilcar	F 2 (c)
General Aircraft Monospar ST-25 Jubilee	C 1 (a)
General Atomics RQ-1 Predator	F 4
General Dynamics BGM-109 Tomahawk	F 4
General Dynamics F-111	F 3 (a)
Gentleman (light airplane)	see Comte AC-4
Gerfalcon	see Saab Gerfalcon
Gerle 13 Scout	F 1
German Navy airships	see L-9. L-13, L-31
Giffard, Henri	A 1 (a), A 2 (a)
Gipsy Moth (light airplane)	see de Havilland DH.60G
Gladiator (fighter)	see Gloster Gladiator I
Glen	see Yokosuka E14Y Glen
Glider No. I (Wright Brothers)	A 4 (a)
Glider No. II (Wright Brothers)	A 4 (a)
Glider No. III (Wright Brothers)	A 4 (a)
Glider No. IV (Wright Brothers)	A 4 (a)
Globemaster II (transport)	see Douglas C-142C
Globemaster III (transport)	see Boeing (McDonnell Douglas) C-17
Gloster VI (seaplane)	D (b)
Gloster G.41 Javelin F.A.W.7	F 3 (a)
Gloster Gamecock	F 2 (a)
Gloster Gauntlet II	F 2 (a)
Gloster Gladiator I	F 2 (a)
Gloster Sea Gladiator	F 3 (a)
Gloster G.41 Meteor Mk I	F 3 (a)
Gloster G.41 Meteor Mk III	F 3 (a)
Gloster Whittle E28/39	G
Gnat (jet fighter)	see Hindustan Aircraft Ajeet
Gnat (jet trainer)	see Folland Fo.141 Gnat T1
Godard, Eugene (balloonist)	A 1 (a)
Goeland (airliner)	see Caudron C-445
Golden Flyer (early)	see Curtiss Golden Flyer
Goliath (airliner)	see Farman F.60
Goodyear airships	A 2 (a)
Goose (amphibian)	see Grumman G-21
Goose (flying boat)	see Grumman Mackinnon G-21 C
Gordon (bomber)	see Fairey Gordon
Goshawk	see Curtiss 67 Goshawk
Gotha G.V	F 1
Goupy 1	see Ambroise's Goupy 1
Gourdou-Leseurre GL832	D (d)
Government Aircraft Factory (GAF) N22B Nomad	C 2 (a)
Government Aircraft Factory (GAF) N24A Nomad	C 2 (a)
Grade monoplane	B
Graf Zeppelin (airship LZ-127)	A 2 (b)
Graf Zeppelin II (airship LZ-130)	A 2 (b)
Granville Brothers'	see Gee Bee
Green, Charles (balloonist)	A 1 (a)
Grigorovich M-5 (flying boat)	D (c)
Gripen	see Saab JAS39 Gripen
Grizodubov No. 2 biplane	B
Gronland Wal (Dornier Do-J Wal)	D (b)
Gross Basenach II (airship)	A 2 (a)
Grumman A6 Intruder	F 3 (b)
Grumman E-2C Hawkeye	see Northrop Grumman
Grumman F4F Wildcat	F 2 (a)
Grumman F6F Hellcat	F 2 (a)
Grumman FF-1	F 2 (a)
Grumman F3F	F 2 (a)
Grumman F7F-3N Tigercat	F 2 (a)
Grumman F8F-2 Bearcat	F 2 (a)
Grumman F9F Cougar	F 3 (a)
Grumman F-14 Tomcat	F 3 (a)
Grumman F-14A Tomcat	F 3 (a)
Grumman FM-2 Wildcat	F 2 (a)

Grumman G-21 Goose (amphibian)	D (a)
Grumman Mackinnon G-21C	D (a)
Goose (flying boat)	D (a)
Grumman Mackinnon G-21E Turbo Goose	D (a)
Grumann G-44 Widgeon	D (a)
Grumman G-1159 Gulfstream III	C 2 (c)
Grumman SA-16 Albatross (flying boat)	D (a)
Grumman TBF Avenger	F 2 (b)
Grumman X-29	G
Guba (flying boat)	see Consolidated PBY-5 Catalina
Gulfstream III	see Grumman Gulfstream III
Gulfstream Aerospace Gulfstream III The American Dream	C 2 (c)
Gulfstream American AA-1 Yankee	C 2 (e)
Gulfstream American AA-1 Tiger	C 2 (e)
Gull Six (long distance)	see Percival P.3
Guyot (balloonist)	A 1 (a)

H

HA-B-501 (airship)	A 2 (a)
Haarlem Spin (Fokker)	B
Hadley triplane	B
Hadrian (glider)	F 2 (c)
Haefeli DH-3	C 1 (c)
HAL HT-2	F 2 (c)
HAL HF-24 Marut	F 3 (a)
HAL LCA	F 3 (a)
HAL Dhruv	E (c)
HAL (Hindustan Aircraft) Ajeet	F 3 (a)
HAL (Hindustan Aircraft) Chetak	E (b)
HAL (Hindustan Aircraft) Pushpak	C 2 (e)
HAL/Dornier 228	C 2 (c)
Halifax (bomber)	see Handley Page H.P.61. Halifax
Hamilcar (glider)	see General Aircraft G . A . L.49
Hamilton (airliner)	see Handley Page H. P.26 W.8e
Hampden (bomber)	see Handley Page Hampden
Handley Page 0/400	F 1
Handley Page Hampden	F 2 (b)
Handley Page H.P.18 W8b	C 1 (a)
Handley Page H.P.24 Hyderabad	F 2 (b)
Handley Page H.P.25 Hendon	C 1 (c)
Handley Page H.P.26 W.8e	
Hamilton O-BAHO Princess Marie Jose	C 1 (b)
Handley Page H.P.42	C 1 (a)
Handley Page H.P.45	C 1 (a)
Handley Page H.P.50 Heyford	F 2 (b)
Handley Page H.P.61 Halifax A.IX	F 2 (c)
Handley Page H. P.67 Hastings	F 2 (c)
Handley Page H.P.80 Victor K2	F 3 (c)
Handley Page H.P.115	G
Handley Page H.P.R.5 Marathon	C 2 (a)
Handley Page H.P.R.7 Herald	C 2 (a)
Handley Page H.P.R.7 Herald Series 200	C 2 (a)
Hanlein, Paul (airships)	A 2 (a)
Hanriot HD-1	F 1
Hanriot XIV	F 2 (c)
Hansa (airship LZ-13)	A 2 (b)
Hansa Brandenburg C-I	F 1
Hansa Brandenburg D-I	F 1
Harbin (HAMC) Y-11	C 2 (d)
Hargrave, Lawrence (inventor)	A 3 (b)
Harpoon	see Lockheed PV-Z Harpoon
Harrier (jet fighter)	see Hawker Siddeley Harrier
Hart (bomber)	see Hawker Hart
Hartbees (bomber)	see Hawker Hartbees
Harvard (trainer)	see North American AT-6
Hastings (transport)	see Handley Page H.P.67
Have Blue	see Lockheed Have Blue
Hawk (jet trainer)	see British Aerospace Hawk T.1
Hawk 75 (fighter)	see Curtiss Hawk 75
Hawkeye	see Grumman E-2 Hawkeye
Hawk Speed Six	see Miles Hawk Speed Six
Hawk 200 (fighter)	F 3 (a)
Hawker 800	see Raytheon Hawker 800
Hawker Demon	F 2 (a)
Hawker Fury	F 2 (a)
Hawker Hart	F 2 (b)
Hawker Hartbees	F 2 (b)
Hawker Horsley	F 2 (b)
Hawker Hunter	F 3 (a)
Hawker Hunter F.6	F 3 (a)
Hawker Hunter FGA.76	F 3 (a)
Hawker Hurricane Mk I	F 2 (a)
Hawker Hurricane Mk II	F 2 (a)
Hawker Hurricane Mk IIC	F 2 (a)
Hawker Nimrod	F 2 (b)
Hawker Osprey	F 2 (b)
Hawker Sea Fury	F 2 (a)
Hawker Woodcock	F 2 (a)
Hawker 1000	C 2 (c)
Hawker Siddeley Andover CC.2	F 2 (c)
Hawker Siddeley Buccaneer S2B	F 3 (a)
Hawker Siddeley Comet 4	C 2 (b)

Hawker Siddeley Dove (airliner)	see de Havilland DH.104
Hawker Siddeley H.S.125	C 2 (b)
Hawker Siddeley H.S.748	C 2 (a)
Hawker Siddeley H.S.801 Nimrod M.R.1	F 3 (c)
Hawker Siddeley H.S.801 Nimrod M.R.2	F 3 (c)
Hawker Siddeley H.S.801 Nimrod M.R.2P	F 3 (c)
Hawker Siddeley H.S.801 Nimrod Mk RIP	F 3 (c)
Hawker Siddeley (Folland) Gnat	F 3 (a)
Hawker Siddeley Harrier	F 3 (a)
Hawker Siddeley Harrier GR.1A	F 3 (a)
Hawker Siddeley Harrier GR.3	F 3 (a)
Hawker Siddeley Harrier II GR7	F 3 (a)
Hawker Siddeley Sea Harrier	F 3 (a)
Hawker Siddeley Trident	C 2 (b)
Hawker Tempest	F 2 (a)
Hawker Typhoon IB	F 2 (a)
Heinkel He 70 Blitz	C 1 (a)
Heinkel He 111C	C 1 (a)
Heinkel He 111H	F 2 (b)
Heinkel He 112	F 2 (a)
Heinkel He 116A	C 1 (a)
Heinkel He-178	G
Helios	see AeroVironment Helios
Hellcat (fighter)	see Grumman F6F
Helldiver (bomber)	see Curtiss SB2C
Hendon (bomber)	see Fairey Hendon
Hendon (mail)	see Handley Page H.P.25
Henry Farman III (early)	see Farman H. F.III
Henschel Hs 129B	F 2 (a)
Henson, William Samuel (inventor)	A 3 (b)
Hercules (airliner)	see de Havilland DH.66
Hercules (flying boat)	see Hughes H-4
Hercules (transport)	see Lockheed C-130
Heron (airliner)	see de Havilland DH.114
Heston Phoenix	C 1 (a)
Heyford	see Handley Page Heyford
HFB 320 Hansa	C 2 (c)
Hien (fighter)	see Kawasaki Ki 61
Hiller 12C "Skeeter"	E (b)
Hiller 12E	E (b)
Hindenburg (airship LZ-129)	A 2 (b)
Hirtenburg HV 15	C 1 (a)
Hirth Acrostar	C 2 (e)
Hiryu (bomber)	see Mitsubishi Ki-67
Hispano HA200B .	see Al Kahira
Holste MH 1521 Broussard	C 2 (d)
Horizon Gardan	see Boeing (McDD) F/A18 Hornet
Horizon Hornet	see Hornet
Hornet Moth (light airplane)	see de Havilland DH.87B
Horsa (glider)	see Airspeed A.S.51 Horsa
Horsley	see Hawker Horsley
Horvath monoplane	B
Hotol space plane	G
Hudson (bomber)	see Lockheed 414
Huey Cobra	see Bell AH-1 Huey Cobra
Hughes H-1	C 1 (b)
Hughes H-4 Hercules (flying boat)	G
Hughes 369 Viking	E (b)
Hughes 500	E (b)
Hughes 500D	E (b)
Humber Sommer biplane	B
Hunter (jet fighter)	see Hawker Hunter
Hunting Pembroke	F 2 (c)
Hunting Percival Jet Provost	F 3 (c)
Hurricane (fighter)	see Hawker Hurricane
Husky (light airplane)	see Auster D.5/160
Hustler (jet bomber)	see Convair B-58A
Hyderabad	see Handley Page HP24 Hyderabad
Hydravion (Fabre)	B
Hypersonic airliner	G
Hythe (flying boat)	see Short Hythe

I

I.A.R. 35	C 2 (e)
I.A.R.80	F 1 (a)
I.A.R.316	E (b)
I.A.R. 817	C 2 (d)
I.A.R.818H (seaplane)	D
I.C.A.R. Comercial	C 1 (a)
Ilya Murometz (bomber)	see Sikorsky Ilya Murometz
Ilyushin Il-2M3 Stormovik	F 2 (b)
Ilyushin Il-4 DB-3	F 2 (b)
Ilyushin Il-12	C 2 (a)
Ilyushin Il-14M	C 2 (a)
Ilyushin Il-14P	C 2 (a)
Ilyushin Il-18	C 2 (a)
Ilyushin Il-18 (with piston engines)	G
Ilyushin Il-28	F 3 (b)
Ilyushin Il-62	C 2 (b)
Ilyushin Il-62M	C 2 (b)
Ilyushin Il-72	C 2 (a)
Ilyushin Il-76	C 2 (b), F 3 (b)
Ilyushin Il-78	F 3 (c)
Ilyushin Il-86	C 2 (b)
Ilyushin Il-96	C 2 (b)

Name	Classification
SEPECAT Jaguar	F 3 (a)
'Seven Seas' (airliner)	see Douglas DC-7C
Severo, Auguste (airship *Pax*)	A 2 (a)
Seversky P-35A	F 2 (a)
Shackleton (reconnaissance)	see Avro Shackleton
Shenyang/Tianjin F-6	F 3 (a)
Shenyang F-8	F 3 (a)
Shenandoah (airship)	A 2 (a)
ShinMaywa SS-2	D (d)
Shooting Star (jet fighter)	see Lockheed F-80
Short S.5 Singapore I (flying boat)	D (b)
Short S.5 Singapore III (flying boat)	D (d)
Short S.8 Calcutta (flying boat)	D (a)
Short S.16 Scion II	C 1 (a)
Short S.17 Kent (flying boat)	D (a)
Short S.20 *Mercury* (Short-Mayo composite) .	G
Short S.21 *Maia* (Short-Mayo composite)	G
Short S.23 Empire "C" Class (flying boat)	D (a)
Short S.25 Hythe (flying boat)	D (a)
Short S.25 Sandringham (flying boat)	D (a)
Short S.25 Sandringham 4 (flying boat)	D (a)
Short S.25 Sandringham 7 (flying boat)	D (a)
Short S.25 Sandringham 7 Bermuda (flying boat)	D (a)
Short S.25 Sunderland (flying boat)	D (d)
Short S.26 "G" Class (flying boat)	D (a)
Short S.30 modified "G" Class (flying boat)	D (a)
Short Type 38	F 1
Short S.45A Solent 2 (flying boat)	D (a)
Short S.45A Solent 3 (flying boat)	D (a)
Short SC.5 Belfast	F 2 (c)
Short Stirling Mk I	F 2 (b)
Short Type 184 (seaplane)	F 1
Short-Mayo composite	see Short S20/21
"Shorthorn" (early)	see Farman M.F.11
Shorts S.7 Skyvan	C 2 (a)
Shorts 330	C 2 (a)
Shorts 360	C 2 (a)
Shvarov Sh-2 (flying boat)	D (a)
SIAI-Marchetti SF 260	F 3 (c)
Sikorsky *Bolshoi Baltiskii*	B
Sikorsky *Ilya Murometz*	F 1
Sikorsky *Russia A*	B
Sikorsky *Russky Vityaz*	B
Sikorsky MH-53 Pave Low	E (c)
Sikorsky S-37	C 1 (a)
Sikorsky S-38 (flying boat)	D (a)
Sikorsky S-38A (flying boat)	D (a)
Sikorsky S-40 (flying boat)	D (a)
Sikorsky S-42 (flying boat)	D (a)
Sikorsky S-42A (flying boat)	D (a)
Sikorsky S-42B (flying boat)	D (a)
Sikorsky S-43 (amphibian)	D (a)
Sikorsky VS-44A (flying boat)	D (a)
Sikorsky S-51	E (b)
Sikorsky S-55	E (b)
Sikorsky S-58	E (b)
Sikorsky S-61B Sea King	E (c)
Sikorsky S-61B SH-3 Sea King	E (c)
Sikorsky S-61N	E (b)
Sikorsky S-65 CH-53 Sea Stallion	E (c)
Sikorsky S-70 (UH-60) Black Hawk	E (c)
Sikorsky S-76 Spirit	E (b)
Sikorsky VS-300A	E (a)
Sikorsky VS-316A	E (a)
Sikumbang (trainer)	see Nurtiano Nu-2 Sikumbang
Silver Dart (McCurdy biplane)	B
Silver Queen II (Vickers Vimy)	C 1 (b)
Simmonds Spartan (seaplane)	D (b)
Simoun (light airplane)	see Caudron C-635
Singapore (flying boat)	see Short S.5 Singapore I, Short S.5 Singapore III
Siniger	see DAR-9 Siniger
Sirius (long distance)	see Lockheed 8
Siskin (fighter)	see Armstrong Whitworth Siskin IIIA
Skipper 77 (light airplane)	see Beechcraft Skipper 77
Skyhawk (jet bomber)	see Douglas A-4
Skyhawk (light airplane)	see Cessna 172
Skylane (light airplane)	see Cessna 182
Skymaster (airliner)	see Douglas DC-4
Skymaster (transport)	see Douglas C-54
Skynight (executive/feeder)	see Cessna 310L
Skynight (jet fighter)	see Douglas F3D Skynight
Skyray	see Douglas Skyray
Skyrocket (experimental)	see Douglas Skyrocket
Skyservant (utility)	see Dornier Do-28D
Skytrain (transport)	see Douglas C-47
Skyvan (airliner)	see Short S.7
Skywarrior (jet bomber)	see Douglas A-3
SL-11 (airship)	see Schutte Lanz SL-11
SME MDZ-160M (light airplane)	C 2 (e)
Smolik S.19	C 1 (a)
Snipe (fighter)	see Sopwith Snipe
Socata RF-6B Sportsman	C 2 (e)
Socata TB-10 Tobago	C 2 (e)
Sokolov A-90 Orlyonok (ekranoplan)	G
SOKO Galeb 3	F 3 (c)
SOKO G-4 Super Galeb	F 3 (c)
Sokol	see PLZ Sokol
Solent (flying boat)	see Short S.45A
Sopwith Atlantic	C 1 (b)
Sopwith Bat Boat	B
Sopwith Baby	F 1
Sopwith Camel	F 1
Sopwith Dove	F 1
Sopwith Pup	C 1 (c)
Sopwith Snipe	F 1
Sopwith Strutter	F 1
Sopwith Tabloid	F 1
Sopwith 5 F.1 Dolphin	F 1
Southampton (flying boat)	see Supermarine Southampton
Southern Cross (long distance)	see Fokker F.VIIa/3m
SPAD 33	see Bleriot SPAD 33
SPAD VII	F 1
SPAD XIII	F 1
SPAD XVI	F 1
Spartan Arrow (light aircraft)	C 2 (e)
Spartan Executive	C 1 (c)
Spartan (seaplane)	see Simmonds Spartan
Sparviero (bomber)	see Savoia Marchetti S.M.79-11
Spelterini, Eduard (balloonist)	A 1 (a)
Spirit (bomber)	see Northrop Grumman B-2A Spirit
Spirit (helicopter)	see Sikorsky S-76
Spirit of St. Louis (Ryan NYP Special)	C 1 (b)
Spitfire (fighter)	see Supermarine Spitfire
Sportsman	see Socata RF-6B
Stal-2 (light airplane)	see Putilov Stal-2
Stampe SV-4	C 1 (a)
Staggerwing	see Beech Model 17
Standard (biplane)	see Lincoln Standard
Starfighter (jet fighter)	see Lockheed F-104
Starfire	see Lockheed F-94
StarLifter (jet transport)	see Lockheed C-141A
Starliner (airliner)	see Lockheed L.1649A
Stationair (executive/feeder)	see Cessna 206, Cessna 207
Stearman C-3MB	F 2 (c)
Stearman PT-17 Kaydett	F 2 (c)
Stearman 75	F 2 (c)
Steglau No. 2	B
Steiglitz (light airplane)	see DAR-9
Stinson Junior	C 1 (a)
Stinson Pilot Radio (seaplane)	D (b)
Stinson SM-1 Detroiter	C 1 (a)
Stinson-Faucett F.19	C 1 (a)
Stinson SR-5 Reliant	C 1 (a)
Stinson SR-8B Reliant	C 1 (c)
Stinson-Faucett F.19 (seaplane)	C 1 (a)
Stirling (bomber)	see Short Stirling
Stormovik (fighter)	see Ilyushin Il-2M3
Stout Air Pullman	C 1 (a)
Stranraer (flying boat)	see Supermarine Stranraer
Stratocruiser (airliner)	see Boeing 377
Stratofortress (jet bomber)	see Boeing B-52
Stratojet (jet bomber)	see Boeing B-47
Stringfellow, John (inventor)	A 3 (b)
"Stuka" (bomber)	see Junkers Ju 87B
Stuwer, Johann (balloonist)	A 1 (a)
Sud Aviation SA 330 Puma	E (c)
Sud Aviation SA 330E Puma	E (c)
Sud Aviation SA 341 Gazelle	E (b)
Sud Aviation SE 210 Caravelle Series 10	C 2 (b)
Sud Aviation SE210 Caravelle Series 11	C 2 (b)
Sud Aviation SE 210 Super Caravelle Series 12	C 2 (b)
Sud Aviation SE 3130 Alouette II	E (b)
Sud Aviation SE 3160 Alouette III	E (b)
Sud Aviation SO 1221 Djinn	E (b)
Sud Aviation SO 4050 Vatour IIA	F 3 (b)
Sud Est SE 161 Languedoc	C 2 (a)
Sud Est SE 2010 Armagnac	C 2 (a)
Sud Ouest SO.30P Bretagne	C 2 (a)
Sud Ouest SO.90 Cassiopees	C 2 (a)
Sud Ouest SO.95 Corse II	C 2 (a)
Sukhoi Su-24 Fencer	F 3 (a)
Sukhoi Su-25 Frogfoot	F 3 (a)
Sukhoi Su-25 Scorpio	F 3 (b)
Sukhoi Su-27 Flanker	F 3 (c)
Sukhoi Su-27 UB	F 3 (a)
Sukhoi Su-30 Flanker	F 3 (a)
Sukhoi Su-35 Flanker E	F 3 (a)
Sunderland (flying boat)	see Short S.25
Super Caravelle (jet airliner)	see Sud Aviation SE 210
Super Cloudmaster (airliner)	see Douglas DC-6B
Super Constellation (airliner)	see Lockheed L.1049, Lockheed L.1049G
Super Cub (light airplane)	see Piper PA-18
Super DC-3 (airliner)	see Douglas Super DC-3
Super Electra (airliner)	see Lockheed 14 Super Electra
Super Emeraude (light airplane)	see Scintex CP 1310
Super Galeb	see SOKO G-4 Super Galeb
Super King Air (executive/feeder)	see Beech 200 Super King Air
Super Mystere (jet fighter)	see Dassault Super Mystere SMB-11
Super Puma (helicopter)	see Eurocopter AS-332M Super Puma
Super Sabre (jet fighter)	see North American F-100
Super Skymaster (executive/feeder)	see Cessna 337
Super Skywagon (executive/feeder)	see Cessna 205
Super Sportster (racer)	see Gee Bee Super Sportster R1
Super Starfighter (jet fighter)	see Lockheed F-104G
Super Trimotor (airliner)	see Fokker F.10A
Super Tucano	see EMBRAER EMB 314
Super Universal (airliner)	see Fokker Super Universal
Superfortress (bomber)	see Boeing B-29
Supermarine Attacker	F 3 (a)
Supermarine Channel MkII	D (b)
Supermarine S6B (seaplane)	D (d)
Supermarine Scapa (flying boat)	D (d)
Supermarine Sea Eagle (amphibian)	D (a)
Supermarine Seafire Mk III	F 2 (a)
Supermarine Southampton I (flying boat)	D (d)
Supermarine Southampton II (flying boat)	D (d)
Supermarine Spitfire	F 2 (a)
Supermarine Swift	F 3 (a)
Supermarine Stranraer	D (d)
Supermarine Walrus Mk I (amphibian)	D (d)
Supermarine Walrus II (flying boat)	see Vickers Supermarine
Swallow (biplane)	see Laird Swallow
Swallow (light airplane)	see British Aircraft Swallow
Swearingen Merlin IIIA	C 2 (e)
Swordfish (torpedo bomber)	see Fairey Swordfish
Sycamore	see Bristol Type 171 Sycamore

T

Name	Classification
Talon (jet trainer)	see Northrop T-38A
Tanski, Czeslaw (aviator)	A 3 (a)
Taube (early)	see Etrich/Rumpler Taube
Taylorcraft Auster AOP.5	F 2 (c)
Teledyne Ryan Firebee	F 4
Teledyne Ryan Tier II Plus	F 4
Tempest (fighter)	see Hawker Tempest
Tempete (light airplane)	see MJ-2 Tempete
Testu-Brissy, Pierre (balloonist)	A 1 (a)
Texan (trainer)	see North American T-6
The Dolphin (Pauley and Egg's balloon)	A 1 (a)
The Globe (Charles' balloon)	A 1 (a)
The Tiny Fly	A 3 (b)
Teodore, Adolfo (balloonist)	A 1 (a)
Thrush Commander (utility)	see Rockwell Thrush Commander
Thulin Type D	F 1
Thunderbolt (fighter)	see Republic P-47
Thunderchief (jet fighter)	see Republic F-105D
Thunderjet (jet fighter)	see Republic F-84G
Tiger	see Gulfstream American Tiger
Tiger II (jet fighter)	see Northrop F-5, Northrop F-5E
Tiger Moth (light airplane)	see de Havilland DH.82
"Tin Goose" (airliner)	see Ford "Tin Goose"
Tips' biplane	B
Tissandier Brothers (airship)	A 2 (a)
Tissandier, Gaston (balloonist)	A 1 (a)
Tobago (light airplane)	see Socata TB-10
Tomahawk (fighter)	see Curtiss P-40B
Tomahawk (light airplane)	see Piper PA-38-112
Tomcat (jet fighter)	see Grumman F-14
Tornado (jet fighter)	see Panavia Tornado
1oth's, monoplane	B
Tournachon, Felix (Nadar) (balloonist)	A 1 (a)
Transall C-160	F 2 (c)
Transporter (airliner)	see de Havilland DHC-5
Transporter Allianz C-160	see Transall C-160
Travel Air 4000	C 1 (c)
Tremml's *Eagle*	G
Trener (light airplane)	see Zlin Z-226, Zlin Z-526
Trident (jet airliner)	see Hawker Siddeley Trident
Triplane	see Avro Triplane
Trislander (executive/feeder)	see Britten Norman Trislander
TriStar (jet airliner)	see Lockheed L-1011
Trojan	see North American F-28 Trojan
Trooper (helicopter)	see Bell 47G
Troopship (transport)	see Fokker F.27A
TsAGI 1-EA (helicopter)	E (a)
Tucano (trainer)	see Embraer EMB-312
Tudor (airliner)	see Avro Type 688
Tupolev ANT-2	C 1 (a)
Tupolev ANT-3	C 1 (b)
Tupolev ANT-3 R-3	C 1 (b)
Tupolev ANT-4	F 2 (b)
Tupolev ANT-4 TB-1	F 2 (b)
Tupolev ANT-6	F 2 (b)
Tupolev ANT-6 TB-3	F 2 (b)
Tupolev ANT-9	C 1 (a)

Sectional Index

Entries are arranged under the following headings:

A. FORERUNNERS
1. Balloons
   (a) Identified balloonists
   (b) Other named or dated balloons
   (c) Other unidentified balloons
2. Airships
   (a) Identified airships
   (b) Zeppelin airships
   (c) Unidentified airships
3. Pre-flight machines
   (a) Gliders to 1914
   (b) Powered machines
4. The Wright Brothers
   (a) Gliders
   (b) Powered machines

B. POST-WRIGHT AIRCRAFT TO 1914

C. CIVIL AIRCRAFT
1. 1919 to 1939
   (a) Passenger aircraft
   (b) Long distance, exploration and racers
   (c) Light aircraft and mailplanes
2. 1940 to date
   (a) Civil airliners - propeller driven
   (b) Civil airliners - jet powered
   (c) Executive and feeder aircraft
   (d) Utility and general purpose aircraft
   (e) Light aircraft

D. FLYING BOATS AND SEAPLANES SINCE 1919
   (a) Civil - passenger carrying
   (b) Long distance and racers
   (c) Utility and mail planes
   (d) Military

E. HELICOPTERS
   (a) All types to 1939
   (b) General purpose helicopters
   (c) Military helicopters

F. MILITARY AIRCRAFT
1. 1914 to 1918 - all types (including post-war civil conversions not listed elsewhere)
2. 1919 to date - propeller driven
   (a) Fighters
   (b) Bombers
   (c) Miscellaneous - transport, reconnaissance and trainers, etc.
3. Jet-powered
   (a) Fighters
   (b) Bombers
   (c) Trainers, reconnaissance and transports
   (d) Unmanned aerial vehicles (UAVs)

G. EXPERIMENTAL AND NON-PRODUCTION AIRCRAFT

H. GLIDERS SINCE 1914
   (a) Gliders
   (b) Hang-gliders
   (c) Microlights and powered gliders
   (d) Paragliding

I. MODEL AIRCRAFT
   (a) Model airplanes
   (b) Model gliders

J. AIRPORTS

K. AIRCRAFT OVERPRINTS

A. FORERUNNERS

1. BALLOONS

(a) Identified Balloonists
ADORNE: *Aerostat* - ascent at Strasbourg, March 1794
Cook Islands 940 **MS**945
ANDREE, Salomon: *Ornen* - Polar flight, 11 July 1879
Guinea-Bissau 731
Kampuchea 450
Liechtenstein 266
Mongolia 1497
Sweden 748
Upper Volta 657
BALDWIN BROTHERS: ascent at Hong Kong, 3 January 1891
Hong Kong 453
BLANCHARD. Jean Pierre: Attempt at propulsion, 2 March 1784
France 4233
Gambia **MS**1533
Rwanda 1196
Vietnam 1960
Ascent at Chelsea, 16 October 1784
Chad 667
First Channel crossing with Jeffries, 7 January 1785
Anguilla 566

Barbuda 665
Central African Republic 964
Comoro Islands 507
Cook Islands **MS**944
Czechoslovakia 2360
Grenada 1631 1751 2637 2640 **MS**2643
Kampuchea 449
Korea (North Korea) N2260
Laos 647
Libya 1388
Mongolia 1495
Poland 2722
Rwanda 1198
Uganda 1064
Upper Volta 655
Vanuatu 368
Vietnam 548
Yemen People's Democratic Republic **MS**312
Ascent at Berlin, September 1788
Chad 653
Ascent with Mme. Madeleine Blanchard (date not determined)
Rwanda 1197
First balloon flight in the U.S.A., 9 January 1793
Antigua 1851 **MS**1855
Dominica **MS**1729
Grenadines of Grenada 1727 **MS**1733
Maldive Islands **MS**1918
St. Vincent 2300 2304/5
Sierra Leone 1058
Tanzania 1787 1789 **MS**1790b
BLINO, Jose Domingo: first Cuban balloonist, 1831
Cuba 1752 **MS**2888
BOSEMAN, Jan - PH-BOX
Haiti 1104/5
BRADLEY, Eduardo: trans-Andean flight in *Eduardo Newbery*, 1916
Argentine 1478 2257
BRANSON, Richard: *Virgin Otsuka Pacific Flyer*, 1991
Uganda 1063 1066
CHARLES, Jacques: *The Globe*, 27 August 1783
Turks and Caicos Islands 754
Upper Volta 654
First manned hydrogen balloon flight, 1 December 1783
Andorra F329
Azerbaijan 249
Central African Republic **MS**969
Chad 652
Cuba 2882
Czechoslovakia 1718
Ecuador 1911
France 2577
French Southern & Antarctic Territories 190
Guinea-Bissau 728
Ivory Coast 761
Kampuchea 448
Korea (North Korea) N2258
Laos 646
Latvia 228
Mauritania 753
Niger 927
Rwanda 1196
Surinam 1151
Togo 392/3
Vanuatu 367
Vietnam 545 1959
Yemen People's Democratic Republic **MS**312
Zaire 1202
COLDING, Johan: Balloon Post, 1808
Denmark 594
CROSBIE, Richard: first ascent by an Irishman, 1785
Ireland 608
DE ANCHORENA, Aaron: *Pampero* - first flight across R. Plate, 25 April 1907
Argentine 1237
DE GUSMAO, Bartolomeu: *Aerostat*
Brazil 703
Portugal 1937
La Passarola
Belize 737
DE LANA-TERZI, Francesco: "Flying Ship"
Belize 736
Mali 141
Zaire 927 1214
DE MORVEAU, Guyton: 25 April 1784
Belize 738
Korea (North Korea) N2246
DEGEN, Jacob: balloon assisted "Ornithopter", 1809
Surinam 1339
Drop of Hope
Senegal 1442
DUNKER: Utopic Balloon Post
Korea (North Korea) N2253
GALLIFET
Haiti 1106/11
GARNERIN, Andre Jacques. first parachute descent from balloon, 22 October 1797
Chad 666

GAY-LUSSAC, Joseph: high altitude flight, 1804
Central African Republic 965
GIFFARD, Henri: *Le Grand Ballon Captif*, Paris 1878
Bhutan **MS**510
Djibouti 871
Korea (North Korea) N2261
Uganda 1069
GODARD, Eugene: Quintuple "acrobatic" balloon, 1850
Cook Islands 943 **MS**945
Cuba 2885
Poland 2723
Yemen People's Democratic Republic **MS**312
L'Aigle, 1864
Vietnam 547
GREEN, Charles: *Royal Vauxhall*, 7/8 November 1836
Belize **MS**742
Chad 654
Cuba 2887
Guinea-Bissau 729
Mongolia 1496
Seychelles 563
GUYOT: Balloon with sails, 1785
Gambia 1527
JONES, Brian, Breitling Orbiter 3
Guyana 5648
KRYAKUTNI: flight over Moscow, 1731
Russia 2034
LENNOX, Comte de: *Eagle*, 17 August 1834
Korea (North Korea) N2249
LOWE, Thaddeus: *Intrepid*, 1862
United States of America 2017
Washington, 1862
Grenada 1812
LUNARDI, Vicenza: London, 15 September 1784
Comoro Islands 506
Laos 648
Wallis and Futuna Islands 421
London, 13 May 1785
Barbuda 663
Palau 340
Yemen People's Democratic Republic **MS**312
MASSE: oar-powered balloon, 1784
Korea (North Korea) **MS**N2252
MENNER: Budapest, 1811
Hungary 3483
MEUSNIER, Jean-Baptiste: Dirigible balloon design, 1784
Azerbaijan 251
Cuba 3632
Libya 1387
MONTGOLFIER, Joseph and Etienne, unmanned flight, 4 June 1783
Central African Republic 963
Cuba 2886
French Southern & Antarctic Territories 190
Ghana 3536
Libya 1390
Niger 348 355
Rwanda 1194
St. Vincent 4268
Upper Volta 652
Vietnam 1958
Yemen People's Democratic Republic 311
Le Martial - flight with animals, 19 September 1783
Chad 664
Korea (North Korea) N2255
Rwanda 1194
Surinam 1149
Turks and Caicos Islands 756
Tethered flight at Chateau de Reveillon, 15 October 1783
Anguilla 565
Brazil 2058
Central African Republic **MS**934
Chad 665
Comoro Islands 505
Djibouti 870
Guinea-Bissau 727
Korea (North Korea) N2254
Mongolia 1494
Upper Volta 653
Vietnam **MS**551
First manned free flight, 21 November 1783
Andorra F329
Barbuda 664
Belize **MS**742
Brazil **MS**2033
Bulgaria 1876
Chad **MS**656
Congo (Brazzaville) 913
Cook Islands 939 **MS**945
Cuba 2883
Ecuador 1910 **MS**1912
Fiji 659
France 546 2576
French Southern & Antarctic Territories 191 302

Gabon 488 858/9
Gambia 522
Germany (West Berlin) B547
Grenadines of Grenada 566
Grenadines of St. Vincent 250
Guinea 1082
Hungary 1822 3142
India 1105
Ivory Coast 760
Kampuchea 446
Korea (North Korea) N2256 N2758
Lesotho 545
Liechtenstein 260 817
Malagasy Republic **MS**487
Maldive Islands 272 276 3175
Mali 182 202 323 953
Mauritania 364 752 768 **MS**772
Monaco 1613
Mongolia 1099
Montserrat 586
Nevis 122
Nicaragua 2173 3913 3919
Niger 926
Niue 496 **MS**502
Portugal 1938
Rwanda 1195
St. Kitts 129
San Marino 1214
Sierra Leone 755
Solomon Islands 493
Somalia 613
Surinam 1150
Swaziland 431
Tonga 836/7 1058 O219
Turks and Caicos Islands **MS**758
Tuvalu 225
Uganda 1067
Upper Volta 493
Vanuatu 366
Vietnam 544
Zaire 1201
Le Flesselles, 19 January 1784
Chad **MS**670
Congo (Brazzaville) 914
Le Gustave, 4 June 1784
Cuba 2884
Zaire 1203
Marie Antoinette, 23 June 1784
Guinea 1083
NADAR (Felix Tournachon): *Le Geant*, 4 October 1863
Bulgaria 3626
Guinea **MS**1088
Maldive Islands **MS**996
Uganda 1065
Vietnam 549
PARIS BALLOON POST: *Armand Barbes*, 7 October 1870
France 1245
Ivory Coast 762
Surinam 1152
Tunisia 392
L'Armee de la Loire, 31 December 1870
Jersey 89
Le Neptune, 23 September 1870
Cook Islands 641 695
Uganda 1068
Ville d'Orleans, 24 November 1870
Central African Republic 932
Congo (Brazzaville) **MS**917 **MS**984
France 1907
Nicaragua **MS**2367
Other unidentified balloons, 1870
Central African Empire 560 622
Comoro Islands **MS**509 **MS**554
Guyana 2726
Ivory Coast 762
Laos 1188
Monaco 565 567 575 D490
Tonga **MS**1063
Turks and Caicos Islands 561
PAULEY and EGG: *The Dolphin*, 1818
Korea (North Korea) N2244
PEREZ, Matias
Cuba 1232/3
PICCARD, Auguste: stratosphere balloon *F.N.R.S.*, 27 May 1931
Belgium 621/3
Central African Republic 1032 1060
Congo (Brazzaville) 915
Guinea 1127
Kampuchea 451
Laos 651
Mali 664
Monaco 1658
Mongolia 1499
Rwanda 1199
San Marino 1210
Upper Volta **MS**658
Vietnam 1964
Wallis and Futuna Islands 516
Zaire 1205
PICCARD, Bertrand, Breitling Orbiter 3
Guyana 5645 5646 5647 **MS**5649
PILATRE DE ROZIER, Jean-Francois and ROMAIN, Jules: first balloon fatality, 15 June 1785
Libya 1389
Poland 2721

over English Channel, 1785
Vietnam 1961
REICHART, Wilhelmine: Munich, October 1820 Germany (Federal Republic) 1856
ROBERT BROTHERS and COLIN HULLIN: 19 September 1784
Central African Republic 930
Uganda **MS**1190
ROBERTSON, Etienne
Liechtenstein 263
SANTOS-DUMONT *Brasil*, 1897
Brasil 2957
SPELTERINI, Eduard: first flight across the Alps, 1898
Switzerland 924
STUWER, Johann: Vienna, 6 July 1784
Austria 924
TEODORE, Adolfo: first ascent in Cuba, 1830
Cuba 1753
TESTU-BRISSY Pierre: ascent on horseback, 1798
Cook Islands 942 **MS**945
Korea (North Korea) N2257
Upper Volta 656
Yemen People's Democratic Republic 310
TISSANDIER, Gaston: *Zenith* 15 April 1875
Guinea-Bissau 730
Korea (North Korea) N2259
VERNE, Jules: *Around the World in 80 Days*
Congo (Brazzaville) 453
Grenada 996
Nicaragua 2170
Five Weeks in a Balloon
Congo (Brazzaville) 452
France 2549
Grenadines of Grenada 330
Guinea 1003
Monaco 529
Nicaragua 2168
L'Ile Mysterieuse
Monaco 1331
VERT, Camille: *Poisson Volant*, 1859
Korea (North Korea) N2250
WISE, John: *Atlantic*: 1/2 July 1859
Central African Republic 931
Mauritania 769
Yemen People's Democratic Republic **MS**312
Jupiter, 17 August 1859
United States of America A1132

(b) Other named or dated balloons
1784 First balloon over Warsaw
Poland 2955
1784 First balloon ascent in Mauritius
Mauritius 660
1785 *Comte d'Artois*
Gambia 1531
1789 Contemporary "sail steered" balloon print
Cook Islands 941 **MS**945
Mongolia 819
1794 *L'Entreprenant* - Battle of Fleurus
Upper Volta 656
1862 First balloon ascent in Mexico
Mexico 1010
1890 Massed balloon ascent
Laos 650
1892 Pioneer balloon flight over Plovdiv
Bulgaria 2605
1896 Observation balloon at Budapest Exhibition
Hungary 3484
1898 Parseval Sigsfeld kite-type observation balloon
Romania 5498
Vietnam 546
1904 Balloon and car pursuit race
Hungary 3485
1906 First Gordon Bennett Race
Mongolia 1498
1914 Caquot observation balloon
Central African Republic 968
Italy 1235
Romania 5499
1927 *Pannonia*
Hungary 3486
1933 *Kosciusko* SP-ADS
Poland 2724
1933 Stratosphere balloons U.S.S.R.-1, *USSR-VR-62*
Mongolia 1500
Russia 634/6 5346
1934 Stratosphere balloon *Osoaviakhim*
Russia 659/61 1042/4
1935 Stratosphere balloon *Explorer II*
Guinea-Bissau 732
United States of America 2020
1935 *Polonia II* SP-AMY
Poland 2725
1936 *L.O.P.P.* SP-BCU
Poland **MS**2727
1937 Demuyter's *Belgica*
Rwanda 1199
1978 *Double Eagle II*

SECTIONAL INDEX

Sierra Leone 3036
SUD EST SE 161 Languedoc, 1939
France 2965
French Morocco 283/8 289 311 338/40 345/6 349/50 465/7
New Caledonia 325/7
Tunisia 323/5
Turkey 1422
Uruguay 941/4
Wallis and Futuna Islands 157/8
SE 2010 Armagnac, 1949
Laos 155
SUD OUEST SO.30P Bretagne, 1945
Cambodia 41 43 45 47/8
France 968 970
Guadeloupe 230
Reunion 327 329
SO.90 Cassiopees, 1943
Monaco 320/1 323/6c
SO.95 Corse II, 1947
Cameroun 262a 297a
France 969
French Guiana 243
Monaco 333/4 340/1
Reunion 328
Togo 181
TUPOLEV Tu-114 Rossiya, 1957
Bulgaria 1577
Russia 2226 2245
VICKERS 952 Cargoliner, 1961
Grenada 1399
953 Vanguard, 1959
Czechoslovakia 1692
Gibraltar 465 1176
Jersey 676
Malta 731
953 Merchantman, 1961
Marshall Islands 1543
Viking 1A, 1945
Trinidad and Tobago 783
Viking 1B, 1947
Cayman Islands 479
Gibraltar 461
Iraq 330/7
Rhodesia 574
Turkey 1400 1403 1456
Viscount 630, 1948
Palau MS1986a
Viscount 700, 1948
Barbados 1236
Egypt 545
Iceland 366
Jersey 26 54 1078
Jordan 432/9
Kuwait 153 160
Malawi 408
Malta 732
Philippines 1950
Rhodesia 395 454
Rhodesia and Nyasaland 28
San Marino 576
Trinidad and Tobago 784
Turkey 1853 2180
Viscount 800, 1956
Austria 1329
Barbados 728
Germany (West Berlin) B589
Gibraltar 463 1177
Guernsey 88 421
Isle of Man 270
Jersey 412
Mali 554
Rhodesia 450
San Marino 736
Saudi Arabia 428/42 490/2
Singapore 1327 MS1329
Uruguay 1910
Yemen 258 307/8
YAKOVLEV Yak-16, 1948
Bulgaria 935/44

(b) Civil Airliners — jet powered
AIRBUS INDUSTRIE A300, 1972
Antigua 738
Bahamas 802
Brazil 2124 2347
Burkina Faso 785 787
France 1999 2524 3679 3864
Germany (Federal Republic) 1920
Greece 1582
Hungary 3137
India 834 1186
Iran 2373
Jamaica 850
Kampuchea 777
Korea (North Korea) MSN1776
Madagascar 1149
Marshall Islands 1827
Mongolia 1598
Nevis 1206
Nicaragua 2787
Sierra Leone 2385
Thailand 1200 1278
Togo 1819
Ukraine 70
A310, 1982
Austria 2823
Bulgaria 3705
Cambodia 1174

Jamaica 946 947
Kenya 489
Libya 1611
Macao MS1441
Madagascar 1148 1153
Maldive Islands 2160
New Caledonia 1238
Papua New Guinea 699 MS820
Portugal 2808
Romania 5642 6429
Wallis and Futuna Islands 560
A319, 1995
El Salvador 2736
A320, 1987
Austria 2913
Bahrain 453/6
Barbados 1091
Bolivia 1356
Costa Rica 1608
Cuba 4382
Falkland Islands 1101
Finland 1701
Germany (Federal Republic) 2241
Ireland 694
Jamaica 948
Malta 972 1179 MS1180
Mexico 2560
Oman 654
Peru 1929
Romania MS5179
Singapore 1323 MS1329
Slovenia 371
Vietnam 1672 2057
A330, 1992
Cuba 4773
New Caledonia 1302
A340, 1991
Austria 2543
French Polynesia 1096
Germany 3543 3546
Great Britain 2284
Jamaica 949
Kuwait 1810/11
Korea (North Korea) N4441
New Caledonia 997
Portugal 2485
Singapore 1319 MS1329
Vietnam 1673
A380, 2006
Alderney A209
France 4201
Germany 3543 3546
Isle of Man 1972
Tajikistan 277/80
ANTONOV An-74, 2001
Russia 7381
Ukraine 188
AVRO RJ 85
Belgium 3427
BOEING 707, 1954

It is virtually impossible to distinguish between the 707 and 720/720B on stamps. The identifications provided are based on postal authority information or known users. In the absence of such assistance the aircraft have been listed as the 707. This machine came in four basic models: Series 120/220 Domestic and Series 320/420 Intercontinental. A suffix 'B' usually indicated the use of turbofan engines. No distinction has been made between these in the Index although it is possible, with care, to identify some individual Model types. It is likely that the majority are the Intercontinental series.

Ajman 138 147
Algeria 1008
Angola 611 633/42 698 752 1011
Antigua 1274
Argentine 1563 2217
Australia 477/8
Bahamas 258 284 306
Bahrain 205/8
Bangladesh 218 349
Barbados 879
Barbuda 1119
Belgium 1704 1740/2
Benin 688
Bophuthatswana 180
Brazil 1216
Burkina Faso 839
Burundi 325
Caicos Islands 20 55
Cameroun 307
Cape Verde Islands 391
Central African Republic 24
Chad 87
Chile 684
Comoro Islands 162
Congo (Brazzaville) 12 D30
Congo (Kinshasa) 460/3 501/6 507/10 644
Czechoslovakia 1693
Dahomey 163 194/7 P278/81
Dominica 849
Dominican Republic 1331
Ecuador 1230/1

Egypt 742/3 965 1629
Ethiopia 775 777
Fiji 320
French Polynesia 196 1005 1007
Gabon 184 359 412
Gambia 1037
Germany (Federal Republic) 1483
Germany (West Berlin) B225
Ghana 599
Greece 1018
Grenadines of Grenada 663
Guinea 861
Haiti 736/8 740 778 O742/4 O746
India 435
Iran 145B 1600/2
Iraq 1893/5
Ireland 1268
Israel 237 351
Ivory Coast 213
Jordan 1121
Katanga 74 76
Kenya 204 282 310
Korea (South Korea) 876
Kuwait 430/3 578/80
Liberia 1188 1190 1379
Liechtenstein 396
Macao 481/5
Malagasy Republic 44
Maldive Islands 273 278
Mali 470/1
Malta 605 608 682
Manama 12
Mauritania 150
Mauritius 415/16 432/3 527
Micronesia 881
Mongolia MS355a
Montserrat 974
Morocco 589
Mozambique 548
Netherlands Antilles 452
New Caledonia 477
Niger 119/20 121 142/3 311
Nigeria 489
Pakistan 379 624
Panama 700/2 710
Papua New Guinea 182
Paraguay 908 1222/3
Peru 962 987/91 1346
Portuguese Guinea 364
Romania 3927/8 4223 MS4303 4451 4794 4881
St. Lucia 547 O11
St. Pierre et Miquelon 410
St. Thomas and Prince Islands 441
San Marino 733 735 742
Saudi Arabia 462/6
Senegal 249
Sierra Leone 650 MS866 2833
Solomon Islands MS1054
Somalia 376/82
South Africa 220 803 1461
Sri Lanka 678
Surinam 466 556 558/9 843f 843h
Thailand 1755
Togo 325 394/6 445 450 1730
Tonga 845/6
Trinidad and Tobago 461/3 505 724 785
Uganda 447
Upper Volta 95
Uruguay 1778/80 1911
Wallis and Futuna Islands 243
Yemen 262/4 265 268 271 306/9 425 428 431
Yemen People's Democratic Republic 254
Yugoslavia 1594
Zaire 932 1036 1324
Zambia 527
707 Air Force One
Togo 1995
720, 1959
Belize 505 MS513
Cyprus (Turkish Cypriot Posts) 67
Ecuador 2021
Ethiopia 1952
Ireland 184/5
720B, 1960
Burundi 978/9 986/7 1350 1439
Colombia 1077/9 1085 1167 1241/2 1250/1 E1143
Ethiopia 626
Israel 377/86
Malta 517 519 521 606 609 730
Pakistan 155
Rhodesia 575
Saudi Arabia 585/610c 716/21 724/37 741/4 812/13
Somalia 615
BOEING 727 (Series not determined)
Algeria 1006 1129
Benin 991
Cayman Islands 672
Christmas Island 177
Comoro Islands 311
Djibouti 927
Egypt 1197
Ethiopia 1357 1387
Guatemala 1275/6
Iceland 463 693

Jamaica 849
Kenya, Uganda & Tanganyika 375
Kiribati 680
Kuwait 1808
Libya 762 2306 2352 2413/14 2435 2853 MS3008
Malawi 679
Maldive Islands MS940 2933
Marshall Islands 216
Micronesia 186
Mongolia MS2435
Morocco 589 840
Nauru 284 287 309 311 321
Nepal 431 572
Nigeria 326 395
Palau 264 381
Samoa 769/71 774 777
Turkey 2812
Upper Volta 663
Uruguay 1698
Yemen 724/6
727-100, 1963
Burundi 326 328
China (Taiwan) 601 602/3 907
Cocos (Keeling) Islands 69 166
Colombia E1168
Djibouti 855
Egypt 892
Germany (Federal Republic) 1394
Gibraltar 464
Guinea 1011
Haiti 1084/9
Iran 1391
Libya 1614
Marshall Islands 78
Micronesia 21
Nauru 222
Nepal 373
Nicaragua 2358 MS2495
Papua New Guinea 179
San Marino 740
Trinidad and Tobago 360 378 451
727-200, 1967
Afghanistan 714/15
Bahamas 810
Brazil 1758
Cayman Islands 580
Costa Rica 1052/4 1606
Dominican Republic 1200
Ecuador 2023
Gabon 415
Grenadines of Grenada 662
Kiribati 182
Libya MS860 1014
Mali 1080 1188
Mexico 1311
Micronesia 254
Netherlands Antilles 608
Panama 1607
Peru 1411
St. Lucia 310 543 566 O7
Turks and Caicos Islands MS720
737, 1967
Algeria 1056/7
Angola 1367 MS1378
Bahamas 800 810 868
Brunei 241/3
Bulgaria MS1614
Cayman Islands 764 825
Chile 1453
China (Taiwan) 1519 1521
Cyprus 721 859
Djibouti 782
Egypt 1478
El Salvador 1683/5
Fiji 686
French Polynesia 204
Ghana 921
Gibraltar 468 589 1178
Hungary 4529
India 944
Iran 2483
Iraq MS1886
Jamaica 652
Jersey 477 810
Jordan 1574 1746/8
Madagascar 1141 1152 1156
Malagasy Republic 188
Malaysia 110/12
Maldive Islands 789 936/7 1059 2935
Mali 806 968 Malta 729
Marshall Islands 214
Mauritania 858
Mexico 2004 2005 2017
Morocco 830
Mozambique 1170
Nauru 152 201/2 223 254 318 424
New Caledonia 763
New Zealand 980 1421
Niger 1037
Nigeria 553
Niue MS926
Norfolk Islands 865
Norway MS862 1324
Oman 418
Pakistan 1056
Panama 1068
Portugal MS2970
Romania 5641 5694/5 6723

Samoa 501 595 617 767 776
Serbia & Montenegro 167
Seychelles 835
Singapore 1325 MS1329
Tanzania 406/7 MS534 714 1822
Togo 2103
Tonga 720/30 1057
Uganda 229 231 275 277
United Arab Emirates 205/6 222/3 245
United States of America A1610/11
Uruguay 2205
Vanuatu 372 383 671 682 724 1018 1019 1022
Venezuela 2696
Vietnam 1914/15
Wallis and Futuna Islands 309 351 761
Yemen 724/6
Yugoslavia 3350
Zambia 400
Zimbabwe 692 784 1044
737-300/500, 1989
Cayman Islands 983
France 3100
New Caledonia 976
Solomon Islands 729 807/8
Vanuatu 526

It is possible that some of the main listing may be this type. It should be noted that the Airbus has a very similar configuration and can be easily confused with the 737.

737 Special ("Short runway")
Faroe Islands 124
747 "Jumbo Jet", 1969
Antigua 486 696
Barbados 504
Barbuda 322 597
Benin 728 914 923 1076
Cameroon 1030
China (Taiwan) 1025 1099 1122f 1150 1215 1520 1645
Dahomey 439
Fiji 663 932
French Territories of the Afars and the Issas 916
Gabon 609 641
Germany (Federal Republic) 2201
Germany (West Berlin) B778
Guinea 1049
Hong Kong 517
India 686 945 1185
Indonesia 1919
Israel 1719
Japan 1535 2314/15 2316 3304a
Korea (South Korea) 1116 1699/1700 1886 2122/2132a 2486
Kuwait 848/9 1812
Luxembourg 1224
Macao 912/16
Madagascar 1145
Malagasy Republic 802 824
Malawi 679
Malaysia 382 475 581/4 641/2 685 687 827
Maldive Islands 509 1010
Marshall Islands 1239
Micronesia MS1226b
Morocco 655
Netherlands 1135
New Caledonia 1188
New Zealand 2145
Nigeria 488
Norway 1323
Oman 173
Saudi Arabia 1260
Solomon Islands MS1054
Switzerland (International Telecommunication Union) LT12
Tanzania 2168
Thailand 1057 1144 2032
Tunisia 922 1160
Turks and Caicos Islands 930
United Nations (Geneva) G310 G320
Upper Volta 544
Venezuela 2592
747-100 (with only three windows on the "bubble")
Antigua 392 424 MS742 937
Bahrain 195
Barbuda 160/1 824
Bermuda 333
British Virgin Islands 527 MS530
Cameroun 900 Chad 730/4 809 826
China (Taiwan) 1234/5 1304/5 1495
Dominica 442/3
Germany (Federal Republic) 1921
Grenada 630
Grenadines of Grenada 27
Hungary 3138
Laos 906
Malta 529
Mauritius 526
Nicaragua 2065 2786
Philippines 1385/6 2599 2602 2632 3088 3361
Seychelles 517
Spain 2118 3599 3878
Switzerland 828

D. FLYING BOATS AND SEAPLANES SINCE 1919

Seaplane version of landplanes are not listed here unless they are only represented on stamps as seaplanes.

F. MILITARY AIRCRAFT
1. 1914 TO 1918 - ALL TYPES
Including post-war civil conversions not
listed elsewhere.

2. 1919 TO DATE - PROPELLER DRIVEN
(a) Fighters
Including scouts, fighter-bombers and
ground attack.

K. AIRCRAFT OVERPRINTS

See more with the
Zoom Digital Microscope

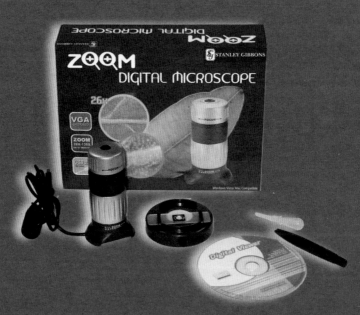

Item: R7521

The **Zoom Digital Microscope** is a powerful digital microscope that displays the magnified image right on to your computer screen allowing you to see intricate details of ordinary objects you never knew existed!

Features:

- Integrated Digital Camera – capture still images and VIDEO at the click of a button and view them on your PC monitor
- 26x -130x digital zoom – allows you to see details of ordinary objects you never knew existed
- 5x optical zoom
- Built in illuminator for clear and bright magnified images
- Image resolution of 640 x 489 pixels (VGA)
- Battery-free and connects right to your PC via USB
- Compatible with Windows 98SE, ME, 2000, XP & Vista

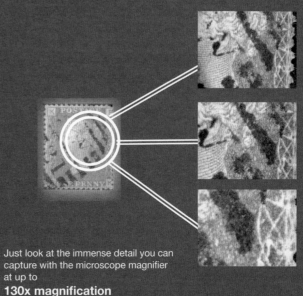

Just look at the immense detail you can capture with the microscope magnifier at up to
130x magnification

ORDER YOURS TODAY FOR JUST £79.95

Price correct as of February 2009 and subject to change

Stanley Gibbons Publications, 7 Parkside, Christchurch Road, Ringwood, Hampshire, BH24 3SH
Tel: 01425 472 363 **Email**: info@stanleygibbons.co.uk
www.stanleygibbons.com

STANLEY GIBBONS
The Home of Philately since 1856

AN IMPORTANT MESSAGE TO YOU

Dear Catalogue User,

As a collector and Stanley Gibbons catalogue user for many years myself, I am only too aware of the need to provide you with the information you seek in an accurate, timely and easily accessible manner.

Naturally, I have my own views on where changes could be made, but one thing I learned long ago is that we all have different opinions and requirements.

I would therefore be most grateful if you would complete the form overleaf and return it to me (or send your answers on a separate sheet if you prefer not to cut the page out of your catalogue).

If you would like the form to be sent to you by email, let me know at hjefferies@stanleygibbons.co.uk

Very many thanks for your help.

Yours sincerely,

Hugh Jefferies,
Editor.

Hugh Jefferies (Catalogue Editor)
Stanley Gibbons Limited
7 Parkside, Ringwood
Hampshire BH24 3SH
United Kingdom

Questionnaire

Please complete and return it to:

Hugh Jefferies *(Catalogue Editor)*
Stanley Gibbons Limited
7 Parkside, Ringwood   or   email: *hjefferies@stanleygibbons.co.uk*
Hampshire BH24 2LE
United Kingdom

2009 Collect Aircraft On Stamps

1.   Level of detail
Do you feel that the level of detail in this catalogue is:
a)   too specialised ☐
b)   about right ☐
c)   inadequate ☐

2.   Frequency of issue
How often would you purchase a new edition of this catalogue?
a)   Annually ☐
b)   Every two years ☐
c)   Every three to five years ☐
d)   Less frequently ☐

3.   Design and Quality
How would you describe the layout and appearance of this catalogue?
a)   Excellent ☐
b)   Good ☐
c)   Adequate ☐
d)   Poor ☐

4.   *How important to you are the prices given in the catalogue:*
a)   Important ☐
b)   Quite important ☐
c)   Of little interest ☐
d)   Of no interest ☐

5.   *Would you be interested in an electronic version of this catalogue?*

a)   Yes ☐
b)   Maybe ☐
c)   No ☐

6.   *Is there anything you would like to see in this catalogue that is not currently included?* ....
....
....
....
....
....
....
....

7.   *Would you like us to let you know when the next edition of this catalogue is due to be published?*
If so please give your contact details below.

Name: ....
Address:...
....
....
....
Email: ....
Telephone: ....

8.   *Are there any other Stanley Gibbons Catalogues which you would like to be informed of when published.*
1.
2.
3.

Many thanks for your comments.